WENNER-GREN CENTER
INTERNATIONAL SYMPOSIUM SERIES

VOLUME 7

THE FUNCTIONAL ORGANIZATION
OF THE
COMPOUND EYE

Already published in this series:

OLFACTION AND TASTE   *Edited by* Y. Zotterman, 1963.

LIGHTING PROBLEMS IN HIGHWAY TRAFFIC   *Edited by* E. Ingelstam, 1963.

THE STRUCTURE AND METABOLISM OF THE PANCREATIC ISLETS *Edited by* S. E. Brolin, B. Hellman and H. Knutson, 1964.

TOBACCO ALKALOIDS AND RELATED COMPOUNDS   *Edited by* U. S. von Euler, 1965.

MECHANISMS OF RELEASE OF BIOGENIC AMINES   *Edited by* U. S. von Euler, S. Rosell and B. Uvnäs, 1966.

COMPARATIVE LEUKAEMIA RESEARCH   *Edited by* G. Winqvist, 1966.

H. K. Hartline.

THE FUNCTIONAL ORGANIZATION
OF THE
COMPOUND EYE

*Proceedings of the International Symposium
held in Stockholm
October 1965*

EDITED BY

C. G. BERNHARD

SYMPOSIUM PUBLICATIONS DIVISION

PERGAMON PRESS

OXFORD · LONDON · EDINBURGH · NEW YORK
TORONTO · SYDNEY · PARIS · BRAUNSCHWEIG

Pergamon Press Ltd., Headington Hill Hall, Oxford
4 & 5 Fitzroy Square, London W.1

Pergamon Press (Scotland) Ltd., 2 & 3 Teviot Place, Edinburgh 1

Pergamon Press Inc., 44–01 21st Street, Long Island City, New York 11101

Pergamon of Canada, Ltd., 6 Adelaide Street East, Toronto, Ontario

Pergamon Press (Aust.) Pty. Ltd., 20–22 Margaret Street, Sydney, New South Wales

Pergamon Press S.A.R.L., 24 rue des Écoles, Paris 5e

Vieweg & Sohn GmbH, Burgplatz 1, Braunschweig

First edition 1966

TYPESETTING BY TAYLOR GARNETT EVANS & CO. LTD
WATFORD, HERTS.
PRINTED IN GREAT BRITAIN BY THE ANCHOR PRESS LTD
TIPTREE, ESSEX

International Symposium

on

THE FUNCTIONAL ORGANIZATION

OF THE

COMPOUND EYE

held in Stockholm, October 25–27, 1965

Sponsored by

European Office of Aerospace Research

Ministry of Education

Swedish Medical Research Council

Swedish Natural Science Research Council

Karolinska Institutet

Committee for Cooperation between
Swedish Research Councils and the
Wenner-Gren Center Foundation for Scientific Research

This symposium has been sponsored by the
AIR FORCE OFFICE OF SCIENTIFIC RESEARCH
under Grant AF EOAR 65–73 through the European Office of
Aerospace Research (OAR), United States Air Force

LIST OF PARTICIPANTS

A. R. ADOLPH
  Retina Foundation, Boston, USA

M. W. ATWOOD
  Dept. Zoology, University of Wisconsin, Madison, USA

R. R. BENNETT
  Dept. Zoology, University of Wisconsin, Madison, USA

R. M. BENOLKEN
  Dept. Zoology, University of Minnesota, Minneapolis, USA

C. G. BERNHARD
  Dept. Physiology, Karolinska Institutet, Stockholm, Sweden

D. BURKHARDT
  Dept. Zoology, University of Frankfurt, Frankfurt am Main, Germany

E. T. BURTT
  Dept. Zoology, University of Newcastle, Newcastle upon Tyne, Great Britain

D. CARLSTRÖM
  Dept. Medical Physics, Karolinska Institutet, Stockholm, Sweden

W. T. CATTON
  Dept. Zoology, University of Newcastle, Newcastle upon Tyne, Great Britain

R. DEVOE
  Dept. Physiology, The Johns Hopkins University School of Medicine, Baltimore, USA

F. A. DODGE
  The Rockefeller University, New York, USA

E. EGUCHI
  Dept. Biology, Yale University, New Haven, USA

M. G. F. FUORTES
  Ophthalmology Branch, N. I. Neurol. Dis. Blindn., N. I. H., Bethesda, USA

G. GEMNE
  Dept. Physiology, Karolinska Institutet, Stockholm, Sweden

L. GIULIO
  Dept. Physiology, Faculty of Veterinary Medicine, University of Perugia, Perugia, Italy

T. H. GOLDSMITH
  Dept. Biology, Yale University, New Haven, USA

J. L. HARTMAN JR.
  European Office of Aerospace Research, Brussels, Belgium

B. HASSENSTEIN
Dept. Zoology, Albert Ludwig University, Freiburg im Breisgau, Germany

G. HÖGLUND
Dept. Physiology, Karolinska Institutet, Stockholm, Sweden

G. A. HORRIDGE
Gatty Marine Laboratory, University of St. Andrews, St. Andrews, Great Britain

H. KIRSCHFELD
Max Planck Institute of Biology, Tübingen, Germany

L. H. KLEINHOLZ
Dept. Biology, Reed College, Portland, USA

J. W. KUIPER
Dept. Biophysics, University of Groningen, Groningen, The Netherlands

D. LANGE
The Rockefeller University, New York, USA

H. LANGER
Dept. Pathology, Karolinska Institutet, Stockholm, Sweden

J. R. LARSEN
Dept. Entomology, University of Illinois, Urbana, USA

J. T. LEUTSCHER-HAZELHOFF
Dept. Biophysics, University of Groningen, Groningen, The Netherlands

F. MAGNI
Dept. Physiology, University of Pisa, Pisa, Italy

G. A. MAZOKHIN-PORSHNJAKOV
Academy of Science, Moscow, USSR

G. D. McCANN
Willis H. Booth Computing Center, California Institute of Technology, Pasadena, USA

W. H. MILLER
Dept. Physiology, Yale University School of Medicine, New Haven, USA

A. R. MØLLER
Dept. Physiology, Karolinska Institutet, Stockholm, Sweden

K. NAKA
Shionogi Research Laboratory, Osaka, Japan

R. F. NUNNEMACHER
Dept. Biology, Clark University, Worcester, USA

D. OTTOSON
Dept. Physiology, Karolinska Institutet, Stockholm, Sweden

H. D. POTTER
Dept. Zoology, University of Wisconsin, Madison, USA

R. L. PURPLE
Dept. Physiology, University of Minnesota Medical School, Minneapolis, USA

F. RATLIFF
The Rockefeller University, New York, USA

W. REICHARDT
Max Planck Institute of Biology, Tübingen, Germany

P. RUCK
Dept. Zoology, University of Wisconsin, Madison, USA

P. R. B. SHEPHEARD
Gatty Marine Laboratory, University of St. Andrews, St. Andrews, Great Britain

B. THORELL
Dept. Pathology, Karolinska Institutet, Stockholm, Sweden

O. TRUJILLO-CENÓZ
Inst. Invest. Biol. Sci., Montevideo, Uruguay

H. G. WAGNER
Naval Air Engineering Center, Philadelphia, USA

J. B. WALTHER
Dept. Zoology I, University of Göttingen, Göttingen, Germany

T. H. WATERMAN
Dept. Biology, Yale University, New Haven, USA

Y. ZOTTERMAN
Dept. Physiology, Royal Veterinary College, Stockholm, Sweden

CONTENTS

Part III. Receptor excitation · Quantum sensitivity.

Part IV. Integration of visual input.

The papers on non-compound eyes by R. DeVoe, F. Magni and J. B. Walther have been included because of their relevance for the problems discussed in this volume.

OPENING ADDRESS

C. G. BERNHARD

Department of Physiology, Karolinska Institutet, Stockholm, Sweden

IT GIVES me great pleasure to welcome you to this conference, in the course of which we are to consider fundamental problems in sensory physiology and discuss them on the basis of data obtained in experiments on the arthropod eye. We have, amongst us, representatives of many fields of science, but we share a common interest. Whether we are regarded as biochemists, entomologists, histologists, pathologists, physicists, physiologists or zoologists, we are all concerned, in one way or another, with problems in vision which can be studied to advantage in the compound eye—this most intricate organ which has fascinated so many scientists for centuries and aroused their admiration.

I am especially happy that almost all who have been invited to attend have found it possible to come to Stockholm. For many, this is a far off corner of the world, although perhaps not so remote as it was in Linnaeus' time, when, in 1739, he delivered his lecture entitled "A Talk about the Marvels in Insects" to the Royal Swedish Academy of Sciences (Fig. 1). In the course of this, he said "We are all amazed by the sharpness of vision possessed by the lynx and the snake, and by the ability of the owl to see in darkness. Yet there are a very few who look at the eight eyes in a spider's skull or at the eyes of the gadfly and dragonfly, each of which is composed of many small eyes within the single large one." The two volumes of Jan Swammerdam's posthumous work *Biblia Naturae* had appeared in 1737–8, with an introduction by Herman Boerhaave (Fig. 2). It is obvious that Linnaeus had this work in mind when, in paragraph 51 in the same lecture, he told his audience to "let Swammerdam anatomize* a louse before you and he will divide* her as though he had the largest of oxen in front of him and you will admit that it is the most accurate* that the world has seen". We still admire the beauty of Swammerdam's drawings of the bee's eye, showing the separation of the receptor and ganglionic elements and delineating the facets and anatomical units behind each lenslet (Fig. 2).

Swammerdam's friend Antoni van Leeuwenhoek was also fascinated by the optics of these lenslets. The majority of his observations he presented in the form of letters to the Royal Society in London (Fig. 3) and one can find therein his description of the transmission of light through the facets: "I

* The word is Linnaeus'.

have frequently examined the flying insect, moth or butterfly produced from the aurelia or chrysalis of the silk-worm; and . . . I placed before the microscope one of those organs of sight, which in this animal is commonly deemed one eye. . . . When this little part, cleared from the optic nerves within it, was placed before the microscope, all the surrounding objects were clearly to be seen through each of the small optical organs . . . though wonderfully diminutive; for the great tower or steeple of our new church in Delft, which is 300 feet high, and about 750 feet distant from my house,

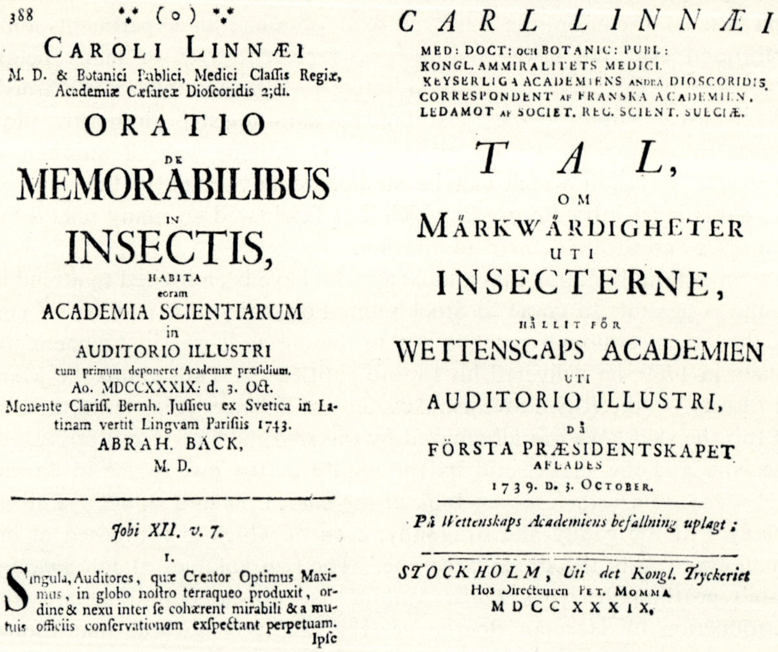

388   ·.· (o) ·.·
CAROLI LINNÆI
M. D. & Botanici Publici, Medici Classis Regiæ,
Academiæ Cæsareæ Dioscoridis 2;di.

ORATIO
DE
MEMORABILIBUS
IN
INSECTIS,
HABITA
coram
ACADEMIA SCIENTIARUM
in
AUDITORIO ILLUSTRI
cum primum deponeret Academiæ præsidium.
Ao. MDCCXXXIX; d. 3. Oct.
Monente Clariss. Bernh. Jussieu ex Svetica in Latinam vertit Lingvam Parisiis 1743.
ABRAH. BÄCK,
M. D.

Jobi XII. v. 7.
I.
Singula, Auditores, quæ Creator Optimus Maximus, in globo nostro terraqueo produxit, ordine & nexu inter se cohærent mirabili & a mutuis officiis conservationem exspectant perpetuam.
Ipse

CARL LINNÆI
MED: DOCT: OCH BOTANIC: PUBL:
KONGL. AMMIRALITETS MEDICI.
KEYSERLIGA ACADEMIENS ANDEA DIOSCORIDIS,
CORRESPONDENT AF FRANSKA ACADEMIEN,
LEDAMOT AF SOCIET. REG. SCIENT. SULCIÆ.

TAL,
OM
MÄRKWÄRDIGHETER
UTI
INSECTERNE,
HÅLLIT FÖR
WETTENSCAPS ACADEMIEN
UTI
AUDITORIO ILLUSTRI,
DÅ
FÖRSTA PRÆSIDENTSKAPET
AFLADES
1739. D. 3. OCTOBER.

På Wettenskaps Academiens befallning uplagt:

STOCKHOLM, Uti det Kongl. Tryckeriet
Hos Directeuren Pet. MOMMA
MDCCXXXIX.

FIG. 1

Carl Linnaeus (1707–78), who was one of the founders of the Swedish Academy of Sciences (2 June 1739), was chosen president by lot for a 4 months' period. At the end of this first presidential period he delivered the lecture entitled "A Talk about the Marvels in Insects". This is the first of Linnaeus' addresses printed in Swedish (1739; front page, to the right). The first printing (by P. Momma) was technically unsatisfactory and a second Swedish edition was prepared in 1747 (printed by L. Salvius) to which Linnaeus made some additions. A third edition without any further alterations appeared in 1752. It was translated into Latin in 1743 by Linnaeus' friend, Abraham Bäck, and was printed in 1751 in *Amoenitates Academicae* (front page, to the left). An English edition appeared in 1781. The quotations in the text (translated into English by the present author) are from a late Swedish edition (A. Uggla, 1954) which is based on the third edition.

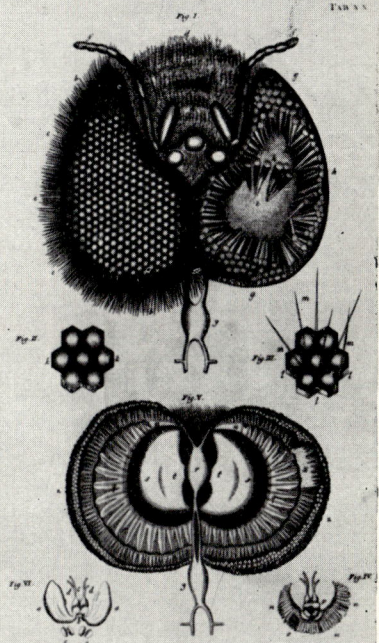

FIG. 2

Jan Swammerdam (1637–80). His productive period in biology after graduation at Leyden 1667 lasted for only 6 years. Thereafter, he was beset by personal troubles and illness. Unpublished manuscripts which he bequeathed to his friend Thevenot in Paris passed through many hands, until they were purchased by Boerhaave, who published them in two volumes in Dutch and Latin during 1737–8, under the title *Bybel der Natuure* (front page, above). The *Bybel* also included earlier published work by Swammerdam on insect anatomy which demonstrates Swammerdam's great skill in evertebrate anatomy. Figure 20 in Volume II (to the right) shows his drawing of the dissected head of the bee illustrating the compound eye.

when viewed through any of these optical organs, appeared no larger than the point of a small needle seen with the naked eye . . ." (Fig. 4).

In an earlier letter (1674) written to the Secretary of the Society, Leeuwenhoek wrote "Dr. Swammerdam hath again within this fort-night visited me twice, accompanied with a Gentleman, to both which I have shew'd many of these microscopical observations, and of such others as I had formerly spoken to him about; perceiving that his speculations are busy upon this subject, and that probably he will discourse more largely of it than I have

FIG. 3

Antoni van Leeuwenhoek (1632–1723) described his observations, including his discoveries on the optical characteristics of the corneal facets, in letters to the Royal Society. He found that each lenslet forms a reduced inverted image located in the eye close to the cornea. Above is a photoprint of one of the pages from a letter of 9 May 1698 to the Society, the lower part of which says: ". . . and this being so, we should have a hundred objects of the eyes that are in the cornea, seen at once, but very small; for the steeple of our new church, whose distance is great, as I have related in my former letters"—and continues—"seems, through the eyes of the beetle, no bigger to me than the point of a small needle. Here we see, now, how these are mistaken, that take the beetle to be blind, and how sufficiently this small animal is provided with sight, not to speak of the other parts of his body; which insect, when we meet it, we tread under our feet, as having no esteem for so black a creature." Translation to English in *Philosophical Transactions* 1698. Acknowledgment is made to the Royal Society for permission to reproduce Leeuwenhoek's letter. The copyright of the letter is the property of the Royal Society.

FIG. 4

What Leeuwenhoek probably saw when he placed the cornea of "the butterfly produced from the aurelia or chrysalis of the silk worm" under his microscope and looked at the "new church in Delft" through the facets.

done hitherto."* One can easily imagine the meeting of these two eminent biologists and their scientific discussions, in the course of which they may well have discussed the optics and image formation of the faceted eye. If so, our present meeting might well be called the Second Symposium on the Compound Eye.

Questions concerned with the definition of the functional sensory unit and the integration of the activity from several units were tackled 150 years later by Johannes Müller. His mosaic theory, presented in 1826 in *Physiologie des Gesichtsinnes* (Fig. 5), was further developed by Exner. Exner also took into account the pigment movements as a dynamic factor in the super-position eye and referred to Leydig's observation on the appearance of the strong reflection of light from the bottom of the dark-adapted eye (Fig. 6) of the type thus designated. The mosaic theory—right or wrong—stimulated work for generations, for it was concerned with challenging problems of fundamental visual mechanisms both at the level of the receptor unit and at that of the integrative functions which we are to discuss this week.

* The Secretary of the Royal Society at this time was H. Oldenburg who, as a theologian, had moved to England from Bremen in 1640. He had spent some time at Oxford—studying literature and physics—and was elected Secretary of the newly founded Royal Society. In this capacity he carried on a correspondence with most of the continental scientists. Fearing that this extensive correspondence might lead to his being suspected of espionage, he invited his correspondents occasionally to direct letters to him under another name, for instance Grubendol. In spite of these precautions he was sent to the Tower, but was released after a few months. (From *Alle de brieven van Antoni van Leeuwenhoek*, Deel I, p. 409, 1939.)

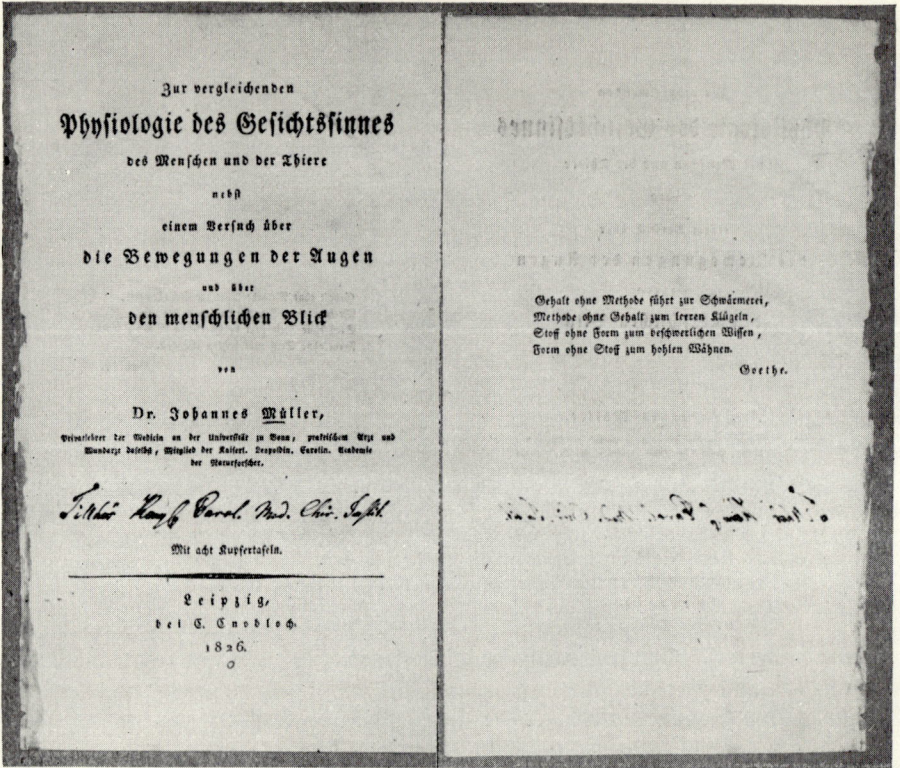

FIG. 5

Johannes Müller (1801–58), one of the founders of the German School of Physiology of the 19th century, presented his conception of the specific nerve energies in *Zum vergleichenden Physiologie des Gesichtssinnes* (front page and second page, above). The same volume also contains his mosaic theory to explain the optical properties of the compound eye.

Des Experimentirens müde, sperre ich das Thier in eine ausgeräumte Kommodeschublade. In aller Frühe des andern Morgens sehe ich nach dem Windig; ich ziehe behutsam die Schublade etwas hervor, der Falter sitzt ruhig am Rande, ich blicke nach seinen Augen — und sie leuchten jetzt prächtig „wie glühende Kohlen".

FIG. 6

Franz Leydig (1821–1905) published in 1864 a paper *Das Auge der Gliedertiere* (Gratulationsschrift der naturwissenschaftlichen Facultät in Tübingen zum fünfzig-jährigen Doctorjubiläum des Kais. Russ wirklichen Staatsraths Carl Ernst v. Bär in St. Petersburg) in which the above description of his observation on the reflection of light (the glow) in the dark-adapted night moth is to be found.

When, in 1906, Ramon y Cajal together with Golgi was honoured here in Stockholm—he came, as he relates in his temperamental autobiography, with some hesitation—reference was made to his "valuable work in the new research on nervous anatomy" (Mörner, 1906), which included discoveries relating to the fine structure of the vertebrate retina. Later, as we know, there appeared his fundamental papers on the arthropod eye in which he described the intricate network within and leading to the insect optic ganglion (Cajal, 1909, Fig. 7; see also Cajal and Sánchez, 1915).

In our present-day efforts to explain, at the molecular level, the mechanisms determining properties of vision, various methods are employed. And much of our discussion will deal with the correlation between electrophysiological, ultrastructural and biochemical data. One of the great rewards of being concerned with experimental work in vision is the stimulus that the experimenter obtains from studying the work of Hartline, from the time

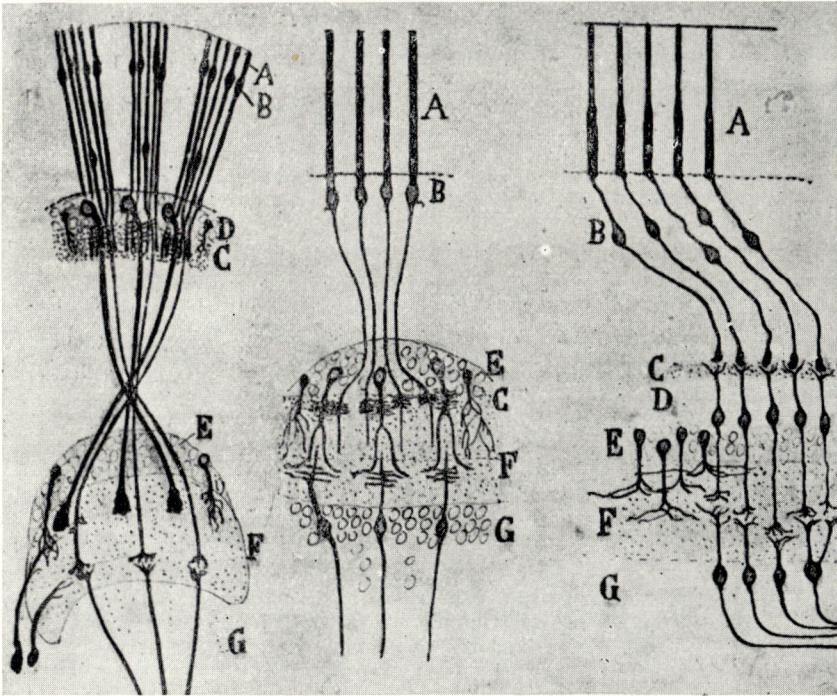

FIG. 7

Cajal (1852–1934) received the Nobel Prize in 1906. Three years later he published his first paper on the compound eye in which the retinoganglionic connections in *Musca* were described. In this paper, arthropod (left), cephalopod (middle) and vertebrate (right) retinal structures were compared. From *Nota sobre le estructura de la retina de la mosca* by S. R. Cajal, 1909.

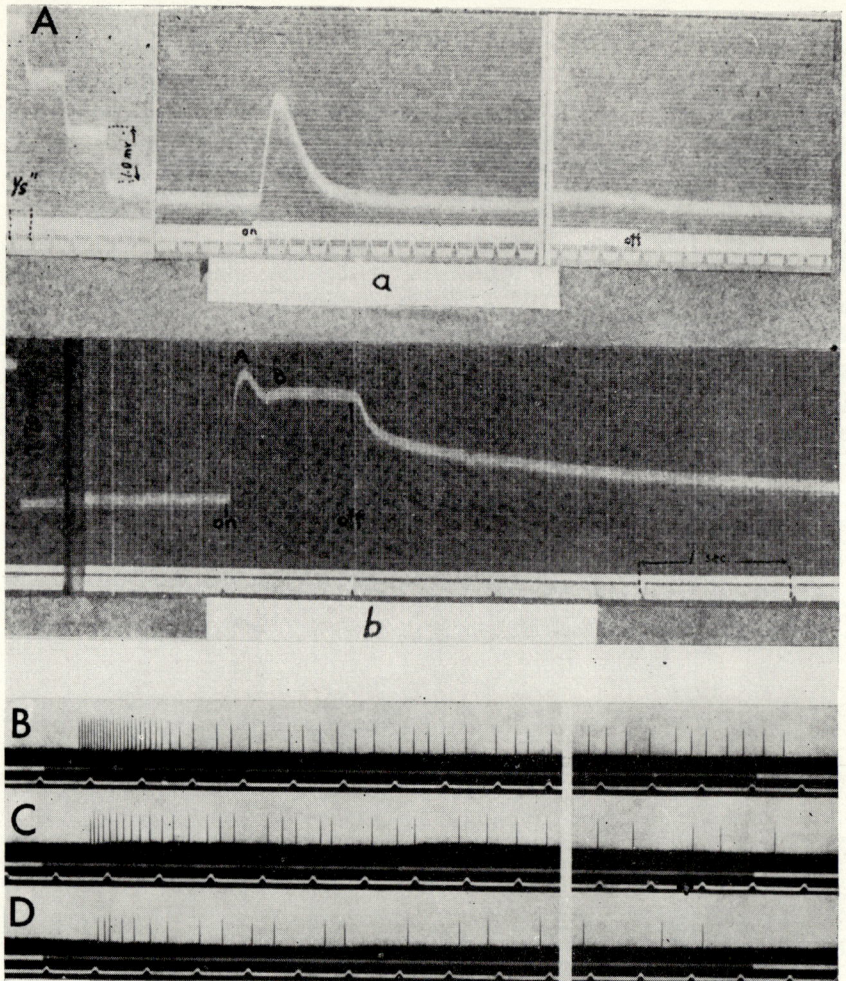

FIG. 8 A

Electric responses to illumination obtained from arthropod eyes. *a*, response from excised lateral eye of a young horseshoe crab, *Limulus polyphemus* (5 cm across carapace). Illumination on eye *ca.* 85,000 meter candles. Area of image 0·1 mm². Calibration at left, 1 step = 1·0 mV. *b*, from grasshopper, *Melanoplus femur-rubrum*. Calibration at left 7·70 mV. Area of image 0·17 mm². Illumination on eye 8500 meter candles. From Hartline, 1928.

FIG. 8 B–D

Action potentials of a single nerve fibre. Complete dark-adaptation of eye. Intensity of stimulation, respectively 0·01, 0·001, and 0·0001 in arbitrary units (1 unit = 630,000 meter candles on the surface of the eye). The gap in each of the records represents an interval of 1·4 sec, 4·5 sec, and 3·3 sec, respectively. From Hartline and Graham, 1932.

when he first recorded the electrical response of the compound eye (Fig. 8, A) and the single fibre activity in the eye of the horseshoe crab (Fig. 8, B–D). A further development—one of the main topics of this symposium—is the recent treatment of the excitatory and inhibitory neuronal interplay taking place in the pathways to the optic ganglion.

The integrative function of this brainlet will also be discussed at our symposium. In this context, I would like to refer to a lecture on biological experimentation by A. V. Hill (1929), in which he said: "By the methods of comparative physiology or of experimental biology, by the choice of the suitable organ, tissue or process, in some animal far removed in evolution, we may often throw light upon some function process in the higher animals, or in man." This is certainly true for our knowledge of the processing of sensory information obtained in experiments on the horseshoe crab (see

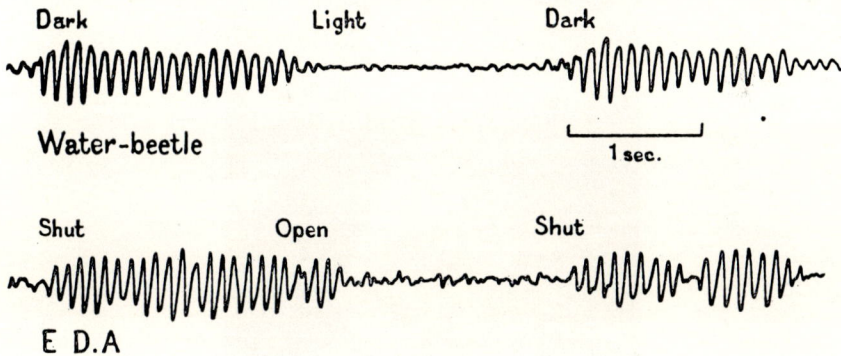

FIG. 9

Comparison of waves from water-beetle preparation in darkness and light (upper record) and from human subject (E.D.A.) with eyes closed and open (lower record). In both the rhythm is abolished during visual activity. From E. D. Adrian and B. H. C. Matthews, 1934.

Ratliff, 1965), this archaic and aquatic super-spider which Linnaeus happened to classify wrongly as monocular (Linnaeus, 1758; cf. André, 1782). It also holds true for the study of higher central nervous functions, and it may be added that the water-beetle suddenly found itself in the centre of neurophysiological, neurological and, strange though it may sound, psychiatric interest when Adrian and Matthews, in 1934, compared the optic ganglion activity in the beetle with the electrical activity of Adrian's own brain (Fig. 9). These now classical records are to be found in a paper in which the observations of the German psychiatrist Berger on the human EEG were confirmed and the synchronization of slow wave activity in the human brain analysed.

When I visited Lord Adrian in Cambridge last month, he told me that he very much regretted his inability to be back in Europe in time for this symposium from a Memorial Lecture he had undertaken to give in Australia. He asked me to convey his best wishes for the success of our deliberations. Good wishes have also come from Professor Karl von Frisch (Fig. 10) who, through his brilliant studies of the ability of the bee's eye to analyse polarized light and of the importance of this capacity to the insect's navigation, has demonstrated so superbly the marvels of the compound eye (see von Frisch, 1960). I would like to quote from his letter: "Ich wünsche Ihrer Veranstaltung den besten Verlauf. Es gibt ja auf diesem Gebiet so viele aufregende Neuigkeiten, dass es bestimmt eine anregende Tagung wird."

This is also my sincere hope, and I thank you all most warmly for your presence here today.

FIG. 10
Karl von Frisch at work in the field.

REFERENCES

ADRIAN, E. D. and MATTHEWS, B. H. C. 1934. The Berger rhythm: potential changes from the occipital lobes in man. *Brain* **57**, 355–85.

ANDRÉ, W. 1782. A microscopic description of the eye of the *Monoculus Polyphemus Linnaei*. *Philos. Trans.* **72**, 440–4.

CAJAL, S. R. 1909. Nota sobre la estructura de la retina de la mosca. *Trab. Lab. de Invest. Biol. Madrid* **7**, 217–57.

CAJAL, S. R. and SÁNCHEZ, D. 1915. Contribución al conocimiento de los centros nerviosos de los insectos. *Trab. Lab. de Invest. Biol. Madrid* **13,** 1–168.

EXNER, S. 1891. *Die Physiologie der Facettierten Augen von Krebsen und Insecten.* F. Deuticke, Leipzig and Vienna.

VON FRISCH, K. 1960. *Sprache und Orientierung der Bienen.* Dr. Alb. Wander-Gedenkvorlesung, Heft 3, Fünfte Gedenkvorderung, 19 Nov. 1960, Verlag Hans Huber, Berne and Stuttgart, 1964.

HARTLINE, H. K. 1928. A quantitative and descriptive study of the electric response to illumination of the arthropod eye. *Amer. J. Physiol.* **83,** 466–83, 1927–8.

HARTLINE, H. K. and GRAHAM, C. H. 1932. Nerve impulses from single receptors in the eye. *J. Cell. Comp. Physiol.* **1,** 277–95.

HILL, A. V. 1929. Experiments on frogs and men. "Popular Lecture" given at the annual meeting of the British Medical Association, Manchester on 27 July 1929. In *The Ethical Dilemma of Science and Other Writings.* The Rockefeller Institute Press, New York, 1960, pp. 24–38.

VAN LEEUWENHOEK, A. *The Select Works of Antoni van Leeuwenhoek.* Translated from the Dutch and Latin editions published by Samuel Hoole, London. Printed by G. Sidney, 1800.

VAN LEEUWENHOEK, A. *Alle de brieven van Antoni van Leeuwenhoek* (in Dutch and English). Deel I, 1939. Swets and Zeitlinger, Amsterdam.

LEYDIG, F. 1864. *Das Auge der Gliedertiere.* Laupp und Siebeck, Tübingen.

VON LINNÉ, C. Tal om märkwärdigheter uti insecterne. In *Tre tal,* published by A. H. Uggla, Almqvist & Wiksells, Uppsala, 1954, pp. 3–26.

LINNAEUS, C. 1739. *Tal om märkwärdigheter uti insecterne.* Stockholm, Uti det Kongl. Tryckeriet hos directeuren Pet. Momma.

LINNAEUS, C. 1751. Oratio de memorabilibus in insectis. In *Caroli Linnaei Amoenitates Academicae.* **2,** 388–407. L. Salvius, Stockholm.

LINNAEUS, C. 1758. *Systema naturae,* **2,** 634. L. Salvius, Stockholm.

MÖRNER, K. A. H. 1906. Le Prix Nobel de Physiologie et de Médicine. In *Les Prix Nobel* 1906, pp. 31–35, P. A. Norstedt & Söner, Stockholm, 1908.

MÜLLER, J. 1826. *Zum vergleichenden Physiologie des Gesichtsinnes.* C. Cnobloch, Leipzig.

RATLIFF, F. 1965. *Mach Bands: Quantitative Studies on Neural Networks in the Retina.* Holdenday, San Francisco, London, Amsterdam.

SWAMMERDAM, J. *Bybel der Natuure.* Vols. I-II. Published by H. Boerhaave, 1737–8. Severinus, B. Vander and P. Vander, Leyden.

PART I

Optics. Control of light admission

THE STRUCTURE OF CHITIN

D. Carlström

Department of Medical Physics, Karolinska Institutet, Stockholm, Sweden

Chitin in its α-form is the major constituent of the rigid parts of most arthropods and its structure on the molecular level may be of interest for those studying the physical properties of the compound eye. The polysaccharide chain of chitin consists of chitobiose residues linked together by 1–4-β-glucosidic bonds. Each chitobiose residue contains two acetyl glucosamine units according to the structural formula of chitin.

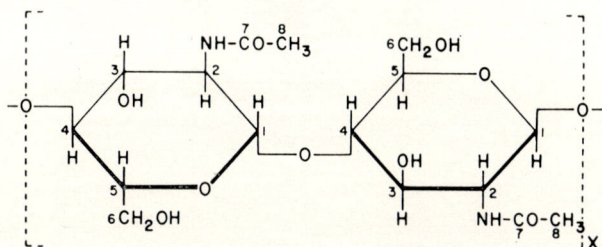

Chitin forms a fibrous matter of considerable chemical inertness and mechanical strength. In some biological samples, such as lobster tendons, the chitin fibres are almost perfectly aligned. Specimens of this kind yield X-ray diffraction patterns (fibre diagrams) fairly rich in information (Fig. 1). Chitin is thus crystalline, but it does not have the high internal order characteristic of single crystals. Nevertheless, it is possible to interpret a fibre diagram in terms of a three-dimensional picture of the molecular structure even if a structure determination based on a fibre pattern can never attain the accuracy possible in single crystal work.

One essential feature in the X-ray diffraction pattern of chitin was observed already in 1926 by Gonell who found that the repeating distance along the fibre direction was 10·4 Å. In 1935 Meyer and Pankow presented a model of the structure of chitin involving four polysaccharide chains, two and two running in opposite directions. The unit cell of this model (the unit cell is the smallest volume of a crystalline material which repeats itself in three dimensions along the crystallographic axes) was found to be orthorhombic with axial dimensions of: 9·40 Å, 10·46 Å (fibre axis) and 19·25 Å, and it contained four chitobiose residues. A schematic drawing of the Meyer and

15

Pankow model, showing the proposed arrangement of the chains, is seen in Fig. 2 A. At that time the knowledge of the size and shape of the pyranose ring and other essential parts of the acetyl glucosamine molecule was not accurate and it is no wonder that this model later had to be revised. More and more structural information was gathered about mono- and disaccharides and the time was finally ripe for a redetermination of the chitin structure.

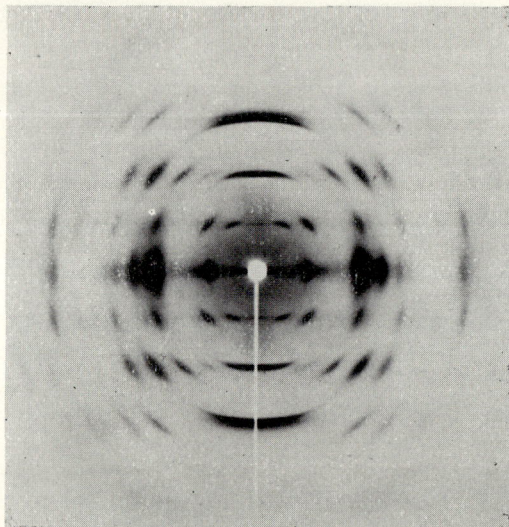

FIG. 1

X-ray diffraction pattern of a well-oriented specimen of pure chitin. Fibre axis vertical. Note the horizontal arrays of diffraction spots arising from a fundamental repeating period of 10·3 Å.

This was made by the author in 1957 and the following presentation is based mainly on that work.

α-chitin (poly N-acetyl-D-glucosamine) is orthorhombic.

$$\textit{Space group:} \quad P\ 2_1 2_1 2_1.$$

$$\textit{Unit cell dimensions:} \quad a = 4 \cdot 76 \text{ Å},$$
$$b = 10 \cdot 28 \text{ Å (fibre axis)},$$
$$c = 18 \cdot 85 \text{ Å}.$$

$$\textit{Density:} \quad 1 \cdot 425 \text{ g/cm}^3 \text{ (observed)},$$
$$1 \cdot 462 \text{ g/cm}^3 \text{ (calculated for two chitobiose}$$
$$\text{residues per unit cell)}.$$

This unit cell had only half the size of the one proposed earlier and contained, accordingly, only two chain fragments running in opposite directions.

For comparison, a schematic drawing of the general arrangement of the chains is shown in Fig. 2 B. A more detailed picture of the structure was derived by constructing models fulfilling all sterical requirements. The diffraction patterns of the three axial projections of a great number of sterically possible models were recorded by aid of an optical diffractometer and these diffraction patterns were compared with the actual diffraction

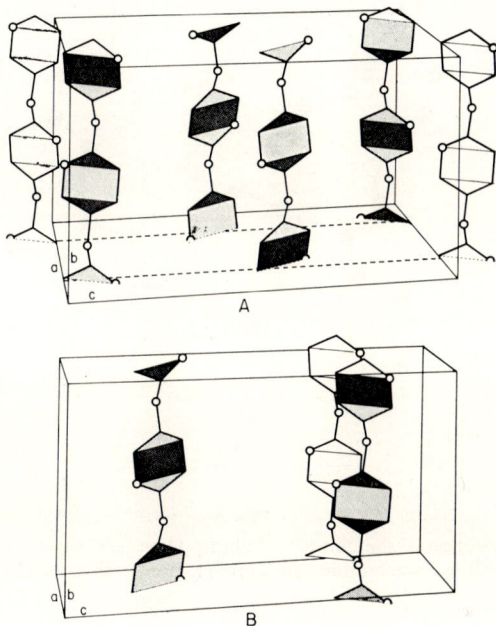

FIG. 2

A, Schematic drawing of the Meyer and Pankow (1935) model of the chitin structure showing the proposed arrangement of the chains within the unit cell. Two chains are running in the opposite direction to the other two. B, Schematic drawing of a revised model of chitin with a unit cell having an *a*-axis of half the length of that in (A). The cell content here is only two instead of four chitobiose residues. In both (A) and (B) the ring and bridge oxygens are represented by open circles. The side groups are omitted.

pattern of chitin. Some information regarding the structure was in addition gained by polarized infrared spectroscopy. Finally, a model was derived which fitted the observed data amazingly well. A projection along the *a*-axis of this model of the chitin structure is shown in Fig. 3. As can be seen, the chains are not straight when viewed perpendicularly to the pyranose rings; they are slightly buckled. Such an arrangement brings an OH-group of one ring closer to the ring oxygen of the next glucosamine unit, thereby making an intramolecular hydrogen bond possible. This feature increases the strength

C.E.—C

and stability in the direction of the chain. The same hydrogen bond was later shown to be present in the closely related disaccharide cellobiose (Jacobson *et al.*, 1961). Another hydrogen bond in the chitin structure is the $- NH \cdots O =$ intermolecular hydrogen bond connecting chains running in the same direction. This bond is not visible in Fig. 3 since it almost coincides with the

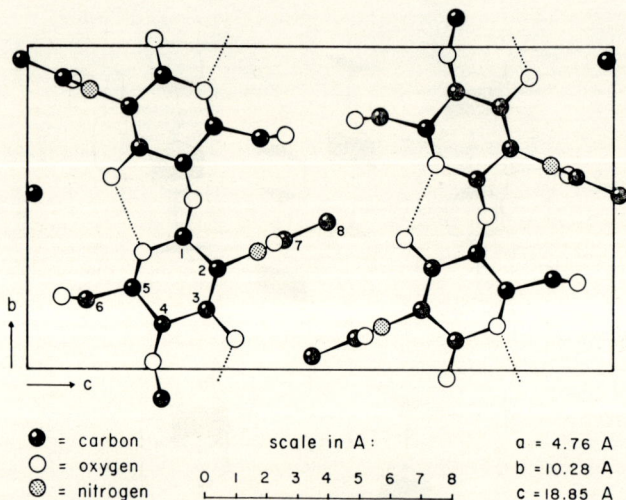

FIG. 3

An *a*-axis projection of the unit cell of chitin. Hydrogen bonds are indicated by dotted lines. All hydrogen atoms are omitted. (Redrawn after Carlström, 1957.)

a-axis direction. Chains running in opposite directions seem only to be held together by ordinary van der Waals' forces. In a thorough analysis of the infrared absorption spectra of chitin, Pearson *et al.* (1960) confirmed the general features of the above model. However, no signs of a free OH stretching frequency was observed and these authors concluded that the OH connected to the sixth carbon atom should also be hydrogen bonded. A bifurcated intramolecular hydrogen bond both to the bridge oxygen and the nitrogen atom in the adjacent glucosamine unit was suggested. Recently, an X-ray diffraction investigation of chitin was carried out by Dweltz (1960) resulting in a model which in its general features was very similar to that described above. In details, however, this model showed severe discrepancies and, moreover, was found to be stereochemically less satisfactory (Carlström, 1962; Ramachandran and Ramakrishnan, 1962).

Although our present picture of the molecular structure of chitin seems to be well established, there are still many problems related to structure to be solved. The actual material of the dense parts of the compound eye, as well as most other chitin-containing structures encountered in nature, is not pure chitin but an intimate chitin–protein complex (Fraenkel and Rudall, 1947). The molecular structure of this important complex is practically unknown. So is the organization on the ultrastructural level of the chitin fibres within the insect cornea. It is evident that the spatial arrangement of the fibrous matter will influence the optical properties, especially the birefringence, of the image-forming elements of the compound eye.

REFERENCES

CARLSTRÖM, D. 1957. The structure of α-chitin. *J. Biophys. Biochem. Cytol.*, **3**, 669–83.

CARLSTRÖM, D. 1962. The polysaccharide chain of chitin. *Biochim. Biophys. Acta*, **59**, B 134, 111–43.

DWELTZ, N. E. 1960. The structure of chitin. *Biochim. Biophys. Acta*, **44**, 416–35.

FRAENKEL, G. and RUDALL, K. M. 1947. The structure of insect cuticles. *Proc. Roy. Soc.* B 134, 111–43.

GONELL, H. W. 1926. Röntgenographische Studien an Chitin. *Z. physiol. Chem.* (Hoppe-Seyler's) **152**, 18–30.

JACOBSON, R. A., WUNDERLICH, J. A. and LIPSCOMB, W. N. 1961. The crystal and molecular structure of cellobiose. *Acta Cryst.*, **14**, 598–607.

MEYER, K. H. and PANKOW, G. W. 1935. Sur la constitution et la structure de la chitine. *Helv. Chim. Acta*, **18**, 589–98.

PEARSON, F. G., MARCHESSAULT, R. H. and LIANG, C. Y. 1960. Infrared spectra of crystalline polysaccharides. V. Chitin. *J. Polymer Sci.*, **43**, 101–16.

RAMACHANDRAN, G. N. and RAMAKRISHNAN, G. 1962. The structure of chitin. *Biochim. Biophys. Acta*, **63**, 307–9.

THE CORNEAL NIPPLE ARRAY

W. H. Miller*, A. R. Møller† and C. G. Bernhard†

In the eyes of certain arthropods the front surface of the cornea is completely covered by an hexagonal array of nipple-like structures that effectively suppress the reflection of light from the corneal front surface and correspondingly increase the transmission of light through the cornea (Bernhard and Miller, 1962; Bernhard, Miller and Møller, 1963; Miller, Bernhard and Møller, 1964; Bernhard, Miller and Møller, 1965). On the basis of results obtained in microwave model experiments and spectrophotometric investigations, and by using a mathematical model, it was concluded that the nipple array acts as an impedance transformer to match the characteristic impedance of air to that of the chitinous cornea.

In the work described below we will report on additional observations of the fine structure and function of the corneal nipple array.

STRUCTURE

Smooth-surfaced corneas. All front surfaces of arthropod compound eyes appear smooth when examined by the light microscope. For a number of arthropods this is also the case when the higher resolving power of the electron microscope is used. Some animals possessing smooth corneal front surfaces are beetles, bees, and grasshoppers. In order to view such corneas with the electron microscope we replicated and shadowed them. Figure 1 is an electron micrograph of a replica of the cornea of the grasshopper, *Melanoplus*. One full facet face and parts of its six neighbors are seen. While there are a number of small pits, scars, and contaminants, these facets are relatively smooth.

Nipple-in-air-array. The corneal front surfaces of some other arthropod compound eyes display distinctive structural attributes. Figure 2 shows the appearance of a gold-coated moth cornea as seen at four different magnifications using an electron flying spot microscope. The lowest magnification picture shows the whole cornea of one eye. The next higher magnification resolves the individual facets, while the two pictures at highest magnification show that the entire cornea is surfaced with minute protuberances—the

* Departments of Physiology and Ophthalmology, Yale University School of Medicine, New Haven, Connecticut.
† Physiology Department II, Karolinska Institutet, Stockholm, Sweden.

corneal nipples. These flying spot microscope pictures give a good general view of the hexagonal array of the nipples, but conclusions concerning the exact form of the individual nipple should be made with caution. Thus, it should be mentioned that the specimen, the micrographs of which were taken at an accelerating potential of 20 kV, was coated with a 500 Å thick layer of gold. Subsequent inspection of sections of the gold-coated specimen in an ordinary electron microscope revealed that the coating was not distributed

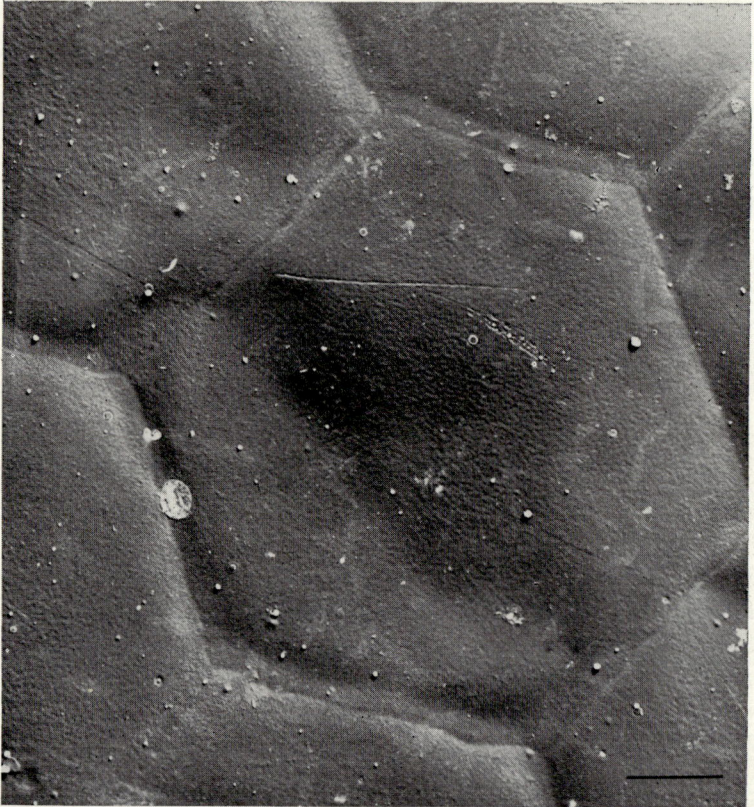

FIG. 1

Electron micrograph of replica of the front surface of the cornea from the compound eye of the grasshopper *Melanoplus*. One full facet face and parts of neighboring six facets are seen. Magnification marker, 5 μ. This electron micrograph and those of Figs. 5, 6, and 8 were all made using the same technique. Negative formvar casts of corneal front surfaces were coated with carbon at normal incidence. The formvar was dissolved away and the remaining carbon positive replica was shadowed at 45° with a mixture of 80% platinum and 20% palladium. The electron micrographs are all negative prints that reverse the intensities so as to make the replicas look as they would appear if they had been illuminated by light rather than metals.

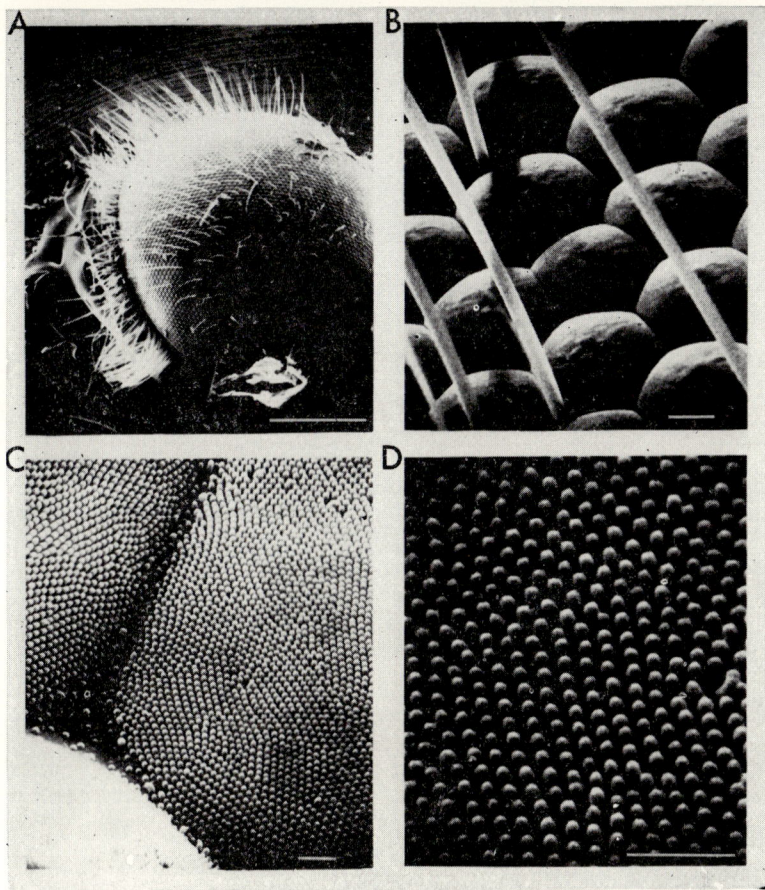

FIG. 2

The eye of a night moth as it appears in the scanning electron microscope. (Pictures taken with the "Stereoscan" at the Electron Probe Development Laboratory of Cambridge Instrument Company; Head, A. D. G. Stewart.) The surface of the eye is covered with 500 Å. thick gold coating and the pictures are taken at an accelerating potential of 20 kV. Magnification markers: A, 0·5 mm; B, 10 μ; C and D, 1 μ (in collaboration with G. Gemne).

uniformly but showed a piling up of the gold around the tips of the nipples (Fig. 3). The tips of the nipples therefore appear too blunt in the flying spot micrographs. However, it appeared that micrographs could be taken at an accelerating potential of 3 kV with no conducting coating on the specimen as shown in Fig. 4. Although the picture is not as sharp as those in Fig. 2 it shows that the tips of the nipples actually are more sharply tapered, as indicated by our earlier investigations (Bernhard, Miller and Møller, 1965; see Fig. 5) and shown by the replica technique.

Figure 5 is an electron micrograph of a replica of the cornea of the moth *Erebus odora* at low magnification. It depicts the pattern of nipple placement over the entire facet face. There are a few artifactual defects, but by and large the entire face shows hexagonal packing that even extends through the borders between neighboring facets.

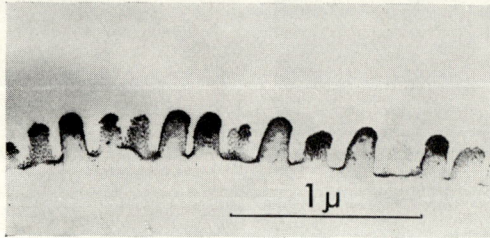

FIG. 3

Electron micrograph of a section of a gold-coated cornea (as in Fig. 2). Magnification marker, 1 μ (in collaboration with G. Gemne).

FIG. 4

Scanning electron microscope picture of the surface of a facet of a night moth without gold coating, taken at an accelerating potential of 3 kV with the same instrument as that used in Fig. 2 (in collaboration with G. Gemne).

At higher magnification a number of additional details can be discerned. The replica depicted in Fig. 6 was shadowed at 45°, which gives the appearance, on this negative print, of cones viewed from above under strong illumination coming from 2 o'clock. Accordingly, the nipples appear brightly illuminated or white on one side, and they cast triangular shadows, the lengths of which indicate that the nipples are about 200 mμ high. The center-to-center spacing of the nipples is likewise about 200 mμ.

On the basis of thin sections of the cornea it was assumed that the nipples are roughly conical and placed as closely together as possible (Bernhard, Miller and Møller, 1965). The pictures of replicas confirm these assumptions in general, but they also suggest that these assumptions may be oversimplified. At first glance the nipples in Fig. 6 appear to be separated from one another

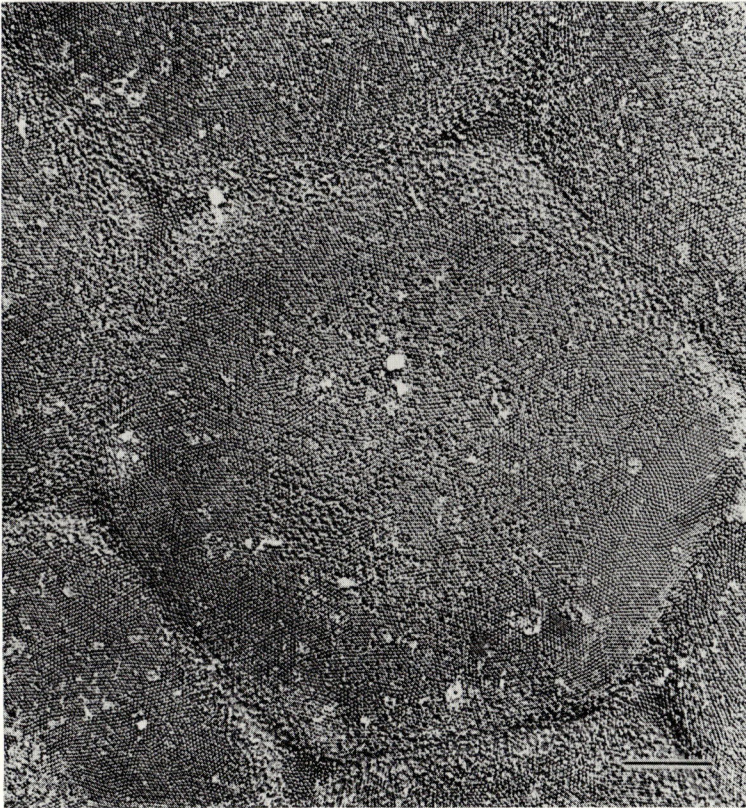

FIG. 5

Electron micrograph of replica of corneal front surface of the moth *Erebus odora* showing one full facet face and parts of six neighboring facets. Magnification marker, 5 μ.

at the corneal surface. In fact, though, they are connected to each other by a highlighted ridge. This highlighted ridge would be expected on a shadowed replica if the slope of the nipple were to change abruptly near the base so that the nipples start at the corneal surface with a hillock. The distal position of the nipple is built on this hillock. It is clearly visible in our earlier sections, and an example is shown in Fig. 7 (arrow). On some nipples the hillock will not show clearly, as one might expect if the plane of the section passes through or near its bottom.

FIG. 6
Same as Fig. 5 at higher magnification. Magnification marker, 200 mμ.

Comparisons between the replicas and sections are useful in arriving at an accurate notion of the three-dimensional structure of the nipple array, even if these methods do not agree in every detail. Thus there is one prominent marking that appears on the replicas that has no obvious counterpart in the sections. That marking consists of helical ridges seen along the sides of the nipples. It is conceivable that these ridges represent inflection points where the slope of the nipple's sides change, but in the absence of more definite proof they may be considered an artifact of unknown origin.

To summarize, the corneal nipple array is invisible in the light microscope. The array has been observed using the electron flying spot microscope and the electron microscope. The nipples are arranged in a more or less perfect hexagonal array that completely covers the corneal surface. They are placed as closely together as possible and each nipple starts at the corneal surface with a gently tapered hillock. The exact shape of the nipple's distal portion is unknown, but it seems to be roughly conical, or perhaps rather more cylindrical near the bases and more sharply tapered distally, as are the nipples seen in the section to the right and left of the arrow in Fig. 7. It should be mentioned that while an off-center section gives the appearance of a sharply tapered cone, consideration of sectioned views as a whole together with the electron

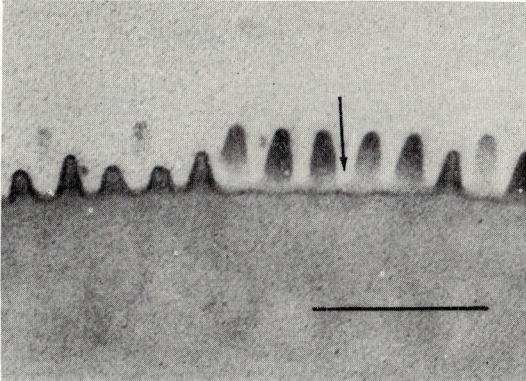

Fig. 7

Electron micrograph of cornea of the moth of southern army grass worm (*Prodenia*) taken in a plane perpendicular to corneal surface. Arrow points to corneal hillock on which the nipples are mounted. Magnification marker, 1 μ.

flying spot and replica pictures suggest that the nipples resemble tapered rods, which is to say they are not as pointed as the word "cone" implies. The nipple-in-air array has been observed in the eyes of butterflies, moths, mosquitoes, net flies, and caddis flies.

The subsurface nipple array. Of the compound eyes we have examined, some common flies, such as *Musca* and *Calliphora* and those of the skipper butterflies and the giant silk worm moth, *Cecropia*, have a subsurface nipple array. In these corneas the nipple array is not on the surface at the corneal–air interface. The nipples are embedded in the cortical layer of the cornea so that the corneal front surface shows only flattened tops that sometimes appear to coalesce, as shown in the replica depicted in Fig. 8. When a cornea such as this is examined in section perpendicular to the surface (Fig. 9), the nipples resemble icebergs in that only their very tips are above the surface. Dense nipples are seen under the corneal surface and there is a less dense corneal material in between. Underlying this cortical layer the nipples are based on small hillocks in the cornea. These hillocks seem to correspond to those that the nipples-in-air are based on. In comparing these variants of the nipple array it is interesting to note that the nipples in the subsurface variety are denser to the electron beam than the cornea proper, while the material between the nipples has about the same density as the rest of the cornea. This contrasts with the nipples-in-air in that these nipples have about the same density as the rest of the cornea. In both cases, however, the nipples are denser than the intervening material (air in the one case and cornea in the other).

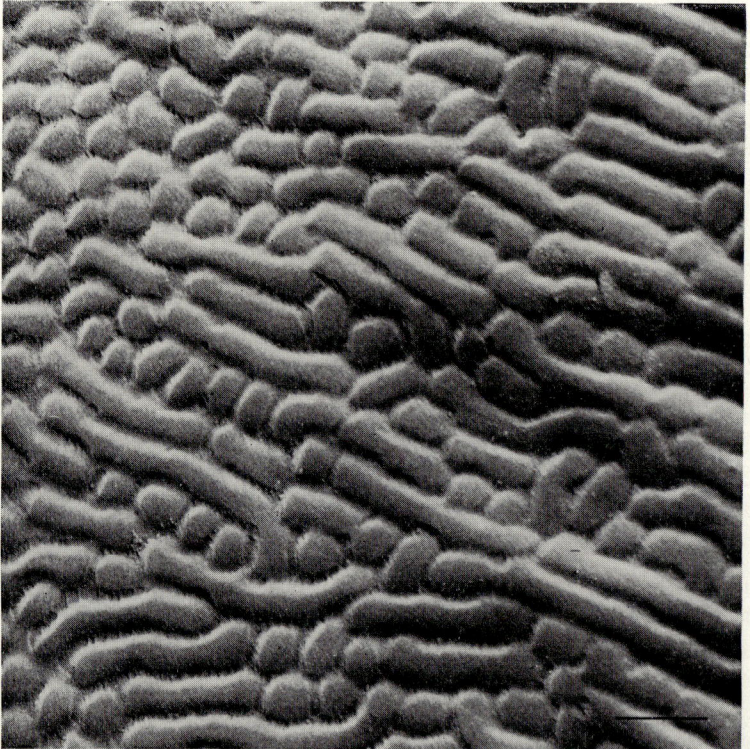

FIG. 8

Electron micrograph of replica of part of facet surface of the fly *Calliphora*.
Magnification marker, 0·5 μ.

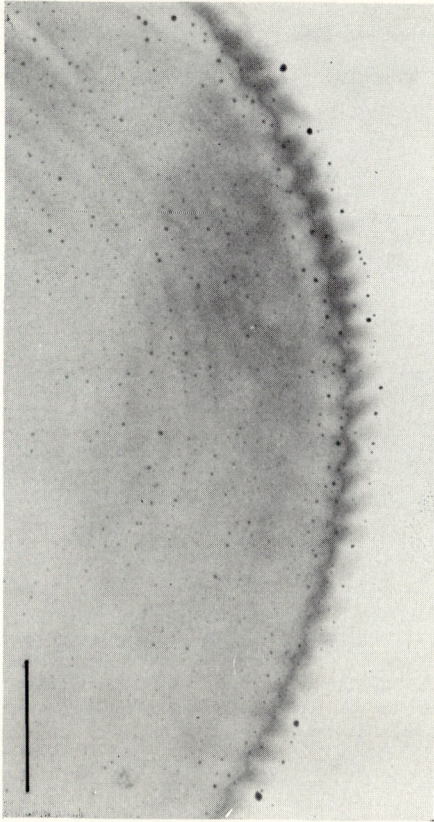

FIG. 9

Electron micrograph of section taken normal to corneal surface of the fly *Musca* showing subsurface nipple antenna array. Magnification marker, 1 μ.

Corneal nipples in fossils. We have examined the corneas of the compound eyes of one fossil insect: an unidentified Diptera from Baltic amber judged to be about 50 million years old (Eocene epoch). The compound eyes of this fossil insect proved to have the subsurface variant of nipple structure with nipples embedded within the corneal cortex. The corneal front surfaces of this animal were in poor condition. The corneal cortex was rarely found intact. In section, the fossil cornea usually appeared as in Fig. 10A. In this figure the structures that resemble teeth in a circular saw are not the nipples but rather the hillocks upon which they rest. The actual nipples may have been lost to the ages. Figure 10B depicts a part of the intact cortical layer, which may be compared with its modern counterpart in Fig. 9.

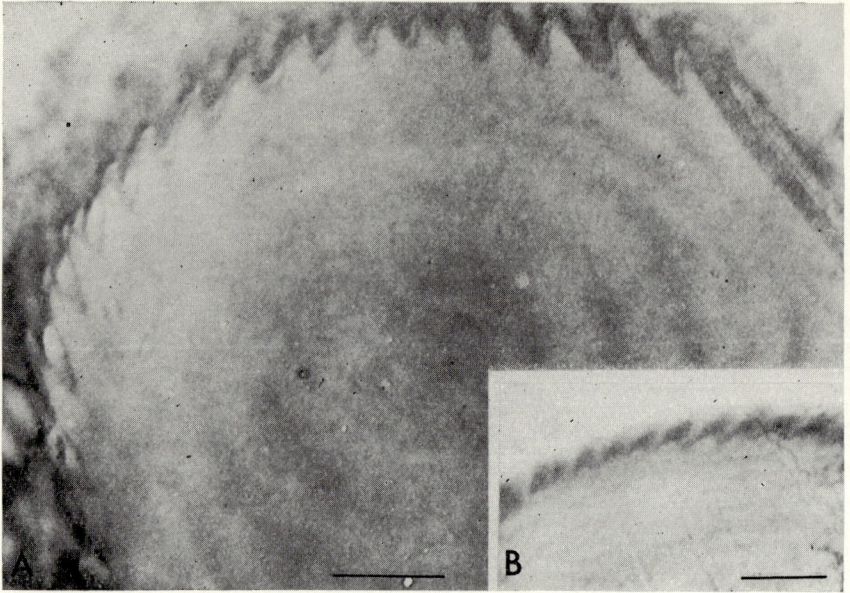

FIG. 10

A, electron micrograph of cornea from unidentified fossil Diptera showing hillocks and damaged nipples of subsurface variety. Magnification marker, 0·5 μ. Fossil from the collection of Naturhistoriska Riksmuséet, Stockholm. B, same as in A but showing section with corneal cortex intact. Magnification marker, 0·5 μ.

Obviously, the subsurface nipple array is no modern innovation. Because it is also present in modern forms we infer that this variant is a stable end product. Whether it is also a precursor of the nipple-in-air variety is unknown.

FUNCTION

The nipple-in-air array reduces the intensity of radiant energy reflected from the corneal front surface and correspondingly increases the transmission of energy through the cornea. We know this from experiments performed with scaled dielectric models in which we measured the intensities of microwave radiation reflected from the model's front surface and through the model (Bernhard, Miller and Møller, 1963, 1965). The results of experiments using models were confirmed by spectrophotometric measurements of the intensity of light reflected from the corneal front surfaces of the eyes of several insects. These measurements were performed on corneal fragments like those shown in Fig. 11 which are mounted on india ink. The corneas of Fig. 11 were used for additional reflection measurements described below.

In their theoretical treatment used to describe the function of the nipple-in-air array, Bernhard, Miller and Møller (1965) utilized a mathematical model assuming the nipple-array layer to be homogeneous in that the individual nipples are not "discerned" by incoming light waves, but heterogeneous for refractive index. The proportion of corneal material changes from 0% at the nipple tips to 100% at the nipple bases, giving rise to a transition in refractive index from 1·0 to 1·57. The nipple layer was divided into 20 equal layers, and the refractive indices for a number of wavelengths were calculated for the plane in front of each successive layer, ending with the layer in front of the nipples' tips. Because the refractive index is the inverse of characteristic impedance, this corresponds to considering each of the 20 layers as a minia-ture transmission line and calculating the input impedance for each stage in order to arrive at the input impedance of the system. With this figure the intensity of light reflected from the nipple array for radiation at normal incidence and, finally, the theoretical reduction in reflection caused by the nipple array, were calculated. The usefulness of this model is illustrated by the agreement between the calculations (solid curve Fig. 12) and comparable experimental measurements (crosses in Fig. 12).

As shown by the replica in Fig. 1, the grasshopper cornea, like that of the bee, has a relatively smooth surface. The crosses in Fig. 12 represent the

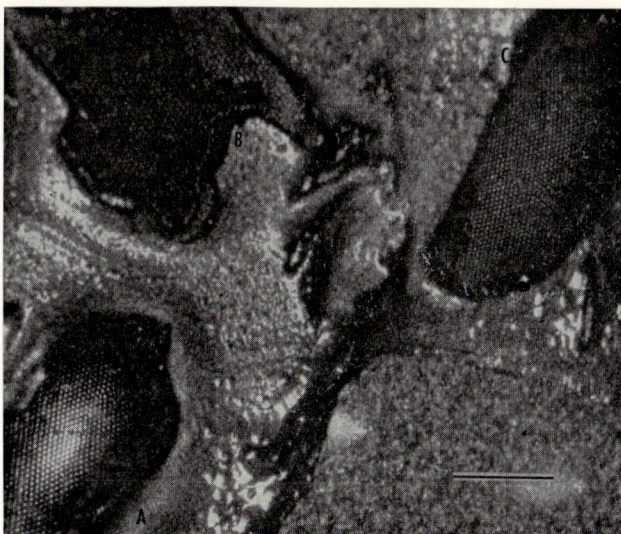

FIG. 11

Photograph of corneal fragments from the grasshopper *Melanoplus* (A), the moth *Sphynx* (B), and the fly *Calliphora* (C) with both the illumination and observation at normal incidence. The preparation depicted here was used for the measurements of Fig. 12. Magnification marker 0·5 mm.

values of the differences in intensity in log units of light reflected at the front surfaces of a moth cornea having a nipple-in-air array and a grasshopper's cornea. The open circles give the values of the corresponding differences in light reflection at the surfaces of a moth cornea and a fly cornea with a sub-surface nipple array. Light of 11 mμ bandwidth was projected at normal incidence on to fragments of the three corneal types which were mounted on india ink in order to minimize reflection from the corneal back surfaces. Observations were made with a microscope perpendicular to the plane of the corneas by direct photometric comparison of the brightness of the various corneas. The brightest corneal front surface was that of the grasshopper *Melanoplus*, which is smooth-surfaced. The next brightest was that of the fly *Calliphora*, which carries the subsurface nipple array; while the dimmest was that of the moth *Sphynx* with its nipple-in-air array. The crosses show the measured decrease in reflection resulting from the nipple-in-air array. The filled circles are values obtained by subtraction of the values represented by open circles (moth minus fly) from those marked by crosses (moth minus grasshopper), and they give a measure of the efficiency of the subsurface nipple array.

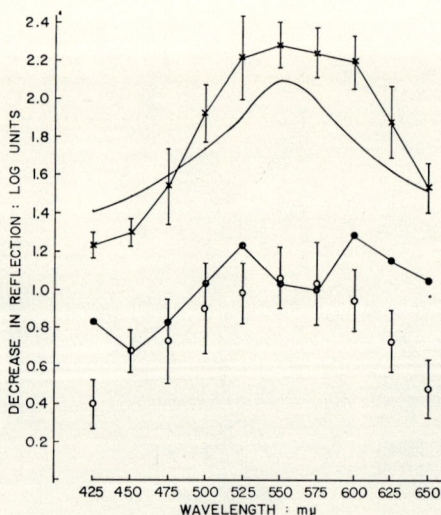

FIG. 12

Direct photometric measurements of reflection intensity differences from corneal fragments of grasshopper *Melanoplus* and moth *Sphynx* (crosses), and moth *Sphynx* and fly *Calliphora* (open circles). Difference between grasshopper and fly are calculated (filled circles). Solid curve is theoretical difference in reflection between grasshopper and moth. Measured points, averages of four measurements. One standard deviation indicated, both above and below each measured value. See text for further details.

We believe that the corneal nipple array enhances camouflage under conditions of bright illumination, and it may also increase the animal's visibility under conditions of dim illumination. For detailed arguments concerning these hypotheses the reader should refer to Bernhard, Miller and Møller (1965). However, special mention should be made of the newly discovered fact that the eyes of certain insects have an absolute threshold to illumination far below that of any known vertebrate eye (see Reichardt, this volume). This additional knowledge gives added probability that the nipple array is useful in increasing visibility under conditions of dim illumination.

ACKNOWLEDGEMENTS

We thank Mr. Charles H. Kreiger for technical assistance. These investigations were supported by the Air Force Office of Scientific Research under Grant AF EOAR 65-9 through the European Office of Aerospace Research (OAR), United States Air Force (to C. G. Bernhard), the Swedish Medical Research Council, Stiftelsen Therese och Johan Andersons Minne, Stiftelsen Gustaf och Thyra Svenssons Minne, Systrarna Wesséns Stiftelse, Anna Cederbergs Stiftelse för medicinsk forskning, United States Public Health Service Grant NB 05730 (to W. H. Miller), and the Connecticut Lions Eye Research Foundation.

REFERENCES

BERNHARD, C. G. and MILLER, W. H. 1962. A corneal nipple pattern in insect compound eyes. *Acta physiol. scand.* **56**, 385–6.
BERNHARD, C. G., MILLER, W. H. and MØLLER, A. R. 1963. Function of the corneal nipples in the compound eye of insects. *Acta physiol. scand.* **58**, 381–2.
BERNHARD, C. G., MILLER, W. H. and MØLLER, A. R. 1965. The insect corneal nipple array. *Acta physiol. scand.* **63** (Suppl. 243).
MILLER, W. H., BERNHARD, C. G. and MØLLER, A. R. 1964. Insect corneal nipple array— A natural impedance transformer. *J. Opt. Soc. Amer.* **54**, 581–2 (Abstract).

ON THE IMAGE FORMATION IN A SINGLE OMMATIDIUM OF THE COMPOUND EYE IN DIPTERA

J. W. KUIPER

Department of Biophysics, Natuurkundig Laboratorium,
University of Groningen, The Netherlands

INTRODUCTION

THE "mosaic theory" of Johannes Müller states that each ommatidium receives the impression of a luminous area which corresponds with the geometric projection of the ommatidium on the visual field.

In this theory the functional unit of the compound eye is the ommatidium. This theory was and still is mainly based on a large number of data obtained in behaviour experiments in Arthropods.

However, observations on the optics indicate that, in some insects, particularly Diptera, the image that is formed by the dioptric apparatus is analysed by the sense cells: optical (Kuiper) and electrophysiological studies (Waterman, 1954; Autrum and Wiedemann, 1962; Washizu and co-workers, 1964; Kirschfeld, 1965) have revealed that the directional sensitivity of a single sense cell is considerably larger than would be expected from the mosaic theory. Quantitatively, however, the agreement between the optical and electrophysiological approaches seems to be poor: the total width of the field of vision of the retinula cells obtained in electrophysiological observations is much greater than that calculated on the basis of diffraction theory (De Vries, 1956).

Because of these discrepancies it seemed worthwhile to study the image formation in the single ommatidium of Diptera somewhat more closely.

GENERAL CONSTRUCTION OF THE EYE, AND STATEMENT OF THE PROBLEM

The dioptric apparatus of the compound eye is formed by the corneal lens and the crystalline cone. The surface of the corneal facets is not constant in area, but varies over the surface of the compound eye (see Fig. 1). Barlow (1952), De Vries (1956) and Kuiper and Leutscher-Hazelhoff (1966) have

35

shown that the square of the diameter of the facets is proportional to the radius of curvature of the whole compound eye, as would be expected from diffraction theory.

In most insects the facets are hexagonal in shape even though the corneal lens is formed by four cells, and in each ommatidium there are, besides the four corneagen cells, four cone cells, four pigment cells and often eight retinula cells. A simple physical explanation can be given for the hexagonal form: the outer surface of the lens is part of a sphere and the minimum spatial arrangement of spherical surfaces gives rise to hexagons. (Of course the intersections of the spherical surfaces are not straight but curved lines.) When the lenses are flat rather than convex on the outside, as in some Crustacea, the minimum spatial arrangement is in some cases over-ruled by the cellular composition, and square or rhomboid facets are found.

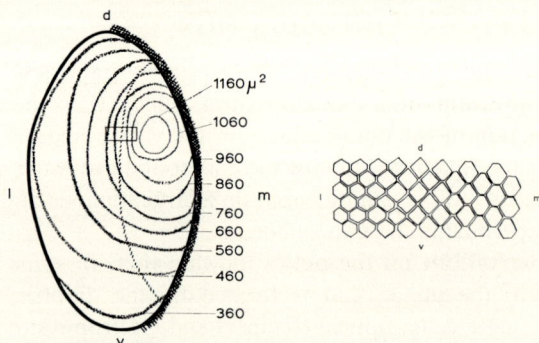

FIG. 1

Map of the left eye of a male *Calliphora*. d = dorsal, m = median, v = ventral. The stippled lines unite facets of equal area. The vertical dotted line separates the facets that are oriented with an edge upwards from those oriented with a side upwards. On the dotted line itself, the facets are rhomboid in shape.

But in Diptera we also find in the dorsal–ventral direction a row of rhomboid facets, and the orientation of the hexagonal facets on either side differs as indicated in Fig. 1. Whether this change in the orientation of the facets is just due to the arrangement of the ommatidia on the non-spherical shape of the whole eye or whether there is a biological significance is unknown.

The thickness of the corneal lenses and the radius of curvature of both the inner and the outer surface vary between species and even for different parts of an individual eye.

For the cone, a great many shapes have been described (see Weber, 1933). In Diptera the cone consists of a fluid; other species have cones of a solid chitin structure. On the proximal side of the cone the retinula cells are arranged around the longitudinal axis of the ommatidium.

The axial part of the retinula cell forms a scructure called the rhabdomere. It has a diameter of about 1μ and a high refractive index, so that physically it behaves as a wave guide. In most insect species the rhabdomeres are fused to form one rhabdome, but in Diptera the rhabdomeres are separated.

Each one of the seven or eight retinular cells forms at its proximal end an axon which penetrates the membrane at the bases of the sense cells. In most cases the ommatidia are surrounded by a sheath of pigment cells that contain dark granules. It is thought that this sheath of pigment has the function of optically isolating the ommatidia from each other.

The function of the corneal lens and crystalline cone is to concentrate light into the rhabdomeres. We will occupy ourselves with the classical problem of how they perform this task, and the importance of the images they form.

GEOMETRICAL OPTICS OF THE DIOPTRIC APPARATUS; CALCULATIONS OF THE FOCAL LENGTH

For the image formation the following parameters are essential: the refractive index of chitin (the substance the lenses are made of) (n); the refractive index of the cone substance (n_c); the diameter of the lens (d); the thickness of the lens (g) (this thickness cannot be neglected, because g is not very small with respect to R_o); the radii of curvature of the outer and inner surfaces of the lens (R_o and R_i).

We calculate the focal length (f) with the formula for a thick lens:

$$f = \frac{nR_oR_i}{(n-1)\ n(R_i-R_o)+(n-1)g} \tag{1}$$

The refractive index of the chitin was determined by embedding the corneal lenses in fluids of a known refractive index. The fluid which gives the minimum contrast in phase-contrast microscopy has a refractive index which corresponds to that of the lens. For *Calliphora* we obtained $n = 1\cdot499 \pm 0\cdot001$. In our calculations we will use $n = 1\cdot5$.

The diameters of the lenses (d) vary between 20 and 40 μ. Within one eye, the large ones are situated in the centre of the eye and the smaller ones are found in the ventral and lateral parts of the eye.

The thickness (g) of the lens is not constant; in our calculations we have used $\frac{1}{3} d < g < d$.

The radius of curvature of the outer surface of the lens was determined in microscopic sections of the cornea. We found that this radius is related to the diameter of the lens, and for a first approximation we used $R_o = d$. In these preparations the inner surface of the lens cannot be seen very well, but in most cases they were evidently concave and not convex, as they are often pictured in literature. However, this is misleading. In *Calliphora* it can be seen even in microscopic sections that for the larger lenses the inner surface is most often flat; only the smaller lenses, found at the ventral and lateral parts of the eye, are biconvex. Therefore we studied the inner surface of the lens in more detail with the aid of reflected light microscopy, both normal and phase-contrast. In these experiments the cornea was freed from adhering tissue, and only the chitin lenses were left. With high magnification it appeared that most lenses are concave on the inner side, but that the central part of each lens is only very slightly curved. The diameter of this central area is $\frac{1}{2}$ to $\frac{3}{4}$ that of the facet and its surface is smoother than that of the surrounding ring. This implies that, particularly for the larger frontal lenses, d is not quite equal to the facet diameter, but rather on the order of $\frac{3}{4}$ of this value. In the case of a flat or nearly flat inner surface, the focal length of the corneal lens amounts to about $2 R_o$. For values of $R_i = 6 R_o$, whether concave or convex, the effect on the focal length (f) is no more than about 10% in eqn. (1). The effect of the variance in g is still smaller.

Taking into account the effect of the crystalline cone, the value obtained with eqn. (1) must be multiplied by the refractive index of the cone substance (n_c) to obtain the focal length in the functioning ommatidium. Using $n_c = 1\cdot33$ and the measured values of R_o, we obtain

$$47 \,\mu < f < 78 \,\mu.$$

These values fall within the range where the tips of the rhabdomeres are found. More detailed information, in this respect, would be welcome, however. For biconvex lenses, smaller values of f will be found. For $\frac{1}{2} R_o < R_i < 2 R_o$, with formula 1, we obtain $\frac{3}{4} R_o < f < 1\frac{1}{2} R_o$, i.e. again using the values measured for R_o and multiplying with $n_c = 1\cdot33$:

$$17 \,\mu < f < 69 \,\mu.$$

These values are not unreasonable, since the cones of the smaller lenses at the ventral and lateral parts of the eye indeed tend to be shorter than those found in the centre, and with the tips of the rhabdomeres therefore closer to the cornea than in the larger lenses.

In conclusion, we may say that the focal length, calculated from the geometry of the lenses and a likely value for the refractive index of the cone, falls within a range where we would expect it. In the next section we will see whether the image observed behind single corneal lenses is in good accordance with the calculated focal length.

OBSERVATIONS OF THE IMAGE FORMED BY SINGLE CORNEAL LENSES

Pieces of cornea were cleaned of all adhering tissue and suspended from a cover slip in a drop of distilled water. Care was taken that there was no water on the outside of the cornea. Using a high power microscope with a water-immersion objective the image behind the corneal lenses was observed. As has been found many times before (see Introduction to this volume, Bernhard), images can be seen of objects that are viewed under an angle of a few degrees. Though there is one position where an optimal image can be observed, there is no sharp focal plane: over a distance of 20–30 μ along the optical axis the image can be seen. This is most clearly demonstrated where the eye is looking at two point sources seen under an angle of 3°. In a number of preparations photographs were taken at several distances from the cornea. Table 1 shows the distances at which the best images were found. These experimental values come quite close to the value calculated from the geometry of the lenses.

The wide range over which an image is observed reminds us of the camera obscura or the pinhole camera. When an image is formed by a small hole, there is not a distinct focal length but a wide range of distances over which the image can be observed. For the image formation in the camera obscura, geometrical as well as diffraction optics have to be taken into account.

TABLE 1

ϕ_f	f	$1/k$	b_o	b'	b''
42	78	1·11 ⎫		1·6	3·2
41	75	1·07 ⎬ 3·1±1		1·5	3·0
35	69	1·15 ⎫		1·7	3·4
33	53	1·11 ⎬ 3·5±0·5		1·4	2·8

ϕ_f, diameter of facet; f, position of best image of an object seen at 3°; k, angular magnification observed; b_o, the size of the central patch of the diffraction pattern measured from photographs; b', calculated size of Airy disc with eqn. (2) for $d = \phi_f$; b'', for $d = \frac{1}{2} \phi_f$. All values in microns.

In the compound eye we are dealing with very small lenses and diffraction becomes important. Therefore we will now consider the effect of diffraction on the focal properties of the small lenses and describe the intensity distribution along the optical axis.

CALCULATION OF THE DIFFRACTION IMAGE FOR A SINGLE LENS

Bottema and Kuiper (1964) succeeded in calculating the intensity distribution function along the axis of a circular lens with a diameter of 20 μ viewing a point source on the optical axis. In his calculations Bottema used the scalar diffraction theory of lens aberrations (see Born and Wolf, 1959); and took into account all the Fresnel diffraction phenomena at a circular opening. His results are reproduced in Fig. 2.

Although the values Bottema used for the diameter of the lenses are on the small side and the focal length $f = 100 \mu$ is too long for *Calliphora*, we will use his figures in order to demonstrate the effect of diffraction on image formation in general. The calculated intensity distribution function perpendicular to the optical axis is given for a number of points in Fig. 3.

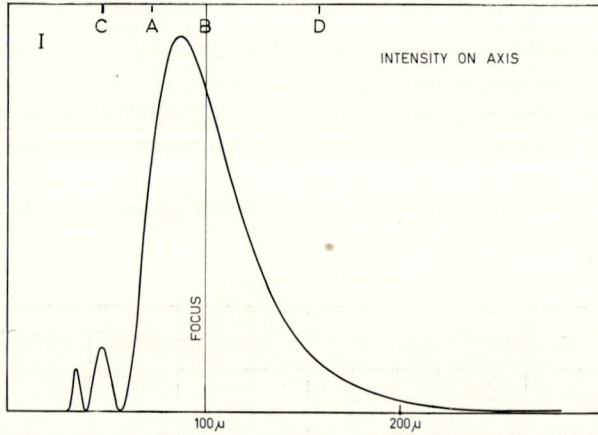

FIG. 2

Intensity distribution function along the optical axis of the ommatidium looking at a point source on the axis. The values were calculated by Bottema for a focal length of 100 μ and a lens diameter of 20 μ. On the abscissa the distance to the cornea is expressed in microns, on the ordinate the intensity is represented. Note that the maximum intensity is found somewhat closer to the cornea than the focal point.

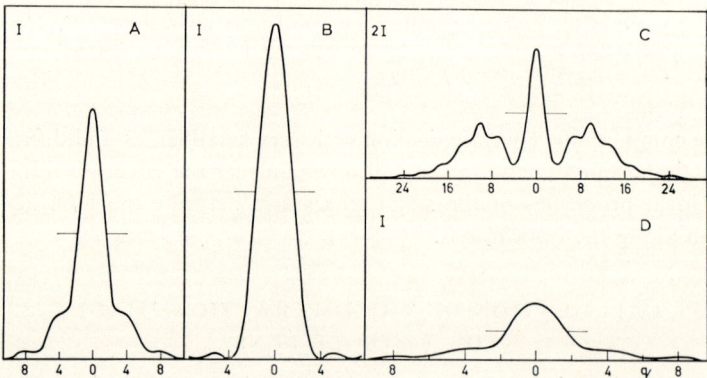

FIG. 3

Intensity distribution perpendicular to the optical axis for four positions indicated in Fig. 2. The value $q = \pi d\sigma / \lambda f$. σ = distance from the optical axis.

In the first place we notice that the position of the point which has the maximum intensity is not in the focal plane, where the Airy diffraction pattern is located, but somewhat closer to the cornea. Secondly, it is seen that for this central maximum the intensity distribution function perpendicular to the optical axis is rather similar to the one found in the focal plane. It is only at larger distances from the axis that the difference in the shape of the curves becomes pronounced. But if we regard only the central maximum, we find that the half-width value does not change much as we move along the optical axis near the focal plane: moving 25 μ in either direction decreases or increases the half-width by no more than 30%. This implies that the image of a point source or of an extended object must be visible over a wide range of depths, and this is exactly what we observe in the actual image formation. Also, the three minima and two maxima that were present in the calculations of the intensity distribution have been observed in later experiments.

Therefore, on the basis of the microscopic observations on single corneal lenses, together with the calculations of the diffraction image, we conclude that the cornea concentrates the light that it receives from a point source on its axis into a narrow "pencil" of light. The fact that this "pencil" extends over quite a range means that, by a similar amount, the distance of the rhabdomeres from the cornea is not critical.

Furthermore, the great depth of the image allows for a wide range of object distances.

Another conclusion is that the narrowness of the "pencil" favours the entrance of the light into the rhabdomeres.

Finally, we conclude that the intensity distribution at the distal end of the rhabdomeres can be described in terms of the intensity distribution of the Airy disc. In doing so, we make a mistake of no more than 30% in half-width value.

THE DIRECTIONAL SENSITIVITY OF THE RETINULA CELL

The directional sensitivity is defined as the relation between the response of the cell to light and the direction that this light comes from. The response may be either photochemical (bleaching of pigment, see Langer and Thorell, this volume) or it may consist of a change of the cell membrane potential or action potentials in the nerve fibre. In all cases the response is determined by the illumination of the sense cell. If the rhabdomere is the site of the primary photochemical event—in other words, the phototransducer—then optically the directional sensitivity of the retinula cell is determined by:

(1) The diameter of the rhabdomere. This is not much more than 1 μ (Fernández-Morán, 1958; Trujillo-Cenóz, 1966).

(2) The intensity distribution and the actual diameter of the diffraction pattern. In the previous section it was demonstrated that the diffraction pattern in the focal plane—that is, the Airy disc—can be used in the first approximation. The intensity distribution has been given in Fig. 3b.

The basic principle of the optical calculation of the directional sensitivity is explained in Fig. 4. The image of a point source is focused on a rhabdomere.

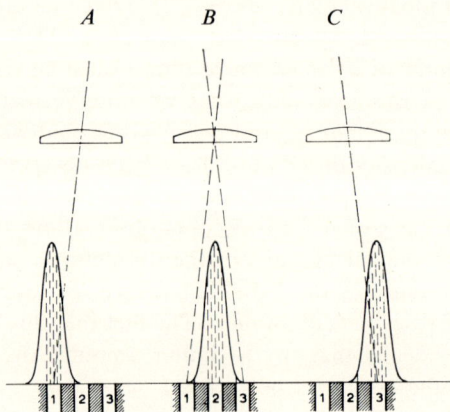

FIG. 4

Illumination of three rhabdomeres (1, 2 and 3) for three positions of a point source (A, B and C). The size of the rhabdomeres and that of the space between them equals $\frac{1}{4}$ of the Airy disc. Note that rhabdomere 2 can receive light from any position between A and C. The angle of directional sensitivity of the rhabdomere therefore corresponds to the angular size of the Airy disc.

The rhabdomere receives light from an angle corresponding to the diameter of the Airy disc (b):

$$b = 2 \times 1 \cdot 22 \frac{\lambda f}{n_c d}. \tag{2}$$

We calculated b for $d = \frac{1}{2}$ facet diameter (see above), and $\lambda = 0 \cdot 5$. There is some agreement between the observed and the calculated values of b, as is shown in Table 1.

The diameter of the central diffraction maximum is 2–3 times the diameter of the rhabdomere. The effect of the ratio between the rhabdomere and Airy disc diameters on the half-width value of the directional sensitivity (expressed in angular diameter of the Airy disc) is almost negligible for rhabdomere diameters that are smaller than $\frac{1}{2}$ of the Airy disc diameter, as is shown in Fig. 5. Therefore the directional sensitivity will be only a little larger than the angular diameter of the Airy disc.

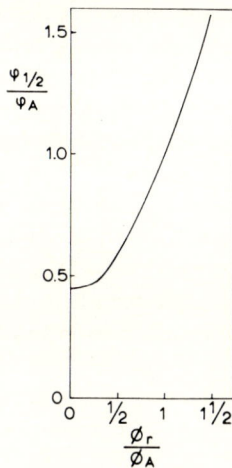

FIG. 5

The half-width of the directional sensitivity as expressed in the angular diameter
of the Airy disc (plotted on the ordinate) as a function of rhabdomere and Airy
disc diameters (plotted on the abscissa). It is seen that the directional sensitivity
does not change very much where the diameter of the rhabdomeres varies between
$\frac{1}{2}$ and $\frac{1}{4}$ of the diameter of the Airy disc.

The angular size of the Airy disc is:

$$\phi_A = 2 \times 1 \cdot 22 \frac{\lambda}{d} \text{ rad.} \qquad (3)$$

Inserting $20\mu < d < 40\mu$, and $\lambda = 0 \cdot 5 \ \mu$, gives for the directional sensitivity:

$$2 \cdot 2° < \phi < 4 \cdot 6°,$$

and for the half-width value $\phi_{\frac{1}{2}}$:

$$0 \cdot 9° < \phi_{\frac{1}{2}} < 2 \cdot 0.$$

The directional sensitivity thus calculated agrees reasonably well with the
values found by observing the light passing through the rhabdomeres (de
Vries and Kuiper, 1958; Kuiper, 1962). In good preparations the total
width of the directional sensitivity was about 4°. Furthermore, in preliminary
photometric measurements of the light passing through a single rhabdomere,
Weyers (not published) obtained a half-width value of 1·3°. In these measurements similar methods were used as described previously: the eye was frozen
and a section was cut with a freeze microtome. The freezing of the eye
might affect the dioptric system in some way, however, and therefore these
measurements should be repeated with fresh unfrozen eyes.

There is one consideration that has not yet been taken into account. We should expect the angular magnification factor (for the angle of incidence of the light in respect to the angle of the image that is formed) to be identical with the refractive index of the cone. This refractive index is unknown, but we have already assumed $n_c = 1 \cdot 33$. However, as is shown in Table 1, for small angles of incidence this magnification factor is close to 1. In our calculations of the directional sensitivity we have therefore neglected this.

The directional sensitivity calculated from the optics and measured optically must now be compared with that obtained electrophysiologically by Washizu, Burkhardt and Streck (1964). They used the membrane potential of single retinular cells, and corrected their response amplitude with the aid of their experimentally obtained relationship between light intensity and response amplitude. Their measurements result in a $\phi_{\frac{1}{2}}$ of 3° and 4° for the horizontal and the vertical plane respectively. This value is about twice that found in our case. However, we must notice that their results were obtained from small facets in the lateral part of the eye. In this area, the value they give for the diameter of the lenses is $10\,\mu < d < 15\,\mu$. We have calculated the directional sensitivity of these lenses, taking into consideration that at the larger angles of incidence which are found here the angular magnification factor may not be neglected as we have done above, and we have accordingly used a value of $1 \cdot 33$.

We find:

$$2 \cdot 7\,\mu < \phi_{\frac{1}{2}} < 4\,\mu.$$

These values calculated from the optics correspond very well with the experimentally found ones.

We have compared the results of Washizu, Burkhardt and Streck (1964) with our calculations in still more detail, using the data of their Fig. 5. These data, corrected by the authors for the effect of the light intensity–response amplitude relationship, should form a curve similar to the one obtained on the basis of diffraction optics. We therefore adapted the maximum and the half-width values to the intensity distribution in the Airy disc. The small but constant effect they recorded at large angles we considered as a zero effect in the calculations which are plotted in Fig. 6. Except at the wider angles the experimental data fit the theoretical directional sensitivity curve rather well. In a previous section it has been shown that the maximum intensity of the diffraction pattern can be described in terms of the intensity distribution of the Airy disc. However, Fig. 3 shows that out of the focal plane the intensity distribution curve fans out somewhat wider at larger distances from the optical axis. For this reason we do not pay much attention to the deviation at the larger angles, and conclude that the directional sensitivity or field of vision of the single retinula cell is mainly determined by diffraction.

We would like to comment on another experimental finding of Washizu, Burkhardt and Streck which we have already mentioned, in passing, namely, the difference they find in directional sensitivity in the vertical and the horizontal plane. In the small biconvex lenses at the lateral border of the compound eye we have noticed a considerable astigmatism: there was a noticeable difference in the position of the focal points for the horizontal and the vertical plane. We think this might be an explanation of their findings.

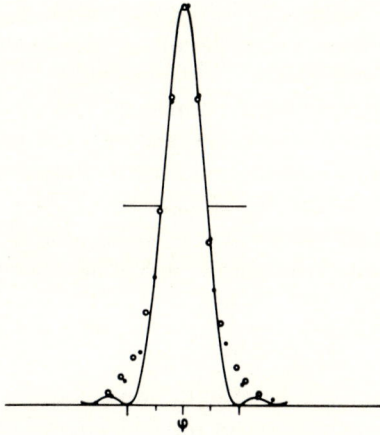

FIG. 6

The solid curve represents the light intensity distribution in the Airy disc and, as such, represents our theoretical directional sensitivity curve. The data from the publication of Washizu, Burkhardt and Streck (1964), corrected for a zero effect and adapted at the maximum and half-width values to fit our curve, are drawn as closed and open circles.

The data presented by Kirschfeld (1965) for the directional sensitivity of single retinula elements of *Musca* are not consistent with our expectations on the basis of diffraction. For a single rhabdomere of this animal we calculated a half-width value about half the value he found.

For an integrated effect of more than one cell we expect a directional sensitivity with at least three peaks, which did not occur.

VISUAL ACUITY WITHIN ONE OMMATIDIUM

The visual acuity of the retinula cells in one ommatidium is determined by diffraction, by the diameter and spacing of the rhabdomeres, and by the minimum detectable difference in radiant energy received by the rhabdomeres.

For a minimum of three rhabdomeres, the minimum angle of resolution has to be larger than the half-width value of the directional sensitivity of the rhabdomeres. This half-width value depends on the width of the diffraction pattern and on the diameter and spacing of the rhabdomeres. As has been shown in Fig. 5, a decrease of the rhabdomere diameter to less than $\frac{1}{2}$ the Airy disc diameter affects the half-width value of the directional sensitivity only very little.

Having very small rhabdomeres would imply that only a very small fraction of the available light is effective. Moreover, when the diameter of the rhabdomeres approaches the wavelength of the light, hardly any light will enter the rhabdomeres. A diameter of $2\,\lambda$, as is found in *Calliphora*, does not seem to be far off the limit.

With respect to the remaining parameters, namely the spacing of the rhabdomeres at the tip of the cone, and the contrast sensitivity of the retinular cells in one ommatidium, there are no data available.

For the moment, therefore, we must restrict ourselves to the conclusion that the minimum angle of resolution within one ommatidium must be larger than the half-width value of the directional sensitivity ($\phi_{\frac{1}{2}}$).

DISCUSSION

Our main conclusion can be that the directional sensitivity of a single retinula cell in the compound eye of the fly *Calliphora* is determined by the diffraction pattern at the tip of the rhabdomere of that cell. Because in Diptera the rhabdomeres are completely separated, the image formed by the dioptric apparatus can be analysed by the retinula cells. In other words, the sense cells within one ommatidium look in different directions, as is indeed observed (Kuiper, 1962; Wiedemann, 1965). In *Limulus*, also, there is evidence that not the ommatidium but the retinula cell is the functional unit (Ratliff, 1966). There are results, obtained with optomotor reactions of flies (Fermi and Reichardt, 1963; Götz, 1965), that can be described with a model in which the ommatidium is the functional unit. However, this does not prove that the information available at the level of the retinula cells is not evaluated by the visual mechanism.

In most other insects the rhabdomeres are fused to form one central rhabdome, and the spacing between the original rhabdomeres is in this case $< \frac{1}{4}\,\lambda$. Thus, "optical crosstalk" between them prevents image analysis within one ommatidium. For such insects there is no evidence that it is not the ommatidium that is the functional unit.

As for the visual acuity, experimental evidence has been presented by Burtt and Catton (1954, 1962) that in locusts and flies visual acuity is better than might be expected on the basis of the diffractive properties of the dioptric apparatus. In the optic lobe and in the thoracal nerve cord they recorded spikes in response to the movement of a black and white grating behind a window. They obtained an activity in the nervous system when the period of the grating was seen under an angle that was three times smaller than the angular resolution calculated on the basis of the Rayleigh criterion ($\frac{1}{2}\phi$). They explained their data with the aid of higher order diffraction images (deep images). These images can be observed especially for stimuli that consist of periodic structures, but only if the medium behind the cornea lens is transparent and isotropic. In the intact eye this is not the case, and therefore I do not think that their presumption is correct. Moreover, the considerable light-gathering power of the rhabdomeres would obliterate the comparatively very faint higher-order diffraction images even if they did exist in intact eyes. In my opinion, a better explanation of the Burtt and Catton effect is provided by Palka (1965) and Barlow (1965). They showed that the responses to these small-angle gratings could be due to events at the edges of the window behind which the gratings are moved.

In Diptera the outer surface of the corneal lens is the important part of the dioptric system. This is not the case in all Arthropods, as can be seen by comparing the compound eyes of terrestrial and aquatic forms. In many aquatic Arthropods we noticed a smooth cornea with lenses that protruded hardly if at all. This is rather unexpected, because when a spherical surface with a radius of curvature R_o separates two media with refractive index n and n', then the focal distance f is given by

$$f = \frac{R_o}{n'-n},\tag{4}$$

Therefore, when an animal moves from air ($n = 1$) into water ($n = 1\cdot3$), the focal length of its lenses will increase with about a factor of two. If the front surface of the lenses is important, we would expect corneal lenses with a smaller radius of curvature in the eyes of aquatic forms. As a general rule this is not true. A suitable animal in which to investigate this seems to be the whirligig beetle *Gyrilus*, a small water beetle moving on the surface of the water. This animal has on both sides two compound eyes; a dorsal eye which is directed upwards into the air and a ventral one which looks downwards into the water (Wigglesworth, 1942).

The refractive index of the chitin was found to be the same in both pairs of eyes. With reflected light interference microscopy we took photographs of both eyes. The photographs are reproduced in Figs. 7, A, B. In this case the whole eye is small and its curvature strong; for this reason no complete set of interference rings could be obtained. In a number of cases we succeeded in measuring the radius of part of the interference fringes, and calculated from these the radius of curvature of the corneal lenses.

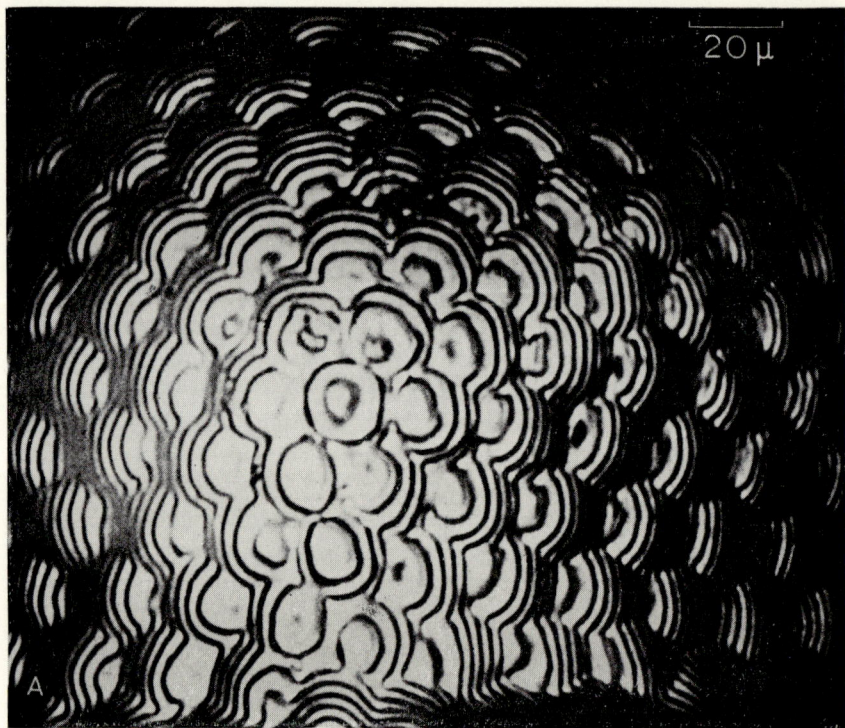

FIG. 7A

Photograph of the upper (A) and lower (B) compound eye of the whirligig beetle *Gyrilus natans*, as seen in reflected light interference microscopy. $\lambda = 5461$ Å. Note that the lenses in the lower eye protrude less than those in the upper eye.

The results are given in Table 2.

TABLE 2

RADIUS OF CURVATURE OF THE OUTER SURFACE OF CORNEAL LENS OF THE UPPER AND LOWER COMPOUND EYE OF GYRILUS (IN MICRONS)

Upper eye	Lower eye
	$129\cdot3\pm 5\cdot4$
$109\cdot8\pm4\cdot4$	$143\cdot2\pm10\cdot8$
$104\cdot0\pm1\cdot1$	$112\cdot2\pm11\cdot4$
	$145\cdot7\pm2\cdot0$

Though the measurements are not very accurate they certainly do not indicate that the radius of curvature of the corneal lens of the lower eye is smaller than it is in the upper eye. Indeed, it is rather the opposite way. This is at least an indication that here the corneal lens is not as important for the image formation as it is in the eyes of Diptera.

In many aquatic forms the dioptric system is more complicated, however; often the cone is a solid and elongated structure terminated on either side by a spherical surface, which will certainly make a contribution to the refractive power of the lens.

We should therefore be aware of the differences which exist between the dioptric systems of different species. They should be studied separately, since the results obtained with *Calliphora* can certainly not be applied throughout.

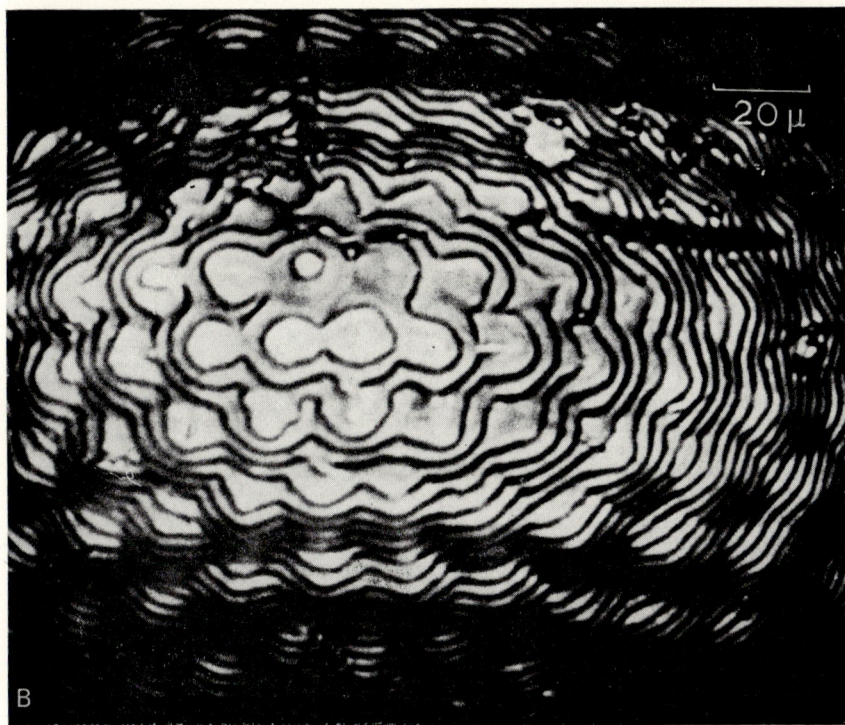

FIG. 7B (*see* opposite)

ACKNOWLEDGEMENTS

I would like to express my gratitude to Dr. Tj. J. de Boer, Dr. M. Bottema, Mr. H. P. Horst, J. J. Schuurman, H. Stal, O. Tilstra and H. Weyers for their collaboration in part of the research reported.

C.E.—E

Thanks are due to Dr. J. T. Leutscher-Hazelhoff for her criticism and aid during the preparation of the manuscript.

REFERENCES

AUTRUM, H. and WIEDEMANN, J. 1962. Versuche über den Strahlengang im Insektenauge. *Z. Naturforsch.* **17b**, 480–2.

BARLOW, H. B. 1952. The size of ommatidia in apposition eyes. *J. Exp. Biol.* **29**, 667–74.

BARLOW, H. B. 1965. Visual resolution and the diffraction limit. *Science* **149**, 553–5.

BERNHARD, C. G. 1966. Opening address. This volume.

BORN, M. and WOLF, E., 1959. *Principles of Optics.* Pergamon Press.

BOTTEMA, M. and KUIPER, J. W. 1964. *Diffraction Optics of the Compound Eye.* Intern. Report Natuurkundig Lab. R.U., Groningen.

BURTT, E. T. and CATTON, W. T. 1954. Visual perception of movement in the locust. *J. Physiol.* (*London*) **125**, 566–80.

BURTT, E. T. and CATTON, W. T. 1962a. Resolving power in the compound eye. *Symp. Exp. Biol.* **16**, 72–85.

BURTT, E. T. and CATTON, W. T. 1962b. A diffraction theory of insect vision. *Proc. Roy. Soc.* (*London*) B. **157**, 53–82.

FERMI, G. and REICHARDT, W. 1963. Optomotorische Reaktionen der Fliege *Musca domestica. Kybernetik* **2**, 15.

FERNÁNDEZ-MORÁN, H. 1958. Fine structure of the light receptors in the compound eye of insects. *Exptl. Cell. Res.* Suppl. 5, pp. 586–644.

GÖTZ, K. G. 1965. Die optischen Uebertragungseigenschaften der Komplexaugen von *Drosophila. Kybernetik* **2**, 13.

KIRSCHFELD, K. 1965. Das anatomische und das physiologische Sehfeld der Ommatidien im Komplexauge von *Musca. Kybernetik*, **2**, 249–75.

KUIPER, J. W. 1962. The optics of the compound eye. *Symp. Soc. Exp. Biol.* **16**, 58–71 (Cambridge University Press).

KUIPER, J. W. and LEUTSCHER-HAZELHOFF, J. T. 1966. Linear and non-linear responses from the compound eye of *Calliphora erythrocephala. Cold Spring Harbor Symposium* **30** (in press).

LANGER, H. and THORELL, B. 1966. Microspectrophotometric assay of visual pigments in single rhabdomeres of the insect eye. This volume.

PALKA, J. 1965. Diffraction and visual acuity of insects. *Science* **149**, 551–3.

RATLIFF, F. 1966. Personal communication.

TRUJILLO-CENÓZ, O. 1966. Structural organisation of the arthropod eye. *Cold Spring Harbor Symposium* **30**, in press.

VRIES, HL. DE. 1956. Physical aspects of sense organs. *Progr. Biophys.* **6**, 208–64.

VRIES, HL. DE, and KUIPER, J. W. 1958. Optics of the insect eye. Conference on Photoreception. *Ann. New York Acad. Sciences* **74**, 196–203.

WASHIZU, Y., BURKHARDT, D. and STRECK, P. 1964. Visual field of single retinula cells and interommatidial inclination in the compound eye of the blowfly *Calliphora erythrocephala. Z. vergl. Physiol.* **48**, 413–28.

WATERMAN, T. H. 1954. Directional sensitivity of single ommatidia in the compound eye of *Limulus. Proc. Nat. Acad. Sci.* (*Wash.*) **40**, 252–7.

WIEDEMANN, I. 1965. Versuche über den Strahlengang im Insektenauge (Appositionsauge). *Z. vergl. Physiol.* **49**, 526–42.

WIGGLESWORTH, V. B. 1942. *The Principles of Insect Physiology*, 2nd ed. Methuen, London.

WEBER, H., 1933. *Lehrbuch der Entomologie.* Fischer Verlag.

PHYSIOLOGICAL OPTICS OF THE COMPOUND EYE OF THE BLOW FLY

D. Burkhardt, I. de la Motte, and G. Seitz

Zoologisches Institut der Universität, Frankfurt am Main, Germany

In order to understand the functioning of any image forming eye one has to know the properties of the dioptric apparatus. In the case of the insect compound eye we are still far from a thorough understanding. Obviously the physical properties of the insect dioptric apparatus are much more complex than those of the lens in the vertebrate eye. Furthermore, in the case of insects, we are dealing with extraordinarily small structures. In the following paper we will discuss one aspect only: the directional sensitivity of the compound eye and of its subunits, namely the ommatidia and the visual cells. The morphological and experimental data are restricted to the species *Calliphora erythrocephala*, but we hope some of the findings and conclusions may hold true for a wider variety of insects.

I. THE TOTAL VISUAL FIELD

To determine which section of space can be seen by the compound eye as a whole we used the phenomenon of the "pseudo-pupil". If the eye is observed from the direction of illumination a characteristic pattern of darkened ommatidia can be seen. Those ommatidia which open towards the light source are dark since they absorb a large amount of the incident light. The surrounding ommatidia are brighter due to scattered reflection of the light. This pseudo-pupil can hardly be observed in normal flies but is readily seen in the eye colour mutant "chalky" which lacks all of the screening pigments.

The experimental subjects are placed under a high power dissecting microscope, the "Zeiss Technoskop", with a built-in light source. The light strikes the object from the observer's direction in the form of a bundle of nearly parallel rays. Under these conditions a regular pattern of about eight ommatidia forms the pseudo-pupil, as can be seen in Fig. 1. The preparation is rotated with respect to the direction of the incident light until the pseudo-pupil—which moves across the rows of ommatidia—has reached the edge of the eye. The resulting angles between the body axis of the fly and the direction of illumination represent a direct measurement of the angular limits of the visual field. Figure 2 shows the results.

51

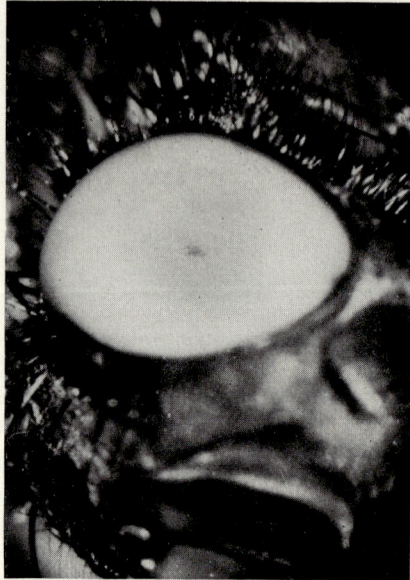

FIG. 1

The pseudo-pupil in the compound eye of the mutant "chalky". It consists of a pattern of a few darkened ommatidia, here positioned near the centre of the eye.

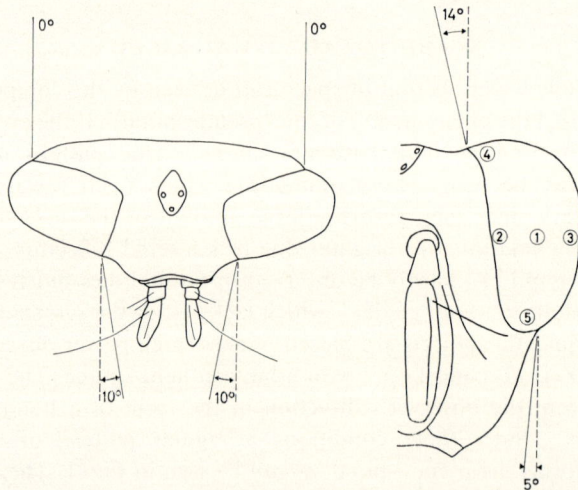

FIG. 2

The total visual field of the compound eye of the blow fly. Left: the extent of the visual field within the horizontal plane; right: within the vertical plane perpendicular to the longitudinal axis of the body. The numbers given in the right eye indicate the regions of the eye which are investigated in Tables 1 and 2.

II. INCLINATION BETWEEN VISUAL AXES OF
NEIGHBOURING OMMATIDIA

In *Calliphora* we found the whole compound eye to be composed of about 5400 ommatidia. There is no significant difference between males and females. Is the distribution of these subunits homogeneous within the total visual field or not? To answer this question one can measure some of the fundamental characteristics of the eye, primarily the angular deviation between the axes of adjacent ommatidia. Usually the data is obtained from histological sections. But this method is not very accurate since the ommatidia at the edge of the eye are curved and the visual axis is not in every case identical with the midline of the ommatidium. The use of the pseudo-pupil will give a more reliable measure. If the eye is rotated just enough so that the pseudo-pupil jumps from one row of ommatidia to the next, the angle of rotation represents the angular distance of the visual axes. Values for different areas of the eye are given in Table 1. We can see that the distribution of the ommatidia is quite uniform within the total visual field, but at the lateral edge of the eye the angle between adjacent visual axes is slightly greater than in the rest of the eye.

TABLE 1

INCLINATION BETWEEN THE VISUAL AXES OF
NEIGHBOURING OMMATIDIA

	Region of the eye (cf. Fig. 3)				
	1	2	3	4	5
Horizontal direction	2·0°	2·0°	4·6°	3·2°	3·4°
Vertical direction	2·6°	3·3°	2·6°	2·6°	3·4°

III. THE VISUAL FIELD OF THE OMMATIDIA

The inclination between the ommatidia is not the only fundamental characteristic of the eye's substructure. Another characteristic parameter to be considered is the width of the visual field of the individual ommatidia. To check whether this is the same in all parts of the total visual field we need only a comparative measure. Again the use of the pseudo-pupil will be of help. The angular limits of the pseudo-pupil darkening inside one particular ommatidium are read off. Of course this will be only a relative measure of the ommatidium's visual field. The subjective decision of the observer whether the pseudo-pupil is still present or not will influence the results, especially since the field is not sharply bordered but fades out gradually. However, as long as different parts of the eye are examined by the same observer, this method will allow comparison. Table 2 gives some of the results. We find the visual fields to be nearly uniform in all parts of the eye, again with the exception of the lateral edge where the visual fields have a somewhat greater area. The horizontal and the vertical limits of the visual fields are the same in individual ommatidia.

TABLE 2

VISUAL FIELDS OF THE OMMATIDIA
AS MEASURED WITH THE PSEUDO-PUPIL

	Region of the eye (cf. Fig. 3)				
	1	2	3	4	5
Horizontal direction	7·1°	6·6°	10·0°	8·0°	10·7°
Vertical direction	7·2°	6·4°	11·7°	8·8°	10·7°

IV. THE DIRECTIONAL SENSITIVITY OF SINGLE VISUAL CELLS

For many years it seemed well established that the ommatidia are the smallest subunits of the compound eye as far as resolving power in space is concerned. But during recent years interest has turned more towards another possibility, namely that the visual cells are the smallest physiological subunits. Observation of the pseudo-pupil provided only relative measurements of the visual field of the ommatidium. When using electrophysiological methods we have the advantage of direct and absolute values for the aforementioned physiological subunits, the single visual cells. The techniques applied have been published in detail in a previous paper (Washizu, Burkhardt and Streck, 1964), therefore we will give only a very short outline in this paper.

Single visual cells are penetrated with fine microelectrodes. The height of the dynamic phase of their graded receptor potential is taken as a measure for the reaction to light. The light source is placed far enough away so that the light beam entering the ommatidium can be regarded as parallel. The diameter of the light point—measured in angular degrees—is small compared

with the morphological opening of an ommatidium. The light source is mounted on a device which allows it to be moved along definite pathways. If we regard the experimental subject as the centre of a sphere, the movements are such as to follow a meridian or a circle of latitude of this sphere. To find the solid angle from which the receptor cell accepts light, one should measure along two sections perpendicular to each other. If one moves the light source along a circle of latitude instead of along a great circle one has to perform some mathematical operations to transform the values obtained into those one would have had measured along the great circle. The situation is shown in Fig. 3.

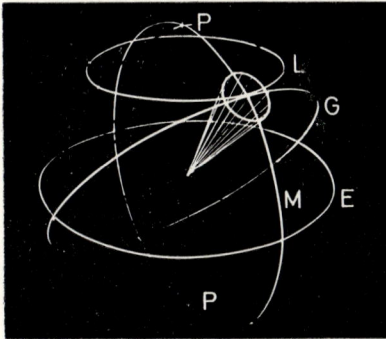

FIG. 3

Schematic drawing of the arrangement used for measuring the solid angle seen by a single visual cell. The cell within the centre of the sphere points with its visual axis towards a certain geographical latitude. The solid angle which is seen by the cell should be gained by measuring along a meridian (M) and a great circle (G), both crossing the visual axis. For practical reasons the light source was moved along the meridian and along a circle of latitude (L). The angle between the edges of the visual field and the centre of the circle of latitude multiplied by the cosine of the geographical latitude gives the angle one would measure along the great circle. (E) Equator, (P) Pole.

We have to confess that this point was missed in the first paper. Unfortunately the absolute coordinates of the cells investigated have not been protocolled in every case. Thus the transformation, a simple multiplication by the cosine of the geographical latitude upon which the light source is moved, cannot be done now. This mistake does not change any of the values obtained moving the light source along the meridian, yet the values given in the previous paper, mentioned above, for the extent of the visual field in the horizontal direction are too large. On account of this the visual fields were described as elliptic but now we believe that their extent perpendicular to the meridian is not greater than their extent along it. In the following we will deal with the values obtained in the vertical or meridian direction; thus we need not care about any transformations. The extent of the visual field is represented by the directional sensitivity curve which is obtained in the following way: first, the light source is brought into the position where it causes the highest action potential. This direction is called the visual axis of the cell. In this position the height of the action potential is measured as a function of varying light intensities. Next, a standard intensity is applied and the light source is moved stepwise to angular positions which deviate more and more from the visual axis. This causes lower action potentials and from the intensity curve one can read off which particular light intensity would cause such a reduced action potential. Thus the reaction of the cell indicates the stimulus effectiveness of oblique light bundles. Figure 4 gives an example for a single

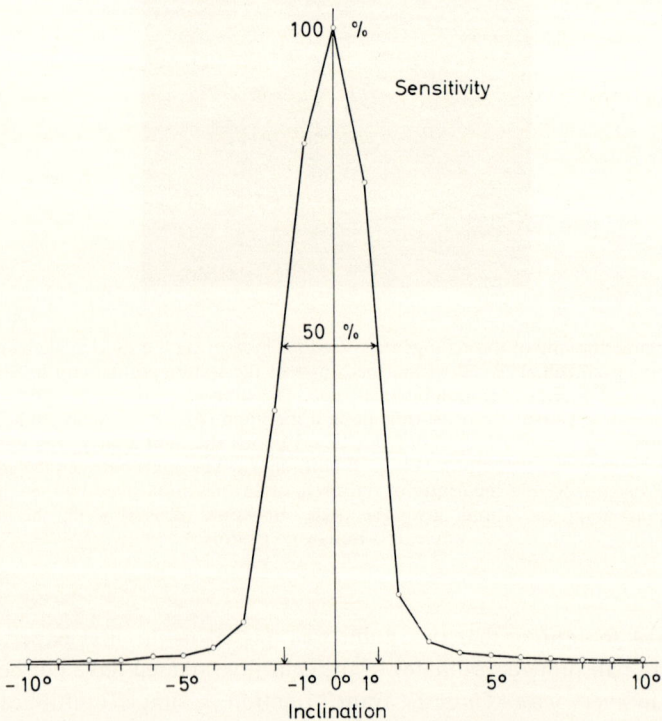

FIG. 4

Directional sensitivity of a single visual cell at the lateral edge of the compound eye of *Calliphora erythrocephala* (wild type). Abscissa: inclination of the light beam relative to the visual axis of the cell. The light source was moved in the vertical plane. Ordinate: relative brightness of the light as calculated from the reaction of the cell; scale: per cent of the maximal value. The arrows indicate the half-width of the directional sensitivity curve.

cell at the lateral edge of the eye (normally pigmented wild type). The directional sensitivity curve is smooth and bell-shaped, gradually flattening with increasing angular deviation from the visual axis. Oscillations or other irregularities are rarely observed, whether white or monochromatic light is used.

Not every single cell shows such a sharp and slender curve as the one seen in Fig. 4. While in that example the half-width is about 3°, we found for twenty cells at the lateral edge of the eye (wild type) an average half-width of 5·2°, in six cells of the frontal region a half-width of 3·3°. This is in agreement with the results from the pseudo-pupil measurements, where the visual fields of the ommatidia at the lateral edge were larger than in other parts of the eye. Besides this systematic variation in the visual fields of cells from different eye regions, there is also variation within the same eye region if the fields of many cells are compared. Finally, we compared the directional sensitivities of normal flies and of eye colour mutants. This is shown in Fig. 5. The midparts of the curves from the normal fly and the mutant "chalky" follow the same course, but at greater angular deviations the curve from the mutant lies above the normal curve. We must conclude, that with large angular deviations from the visual axes the effects of the screening pigments enter the figure.

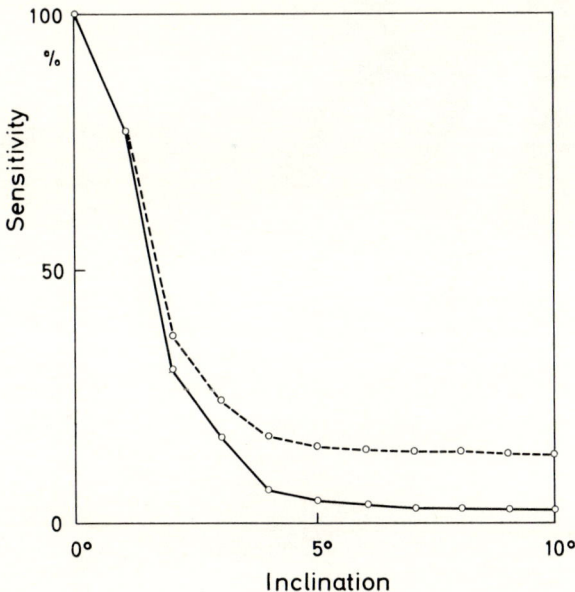

FIG. 5

Average values for the directional sensitivity of 20 single visual cells at the lateral edge of the eye from the wild type (solid line) and 5 cells from the mutant "chalky" (broken line). Abscissa and ordinate the same as in Fig. 4.

DISCUSSION

The electrophysiological measurements have provided precise data about the directional sensitivity of the smallest subunit of the compound eye, the visual cell. This directional sensitivity curve results from the properties of the dioptric apparatus as well as from the properties of the light-accepting structures and finally from the geometrical relation between both.

In *Calliphora* the focal distance of the optic system which about equals the length of the dioptric apparatus is roughly 50–70 μ depending on the region of the eye. As postulated by Exner's theory (Exner, 1891) and proven by direct measurements (unpublished data) the image of the light source is focused near the proximal end of the crystal cone. The light sensitive parts of the visual cells are the rhabdomeres. These rhabdomeres bear small cylindrical processes which approach closely the proximal end of the crystal cone. Figures 6 and 7 show the morphological situation and Fig. 8 gives a schematic representation. A parallel beam of light will be focused by the dioptric apparatus to a small spot in the focal plane. If the light bundle is moved to increasing deviations from the visual axis, the focal intensity

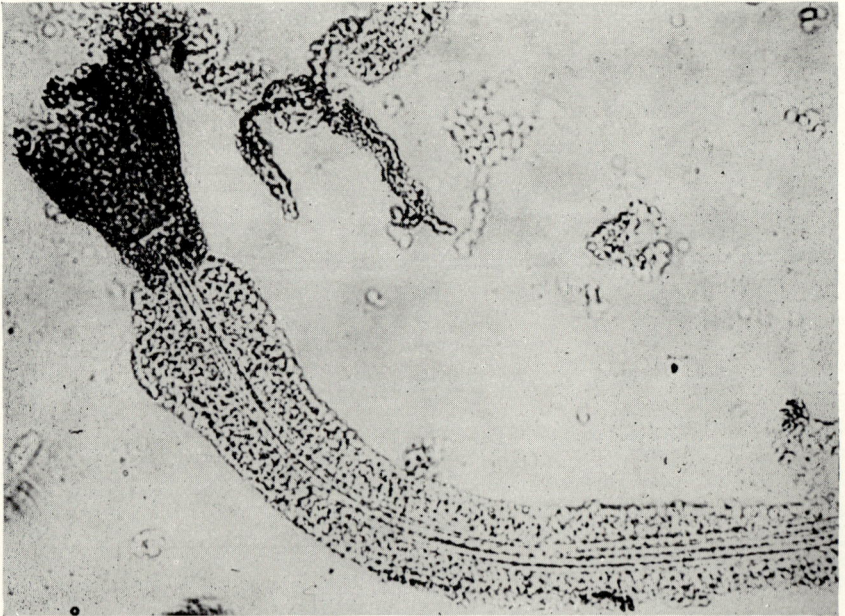

FIG. 6

Microphotograph of an isolated ommatidium. Upper left: crystal cone surrounded by pigment cells. The curved visual cells bear in their centre the group of rhabdomeres, which protrude into the semper cells at the proximal end of the crystal cone. The cornea lens is cut off. (By courtesy of Dr. K. Hamdorf.)

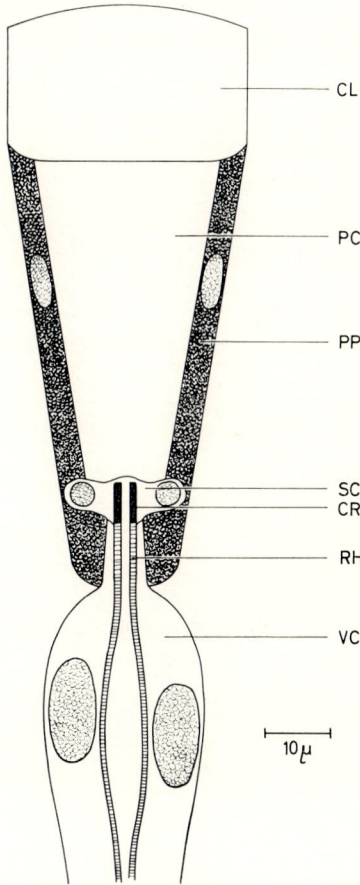

FIG. 7

Slightly schematic drawing of the relationship between the dioptric apparatus and the visual cells. *CL*, cornea lens, *PC*, pseudocone, *PP*, primary pigment cells, *SC*, semper cells, *CR*, amorphous caps covering the ends of the rhabdomeres, *RH*, rhabdomeres, *VC*, visual cells.*

pattern caused by the bundle will be shifted in the focal plane perpendicular to the axes of the rhabdomeres. Under these conditions the directional sensitivity curve of the visual cell will depend on the following four parameters: (1) the size of the focal intensity pattern; (2) the diameter of the light-accepting structures; (3) the focal length of the dioptric apparatus; (4) the effectiveness of light screening between the optic units. Each of these

* We are greatly indebted to Dr. Trujillo-Cenóz for giving us electron microscopical data on which this picture is partly based.

parameters influences the directional sensitivity curve and gives some explanation for our experimental findings. Some simple considerations lead to the following conclusion.

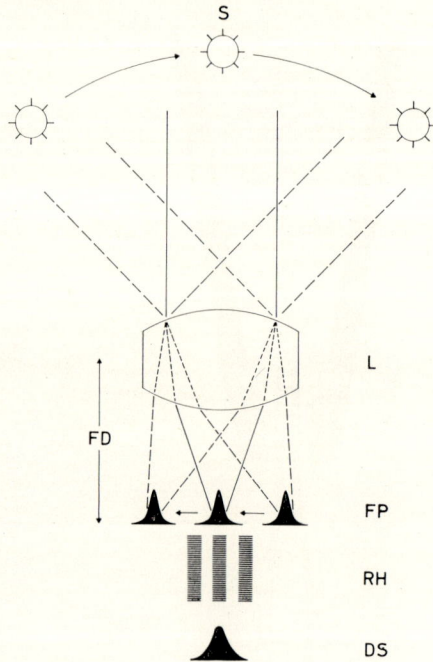

FIG. 8

Schematic drawing of the optical situation leading to the directional sensitivity curve. *S*, light source, moving from left to right, *L*, lens, representing the dioptric apparatus, *FP*, focal intensity pattern, moving direction opposite to that of the light source, *RH*, rhabdomeres as light-accepting structures, *DS*, directional sensitivity of the visual cell, *FD*, focal distance of the lens. The light source is to be regarded as far distant, so that the light beams reaching the lens can be considered as parallel.

CONCLUSION

If the diameter of the light-accepting structure exceeds that of the focal intensity pattern, the central part of the directional sensitivity curve will be flat. As this is not the case in our experimental data, the diameter of the focal intensity pattern must exceed or equal that of a rhabdomere, the latter being about 1 μ. On the other hand, Autrum and Wiedemann (1962) and Wiedemann (1965) were able to show that the seven rhabdomeres within one ommatidium are never illuminated simultaneously by a point source. This means that the diameter of the focal pattern does not exceed the diameter of the group of rhabdomeres, which is about 3 μ. Thus the major portion of the focal intensity pattern should have a diameter between 1 and 3 μ.

The second of the above mentioned parameters, the diameter of the light-accepting structure, is likely to be one source of the scatter in the half-widths of sensitivity curves between visual cells of the same eye region. In fact, within each ommatidium we find a regular pattern of rhabdomeres of different diameters which may vary by nearly a factor of 2.

Point 3, the focal length of the dioptric apparatus, gives some explanation as to the systematic difference in sensitivity curves depending on the region of the eye. At the lateral edge of the eye, we found the half-width to be about 1·5 times greater than in the frontal region. The length of the dioptric apparatus, and hence the focal length, is here about 50 μ, while it is 70 μ in the centre of the eye. With a shorter focal distance, a given angular excursion of the light source would be represented by a smaller movement of the image behind the lens system. This means that the directional sensitivity curve will be broader as compared with a long focus system.

The last point to be discussed is the importance of the screening pigments. Their influence is immediately proven by the experiments with the pigment-less mutant. While the central part of the directional sensitivity curve is the same for the normal fly and the mutant "chalky", the outer parts differ considerably. At larger angular excursions the mutant's curve is well above that of the normal fly. This means that the screening pigments prevent a great portion of the scattered light from stimulating the receptors.

Each of the above mentioned four parameters affects the directional sensitivity curve in some way. But obviously the most important parameter is the focal intensity pattern, which in turn reflects the optical qualities of the dioptric apparatus. Certainly we must not expect to find high standard optical qualities in this system, since even in purely physical systems there is no ideal lens known which can focus a parallel bundle to a point. Thus, if in our biological system the image defects caused by simple lens errors were extremely small (which is most unlikely) there would still be a blurring of the focused point caused by diffraction. Diffraction patterns and their importance for the directional sensitivity of the insect eye have been discussed by several authors (cf. Barlow, 1952). From our results we have to conclude that diffraction is not the limiting factor for the resolving power of the visual cell. If it were so, we should find first and higher order maxima and minima in the course of the directional sensitivity curve of the visual cells. But one of the characteristic features of our results is that with increasing deviations from the visual axes there are no oscillations and the curves decline smoothly. There must be other image defects present which are effective enough to mask any results of diffraction. We hope that experiments which are in progress will bring precise data about the lens system itself in a more direct manner.

SUMMARY

The visual fields of the compound eye and its subunits, the ommatidia and visual cells, have been measured in the blow fly *Calliphora erythrocephala*.

Observing the pseudo-pupil of a pigment-free mutant reveals that the total visual field of one compound eye is larger than 180° in the horizontal as well as in the vertical plane; *Calliphora* therefore has panorama vision and a binocular region with a width of 30° upward, 20° forward and 10° downward.

The pseudo-pupil allows measurement of the angular distance between the visual axes of neighbouring ommatidia, which is about 2° in most regions of the eye, except at the lateral edge, where it increases to about 4°.

The same method allows comparison of the visual fields of ommatidia in different eye regions, which are nearly equal at every place except that they are somewhat larger at the lateral edge. The horizontal and vertical extents of the fields are about equal.

Electrophysiological measurements in single visual cells provide data about the visual fields of these smallest subunits. The sensitivity to oblique light bundles declines as the angle is increased, forming a bell-shaped curve with smooth sides. The half-width of this curve averages 5° at the lateral edge of the eye and 3° in the frontal region.

Four parameters which influence the shape of this directional sensitivity curve are discussed.

ACKNOWLEDGEMENT

The experimental work was supported by a grant from the Deutsche Forschungsgemeinschaft.

REFERENCES

AUTRUM, H. and WIEDEMANN, I. 1962. Versuche über den Strahlengang im Insektenauge (Appositionsauge). *Z. Naturforsch.* **17b**, 480–2.

BARLOW, H. B. 1952. The size of ommatidia in apposition eyes. *J. Exp. Biol.*, **29**, 667–74.

EXNER, S. 1891. Die Physiologie der facettirten Augen von Krebsen und Insekten. *F. Deuticke Verl.* Leipzig und Wien.

WASHIZU, Y., BURKHARDT, D. and STRECK, P. 1964. Visual field of single retinula cells and interommatidial inclination in the compound eye of the blow fly *Calliphora erythrocephala*. *Z. vergl. Physiol.*, **48**, 413–28.

WIEDEMANN, I. 1965. Der Strahlengang im Appositionsauge. *Z. vergl. Physiol.*, **49** 526–42.

THE ROLE OF DIFFRACTION IN COMPOUND EYE VISION

E. T. Burtt and W. T. Catton

Departments of Zoology and Physiology, University of Newcastle upon Tyne, England

THE compound eye has several remarkable structural features. These are clearly seen when during development or phylogeny a number of simple eyes is replaced by a compound eye. This is well seen in Dethier's (1942, 1943) account of the larval eyes of the arctiid moth *Isea* in comparison with Yagi and Koyama's survey (1963) of compound eyes in adult Lepidoptera.

The transition shows the following changes:

(i) Reduction in diameter of the lenses—94–138 μ in *Isea* larva but not more than 42 μ in adult Lepidoptera.

(ii) Greater uniformity in size so that the lenses tend to form a regular mosaic.

(iii) Great increase in depth of the compound eye. The photoreceptor layer in *Isea* larva is 170 μ deep but it may attain a depth of over 600 μ in adult *Papilio*. Here the essential photoreceptor structure, the rhabdome, extends throughout this length.

Why has this change taken place? It is clear that groups of simple eyes are valuable organs of vision. Dethier found that the visual fields of the simple eyes in *Isea* did not overlap and Hundertmark (1937) found a power in the larval eyes of *Lymantria* to discriminate simple forms (e.g. an erect and inverted pyramid).

Müller (1840), in his mosaic theory, regarded the compound eye as in effect an assemblage of simple eyes each of which detected a point of light at the apex of the cone. But he mistook the rhabdomes for the optic nerves and thought the latter ended at the apex of the crystalline cones. Grenacher (1879) corrected this and Exner (1891) added the idea of superposition images formed by the lenses working together in groups, but only being operative in certain types of eyes. Burtt and Catton (1962) and Rogers (1962) have reinvestigated these deeper images as diffractive processes.

The aims of this paper are as follows:

(i) *To examine diffraction images in the compound eye.* We shall claim that these images are generated by the array of lenses which forms the compound eye. The great depth of the receptors is needed to detect these images. This is a re-examination of superposition but it will be seen to be a phenomenon occurring in all compound eyes.

Stress will be laid on the resolving power of the compound eye, and the diffractive images have the higher resolution needed to explain the values observed electrophysiologically by Burtt and Catton (1962, 1966) and behaviouristically by Jander and Voss (1963).

(ii) *To try to explain form vision in the compound eye.* If the depth of the compound eye is needed to make use of the diffraction images, what has become of the type of vision found in a group of simple eyes? Here we shall suggest that the eccentric cells are important and since there is usually only one for each ommatidium this will bring us back to a mosaic theory of form vision, but one based, not on an optical, but rather a neural mosaic.

MOVEMENT DETECTION AND RESOLUTION

The detection of movement is a very obvious power possessed by the compound eye. We shall approach it from two types of experiments.

1. *Detection of Small Movements*

The minuteness of the movements which compound eyes will detect has been shown by recent work to be much smaller than was supposed.

In Crustacea, Kunze (1964) finds that movements of as small as $0.08°$/sec will give responses in *Ocypode* while Horridge and Sandeman (1964) find responses to movements down to $0.001°$/sec in *Carcinus*.

In insects Thorson (1964) recorded the torsion in the neck muscles of *Schistocerca* and found that angular movements as small as $0.03°$ gave consistent responses. Earlier Burtt and Catton (1954, 1956) found that a small source of light could produce spike responses in the optic lobe and nerve cord of *Locusta* when the angular extent of the movement was as small as $0.1°$.

2. *Resolution of Striped Patterns*

In human vision the nature of image formation by the eye is certainly clear in its broad outlines. Here the smallest detectable movement is much less than the smallest resolvable stripe in a continuous pattern.

It is essential therefore to test the resolution of the compound eye to striped patterns. The values using the optomotor responses to striped patterns on whole insects give values of not less than $1°$ for *Apis*. Burtt and Catton (1962) recorded the ventral nerve cord response and stimulated the eye with a pattern of equally spaced black and white stripes moved across a window. They got a threshold in *Locusta* of about $0.3°$ and about $0.25°$ for *Phormia* and *Calliphora*. McCann and Macginitie (1965) have criticized this experiment in that the pattern may have errors causing slight but detectable changes in intensity. If this is so it is surprising that different sizes of pattern give the same angular threshold.

A further criticism of this experiment is that of Palka (1965) and Barlow (1965). Palka repeated Burtt and Catton's experiment but claimed that while he found responses to angular separations below 1°, these responses were greatly reduced if the edge of the window was inclined to the stripes of the pattern. Barlow showed that for a human eye a detectable flicker occurred at the edge of the window when the pattern was moved, even when the human eye could not resolve the stripes of the central pattern. In this way the movement of stripes of $\frac{1}{2}$ to a $\frac{1}{4}$ of the normal resolvable limit could be detected. Burtt and Catton (1966) have repeated their experiment using the type of pattern shown in Fig. 1 where a wheel-like arrangement of equally

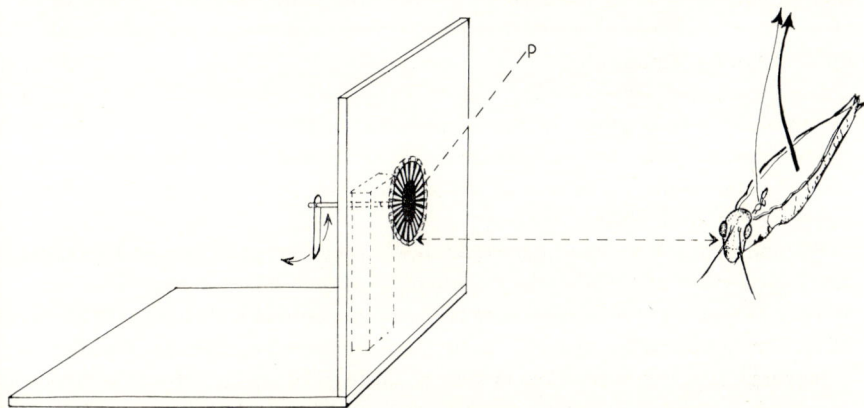

FIG. 1

The *stimulus* consists of a pattern (*P*) of radically arranged, equally spaced black and white stripes (separation shown exaggerated) rotated clockwise or anti-clockwise. The *response* is recorded from the thoracic ventral nerve cord of *Locusta*.

spaced stripes is moved clockwise or anti-clockwise manually. Such an arrangement does not produce edge effects by its very nature and the pattern can be placed in different regions of the visual field, yet the same limit for resolution, i.e. 6·3° is found. This value is the angular separation of the stripes at the edge of the pattern.

Two further interesting effects are seen when using this type of pattern as a stimulus. When the limit of resolution is approached responses are more effective in either a clockwise or anti-clockwise direction. Any given insect is either predominantly clockwise or anti-clockwise for each of its eyes.

A pattern with a central black disc yields a higher resolution than one with a white central disc.

Now that very delicate methods of detecting optomotor responses are available (Fermi and Reichardt, 1963; McCann and Macginitie, 1965;

Thorson, 1964) it would be most interesting to have them applied to problems of resolution.

The work of Jander and Voss (1963) is very relevant. They found that *Formica rufa* could respond differentially to vertical as opposed to horizontal stripes when the separation of the pattern was only 1°. Our measurements of the diameter of the single ommatidial lenses in *Formica rufa* show that this is below the expected resolution of the single ommatidial lens.

IMAGE FORMATION IN THE COMPOUND EYE

All observers from Müller onwards agree that each of the ommatidial lenses forms a minute image at the apex of the cone. Exner's (1891) views on the optical structure of the cone have been widely quoted but in many cases at least (i.e. in *Calliphora* and *Locusta* as measured by the present authors) the focus of the ommatidial lens is much the same whether the medium behind it is the fresh cone substance or is replaced by saline solution. In other words, the main refractive effect is due to the lens.

This matter need not be considered further in this context because the essential functional point is that the system lens and cone forms a minute image at the apex of the cone.

Beyond this well-known image (which we will call the primary image) there are a succession of images which we will term the 2nd, 3rd and 4th images. Burtt and Catton (1962) suggest that these are responsible for the high level of resolution found by them in the eyes of *Locusta*, *Phormia* and *Calliphora*.

Rogers (1962) describes a model consisting of an array of apertures arranged hexagonally which will generate a succession of such images behind it if illuminated from a small source. The effect is the same whether the array consists of small apertures or, as in the insect eye slice, of small lenses. Later (Rogers, unpublished) he has found that small plastic lenses can be constructed to produce this succession of images.

Whether we are dealing with minute lenses or small apertures the first stage is for each lens or aperture to generate a minute primary image which will be nearly coherent. Thus an array of coherent sources is produced and these will in turn generate further away from themselves a repetition of the array. Rogers (1962) has photographs of the succession of images behind such an array illuminated by a monochromatic source and Burtt and Catton (1962) show a closely comparable effect using the array of lenses in the insect eye.

Now if a pattern of fine stripes is placed across the source, it will form images at the level of the repetitions of the array. One can think of each point source being an image of the source with a certain lack of perfection to be discussed later. Hence the stripes will appear in the image. Further (as Rogers' photograph shows), the image of stripes formed by such an array can show a high degree of resolution, much above that possible with one of the pinholes or lenses of the array itself. The process of image formation with arrays is further discussed by Rogers (1963) and by Winthrop and Worthington (1965). We need not go into details for our present account. It is quite certain that an array such as the lenses of the compound eye has the potentiality under certain conditions to generate a succession of diffraction images. The question for students of the physiology of the compound eye is this—are such diffraction images made use of by the compound eye in the living state?

Before bringing evidence we could point out that these images are really the superposition image of Exner but expressed in more general optical terms. A further difference is that there are a succession of such images and not just one as Exner thought.

EVIDENCE FOR THE ROLE OF THE DIFFRACTION IMAGE

I. *Evidence Discussed by Burtt and Catton* (1962)

(1) The diffraction images have higher resolving power than that due to a single lens (Rogers, 1962; Winthrop and Worthington, 1965). This accounts for the high resolution observed in the eyes of *Locusta*.

(2) The diffraction images would be equally effective in detecting small angular movements of a point source.

(3) Their use by the eye necessitates the greatly increased depth which we saw earlier to be so characteristic of the compound eye.

(4) The resolution of the array is fully realized only in certain directions (see Fig. 2). Now Burtt and Catton (1962) claim that there is a marked effect on the resolution of striped patterns by their angle of inclination to the horizontal. Further, it is worth noting that Hertz (1931) in bees, showed that a pattern of radially arranged black rods was far more attractive than the same rods arranged in parallel lines. The radial pattern would be resolved in any orientation of the eye, the parallel only in one orientation.

II. *New Evidence*

Rogers (1962) gives the formula for the position of an image of order n from the array of coherent sources,

$$\text{distance} = d = \frac{3b^2\,\mu}{n\,\lambda},$$

where b is the separation of coherent sources, μ is the refractive index of the medium in which the diffraction images are being formed, λ is the wavelength of light and n is an integer which defines the "order" of the image. This can also be called the focus of the image in question.

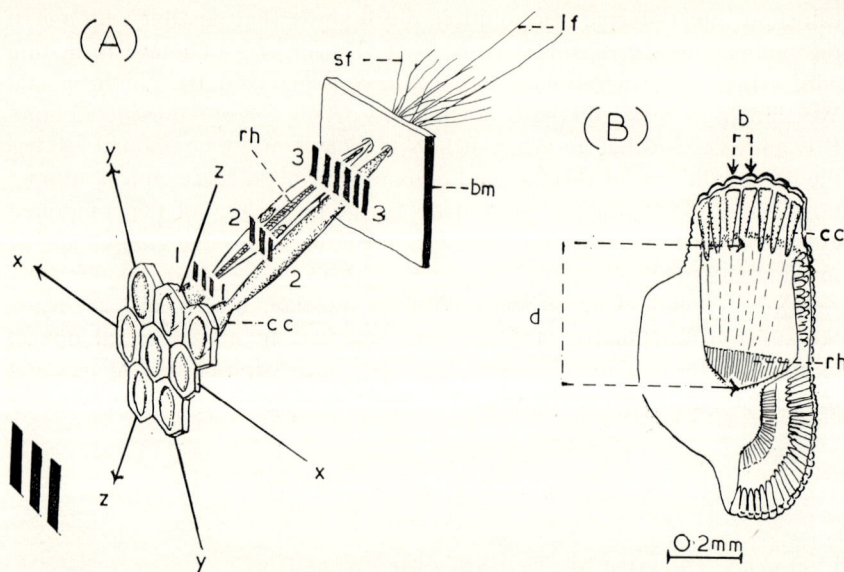

FIG. 2

A, Diagram to show formation of diffraction images in the compound eye. *bm*, basement membrane; *cc*, crystalline cone; *lf*, long retinula cell fibre; *rh*, rhabdome; *sf*, short retinula cell fibre; *x, y, z*, axes for maximal resolution by array of corneal lenses; 1, 2, 3, first, second and third image planes. B, Camera lucida tracing of thick frozen section of compound eye of Euphausiid Crustacean *Stylocheiron longicorne*; *b*, distance of ommatidial separation; *d*, distance between first image and basement membrane. Other lettering as in Fig. 2A.

Measurements have been made on compound eyes which yield interesting results and we can consider them by rearranging the above so that

$$\frac{n\,\lambda}{3\,\mu} = \frac{b^2}{d}.$$

Consider the compound eye of any given insect. If the diffraction images are used by the eye the image must fall before the pigmented basement membrane and one would expect the depth of the latter to be closely related to the position of the diffraction images to whatever number they are made use of. This is comparable with the expectation that the position of the retina in a vertebrate eye will be closely related to the focal length of the corneal and lens optical system.

What will be the effect of increase in size on the eye?

Within any eye it seems likely that the refractive index μ of the cells of the retina will not vary greatly. What about λ? Rogers used monochromatic light in his experiments. Insect eyes show several peaks of maximum sensitivity (Goldsmith, 1961) but a peak around 500 $\mu\mu$ seems general. At least the sensitivity within any one eye seems likely to be constant.

The left-hand side of the equation might be constant and in that case b^2/d should be constant for any one eye.

MEASUREMENTS ON ARTHROPODS WITH DOUBLE EYES

These have been briefly reported by Burtt, Catton and Rogers (1965). They find that in *Bibio varipes* Meig (Diptera) there is good agreement for b^2/d in the upper and lower eyes and the same is true for *Simulium ornatum* L. Recently results have been obtained for two more arthropods, *Chloeon simile* and the Euphausiid Crustacean *Stylocheiron longicorne*. The data for all these four examples of double eyes are set out in Table 1 (also see Fig. 2). There is

TABLE 1

COMPOUND EYES WITH REGIONS OF MARKEDLY DIFFERENT OMMATIDIAL DIAMETER
(each value mean of 9 measurements)

Species	Upper eye (in μ)			Lower eye (in μ)		
	b	d	b^2/d	b	d	b^2/d
Bibio varipes (Diptera)	26	143	4·8	16	54	4·7
Simulium ornatum L. (Diptera)	40	255	6·3	16	42	6·1
Chloeon simile (Ephemeroptera)	24·4	155	3·8	14·6	58	3·7
Stylocheiron longicorne (Crustacea Euphausiidae)	55·5	388	7·9	22·7	67	7·7

good agreement with the depth of the basement membrane on the view that b^2/d is a constant for each of the eyes. This is to be expected on the theory of diffraction images on the basis of the following assumptions:

(1) that the refractive index of the region where Fourier image is forming is the same in both parts of the eye of the arthropod;

(2) that whatever value should be given to λ it is the same for both parts of the eye.

COMPARISON OF THE b^2/d VALUES FOR EYES
OF DIFFERENT ARTHROPODS

It will be noted that while b^2/d appears to be constant for any one of the eyes in Table 1, this ratio is different for each of these four Arthropods. The conclusion from Table 1 is that each of these eyes uses the same order of Fourier image within itself but in passing to another eye a different order may be used. Returning to the relationship $n \lambda/3\ \mu = b^2/d$ we might expect that μ will not vary greatly from eye to eye.

The refractive index change of a solution of bovine plasma albumen is from 1·333 to 1·420 over a concentration of 0–50%.

The least known quantity is λ but from the review of Goldsmith (1961) one can conclude tentatively that the range of insect wavelength sensitivity is broadly comparable and certain peaks (e.g. that near 5000 Å) are of general occurrence.

It is of interest therefore to measure the values of b^2/d for a wide range of arthropod eyes. The results so far are set out in Fig. 3.

If the value of $n \lambda/3\ \mu$ is constant for arthropods one would expect the values of b^2/d to fall into a limited number of groups. Thus some compound eyes would make use of only the first few members of the series of images and others those of higher order.

The results so far are too few to plot out the extended histogram which might show a succession of peaks.

Some points already seem worth noting.

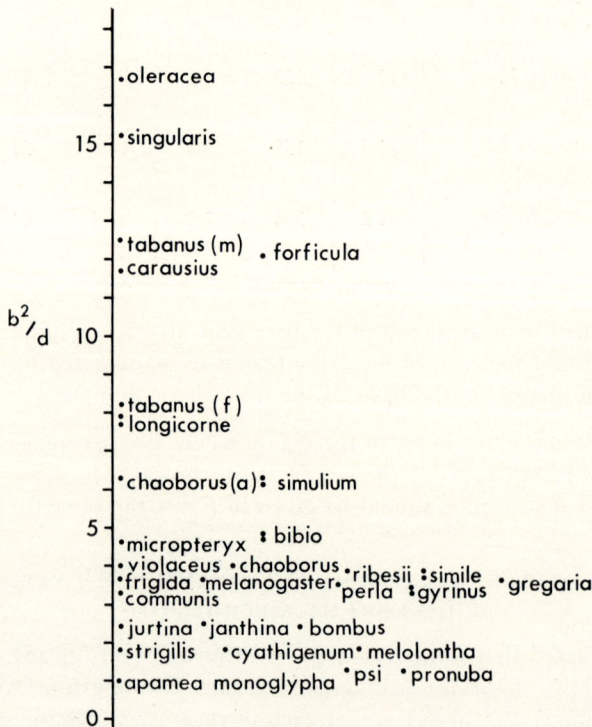

FIG. 3

1. There are some striking agreements, e.g. the Coleopteran *Melolontha*, the Lepidopteran *Procus strigilis* and the Odonatan *Enallagma* all have $b^2/d = 1·80$ and hence on the present theory use the same orders of images. At the other end with $b^2/d = 12$ *Carausius*, *Forficula* and *Tabanus* use the same order of images.

2. There is no sign of any phylogenetic significance in the value of b^2/d. This is comparable with the occurrence of superposition and apposition eyes and is to be expected.

3. When the values of b/d are set out for comparison as a histogram there is little or no sign of grouping (see Fig. 4).

DIFFICULTIES IN THE DIFFRACTION THEORY

How are the images received by the receptors of the eye? If there is a succession of images produced from, let us say, a striped pattern then will they not give rise to confusion on the receptors?

The position would be easier if only the deeper diffraction images were used by the eye. In fact, in some moths (Fernandez-Moran, 1958) the

---

FIG. 3 *opposite*

Values of b^2/d (measured in μ) set out in order of magnitude for 30 different arthropods compound eyes. The names on the graph show the species in the following list:

Crustacea	Euphausiidae	*Stylocheiron longicorne*
Insecta	Ephemeroptera	*Chloeon simile*
	Odonata	*Enallagma cyathigenum*
	Orthoptera	*Schistocerca gregaria*
	Phasmida	*Carausius morosus*
	Dermaptera	*Forficula auricularia*
	Mecoptera	*Panoppa communis*
	Neuroptera	*Chrysopa perla*
	Lepidoptera	*Triphoena janthina*
		Triphoena pronuba
		Maniola jurtina
		Micropteryx sp.
		Apamea monoglypha
		Apatele psi
		Procus strigilis
	Diptera	*Coelopa frigida*
		Drosophila melanogaster
		Chaoborus crystallinus (larva, adult)
		Tipula oleracea
		Simulium ornatum
		Tabanus solstitialis (male and female)
		Bibio varipes
		Syrphus ribesii
	Coleoptera	*Gyrinus* sp.
		Melolontha melolontha
		Otiorrhynchus singularis
		Carabus violaceus
	Hymenoptera	*Bombus terrestris*

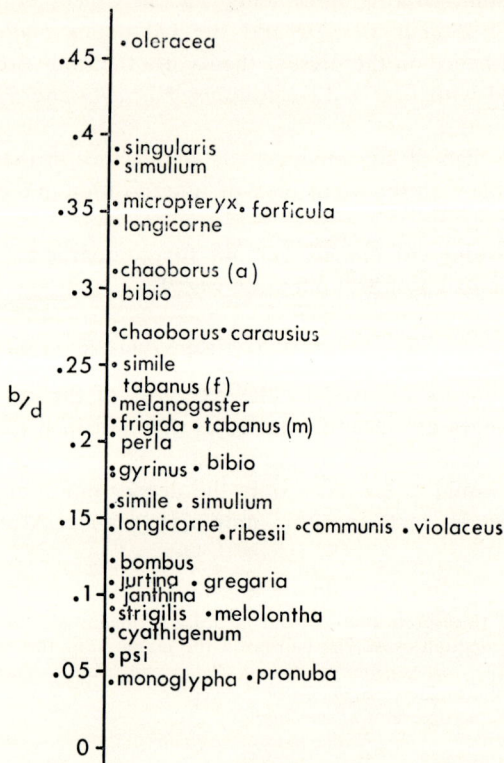

FIG. 4

The same 30 different compound eyes shown in Fig. 3 but here b/d (not b^2/d) is set out in order of magnitude. For comment see text.

rhabdomes are found deep in the eye much below the region where the primary images occur.

However, in *Locusta* and *Calliphora* the rhabdomes extend from the apex of the cone to the basement membrane, and so could be stimulated by any one of the three images shown in Fig. 2.

An explanation may be as follows. The most intense image is that nearest the cone and it is suggested that with large stripes this is dominant and movement will be detected using this image. Now suppose the separation of the stripes is reduced, the primary image will become blurred and no longer resolvable, but the next order image will still be resolved. As the separation is again reduced this image fades and the next order remains resolvable and is the one dominating the receptors.

It is essential for resolution that the separation of the retinula cell rhabdomeres is adequate to resolve the diffraction pattern. Burtt and Catton

(1962) claim that this is so and it is becoming clear from recordings from single retinula cells that they can act as individual units.

FORM VISION IN INSECTS

The evidence given so far is to show (1) that these diffraction images could be formed by the eye, and (2) that the level of resolution of the eye and its dimensions in double compound eyes and perhaps in a comparison of different eyes are in agreement with such images being used. Such images would be useful in detection of movement and resolution, but form vision remains problematical. Winthrop and Worthington (1965) also find form vision a serious difficulty.

How far is there a basis for belief in form vision in insects?

Hertz (1931) found in bees that a circle, a square, a triangle and a rectangle are confused, while a hollow square, an *X*, a *Y*, or parallel lines are also confused but any one of the first group could be separated from any one of the latter. These results by themselves suggest a poor form vision but are to be expected on a basis of diffractive images. However, Mazokhin-Porshnjakov and Wischnevskaya (1965) find that bees can separate simple figures provided they are made up of similar smaller figures, e.g. small separate triangles arranged in a triangular group. The difficulty with Hertz figures might be that the bee detects them at a distance using, as we should suggest, the diffraction images in the eye. Patterns giving more disrupted outlines are certainly more effective as Hertz found and radial patterns particularly so. When the bee alighted on the pattern the figures used by Hertz were too large for the outline to be appreciated, but the smaller figures of Mazokhin-Porshnjakov and Wischnevskaya could be recognized.

The behaviour of many Sphecoidea (Hymenoptera) strongly suggests form vision. Thus *Mellinus* captures Diptera of a wide range of species (Hobby, 1932) with very different colour patterns but suggesting that the common form of these insects is appreciated. *Sceliphron* hunts spiders and again a wide range of species ranging from conspicuously to cryptically coloured are captured (White, 1962). In these cases one cannot eliminate chemical stimuli but the most probable single sensory clue seems to be vision of a common form.

A NEW MOSAIC THEORY

The diffraction images seem to offer little basis for form vision and in any case the groups of simple eyes of caterpillars possess a rudimentary form vision.

We seek then a basis for form vision in some visual mechanism which is present both in compound eyes and in groups of simple eyes.

Elsewhere (Burtt and Catton, 1966) we have drawn attention to the eccentric cells of arthropod eyes and are inclined to look here for the basis of a mosaic type of vision based on neurology rather than optics. This might surmount the difficulties put forward earlier (Burtt and Catton, 1961).

Eccentric cells occur in the Limulus eye and produce a continuous train of spikes. Here they could build up a mosaic image in the manner suggested by Reichardt (1961) in spite of the fact that the receptive fields of ommatidia overlap markedly. What is required is that there should be a central region in the ommatidium of Limulus where illumination and rate of firing of the eccentric cell is maximal.

But do cells with comparable behaviour occur in insects?

Hanström (1927) showed that eccentric cells are of wide occurrence in ommatidia. We need not follow his view that they are necessarily associated with colour vision. Cajal and Sanchez (1915) claimed that in *Calliphora* such cells had a distinct course in the optic lobe. Unlike the rest of the cells in each ommatidium (the short visual fibres) which ended in the first synaptic region, these (the long fibres) ran through the first synaptic region without synapses and ended in the second synaptic region.

Units with continuous activity in light can be detected in the optic lobe (Burtt and Catton, 1960; Horridge *et al.*, 1965) and even in the thoracic nerve cord (Burtt and Catton, unpublished) but so far there is nothing to suggest that these fibres are directly connected to the eccentric cells. Waterman and Wiersma (1963), Waterman *et al.* (1964) also find what they term "seeing" units in the eye of the Crustacean *Podophthalmus*. One guesses that a group of continuously discharging units would be more suitable for building up a total image than on–off units.

We return then to a mosaic of responses from eccentric cells which are usually one in each ommatidium. These would respond to the average illumination of each ommatidium. Thus any behaviour resulting from their action would agree with classical Müllerian mosaic theory. We can thus reconcile the results of work which demands mosaic theory, e.g. that of Hassenstein (1951) on the beetle *Chlorophanus*. The critical experiment here is that in which geometrical interference effects are produced between the repeat distance of the patterns and the ommatidia. The most striking experiment is that in which the movement of the beetle periodically reverses direction in accordance with the relationship between the angular separation of the pattern and the angular separation of the ommatidia. This recalls the effects observed when two periodic arrays are superimposed and moved relative to each other (Moiré patterns). As the periodicity of one is altered relative to the other the impression given to an observer is exactly of this type. The same effect of periodical reversal is noted by Götz (1964), on *Drosophila*. Here the direction of response to the pattern on an optomotor drum changes direction as the angular separation alters from that of ommatidial separation to twice this value.

These results fall naturally into place on the basis of a mosaic type of vision. Are we to conclude that the optomotor responses depend on this kind of vision? If so it would explain why the values for resolution making use of orientation responses seldom fall lower than the order of about 1°. Jander and Voss' (1963) work stands rather apart from this, however.

To conclude with a summing up of the role of diffraction images in insect vision: the characteristic feature which distinguishes the compound eye from an aggregate of simple eyes is its ability to generate and respond to diffraction images. These are of great value in the detection of angular movement and resolution of discontinuities in the visual world. Here the single retinula cell is the functional unit.

Form recognition and perhaps orientated movements may depend on a more primitive aspect of vision (shared with aggregates of simple eyes). In this the single ommatidium appears to be the optical unit. The eccentric cells of the ommatidia might be the functional receptor unit in this case.

REFERENCES

BARLOW, H. B. 1952. The size of ommatidia in apposition eyes. *J. Exp. Biol.* **29**, 667–74.

BARLOW, H. B. 1965. Visual resolution and the diffraction limit. *Science N.Y.*, **149**, 553–5.

BURTT, E. T. and CATTON, W. T. 1954. Visual perception of movement in the locust. *J. Physiol.* **125**, 566–80.

BURTT, E. T. and CATTON, W. T. 1956. Electrical responses to visual stimulation in the optic lobes of the locust and certain other insects. *J. Physiol.* **133**, 68–88.

BURTT, E. T. and CATTON, W. T. 1960. The properties of single unit discharges in the optic lobe of the locust. *J. Physiol.* **154**, 479–90.

BURTT, E. T. and CATTON, W. T. 1961. Is the mosaic theory of insect vision true? *Int. Congr. Ent.* **11**, 670–3.

BURTT, E. T. and CATTON, W. T. 1962. A diffraction theory of insect vision. Part I. An experimental study of visual acuity in certain insects. *Proc. Roy. Soc.* **B157**, 53–82

BURTT, E. T. and CATTON W. T. 1966. Perception by locusts of rotated patterns. *Science N.Y.* **151**, 224.

BURTT, E. T., CATTON, W. T. and ROGERS, G. L. 1965. Optics of the compound eye in relation to increase in size. *Int. Congr. Ent.*, **12**, 227–8.

CAJAL, RAMON Y and SANCHEZ, D. 1915. Contribucion al conocimiento de los centros nerviosos de los insectos. *Trab. Lab. Invest. Biol. Univ. Madr.*, **13**, 1–164.

DETHIER, V. G. 1942. The dioptric apparatus of lateral ocelli. I. The corneal lens. *J. Cell. Comp. Physiol.*, **19**, 301–13.

DETHIER, V. G. 1943. The dioptric apparatus of lateral ocelli. II. Visual capacities of the ocellus. *J. Cell. Comp. Physiol.*, **22**, 116–36.

EXNER, S. 1891. *Die Physiologie der facettierten Augen von Krebsen und Insekten.* Leipzig.

FERMI, G. and REICHARDT, W. 1963. Optomotorische Reaktionen der Fliege *Musca domestica. Kybernetik* **2**, 15–28.

FERNANDEZ-MORAN, H. 1958. Fine structure of insect eyes. *Exp. Cell Res. Suppl.*, **5**, 586/644.

GOLDSMITH, T. H. 1961. The color vision of insects. In *Light and Life* (McELROY, W. D. and Glass, B., Eds.) pp. 771–94. John Hopkins Press.

GÖTZ, K. G. 1964. Optomotorische Untersuchung des visuellen Systems einiger. Augenmutanten der Fruchtfliege *Drosophila. Kybernetik* **2**, 77–92.

GRENACHER, H. 1879. *Untersuchungen über die Sehorgane der Arthropoden.* Göttingen.

HANSTRÖM, B. 1927. Über die Frage, ob Funktionell verschiedene, zapfen- und stäbchen-artige Sehzellen im Komplexauge der Arthropoda vorkommen. *Z. vergl. Physiol.* **6,** 566–97.

HASSENSTEIN, B. 1951. Ommatidienraster und afferente Bewegungs-Integration. *Z. vergl. Physiol.* **33,** 301–26.

HASSENSTEIN, B. 1958. Über die Wahrnehmung der Bewegung von Figuren und unregel-mässigen Helligkeitsmustern. *Z. vergl. Physiol.* **40,** 556–92.

HERTZ, M. 1931. Die Organisation des optischen Feldes bei der Biene. *Z. vergl. Physiol.* **14,** 629–74.

HOBBY, B. M. 1932. Observations on the habits and prey of the fossorial wasp, *Mellinus arvensis* L. *Trans. Ent. Soc. S. Engl.* **7,** 68–80.

HORRIDGE, G. A. and SANDEMAN, D. C. 1964. Nervous control of optokinetic responses in the crab *Carcinus. Proc. Roy. Soc. B*161, 216–46.

HORRIDGE, G. A., SCHOLES, J. H., SHAW, S. and TUNSTALL, J. 1965. Extracellular recordings from single neurones in the optic lobe and brain of the locust. In *The Physiology of the Insect Central Nervous System* (Treherne, J. E. and Beament, J. W. L. Eds.) pp. 165–202. Academic Press. London and New York.

HUNDERTMARK, A. 1937. Das Formunterscheidungsvermögen der Eiraupen der Nonne Lymantria monacha. *Z. vergl. Physiol.* **34,** 562–82.

JANDER, R. and VOSS, C. 1963. Die Bedeutung von Streifenmustern für das Formense-hen der Roten Waldameise (*Formica rufa* L.). *Z. für Tierpsychologie,* **20,** 1–9.

KUNZE, P. 1961. Untersuchung des Bewegungssehen fixiert fliegender Bienen. *Z. vergl. Physiol.* **44,** 656–84.

KUNZE, P. 1964. Eye stalk reactions of the ghost crab Ocypode. In *Neural Theory and Modelling* (Reiss, R. F. Ed.) pp. 293–305. Stanford University Press.

MAZOKHIN-PORSHNJAKOV, G. A. and WISCHNEVSKAYA, T. M. 1965. Beweise der Fähighkeit der Insekten den Kreis, das Dreieck und andere einfachen Figuren zu unterscheiden. *Int. Congr. Ent.* **12,** 340.

McCANN, G. D. and MACGINITIE, G. F. 1965. Optomotor response studies of insect vision. *Proc. Roy. Soc. B*163, 369–401.

MÜLLER, J. 1840. *Handbuch der Physiologie des Menschen.* Coblenz.

PALKA, J. 1965. Diffraction and visual acuity of insects. *Science N.Y.* **149,** 551–3.

REICHARDT, W. 1961. Über das optische Auflösungsvermögen der Facettenaugen von Limulus. *Kybernetik* **1,** 57–69.

ROGERS, G. L. 1962. A diffraction theory of insect vision. II. Theory and experiments with a simple model eye. *Proc. Roy. Soc. B.* **157,** 83–98.

ROGERS, G. L. 1963. The process of image formation as the re-transformation of the partial coherence pattern of the object. *Proc. Phys. Soc. Lond. B*81, 323–331.

THORSON, J. 1964. Dynamics of motion perception in the desert locust. *Science N.Y.* **145,** 69–71.

WATERMAN, T. H. and WIERSMA, C. A. G. 1963. Electrical responses in Decapod Crustacean visual systems. *J. Cell. Comp. Physiol.* **61,** 1–16.

WATERMAN, T. H., WIERSMA, C. A. G. and BUSH, B. M. H. 1964. Afferent visual impulses in the optic nerve of the crab, *Podophthalmus. J. Cell. Comp. Physiol.* **63,** 135–56.

WHITE, E. 1962. Nest building and provisioning in relation to sex in *Sceliphron spirifex* L. (Sphecidae). *J. Anim. Ecol.* **31,** 317–29.

WINTHROP, J. T. and WORTHINGTON, C. R. 1965. Theory of Fresnel Images I. Plane periodic objects in monochromatic light. *J. Opt. Soc. Amer.* **55,** 373–81.

YAGI, N. and KOYAMA, N. 1963. *The Compound Eye of the Lepidoptera.* Shinkyo Press, Tokyo.

PIGMENT MIGRATION AND RETINULAR
SENSITIVITY

G. HÖGLUND

Department of Physiology, Karolinska Institutet, Stockholm , Sweden

THE compound eyes of many arthropods, like the eyes of animals belonging to other phyla, contain light screening pigments whose position varies with the environmental light intensity (see reviews by Parker, 1932; Kleinholz, 1961; and Goldsmith, 1964). In the compound eye of some nocturnal moths, the accessory pigment is the only pigment which exhibits gross movements. The sensitivity of the eye has been shown to be related to the position of this pigment, because the outward migration of the accessory pigment during dark-adaptation is associated with an increase in sensitivity of 2 to 3 log units (Bernhard and Ottoson, 1960a, 1960b, 1964; Bernhard, Höglund and Ottoson, 1963; Post and Goldsmith, 1965). The sensitivity of the eye thus depends both on the excitability of the photoreceptors, i.e. the retinular cells, and on the pigment position. In order to obtain information on the relation between the retinular sensitivity and the pigment position it would be of interest to determine the retinular sensitivity during pigment movements. However, the retinular sensitivity cannot be measured by light passing through the retinal dioptric media since the intensity of the test light needed to elicit a threshold response will vary with the position of the pigment. The present paper describes a series of experiments in which a method was used which permitted the retinular sensitivity changes during the pigment movements to be determined directly.

The principal results described in this paper have been briefly reported by Höglund (1963b). A more detailed account of the method used and the results obtained is awaiting publication (Höglund, 1966).

METHODS

The experiments were carried out on compound eyes from moths of the family Sphingidae. The optic lobes were removed or severed prior to the experiments. The relative light intensity necessary to elicit a threshold mass response of constant amplitude (usually 40 μV, in some experiments 80 μV) was tested in two ways: (1) by test flashes passing through the cornea and

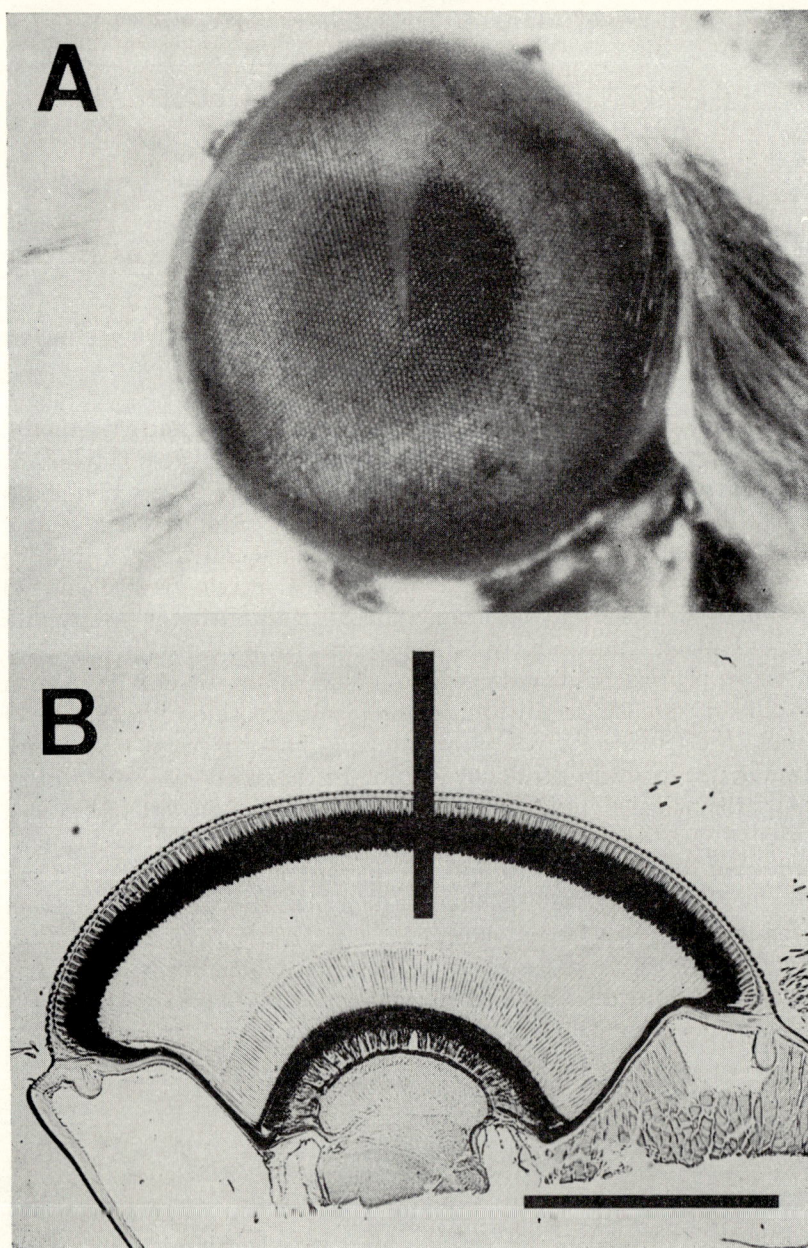

Fig. 1

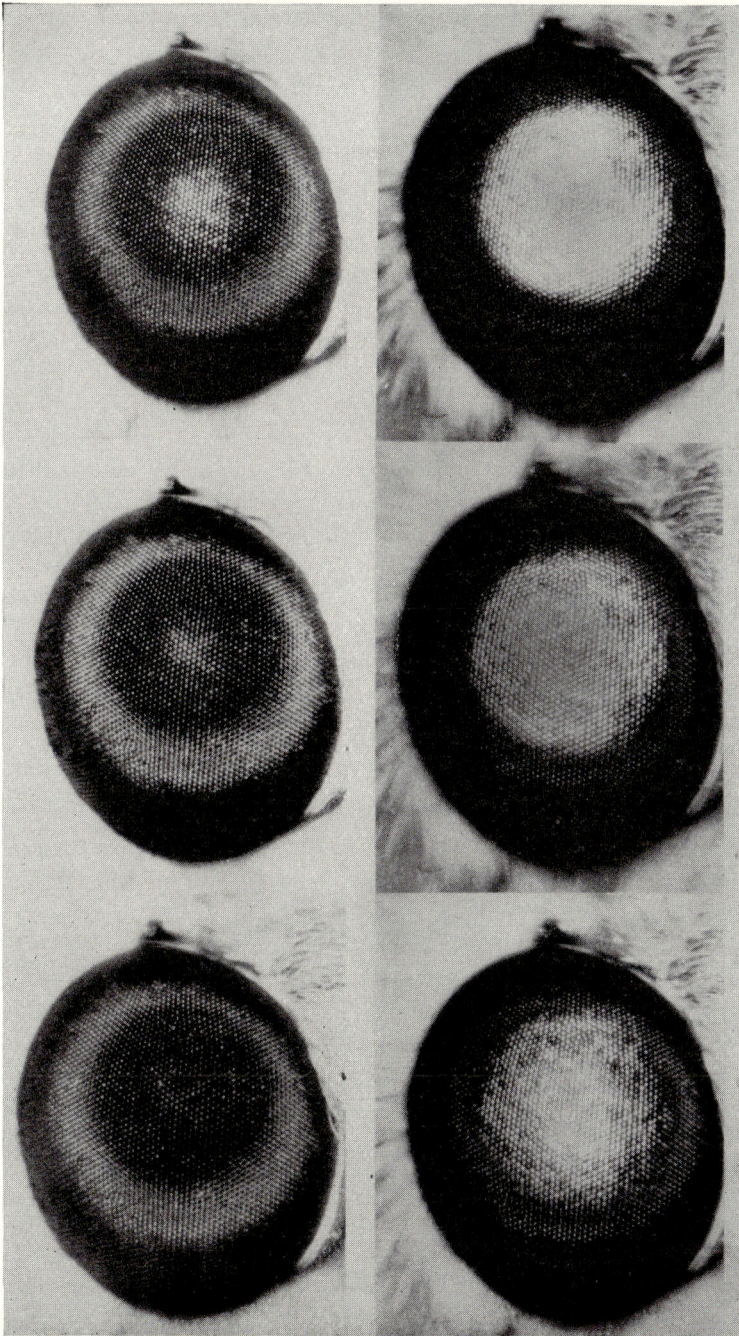

FIG. 2

Gradual increase in size of "glow" in night moth (*Tholera popularis*). Upper left: light-adapted eye. Lower right: fully dark-adapted eye. (From Höglund, 1963a.)

pigment layer in the usual manner; and (2) by test flashes conducted to the rhabdoms through a coated glass fibre inserted into the eye. The total diameter of the fibre was 75 μ. Figure 1 shows a photograph of an eye with the fibre penetrating the cornea (Fig. 1 A), and a histological section of an eye with the fibre drawn to scale (Fig. 1 B). The tip of the fibre was placed between the proximal and accessory pigment layers. When the fibre tip was in this position the light reaching the rhabdoms through the fibre was not attenuated by the accessory pigment.

In the present paper the electrophysiological threshold measured by light passing through the fibre is called the "infrapigment" threshold, and the threshold measured by light passing through the ommatidial dioptric media in the normal manner is called the "transpigment" threshold.

The corneal surface of an eye in which the accessory pigment is in the distal position is seen to "glow" (Fig. 2) if the eye is examined under a light source (Leydig, 1864; Exner, 1891; see reviews by Parker, 1932; and Goldsmith, 1964). The glow is caused by light reflected from internal structures in the eye, and the size of the glow is related to the pigment position. This is illustrated in Fig. 3. The glow is maximal when the pigment is situated distally, near the cornea (Fig. 3 A), and the glow is minimal when the pigment is situated more proximally (for details, see Höglund, 1966). The corneal surface was inspected after each threshold determination, and variations in the size of the glow were taken as an index of pigment movements. All eyes were fully dark-adapted before the threshold measurements were started, and a maximal glow indicated that the accessory pigment was situated distally.

RESULTS AND CONCLUSIONS

In one series of experiments dark-adapted eyes were kept in *darkness* and the transpigment and infrapigment thresholds were measured at intervals. In most of these eyes the pigment started to migrate proximally after some time in darkness. The cause for this pigment migration is not known, but is presumably related to the fact that the eyes were isolated from the rest of the body. Figure 4 shows the effect of the pigment movement on light sensitivity. It can be seen that both the transpigment and infrapigment thresholds were constant for 25 min. During this time the pigment was situated distally,

---

Fig. 1 A

Compound eye of night moth (*Noctua pronuba*) with light-conducting glass fibre penetrating through cornea.

Fig. 1 B

Histological section of eye (*Deilephila elpenor*) showing position of glass fibre. Fibre tip located between distal and proximal pigments. Fibre diameter (75 μ) drawn to scale. Horizontal bar 1 mm. (From Höglund, 1966.)

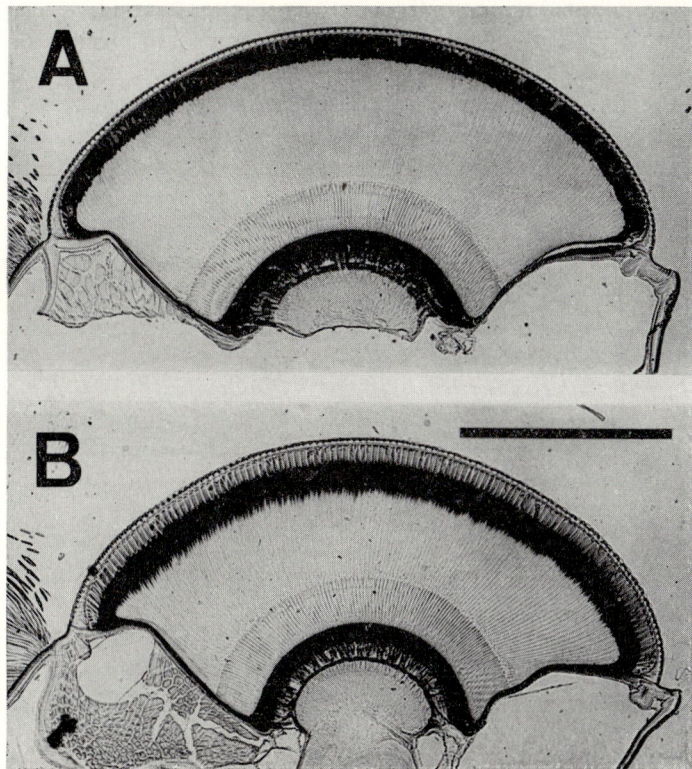

FIG. 3

Position of light screening accessory pigment in eyes (*Deilephila elpenor*) exhibiting maximal glow (A), and minimal glow (B). Note that in eye with minimal glow both proximal and distal borders of accessory pigment layer are located more proximally than in eye with maximal glow. Horizontal bar 1 mm. (From Höglund, 1966.)

as indicated by a maximal glow. The glow then began to diminish, indicating that the pigment was migrating proximally. At the same time, the transpigment threshold was observed to increase. The total increase was 2·6 log units, after which the transpigment threshold remained constant as long as the experiment was continued. Figure 4 shows that, in contrast to the transpigment threshold, the infrapigment threshold remained constant throughout the experiment. Histological sections showed that the pigment had migrated proximally in all parts of the eye during the experiment.

Since the infrapigment threshold was constant throughout the experiment, it can be concluded that the retinular sensitivity remained constant during the pigment migration. According to Exner (1891), the light transmission through the dioptric media varies with the position of the accessory pigment.

The observation that the retinular sensitivity was constant during the experiment shown in Fig. 4 suggests that the increase in transpigment threshold should be attributed to a change in light transmission as postulated by Exner. The threshold increase would thus represent the increase in light intensity necessary to compensate for the decreased light transmission. Therefore the increase in transpigment threshold gives a measure of the light screening effect associated with the pigment migration.

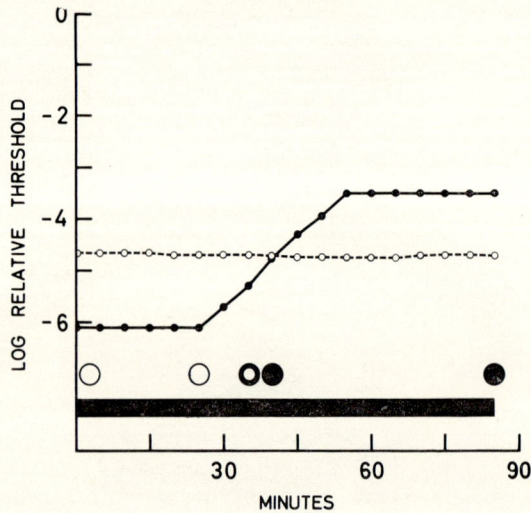

FIG. 4

Transpigment and infrapigment thresholds during inward pigment migration in dark-adapted eye (*Deilephila elpenor*) kept in darkness. Note that pigment migration is associated with an increase in transpigment threshold while infrapigment threshold remains constant. Filled circles connected by solid lines = transpigment threshold. Open circles connected by dashed lines = infrapigment threshold. Horizontal black bar indicates eye kept in darkness. Large circles above horizontal bar indicate size of glow: open circles = maximal glow, filled circles = no glow, filled circle with open centre = intermediate glow. (From Höglund, 1966.)

The threshold changes during *illumination* are shown in Fig. 5. The eye was fully dark-adapted when the experiment began, and a maximal glow indicated that the pigment was situated distally. When the eye was exposed to an adapting light both thresholds increased within 1 min to new values that were maintained for about 3 min. The glow then began to diminish, indicating that the pigment had started to migrate proximally. Beginning at the same time, the infrapigment threshold steadily decreased for about 42 min and then remained constant; the total decrease was 2·9 log units. In contrast to the large decrease in infrapigment threshold, the transpigment threshold remained almost constant as long as the eye was illuminated.

The observation that the infrapigment threshold began to decrease at the same time as the accessory pigment started to migrate suggests that the decrease in infrapigment threshold is caused by the inward migration of the accessory pigment. Experimental results supporting this interpretation are

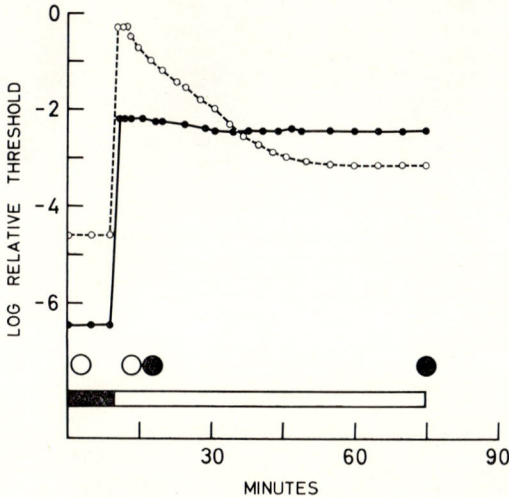

FIG. 5

Transpigment and infrapigment thresholds during illumination (*Deilephila elpenor*). Note that inward pigment migration during illumination is associated with a decrease in infrapigment threshold, while transpigment threshold remains almost constant. Black part of horizontal bar: eye kept in darkness. White part of bar: eye exposed to adapting light. For explanation of other symbols see Fig. 4. (From Höglund, 1966.)

illustrated in Figs. 6 and 7. These figures show the relationship between the pigment position and the decrease in infrapigment threshold during illumination. In Fig. 7 each horizontal line represents the position of the pigment in one eye. Figures 6 and 7 show that the proximal migration of the pigment is accompanied by a gradual decrease in the infrapigment threshold. This relationship is interpreted as follows. As the pigment migrates proximally the illumination of the rhabdoms is gradually decreased, even though the adapting light intensity is constant. The decrease in the infrapigment threshold therefore represents a gradual adaptation of the retinulae to the decreased

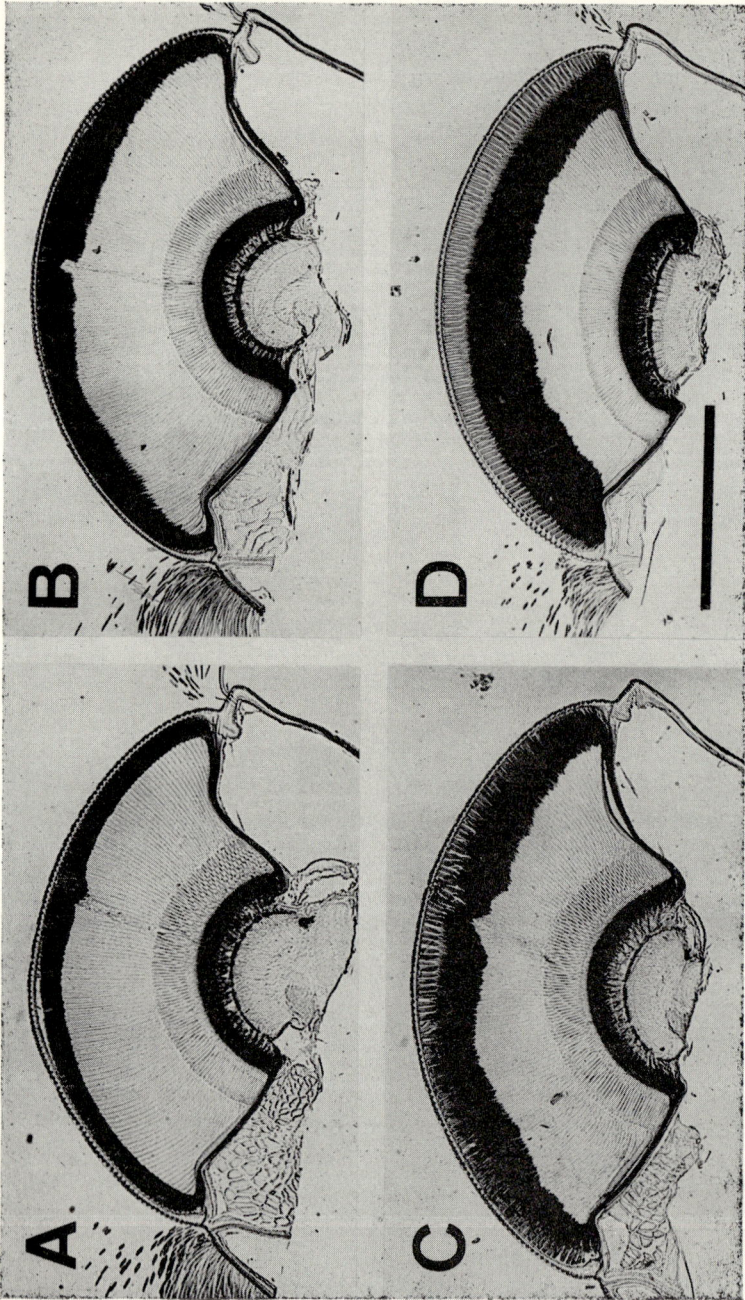

Fig. 6

Histological sections showing pigment position after decrease in infrapigment threshold during illumination (*Celerio euphorbiae*). Threshold decrease in A, 0 log unit; in B, 1·1 log units; in C, 2·1 log units; and in D, 3·0 log units. Horizontal bar 1 mm. (From Höglund, 1966.)

illumination of their rhabdoms. This suggests that the reason for the trans-pigment threshold remaining almost constant in spite of the pigment migra-tion is because the attenuation of the test light intensity is compensated for by the simultaneous increase in retinular sensitivity.

This interpretation is supported by the experiment shown in Fig. 8. The adapting light was turned off when the infrapigment threshold had reached a steady value. During the ensuing dark-adaptation period, the infrapigment threshold decreased to the same value as before the light-adaptation, showing that the retinulae attained the same sensitivity as before the light-adaptation. Histological sections from similar experiments showed that the pigment remains in the proximal position during this dark period, an observation which agrees with the steady value of the infrapigment threshold found during the second illumination period in Fig. 8. During the dark period following the light-adaptation the transpigment threshold decreased to a value that was higher than before the light-adaptation period. Its failure to return to the original dark-adapted value is attributed to the decreased light trans-mission caused by the intervening pigment migration. The difference between the values of the transpigment threshold determined in darkness before and after the pigment migration thus gives a measure of the decrease in light transmission associated with the pigment migration. In the experiment shown in Fig. 8, the pigment migration was associated with a decrease in trans-mission of the adapting light of about 2·8 log units, which was compensated for by an increase in retinular sensitivity of about 2·8 log units. As a result, the transpigment threshold remained almost constant during the pigment migration.

This interpretation is in agreement with the conclusions drawn by Post and Goldsmith (1965) from different experimental evidence. They found that the threshold of most *Galleria* eyes reaches its final value a few seconds after the onset of the adapting illumination, whereas the pigment migration requires minutes for completion (see also Höglund, 1963 a and b). However, in some *Galleria* eyes the pigment migration occurring during the adapting illumina-tion caused a small increase in threshold. Post and Goldsmith concluded that the reason for the slow threshold increase during the pigment migration was that a light attenuation of one log unit by the screening pigment caused the receptor sensitivity to increase by less than one log unit.

In some of the eyes of the present series of experiments the transpigment threshold decreased slightly as the pigment migrated during the illumination. In one example (Fig. 9), the transpigment threshold decreased 0·6 log units during the pigment migration. In this case a reduction in light transmission of about 2·2 log units was accompanied by a decrease in infrapigment thres-hold of about 2·9 log units. One factor contributing to the decrease in trans-pigment threshold may therefore be that the increase in retinular sensitivity overcompensates for the increase in light attenuation. This agrees with the

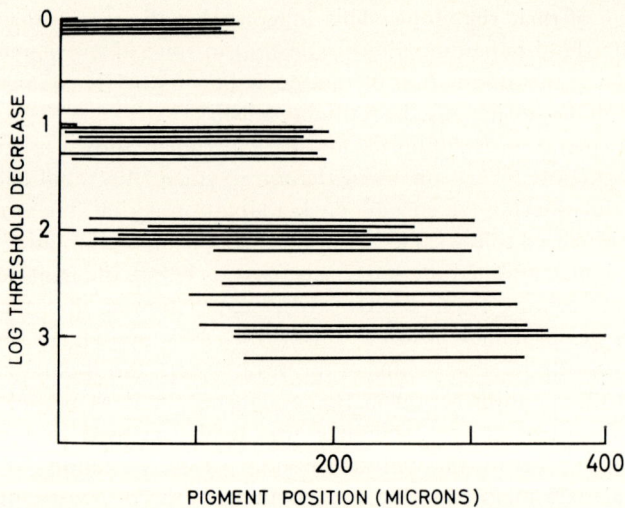

FIG. 7

Relation between pigment position and decrease in infrapigment threshold during illumination (*Celerio euphorbiae*). Values from 27 experiments. Each horizontal line shows position of accessory pigment in one eye. Ordinate: decrease in infrapigment threshold. Abscissa: position of accessory pigment in microns from inner corneal surface. (From Höglund, 1966.)

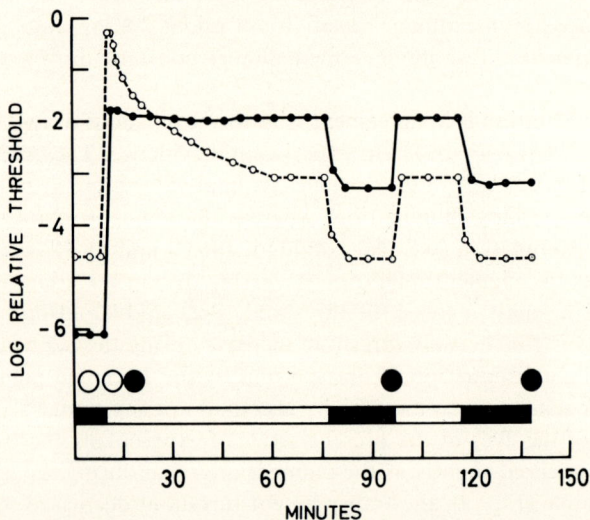

FIG. 8

Transpigment and infrapigment thresholds before, during and after illumination (*Deilephila elpenor*). Transpigment threshold remained almost constant when pigment migrated during first illumination period. For explanation of symbols see Figs. 4 and 5. (From Höglund, 1966.)

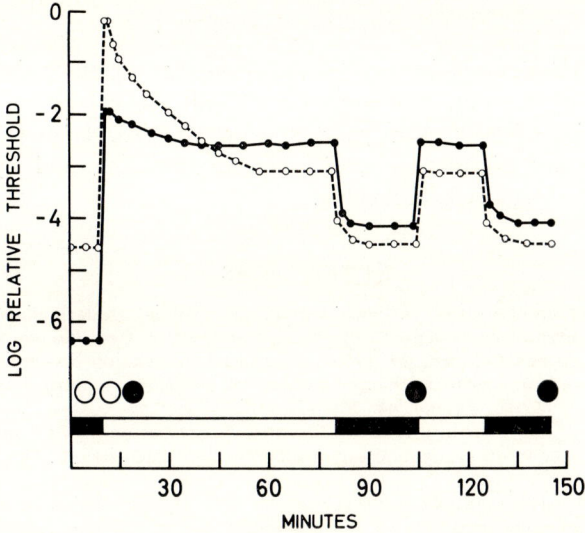

FIG. 9

Transpigment and infrapigment thresholds before, during and after illumination (*Deilephila elpenor*). Transpigment threshold decreased during first illumination period. For explanation of symbols see Figs. 4 and 5. (From Höglund, 1966.)

conclusion by Post and Goldsmith that in some eyes the light attenuation, when expressed in log units of threshold change, is not equal to the increase in receptor sensitivity.

SUMMARY

In dark-adapted eyes kept in darkness, pigment movements may occur with no change in retinular sensitivity although they are accompanied by large changes in the light sensitivity of the eye, which are attributed to variations in light attenuation associated with migration of the accessory pigment. The sensitivity changes give a measure of the light screening effects associated with the pigment migration.

The pigment migration occurring during illumination is associated with a decrease in light transmission which is compensated for by an increase in retinular sensitivity. After the initial rapid decrease in sensitivity upon exposure to light, the sensitivity of the eye therefore remains almost constant in spite of the subsequent pigment migration. However, in some eyes the pigment migration occurring during illumination causes a slight increase in the sensitivity of the eye. The experimental results indicate that one factor contributing to such a sensitivity increase is that the decrease in light transmission is overcompensated for by the increase in retinular sensitivity.

ACKNOWLEDGEMENTS

The research reported in this document has been sponsored by the Air Force Office of Scientific Research under Grant AF EOAR 65-9 through the European Office of Aerospace Research (OAR), United States Air Force, by Reservationsanslaget, Karolinska Institutet, and by Svenska Sällskapet för Medicinsk Forskning.

REFERENCES

BERNHARD, C. G. and OTTOSON, D. 1960a. Comparative studies on dark adaptation in the compound eyes of nocturnal and diurnal Lepidoptera. *J. Gen. Physiol.* **44**, 195–203.

BERNHARD, C. G. and OTTOSON, D. 1960b. Studies on the relation between the pigment migration and the sensitivity changes during dark adaptation in diurnal and nocturnal Lepidoptera. *J. Gen. Physiol.* **44**, 205–15.

BERNHARD, C. G. and OTTOSON, D. 1964. Quantitative studies on pigment migration and light sensitivity in the compound eye at different light intensities. *J. Gen. Physiol.* **47**, 465–78.

BERNHARD, C. G., HÖGLUND, G. and OTTOSON, D. 1963. On the relation between pigment position and light sensitivity of the compound eye in different nocturnal insects. *J. Insect Physiol.* **9**, 573–86.

EXNER, S. 1891. *Die Physiologie der facettirten Augen von Krebsen und Insecten.* Deuticke, Leipzig and Wien.

GOLDSMITH, T. H. 1964. The visual system of insects. In *The Physiology of Insecta* (Rockstein, M., ed.) Vol. 1, 397–462. Academic Press, New York and London.

HÖGLUND, G. 1963a. Glow, sensitivity changes and pigment migration in the compound eye of nocturnal Lepidoptera. *Life Sci.* **2**, 275–80.

HÖGLUND, G. 1963b. Receptor sensitivity and pigment position in the compound eye of nocturnal Lepidoptera. *Life Sci.* **2**, 862–5.

HÖGLUND, G. 1966. To be published in *Acta physiol. scand.* Suppl.

KLEINHOLZ, L. H. 1961. Pigmentary effectors. In *The Physiology of Crustacea* (Waterman, T. H., ed.) Vol. 2, 133–69. Academic Press, New York and London.

LEYDIG, F. 1864. *Das Auge der Gliederthiere.* Laupp and Siebeck, Tübingen.

PARKER, G. H. 1932. The movements of the retinal pigment. *Erg. Biol.* **9**, 239–91.

POST, C. T. and GOLDSMITH, T. H. 1965. Pigment migration and light-adaptation in the eye of the moth, *Galleria mellonella. Biol. Bull.* **128**, 473–87.

HORMONAL REGULATION OF RETINAL PIGMENT MIGRATION IN CRUSTACEANS*

L. H. KLEINHOLZ

Biological Laboratories, Reed College, Portland, Oregon, U.S.A.

I. INTRODUCTION

PHOTOMECHANICAL movements of the retinal pigmentary effectors of the compound eye have been known since the latter decades of the 19th century. Parker (1932), Tuurala (1954), Kleinholz (1961), and Charniaux-Cotton and Kleinholz (1964) have reviewed the physiology of these effectors in crustaceans and several lepidopteran genera. Since this review is concerned with crustaceans and the species most studied have been palaemonids, an ommatidial unit with the normal photomechanical movements of its retinal pigments in such an eye is shown in Fig. 1. Each ommatidium has associated with it three sets of pigments which, in the recent literature, are called the distal, proximal and reflecting retinal pigments. Distal pigment cells, enclosing the axial crystalline cone, each have two processes, one extending distally to the cornea and the other proximally to the retinular cells. In bleached histological preparations three or four myofibrillar structures are demonstrable within each distal pigment cell (Welsh, 1930a); these fibrils are short and thickened in the light-adapted position and attenuated in the dark-adapted position; hence they are suspected of being responsible for the proximal migration of the distal pigment cells.

Retinular cells enclose the photosensitive rhabdom which is actually formed by fusion of the inner faces of these cells; the outer portions of the retinular cells contain the black proximal pigment. The white reflecting pigment is contained in cells described as filling the space between the proximal portions of adjacent ommatidia; in several palaemonid species, however, caps of such pigment are present on the distal ends of the distal pigment cells and are connected by processes to the main mass of the reflecting pigment. The chemical nature of retinal pigments in crustaceans has not been extensively studied. The black pigments of the distal and retinular cells are melanins or ommochromes (Butenandt, 1957; Butenandt et al., 1958a, 1958b). Fisher (1965) indicates from histochemical studies that both the proximal and distal pigments appear to be melanins in euphausiids, while in pelagic decapods

* This review was written during tenure of a grant (NB 02606) from the U.S. National Institutes of Health.

the distal pigment is melanin but the proximal pigment is not. Reflecting pigments in several crustacean species are mixtures of purines and pteridines (Kleinholz, 1959).

Photomechanical movements of the retinal pigments may vary both in the extent of their migrations and in the number of the pigments involved. In some decapod species only one or two of the three pigments may undergo such movements (Kleinholz, 1961). Movements of the distal and proximal pigments screen the rhabdom in bright light and uncover the rhabdom in dim light or in darkness. Despite these general relations, very few precise measurements of threshold and of acuity have been made in the crustacean eye under the various conditions of pigment distribution (de Bruin and Crisp, 1957).

II. ENDOCRINE REGULATION

The early studies on regulation of retinal pigment migration attempted to decide between action as independent effectors or as reflex responses (Parker, 1932; Kleinholz, 1961). In general, the evidence for nervous regulation was unsatisfactory and the results of experiments to demonstrate action as independent effectors were not decisive. The inconclusiveness of the above studies, coupled with the discovery that the eyestalk is a source of hormones regulating integumentary chromatophores (Perkins, 1928) and indications for vascular influence on retinal pigment migration (Bennitt, 1932; Welsh, 1930b) led to a series of investigations that demonstrated hormonal regulation of retinal pigment migration. Injection of crude seawater extracts of eyestalks of *Palaemonetes*, as well as from a variety of other crustacean species, into dark-adapted test *Palaemonetes* effects light-adaptation of the distal and reflecting pigments (Fig. 1) in about 45 min; the proximal pigment remains dark-adapted (Kleinholz, 1936). Similar responses are reported for the prawn, *Paratya* (Nagano, 1947), for the crayfish, *Cambarus*, in which the distal and proximal pigments become light-adapted (Welsh, 1939), and for the crabs *Hemigrapsus* and *Pachygrapsus* (Smith, 1948) in which the retinal glow observable at night in dark-adapted crabs disappears after injection of eyestalk extract. In this latter case it is not known which specific retinal pigments migrated.

Meanwhile, two structures within the eyestalk were examined as possible sources of the chromatophorotropins because of their secretory appearance. One of these was Hanström's *X*-organ, thought to be transformed sensory cells of a rudimentary eye papilla; the other was the sinus gland, generally located between the two middle optic ganglia. Evidence from injection experiments (Carlson, 1935, 1936; Carstam, 1942; Hanström, 1937) indicated that the sinus gland was the probable endocrine source. This discovery permitted deficiency experiments, in which after surgical removal of the sinus gland in *Palaemon* the distal pigment assumes the dark-adapted

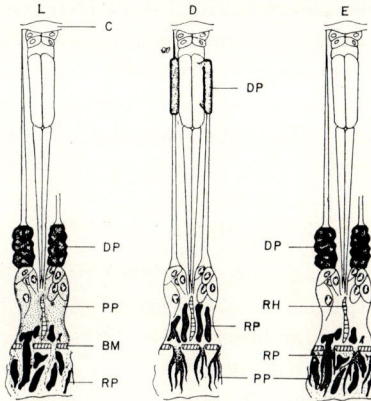

FIG. 1

Ommatidia from the eyes of *Palaemonetes*, showing general structure and the position of the three retinal pigments under various conditions. *L*, from a light-adapted eye; *D*, from a dark-adapted eye; *E*, from eye of a dark-adapted animal 45 min after injection with eyestalk extract. *C*, cornea; *DP*, distal pigment; *PP*, proximal pigment; *BM*, basement membrane; *RP*, reflecting pigment; *RH*, rhabdom. (From Kleinholz, 1936.)

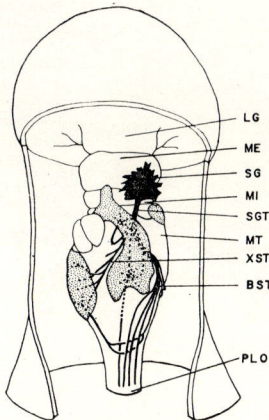

FIG. 2

Dorsal view of the right eyestalk of *Orconectes virilis* showing the eyestalk neurosecretory system. Stippled areas indicate occurrence of neurosecretory cells. The principal neurosecretory fiber tracts leading to the sinus gland are shown. *BST*, brain-sinus gland tract; *LG*, lamina ganglionaris, first optic ganglion of the eyestalk; *ME*, medulla externa; *MI*, medulla interna; *MT*, medulla terminalis; *PLO*, optic lobe peduncle; *SG*, sinus gland; *SGT*, sinus gland tract; *XST*, tract from medulla terminalis *X*-organ to sinus gland. (Modified from Bliss *et al.*, 1954.)

position (Panouse, 1946). More detailed study (Knowles, 1950, 1952) reveals that in *Palaemon* the distal pigment remains in the dark-adapted position, even when animals are kept brightly illuminated, for as long as 10 days after sinus gland removal. Regulation of light-adaptation of the distal pigment by a hormone from the sinus gland thus meets the classical criteria of deficiency and injection experiments.

III. NEUROSECRETION

Results from physiological and morphological studies (Bliss and Welsh, 1952; Bliss *et al.*, 1954; Enami, 1951; Passano, 1953) indicate that the sinus gland is primarily an accumulation of bulbous, secretion-laden axon terminals that come from neurosecretory cells located in various parts of the central nervous system (Fig. 2). Such neurosecretory cells are modified neurons whose hormonal secretion may be transported along the axoplasm to storage sites from which release into the circulation can occur. Distribution of neurosecretory cells in various ganglionic components of the eyestalk and a functional study of the effectiveness of extracts of these and of other

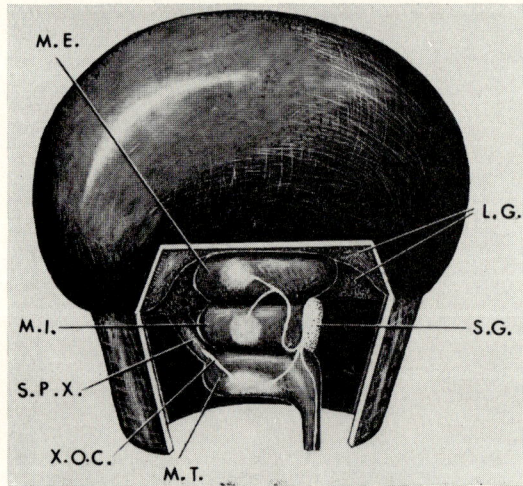

FIG. 3

Dissection of the left eyestalk of *Pandalus borealis*; the mid-dorsal line is towards the right-hand side of the drawing. Only the nervous tissues are shown. Ganglionic *X*-organs show in their natural appearance as whitish patches against their corresponding medullae; from each of them a neurosecretory tract runs to the sinus gland. A tract also runs from the brain to the sinus gland. In life these tracts also appear as white lines against the nervous tissue. Dissection by D. B. Carlisle. *LG*, lamina ganglionaris; *ME*, medulla externa or second optic ganglion; *MI*, medulla interna; *MT*, medulla terminalis; *SG*, sinus gland; *SPX*, sensory pore *X*-organ (Hanström's *X*-organ); *XOC*, *X*-organ connective. (From Kleinholz *et al.*, 1962a.)

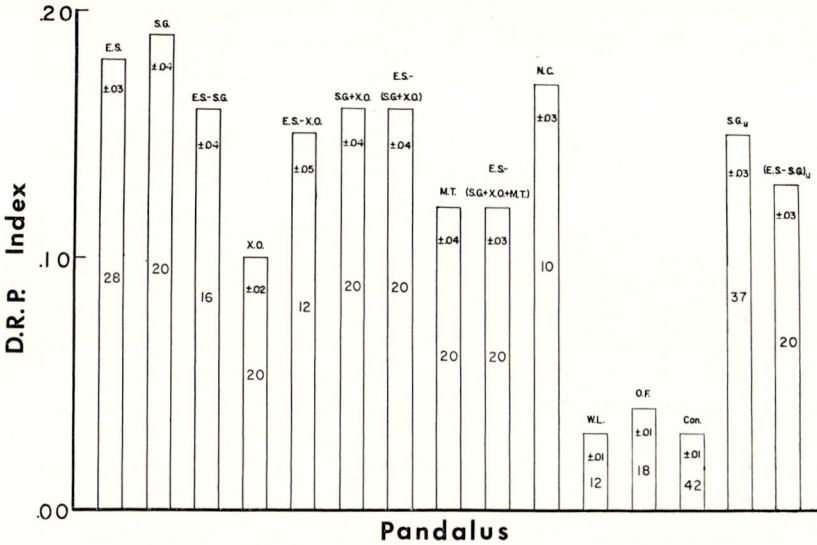

FIG. 4

Distal retinal pigment hormone in *Pandalus* nervous tissues tested on *Palaemon adspersus*. *ES*, extract of whole eyestalks; *SG*, sinus gland; SG_u, unheated sinus gland extract. *ES-SG*, sinus glandless eyestalks; $(ES-SG)_u$, unheated extract of sinus glandless eyestalks. *XO*, Hanström's *X*-organ (*SPX* of Fig. 3); *ES-XO*, eyestalks from which Hanström's *X*-organ had been removed; *MT*, medulla terminalis; *NC*, ventral nerve cord; *WL*, control extracts prepared from walking legs and swimmerets; *OF*, erythrophore-concentrating hormone preparation of Edman, Fänge, and Östlund; *CON*, control uninjected test animals. (From Kleinholz *et al.*, 1962a.)

ganglia of the central nervous system in causing light-adaptation of the distal pigment in *Pandalus borealis* is summarized in Figs. 3 and 4. Light-adapting hormone occurs not only in the sinus gland but in all the ganglia of the central nervous system tested. The only preparations which show no such activity are extracts of walking legs, sea water controls, and a partially purified preparation of chromatophorotropic hormone (Kleinholz *et al.*, 1962a). Such distribution of activity for the distal pigment is similar to that found for chromatophorotropic activity (Bowman, 1949; Brown, 1950; Sandeen, 1950), and has been reported also for the supraesophageal ganglia of several crustacean species (Fingerman and Aoto, 1962); it is consistent with the known presence of neurosecretory cells in these tissues.

IV. ASSAY AND PROPERTIES

Early studies had shown that the degree of light-adaptation of the distal pigment is related to intensity of illumination, and that graded responses from dark- to light-adaptation can be obtained by injecting eyestalk extract in a range between the lower and upper threshold concentrations (Kleinholz, 1938; Kleinholz and Knowles, 1938; Sandeen and Brown, 1952). These observations led to development of an assay for the hormone, with dark-adapted *Palaemonetes vulgaris* as test animal (Fig. 5), although other crustaceans with a good range of movement of the distal pigment would probably serve equally well. The ratio of the distance (a) from the cornea to the distal

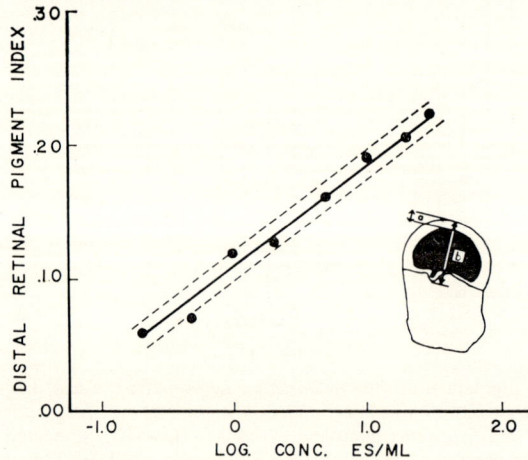

Fig. 5

Regression of distal retinal pigment index (response) on the logarithm of concentration of injected extracts of *Palaemonetes* eyestalks, with the standard error of the estimate shown in broken lines. The inset drawing of an eyestalk shows the measurements made for calculating the response. (From Kleinholz *et al.*, 1962b.)

margin of the distal pigment to the distance (b) from the cornea to the proximal margin of the dorsal pigment spot constitutes the distal pigment index (DPI). Such measurements are made with an ocular micrometer in a compound microscope on eyestalks removed from the test animals 45 min after injection of extract. Distal pigment indices for the dark-adapted state are about 0·050 and about 0·200 for the light-adapted condition. The *Palaemonetes* unit for distal pigment light-adapting hormone is defined as that concentration of eyestalk extract, injected into 10 dark-adapted *P. vulgaris* measuring 35–40 mm in rostrum–telson length, which results in an average DPI of 0·150.

Properties of this light-adapting hormone have been examined as a necessary preliminary to undertaking separation and purification studies and further chemical characterization. It was found (Kleinholz *et al.*, 1962b) that responses obtained with extracts prepared from eyestalks heated at 110°C for 2 hr are as great (average DPI: 0·215 ± 0·01) as those obtained with extracts from fresh eyestalks (average DPI: 0·200 ± 0·02); extracts prepared from lyophilized eyestalks show an average DPI of $0 \cdot 222 \pm 0 \cdot 01$; hormonal activity thus appears to be thermostable. The activity is insoluble in 100% ethanol (average DPI: $0 \cdot 090 \pm 0 \cdot 01$) and can be extracted from the 100% ethanol-insoluble residue with water (average DPI: $0 \cdot 214 \pm 0 \cdot 01$); 95% ethanol, however, extracts a substantial amount of activity (average DPI: $0 \cdot 161 \pm 0 \cdot 04$). The hormone is dialyzable through Visking cellophane tubing, activity (average DPI: $0 \cdot 113 \pm 0 \cdot 02$) being detectable in the dialyzate after 3 hr.

Aqueous extracts of eyestalks, allowed to remain at room temperature, gradually lose activity over 12–24 hr, in contrast with aqueous extracts which, heated for 1 min at 100°C, show full activity after 24 hr. A pH of about 7·5 is optimum for this inactivation. Enzymes that inactivate this hormone are found in a variety of tissues from crustaceans and mollusks. For crustaceans, the tissues used and the percentage inactivation in standardized tests with hormone extract are: heart, 41%; vas deferens, 100%; thoracic muscle, 92%; hypodermis, 97%; blood, 1%; ventral nerve cord, 72%; eyestalks, 42%. Adductor muscle of a mollusk causes 95% inactivation. Treatment of suitably prepared eyestalk extracts with crystalline trypsin or chymotrypsin results in 45–84% inactivation of hormone activity.

V. SEPARATION OF DISTAL PIGMENT LIGHT-ADAPTING HORMONE

With the information from neurosecretory distribution of hormonal activity in eyestalks, and the properties described above, a reasonable basis is established for attempting separation of the light-adapting hormone from lyophilized whole eyestalks, on the assumption that the hormone is a peptide of low molecular weight.

The first large-scale separation of distal retinal pigment light-adapting hormone on Dowex and DEAE-Sephadex columns was reported by Josefsson and Kleinholz (1964). The procedure also separates the retinal hormone from the erythrophore-regulating chromatophorotropin of the eyestalk and confirms earlier physiological (Kleinholz, 1958; Kleinholz et al., 1962a) and paper electrophoretic studies (Fingerman and Mobberly, 1960a) that these hormones are different molecules. Assay on dark-adapted *Palaemonetes* of the distal pigment light-adapting hormone thus obtained, however, shows only 0·4% of the activity present in the original aqueous extract of the eyestalk material. An improved method which yields about 60% recovery of activity was developed by Kleinholz and Kimball (1965); a typical chromatogram for this separation on Sephadex G-25 columns is shown in Fig. 6. The distal pigment hormone is found in the fractions designated IB on the chromatogram; another hormone, MDH, which disperses melanin pigment in brachyuran chromatophores, occurs in the same fractions. These are completely separated from the erythrophore pigment-concentrating hormone which is found in Peak IV.

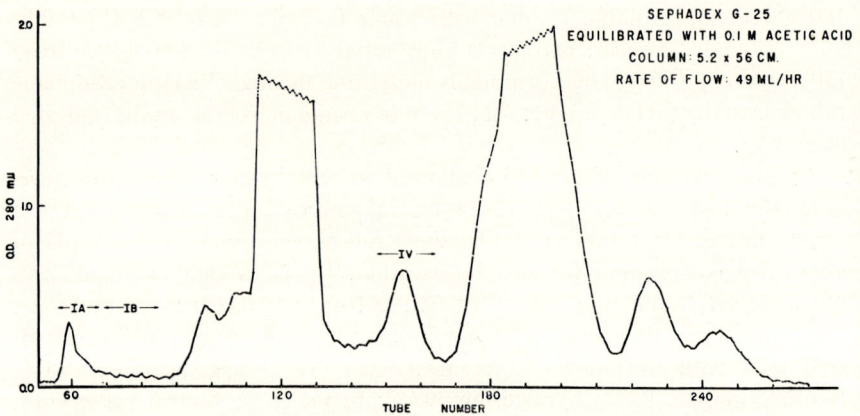

FIG. 6

Separation of pigmentary effector hormones in extracts of crustacean eyestalks on Sephadex G-25 columns. (From Kleinholz and Kimball, 1965.)

VI. DARK-ADAPTING DISTAL PIGMENT HORMONE

The presence of an antagonistic hormone causing migration of the distal pigment towards the dark-adapted position has been postulated by Brown and his collaborators (Brown *et al.*, 1952a, 1952b, 1953). The indirect evidence for such a dark-adapting hormone is based on the kinetics of light- and of dark-adaptation in *Palaemonetes* in which (a) animals, dark-adapted for measured but varying intervals, were given a light stimulus and returned to darkness, and (b) similarly dark-adapted animals were injected with extracts of various tissues after exposure to the light stimulus, and then returned to darkness.

Under the conditions listed in (a), the longer the interval in darkness before applying the light stimulus, the greater is the degree of light-adaptation of the distal pigment, and the faster is the rate of readaptation to darkness following the light stimulus. These results are interpreted as indicating the presence of a dark-adapting hormone. Support for this hypothesis was adduced from injection experiments (b) where, compared with sea water controls, extracts of eyestalks or other parts of the central nervous system not only supplement the degree of light-adaptation evoked by the light stimulus (through the known presence of light-adapting hormone in such extracts) but also produce faster rates of readaptation to darkness (hence, the presence also of dark-adapting hormone). Injection of extract of trito-cerebral commissure into similar experimental animals induces less light-adaptation and a faster rate of readaptation to darkness than does sea water; the interpretation is that commissure extract contains only dark-adapting distal pigment hormone. Attempts to effect dark-adaptation of the distal pigment by injection of tissue extracts into light-adapted *Palaemonetes*, maintained in the light, are unsuccessful. Some of the above experiments were repeated by Fingerman (1957) on another crustacean species, the crayfish *Cambarellus*, and were similarly interpreted.

More direct evidence for a dark-adapting distal pigment hormone is summarized by Fingerman and Aoto (1962). The distal pigment responses of *Palaemonetes* (Fingerman *et al.*, 1959) are shown in Fig. 7 and are representative of the several studies on three different crustacean species made by Fingerman and his collaborators. One eyestalk is removed from the test animals on the assumption that such prawns are less able to antagonize any dark-adapting distal pigment hormone to be injected than are intact test animals. The one-eyed *Palaemonetes* are maintained on black backgrounds at an intensity of illumination such that the distal pigment lies

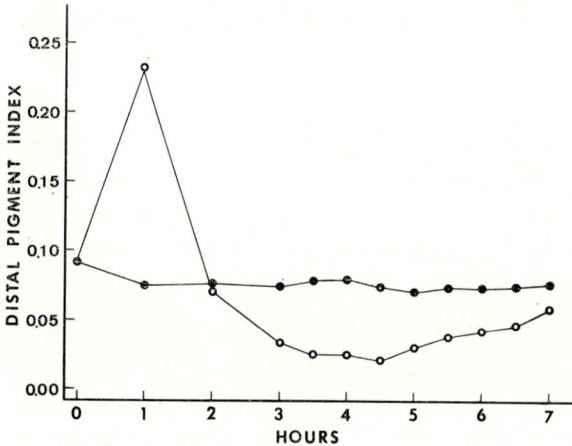

FIG. 7

Light- and dark-adaptational responses of distal retinal pigment of *Palaemonetes* to eyestalk extract (circles); sea water control injections (dots). (From Fingerman *et al.*, 1959.)

between the positions of complete light- and of complete dark-adaptation, and can respond to injected extracts by moving in either direction. *Palaemonetes* thus prepared are each injected 0·02 ml of a sea water extract containing 33 eyestalks per ml. Figure 7 shows that 1 hr afterwards the distal pigment is characteristically light-adapted; after 2 hr, the distal pigment has returned to near the starting index; from the second to seventh hours after injection the DPI remains on the dark-adapted side. Control animals injected an equal volume of sea water show no appreciable change in the DPI. Similarly, injection into each test *Palaemonetes* of sea water extract of three tritocerebral commissures results in slight light-adaptation after 30 min, followed for several hours by a DPI lower than that at time of injection. When extract of the supraesophageal ganglion plus the attached circumesophageal connectives, but from which the tritocerebral commissure has been removed, is injected, marked light-adaptation of the distal pigment occurs initially as expected, but the DPI gradually returns to the level of the controls without showing a dark-adaptational response. Dark-adapted responses are also obtained with extracts of sinus gland and of optic ganglia.

The dark-adaptational response appears to be consistently reproducible in injection experiments, even though very small. In Fig. 7 the change in DPI from the beginning to the maximum dark-adaptational response $4\frac{1}{2}$ hr after injection is about 0·07. In a later report, Fingerman and Mobberly (1960b) use less concentrated extracts (20 eyestalks per ml, with and without denatured trypsin) and show (in their Fig. 5) DPI changes of about 0·07 and 0·09, 5 hr after injection. No appreciable difference in the dark-adaptational response seemingly results from this dosage difference. Whether significant differences can be produced by a suitable range of dosage is not known. The demonstration that eyestalk extract can be separated by paper electrophoresis to give a fraction effecting a statistically significant migration of the distal pigment toward the dark-adapted position (Fingerman and Mobberly, 1960b) raises the possibility that sufficient amounts of this substance might be made available for study of dose–response relations. No further characterization studies of the dark-adapting hormone are available.

VII. PROXIMAL AND REFLECTING PIGMENTS

The mechanisms regulating activity of the proximal retinal pigment are still not clear; the varied results obtained experimentally indicate the possibility of species differences in the control of this effector. Thus, injection of eyestalk extract into dark-adapted *Palaemonetes* (Kleinholz, 1936) and *Paratya* (Nagano, 1947) has no effect on the proximal pigment, although the distal and reflecting pigments become light-adapted. Welsh (1939), however, found that, while injection of extract equivalent to one eyestalk is without effect on the dark-adapted proximal pigment of the crayfish, *Cambarus*, doubling the dosage causes light-adaptation of this effector. Surgical removal of the sinus gland in the crayfish *Pacifastacus* (Kleinholz, 1948) and in the prawn *Palaemon* (Knowles, 1950, 1952) does not interfere with the responses of the proximal pigment to light and to darkness. The proximal pigments of isolated eyestalks of *Pacifastacus* (Kleinholz, 1949) and of *Paratya* (Nagano, 1952) maintained in moist chambers and exposed to light and to darkness, show appropriate movements. De Bruin and Crisp

(1957) find that light-adaptation of the proximal pigment in dark-adapted *Palaemon serratus*, *Pandalus montagui*, and *Praunus flexuosus* requires 4–6 min as compared with about 30 min for *Palaemonetes* (Fingerman *et al.*, 1962). Except for the results observed with *Cambarus*, this group of studies indicates that the proximal pigment may respond as independent effectors; the short response time found by De Bruin and Crisp must, however, be regarded as less reliable evidence for the independent effector possibility.

Fingerman and his co-workers, in fact, propose that light-adaptation of the proximal pigment in *Palaemonetes* is hormonally controlled, based on observations that this effector continues to migrate, in the dark, towards the light-adapted position for several minutes after dark-adapted animals, given a short exposure to light, are returned to the dark-room. Fingerman and Nagabhushanam (1963) report that if the crayfish *Cambarellus* is kept on illuminated black backgrounds the proximal pigment is intermediate between the completely light-adapted and dark-adapted positions. The proximal pigment shows a dark-adaptational response when such animals are injected with the equivalent of two eyestalks; injection of extracts of supraesophageal ganglia and the attached circumesophageal connectives results in a lesser but statistically significant migration toward the dark-adapted position.

Evidence for hormonal regulation of reflecting pigment comes only from injection experiments (Kleinholz, 1936; Nagano, 1947; Fingerman and Oguro, 1963) and suffers from the inadequacies of such limited approaches.

Review of the literature on the physiology of crustacean retinal pigments shows that hormonal control of the distal pigment has been convincingly demonstrated, albeit more so for light-adaptation than for dark-adaptation. Information on the properties and characteristics of the light-adapting hormone is moderately advanced; that for the dark-adapting hormone is still very sparse. Present evidence shows that the proximal pigment may act as an independent effector; in some species, at least, hormonal regulation is indicated. The possibility that the physiological mechanism of control may vary among species, or even that more than one mechanism may be involved in a single species, cannot be overlooked. For the physiology of retinal reflecting pigments our ignorance is more impressive than our knowledge.

REFERENCES

BENNITT, R. 1932. Physiological interrelationship in the eyes of decapod Crustacea. *Physiol. Zool.* **5**, 49–64.

BLISS, D. E. and WELSH, J. H. 1952. The neurosecretory system of brachyuran Crustacea. *Biol. Bull.* **103**, 157–69.

BLISS, D. E., DURAND, J. B. and WELSH, J. H. 1954. Neurosecretory systems in decapod Crustacea. *Z. Zellforsch. u. Mikroskop. Anat.* **39**, 520–36.

BOWMAN, T. E. 1949. Chromatophorotropins in the central nervous organs of the crab, *Hemigrapsus oregonensis*. *Biol. Bull.* **96**, 238–45.

BROWN, F. A., Jr. 1950. Studies on the physiology of *Uca* red chromatophores. *Biol. Bull.* **98**, 218–26.

BROWN, F. A., Jr., FINGERMAN, M. and HINES, M. N. 1952a. Alterations in the capacity for light and dark adaptation of the distal retinal pigment of *Palaemonetes*. *Physiol. Zool.* **25**, 230–9.

BROWN, F. A., Jr., HINES, M. N. and FINGERMAN, M. 1952b. Hormonal regulation of the distal retinal pigment of *Palaemonetes*. *Biol. Bull.* **102**, 212–25.

BROWN, F. A., Jr., WEBB, H. M. and SANDEEN, M. 1953. Differential production of two retinal pigment hormones in *Palaemonetes* by light flashes. *J. Cell. Comp. Physiol.* **41**, 123–44.

BUTENANDT, A. 1957. Über Ommochrome, eine Klasse natürlicher Phenoxazon-Farbstoffe. *Angew. Chem.* **69**, 16–23.

BUTENANDT, A., BIEKERT, E. and LINZEN, B. 1958a. Über Ommochrome, XIII. Isolierung und Charakterisierung von Omminen. *Zeit. f. physiol. Chemie.* **312**, 227–36.

BUTENANDT, A., BIEKERT, E. and LINZEN, B. 1958b. Über Ommochrome, XIV. Zur Verbreitung der Ommine im Tierreich. *Zeit. f. physiol. Chemie.* **313**, 251–8.

CARLSON, S. P. 1935. The color change in *Uca pugilator*. *Proc. Natl. Acad. Sci. U.S.* **21**, 549–51.

CARLSON, S. P. 1936. Color changes in brachyuran crustaceans, especially in *Uca pugilator*. *Kgl. Fysiograf. Sällskap. Lund Förh.* **6**, 1–18.

CARSTAM, S. P. 1942. Weitere Beiträge zur Farbwechsel physiologie der Crustaceen. *Z. vergleich. Physiol.* **29**, 433–72.

CHARNIAUX-COTTON, H. and KLEINHOLZ, L. H. 1964. Hormones in invertebrates other than insects. In *The Hormones* (Pincus, G., Thimann, K. V. and Astwood, E. B., eds.) Vol. IV, 135–98. Academic Press, New York.

DE BRUIN, G. H. P. and CRISP, D. J. 1957. The influence of pigment migration on vision of higher Crustacea. *J. Exptl. Biol.* **34**, 447–63.

ENAMI, M. 1951. The sources and activities of two chromatophotropic hormones in crabs of the genus *Sesarma*. II. Histology of incretory elements. *Biol. Bull.* **101**, 241–58.

FINGERMAN, M. 1957. Regulation of the distal retinal pigment of the dwarf crawfish, *Cambarellus shufeldti*. *J. Cell. Comp. Physiol.* **50**, 357–70.

FINGERMAN, M. and AOTO, J. 1962. Regulation of pigmentary phenomena. Hormonal regulation of pigmentary effectors in crustaceans. *Gen. Comp. Endocrin. Suppl.* **1**, 81–93.

FINGERMAN, M. and MOBBERLY, W. C., Jr. 1960a. Physicochemical properties and differentiation of chromatophorotropins and retinal pigment light-adapting hormone of the dwarf crayfish, *Cambarellus shufeldti*. *Amer. Mid. Nat.* **64**, 474–84.

FINGERMAN, M. and MOBBERLY, W. C., Jr. 1960b. Investigation of the hormones controlling the distal retinal pigment of the prawn, *Palaemonetes*. *Biol. Bull.* **118**, 393–406.

FINGERMAN, M. and NAGABHUSHANAM, R. 1963. Proximal retinal pigment responses and their relationship to total photomechanical adaptation in the dwarf crayfish, *Cambarellus shufeldti*. *Tulane Stud. Zool.* **10**, 49–56.

FINGERMAN, M., LOWE, M. E. and SUNDARARAJ, B. I. 1959. Dark-adapting and light-adapting hormones controlling the distal retinal pigment of the prawn *Palaemonetes vulgaris*. *Biol. Bull.* **116**, 30–6.

FINGERMAN, M. and OGURO, C. 1963. Hormonal control of the reflecting retinal pigment in the isopod *Ligia olfersi* Brandt. *Tulane Stud. Zool.* **11**, 75–8.

FINGERMAN, M., NAGABHUSHANAM, R. and PHILPOTT, L. 1962. Photomechanical responses of the proximal pigment in *Palaemonetes* and *Orconectes*. *Biol. Bull.* **123**, 121–31.

FISHER, L. R. 1965. Pigments of euphasiid eyes. *Symposium on Crustacea*. Mar. Biol. Assoc. India. (Abstracts of Papers.) pp. 54–5.

HANSTRÖM, B. 1937. Die Sinusdrüse und der hormonal bedingte Farbwechsel der Crustaceen. *Kgl. Svenska Vetenskapsakad. Handl.* **16**, (3) 1–99.

JOSEFSSON, L. and KLEINHOLZ, L. H. 1964. Isolation and purification of hormones of the crustacean eye-stalk. *Nature* **201**, 301–2.

KLEINHOLZ, L. H. 1936. Crustacean eye-stalk hormone and retinal pigment migration. *Biol. Bull.* **70**, 159–84.

KLEINHOLZ, L. H. 1938. Studies in the pigmentary system of Crustacea. IV. The unitary versus the multiple hormone hypothesis of control. *Biol. Bull.* **75**, 510–32.

KLEINHOLZ, L. H. 1948. Migrations of the retinal pigments and their regulation by the sinus gland. *Bull. biol. France et Belg.* **33**, Suppl., 127–38.

KLEINHOLZ, L. H. 1949. Responses of the proximal retinal pigment of the isolated crustacean eyestalk to light and to darkness. *Proc. Natl. Acad. Sci. U.S.* **35**, 215–8.

KLEINHOLZ, L. H. 1958. Neurosecretion and retinal pigment movement in crustaceans. In *Zweites Internationales Symposium Über Neurosekretion* (Bargmann, W., Hanström, B. and Scharrer, B. and E., eds.) pp. 110–12. Springer, Berlin.

KLEINHOLZ, L. H. 1959. Purines and pteridines from the reflecting pigment of the arthropod retina. *Biol. Bull.* **116**, 125–35.

KLEINHOLZ, L. H. 1961. Pigmentary effectors. In *The Physiology of Crustacea* (Waterman, T. H., ed.) Vol. II, 133–69. Academic Press, New York.

KLEINHOLZ, L. H. and KIMBALL, F. 1965. Separation of neurosecretory pigmentary effector hormones of the crustacean eyestalk. *Gen. Comp. Endocrin.* **5**, 336–41.

KLEINHOLZ, L. H. and KNOWLES, F. G. W. 1938. Studies in the pigmentary system of Crustacea. III. Light-intensity and the position of the distal retinal pigment in *Leander adspersus. Biol. Bull.* **75**, 266–73.

KLEINHOLZ, L. H., BURGESS, P. R., CARLISLE, D. B. and PFLUEGER, O. 1962a. Neurosecretion and crustacean retinal pigment hormone: distribution of the light-adapting hormone. *Biol. Bull.* **122**, 73–85.

KLEINHOLZ, L. H., ESPER, H., JOHNSON, C. and KIMBALL, F. 1962b. Neurosecretion and crustacean retinal pigment hormone: assay and properties of the light-adapting hormone. *Biol. Bull.* **123**, 317–29.

KNOWLES, F. G. W. 1950. The control of retinal pigment migration in *Leander serratus. Biol. Bull.* **98**, 66–80.

KNOWLES, F. G. W. 1952. Pigment movements after sinus-gland removal in *Leander adspersus. Physiol. Comparata et Oecol.* **2**, 289–96.

NAGANO, T. 1947. Physiological Studies on the Pigmentary System of Crustacea. II. The Pigment Migration in the Eyes of the Shrimps. *Science Repts. Tohoku Univ. Fourth Series*, **18**, 1–16.

NAGANO, T. 1952. Physiological Studies on the Pigmentary System of Crustacea. IX. An Analysis of the Behavior of the Proximal Retinal Pigment in the Shrimp. *Science Repts. Tohoku Univ. Fourth Series*, **19**, 219–20.

PANOUSE, J. B. 1946. Recherches sur les fhénomènes humoraux chez les Crustacés. *Ann. inst. Océanog. Paris* **23**, 65–147.

PARKER, G. H. 1932. The movements of the retinal pigment. *Ergeb. Biol.* **9**, 239–91.

PASSANO, L. M. 1953. Neurosecretory control of moulting in crabs by the X-organ sinus gland complex. *Physiol. Comparata et Oecol.* **3**, 155–89.

PERKINS, E. B. 1928. Color changes in crustaceans, especially *Palaemonetes. J. Exptl. Zool.* **50**, 71–105.

SANDEEN, M. I. 1950. Chromatophorotropins in the central nervous system of *Uca pugilator* with special reference to their origins and actions. *Physiol. Zool.* **23**, 337–52.

SANDEEN, M. I. and BROWN, F. A., Jr. 1952. Responses of the distal retinal pigment of *Palaemonetes* to illumination. *Physiol. Zool.* **25**, 222–30.

SMITH, R. I. 1948. The role of the sinus glands in retinal pigment migration in grapsoid crabs. *Biol. Bull.* **95**, 169–85.

TUURALA, O. 1954. Histologische und physiologische Untersuchungen über die photomechanischen Erscheinungen in den Augen der Lepidopteren. *Ann. Acad. Sci. Fenn.*, Ser. A, **24**, 1–69.

WELSH, J. H. 1930a. The mechanics of migration of the distal pigment cells in the eyes of *Palaemonetes. J. Exptl. Zool.* **56**, 459–94.

WELSH, J. H. 1930b. Diurnal rhythm of the distal pigment cells in the eyes of certain crustaceans. *Proc. Natl. Acad. Sci. U.S.* **16**, 386–95.

WELSH, J. H. 1939. The action of eye-stalk extracts on retinal pigment migration in the crayfish, *Cambarus bartoni. Biol. Bull.* **77**, 119–25.

PART II

Rhabdom structure. Photochemistry. Colour discrimination.
Reaction to polarized light

FINE STRUCTURE PATTERNS IN CRUSTACEAN RHABDOMS

E. Eguchi and T. H. Waterman

Department of Biology, Yale University, New Haven, Connecticut, U.S.A.

INTRODUCTION

ALL currently acceptable hypotheses of compound eye function either imply or directly assume that the rhabdom is the site of the visual pigments and thus the locus of the primary photochemical events in vision. Consequently, detailed knowledge of this structure is essential for improving our still quite imperfect understanding of the functional organization of arthropod and other rhabdom-bearing eyes.

For nearly a decade we have known that rhabdoms comprise characteristic ordered arrays of fine tubules or microvilli arising from the small clusters of retinular cells which form the patterned ranks of neurosensory cells characteristic of retinas of this kind (for reviews see Waterman, 1961; Eakin, 1963; Goldsmith, 1964; Eguchi, 1965; Horridge, 1965). Hence in their coaxial location in the light path, their strikingly exaggerated development of regularly organized lipoprotein membrane systems, and in their presumed enclosure of retinal-opsin, rhabdoms show important analogies with the outer segments of vertebrate rods and cones. Yet in the rhabdom-bearing eyes we still have little direct experimental evidence of their role or its importance.

In pursuit of such knowledge we are engaged in an extensive study of crustacean rhabdom fine structure in search of functional correlations between it and electrophysiological and behavioral responses. The strategy employed involves two approaches: first, a comparative one surveying many and varied species, and second, an experimental alteration of rhabdom organization. In both cases we are looking to these evolutionary and laboratory variations on the typical rhabdom pattern as a means of isolating functional components of this minute complex mechanism.

The present report is a preliminary account of our relevant findings. It first describes a typical brachyuran rhabdom as the norm for decapods and then contrasts this typical structure with a special decapod type from the spiny lobster *Panulirus* as well as a peracaridan variant from the compound eye of the mysid *Mysidium*. The experimental section reports the fine structural changes which occur in the rhabdoms of the crayfish *Procambarus* and the brine shrimp *Artemia* when they are kept in constant darkness for periods of several months.

MATERIAL AND METHODS

The principal crustaceans studied for this report were the following: the mysid *Mysidium gracile* (Dana), the spiny lobster *Panulirus argus* (Latreille) and the swimming crab *Callinectes ornatus* (Ordway), all from Bermuda; *Procambarus clarkii* (Girard) from Louisiana and *Artemia salina* (Linnaeus) laboratory raised from resting eggs of California origin.

Eyes were first fixed for 2 hr with 5% glutaraldehyde buffered in 0·1 M Sorenson's phosphate solution at pH 7·4 (Sabatini, Bensch and Barrnett, 1963). After washing with buffer, the tissues were then post-fixed for another 2 hr with 2·5% osmium tetroxide, also buffered at pH 7·4 with Sorenson's solution. Fixation was followed by acetone dehydration, transfer to propylene oxide, and embedding in epoxy resin (Luft, 1961). Sections were cut with a Porter-Blum MT-2 microtome, stained with uranyl acetate and lead citrate (Reynolds, 1963). Finally, observations were made in an RCA EMU3G or Philips 200 electron microscope.

RESULTS

1. *The Typical Decapod Rhabdom*

Rhabdoms are composite structures derived from the retinular cells of a single ommatidium. Hence knowledge of the relation of rhabdom parts to retinular cells as well as of their complex integrated pattern are basic to any understanding of function. In decapods, as in a number of other arthropod groups, there are most commonly seven or eight neurosensory cells in each retinula. Only seven of these normally contribute a part (rhabdomere) to the rhabdom, while the eighth cell when present usually does not possess a rhabdomere. This eighth cell is ordinarily characterized also by a different size or position from the rest of the retinular cells and will not be considered further here since it is not known to have any functional relation to the rhabdom.

The seven regular retinular cells are arranged radially around the optic axis of the retinula like the sections of a much attenuated orange (Fig. 1). They enclose the rod-like or fusiform rhabdom whose longitudinal axis coincides with that of its ommatidium. Each of the seven rhabdomeres consists of fine tubules or microvilli perpendicular to the optic axis and extending towards it from the more peripheral cytoplasmic part of the parent retinular cell.

The microvilli of decapod (and some other) crustaceans are precisely arranged in alternating layers (Plate 1) with their longitudinal axes regularly

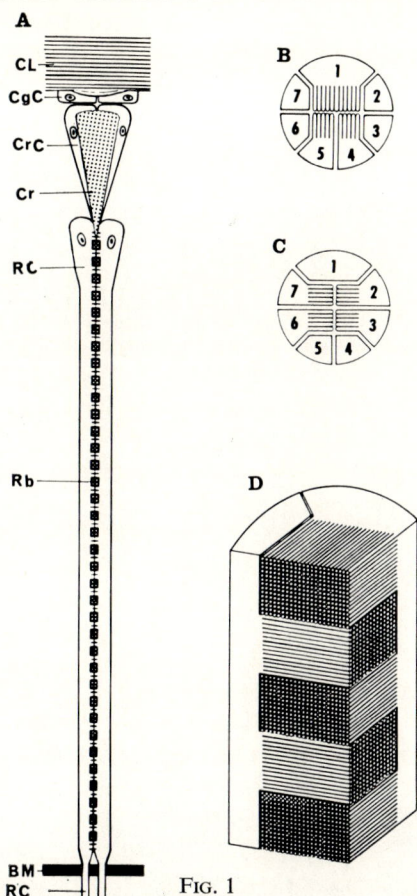

Fig. 1

Ommatidial structure in the typical compound eye of the swimming crab *Callinectes ornatus* (diagrammatic). A, Longitudinal section through the optic axis. In such a typical apposition ommatidium the rhabdom occupies a major part of the ommatidial axis terminating close to the crystalline cone. Along its length the rhabdom shows a characteristic banded appearance due to its fine structure. The surrounding retinular cells continue proximally through the basilar membrane as the primary visual axons. B, Cross-section through the retinula showing the make-up of one rhabdom layer. All its constituent microvilli run closely parallel in one direction. Note that this layer composed three rhabdomeres: a double-sized one from retinular cell 1 and two regular quarter-rhabdom ones from cells 4 and 5. Alternative rhabdom layers are the same as this one. C, Cross-section of an adjacent rhabdom. These have their microvilli regularly oriented in a direction 90° to those in adjacent layers and have their rhabdomeres derived from the other four retinular cells, 2, 3, 6 and 7 each contributing a quarter as shown. D, Stereodiagram showing rhabdom-layered structure with regular close packed microvilli with their long axes all parallel in one set of alternate layers and perpendicular to their counterparts in the other set. Dimensions of the various components of these diagrams are given in Table 1. *BM*, basilar membrane; *CgC*, corneagenous cell; *CL*, corneal lens; *Cr*, crystalline cone; *CrC*, crystalline cone cell; *Rb*, rhabdom; *RC*, retinular cell; *RCA*, retinular cell axon.

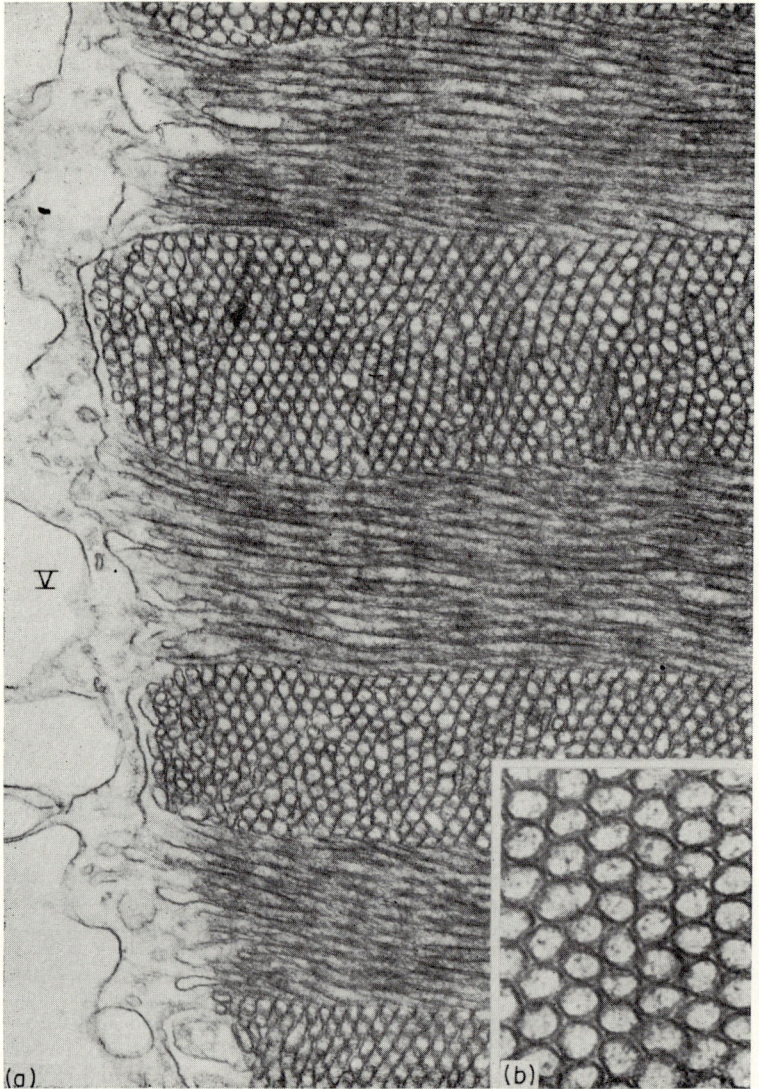

PLATE 1

a, Longitudinal section of part of a rhabdom from the compound eye of *Callinectes ornatus*. The microvilli are seen to run in perpendicular directions in alternate layers (see Fig. 1 for diagrammatic reconstruction). To the left the microvilli parallel to the section can be seen to originate from one of the retinular cells. Also noteworthy are the large perirhabdomal vacuoles (V) at the left edge of the picture. × 34,500. *b*, Higher magnification of microvilli running perpendicular to the sections. The tubule membranes and their dark staining contents are readily seen. × 76,000.

aligned in a given direction for one set and in a perpendicular direction for the alternate layers (Eguchi, 1964, 1965; Rutherford and Horridge, 1965). The number (25–450) and thickness (0·5–5 μ) of these rhabdom layers varies over a considerable range in the species studied (Table 1) but microvillus diameters are less variable (0·05–0·1 μ).

Three retinular cells (1, 4 and 5) contribute all the tubules in one set of alternate layers (Fig. 1, B). Retinular cells 2, 3, 6 and 7 provide rhabdomeres for the other set which has its tubules at right-angles to those from the other three cells (Fig. 1, C).

Rhabdom microvilli extend only half-way across the diameter of the whole structure and with their closed ends meet those of the opposite retinular cells along the diametrical plane normal to the tubule long axis (Plate 2). Because of the odd number of cells contributing to the rhabdom only six are paired (2–7) and each contributes one quarter of the microvilli in its set of layers (Fig. 1, B, C). Cell 1 in contrast produces half the tubules in its layers and is correspondingly larger and sometimes, at least, more electron dense (Plate 2).

Dense cytoplasmic particles are frequently observed within rhabdom microvilli (Plate 1, *b*) but their nature is not known. In all the decapods observed except *Panulirus* and *Procambarus* a vacuole system surrounding the rhabdom is prominent, especially in the distal part of the rhabdom (Plates 1 and 2). Such perirhabdomal vacuoles (called palisade by Horridge and Barnard, 1965), as well as mitochondria, change their position within the retinulas during dark and light adaptation (*Homarus*, Rutherford and Horridge, 1965; *Libinia*, Eguchi and Waterman, 1965, unpublished).

The major features of the typical decapod rhabdom are illustrated in the figures of the *Callinectes* rhabdom (Fig. 1, Plates 1 and 2). Major components commonly seen in the cytoplasm near the rhabdom are the vacuoles cited above, minute vesicles, desmosomes and multivesicular bodies as well as peculiar lamellated structures (onion bodies of the endocrinologists?). Retinular cells contain numerous mitochondria, but in our preparations they are not prominent near the rhabdom but often are conspicuous close to the cytoplasmic membranes of retinular cell axons.

As yet no consistent differences in fine structure pattern have become evident between the rhabdoms of "apposition" and those of "super-position" eyes, as defined by Exner (see review by Waterman, 1961). Thus the present account of the *Callinectes* rhabdom from an apposition eye agrees basically with those of *Procambarus* (Eguchi, 1964, 1965) and *Homarus* (Rutherford and Horridge, 1965), both of which are superposition.

Nevertheless, certain differences which are undoubtedly of physiological importance are evident. For example, although the axial length and the diameter of an ommatidium in a mature swimming crab and an adult crayfish are about the same, the relative size and position of the rhabdom is

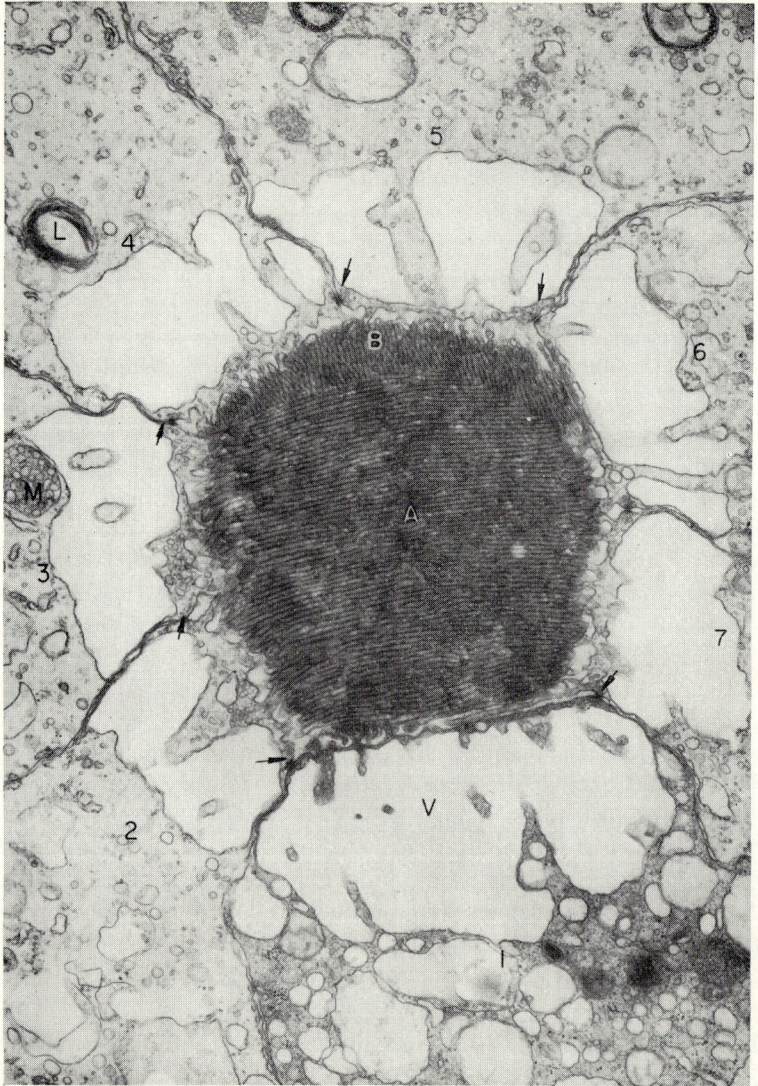

PLATE 2

Cross-section of rhabdom and adjacent parts of the retinular cells in a *Callinectes* ommatidium. Parts of two layers of microvilli (*A* and *B*) are visible in the rhabdom since the section is slightly oblique. The seven surrounding retinular cells are numbered 1 to 7, with 1 corresponding to cell 1 in Fig. 1. Note that its cytoplasm is much denser than that of the other six retinular cells. Desmosomes (arrows), multivesicular bodies (*M*) and curious multilamellar bodies (*L*) as well as the prominent vacuoles (*V*) adjacent to the rhabdom are all clearly shown.   × 14,800.

TABLE 1

QUANTITATIVE COMPARISONS OF OMMATIDIAL STRUCTURE

SPECIES NAME	Eye type	Ommatidium		Retinular cells			Rhabdom		Microvilli				Perirhabdomal vacuoles
		Length[2] (μ)	Diameter (μ)	Number in ommatidium	Length (μ)	Diameter (μ)	Length (μ)	Diameter (μ)	Number of layers	Layer thickness	Length (μ)	Diameter (μ)	
Artemia salina	A[1]	100	13	5 + 1[3]	50	6	50	4	None	—	2 μ	0·06μ	Yes
Mysidium gracile	S	120	9	7	100	5	Dist.[1] 6 Prox.[1] 20	7	Dist. None Prox. 20	Prox. 1	Dist. 3 Prox. 3	Dist. 0·07 Prox. 0·06	No
Procambarus clarkii	S	650	30	7	150	15	120	20	25	5	10	0·08	No
Panulirus argus	S	4000	60	7	200	30	Dist. 50 Prox. 150	Dist. 6 Prox. 50	Dist. 50 Prox. None	Dist. 0·5 Prox. —	Dist. 3 Prox. 3	Dist. 0·1 Prox. 0·1	No
Pagurus bernhardus	A	650	30	7	450	15	350	12	120	3	6	0·06	Yes
Callinectes ornatus	A	600	30	7 + 1[3]	450	15	400	5	450	1	2·5	0·07	Yes
Cardisoma guanhumi	A	680	20	7	350	10	350	5	350	1	2·5	0·07	Yes
Goniopsis cruentata	A	700	30	7	330	15	300	3	300	1	1·5	0·05	Yes
Libinia emarginata	A	370	20	7	250	10	Dist. 200 Prox. 50	Dist. 4 Prox. 15	200	1	Dist. 2 Prox. 7	0·09	Yes
Podophthalmus vigil	A	650	20	7	350	10	350	4	350	1	2	0·05	Yes

[1] A, Apposition type; S, Superposition type; Dist., Distal part of rhabdom; Prox., Proximal part of rhabdom.
[2] Length from corneal surface to basilar membrane.
[3] 1 is a rudimentary cell.

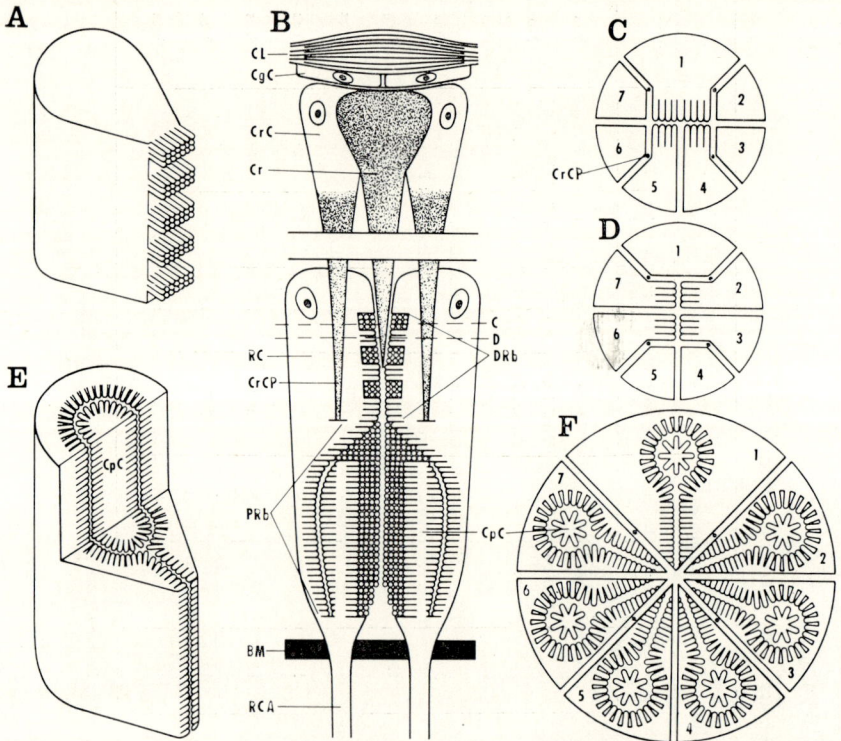

FIG. 2

Ommatidial structure in the unusual compound eye of the spiny lobster *Panulirus argus* (diagrammatic). A, Stereodiagram of the distal part of a single retinular cell bearing a slender but otherwise typical decapod rhabdomere. B, Longitudinal section through the optic axis with the greater part of the distance between crystalline cone and retinula omitted as indicated by the interruption. In such a superposition ommatidium the rhabdom occupies a minor part of the ommatidial axis, being separated from the crystalline cone in this instance by an extraordinarily long cone stalk. The atypical rhabdom is shown to consist of proximal and distal parts with the microvillus pattern being markedly aberrant in the former. C and D, Cross-sections of adjacent distal rhabdom layers (C and D in B) showing that rhabdomere structure and cellular derivation are closely similar to the *Callinectes* rhabdom. E, Stereodiagram of part of the proximal region of a retinular cell showing the intracellular location of the rhabdomere as well as the second array of microvilli arising from the cytoplasmic core. Note that instead of the typical two directions microvilli run in all directions. F, Enlarged cross-section of the proximal rhabdom indicating the relations between the seven rhabdomeres and their parts. Dimensions of the various components of these diagrams are given in Table 1. *BM*, basilar membrane; *CgC*, corneagenous cell; *CL*, corneal lens; *CpC*, cytoplasmic core; *Cr*, crystalline cone; *CrC*, crystalline cone cell; *CrCP*, crystalline cone cell process running proximally almost to the *BM*; *DRb*, distal rhabdom; *PRb*, proximal rhabdom; *RC*, retinular cell; *RCA*, retinular cell axon.

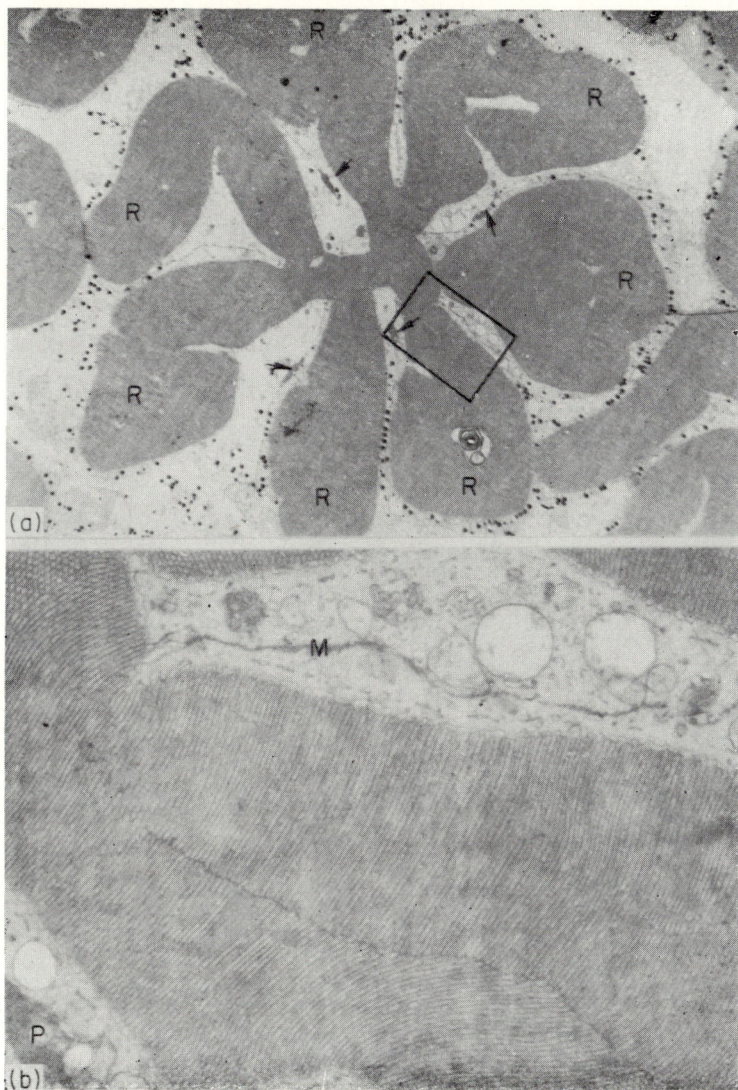

PLATE 3

Cross-sections of *Panulirus argus* proximal rhabdom. *a*, Low-power view showing the branching structure with bent swollen outer edges of the rhabdomeres (*R*). Position of the cell membranes demonstrates that the rhabdomeres lie within the retinular cells. Arrows point to the four crystalline cone cell processes running proximally towards the basilar membrane. Many cytoplasmic pigment granules may be seen. Box indicates the region enlarged in *b*. × 1800. *b*, Higher-power detail of the proximal rhabdom near the ommatidial (optic) axis. Two layers of well-ordered microvilli originating within the same retinular cell face each other in this region which may be identified in Fig. 2, E and F. The rhabdomere is surrounded by a thin layer of cytoplasm belonging to its retinular cell. *M*, retinular cell membrane; *P*, cone cell process. × 14,400.

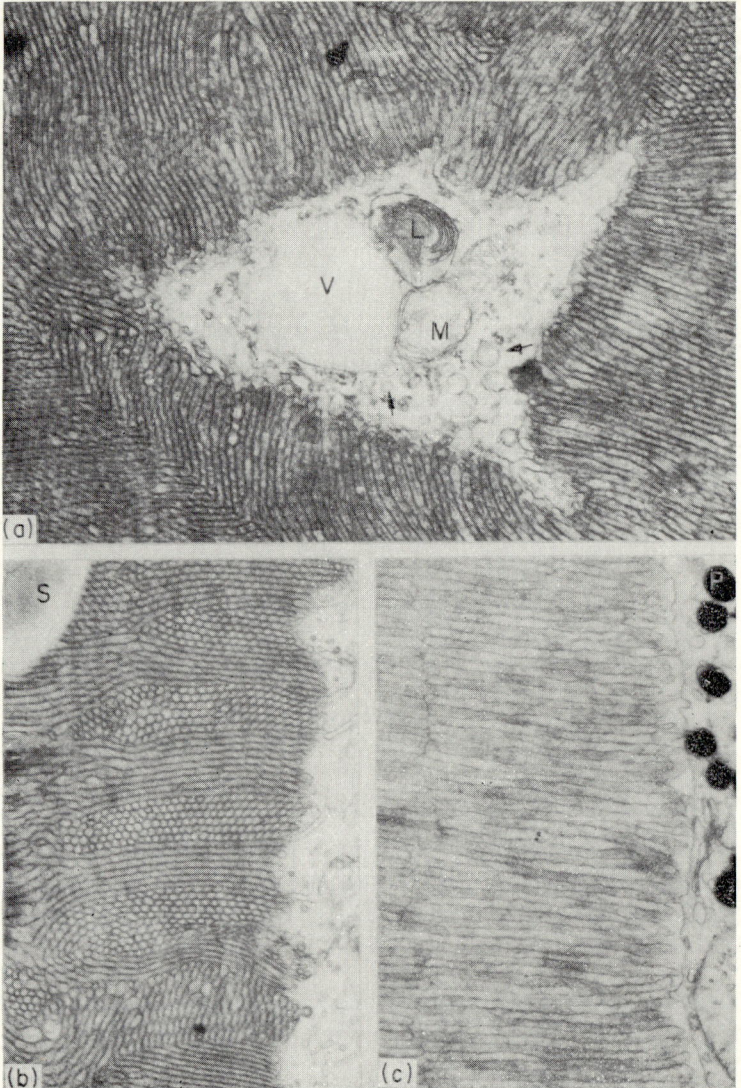

PLATE 4

Further details of *Panulirus argus* rhabdom. *a*, Cross-section through a cytoplasmic core thrusting into the swollen tip of a rhabdomere in proximal rhabdom region. A second set of microvilli facing those from the surrounding cytoplasm are formed from and radiate out from this core. In the latter small vesicles (arrows), a vacuole, mitochondria (*M*) and a lamellated body (*L*) are visible. × 25,000. *b*, Longitudinal section through the distal rhabdom showing the orderly array of microvilli layers lined up in perpendicular directions in adjacent layers, basically similar to the pattern shown in Plate 1. *S* is part of a crystalline cone stalk. × 18,000. *c*, Longitudinal section through the proximal rhabdom showing quite different. Corresponding differences in the length, but not the diameter of the retinular cells, are also evident.

In *Callinectes* the rhabdom and retinular cells are three times as long as those in *Procambarus*, so that the retina occupies 75% of the ommatidial length in the former and only 25% of it in the crayfish. In the latter, however, the rhabdom's diameter at its widest is four times that in the crab so that a rhabdom's volume in the superposition eye is equal to or greater than it is in the apposition example (Table 1).

The occurrence of prominent perirhabdomal vacuoles seems to be strongly correlated with the eye-type in the reptantian decapods so far studied. Such structures are absent in the macrurans, *Procambarus* (Eguchi, 1964, 1965), *Panulirus* (Plates 3 and 4) and *Homarus* (Rutherford and Horridge, 1965). All of these have superposition eyes. (Penaeid shrimps and *Mysidium* also having superposition eyes similarly have no well-developed vacuoles.) But the brachyuran Reptantia, the true crabs, all have well-developed vacuoles around the rhabdom (e.g. Plates 1 and 2).

2. *Variations on the Typical Pattern*

While many more kinds of decapod compound eye need to be studied, some interesting deviations from the type exemplified by *Callinectes* have been found so far. Two examples will be given, the spiny lobster *Panulirus* and the mysid *Mysidium*.

(a) *Panulirus* has one of the most peculiar rhabdoms of any species known even though the standard complement of seven major retinular cells and seven rhabdomeres is present (Fig. 2). The rhabdom consists of quite different proximal and distal parts as described long ago from light microscopy (Viallanes, 1892). The distal part, although both short and thin, nevertheless, is shown by our electron microscopy to have a typical axial and extracellular position as well as alternating layers of microvilli with their long axes at 90° (Fig. 2, A, C, D and Plate 4, *b*).

The proximal rhabdom is much larger, has no layering (Plate 4, *c*) and has its flange-like rhabdomeres mainly intracellular in position although they are interconnected by an axial stand (Fig. 2, B and Plate 3, *a*). Peripherally the rhabdomeres often are folded over or swollen in such a way that one or more cytoplasmic cores are thrust up within (Fig. 2, E, F and Plate 3, *a*). Complex double layers of tubules appear as a result of the actual geometry of this situation (Fig. 2, B, E and F).

---

cont. from p. 114

at the same magnification marked contrast with the distal pattern (*b*). Microvilli are all parallel in this section and no layering is present. Microvilli at the right originate from the retinular cell just visible at the right edge of the picture and abut on the left on their counterparts originating from the opposite side of the cell's cytoplasm. *P*, pigment granules. × 18,000.

In the more peripheral swollen regions contiguous tubule layers arise from enveloping cytoplasm and from the central cytoplasmic core when this is present (Plate 4, *a*). In the more axial regions of the rhabdomere double layers arise from the two sides of the enveloping cytoplasm (Fig. 2, E and Plate 3, *b*). The description and figures make it clear that the proximal rhabdom is a massive structure in which the simple sharply bimodal distribution of the longitudinal axes typical of retinular cells appears to be entirely lost. This patterned arrangement is present, however, in the distal rhabdom.

(b) *Mysidium*, a small subtropical marine mysid, provides a non-decapod, peracaridan example of another rhabdom which is divided into different proximal and distal sections (Plate 5). In this instance, however, the proximal portion is typical in structure and the distal region is aberrant. The typical part consists of about twenty layers showing alternate perpendicular orientation of their constituent microvilli. These originate in the characteristic decapod manner from the seven retinular cells of each ommatidium.

In contrast, the distal rhabdom has no layering of its microvilli all of which are oriented in one direction. This is the same as that in the most distal layer of the proximal rhabdom. Hence the distal portion has rhabdomeres only from cells 2, 3, 6 and 7 whereas cells, 1, 4 and 5 do not contribute to it.

Microvilli in this distal rhabdom differ from the typical pattern in the following additional features. They are less tightly packed and distinctly sinuous in form. They are somewhat larger in diameter and notably less electron dense because they almost entirely lack the dark staining contents typically present in rhabdom microvilli. Some tubules at the boundary between distal and proximal rhabdoms appear to have dense contents through part of their length only while the remainder is clear (Plate 5).

3. *Experimentally Induced Changes*

Light and dark adaptation have long been known to produce certain reversible changes in the ommatidia of crustacean eyes. Movements of pigment granules and of retinal pigment cells have been widely studied (for review, see Kleinholz, 1961). In *Artemia*, migration of the whole rhabdom from a proximal to a distal position has been described during dark adaptation (Debaisieux, 1944) whereas movements of vacuoles and mitochondria toward and away from the rhabdom have been reported for the insect *Locusta* during adaptation (Horridge and Barnard, 1965). Adaptation also affects movements of cytoplasmic components in the spider crab (*Libinia*) retinula (Eguchi and Waterman, unpublished). No alterations in rhabdom fine structure are known to accompany any of these adaptation phenomena.

However, drastic changes which have not yet been demonstrated to be reversible do occur in rhabdoms when darkness is maintained for periods of several months with only occasional minutes of dim red light for feeding, etc.

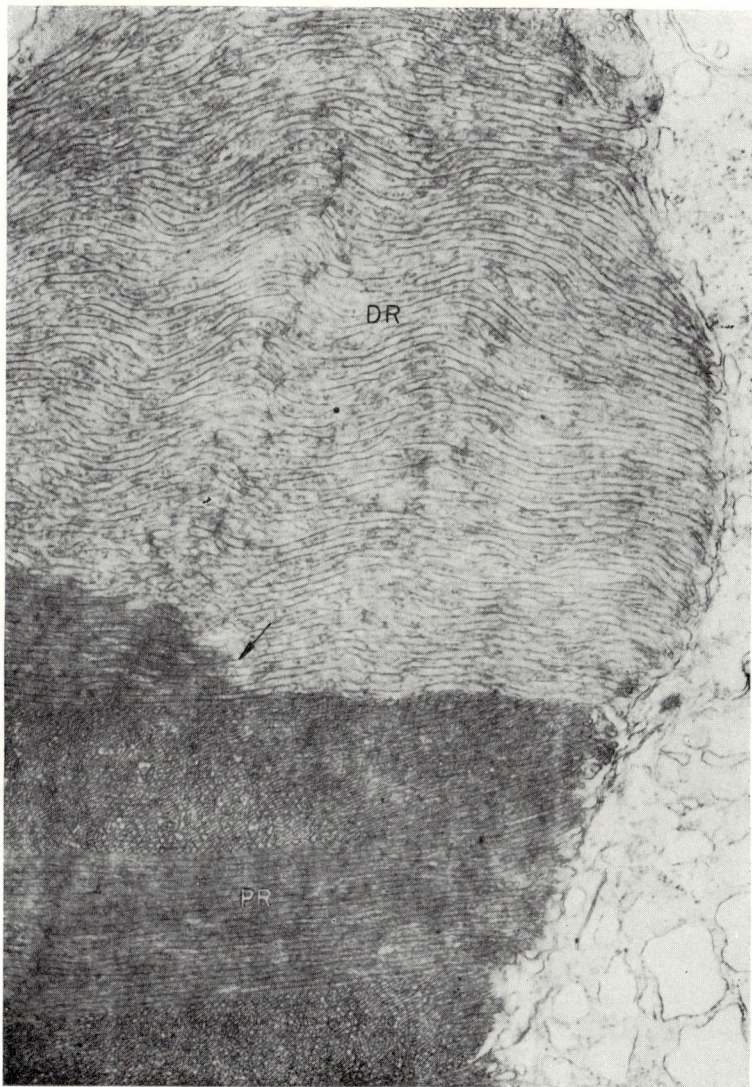

PLATE 5

Longitudinal section through the distal and proximal part of the rhabdom in the compound eye of *Mysidium*. The microvilli in the distal part (*DR*) are sinuous in outline and look much less dense than those in the proximal part (*PR*) of the rhabdom. The proximal retina shows typical layered structure and other details much as in *Callinectes*. At the boundary between the two rhabdom areas the arrow indicates some microvilli which are part light and part dark. × 30,000.

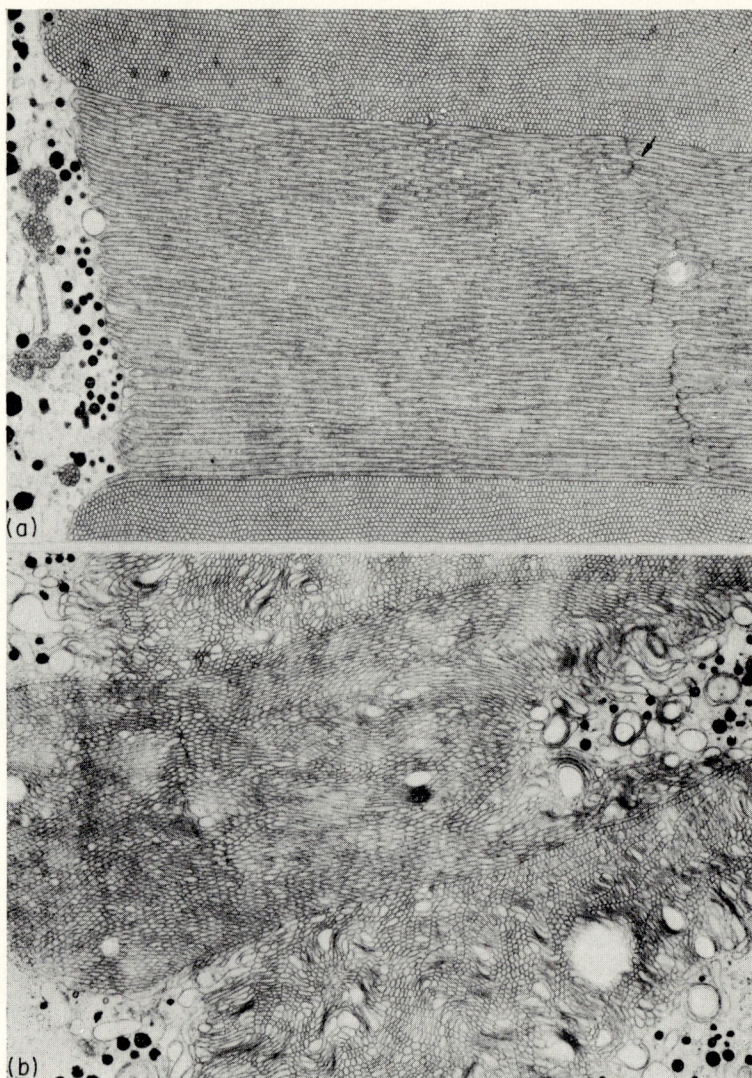

(a)

(b)

PLATE 6

a. Longitudinal section through part of the rhabdom of the compound eye of normal *Procambarus*. Microvilli are regularly arranged in alternate layers parallel and perpendicular to the plane of the section. Microvilli derived from the retinular cell to the left abut on those from the opposite retinular cell (arrow). In the retinular cell cytoplasm, several multi-vesicular bodies and many pigment granules are visible. × 10,300. *b*, Longitudinal section through the part of the *Procambarus* rhabdom from a crayfish kept in the dark for 3 months. The normal regular arrangement of microvilli (Plate 6, *a*) is shown to be markedly disturbed. Even the normal layered structure has almost been lost. × 10,300.

Such treatment of normally epigenous animals results in an irregular arrangement of the microvilli similar to those found in cave animals (Kuwabara and Eguchi, 1960, unpublished). This has previously been studied in *Procambarus* both by electron microscopic and electrophysiological methods (Eguchi, 1964, 1965). We are continuing this work in *Procambarus* and in *Artemia* where it had not been previously studied.

(a) *Procambarus*. After 3 months in darkness striking changes had occurred in the crayfish rhabdom. The strict geometrical arrangement normal for the microvilli (Plate 6, *a*) had been strongly disturbed and some of the tubules had swollen. Many vacuoles had appeared in the rhabdom (Plate 6, *b*). In contrast, other cell constituents such as mitochondria, endoplasmic reticulum and cell membrane appeared normal. Hence the rhabdom is particularly susceptible to the effect of no light.

After only 1 month in the dark small beginnings of the changes observed after 3 months could already be seen, but continuous darkness for 7 months did not appreciably increase the degree of derangement already observed after 3 months.

(b) *Artemia*. The rhabdom of this branchiopod differs in several important respects from the decapod type pattern. No layering is present in the fine tubule array (Plate 7, *a*) but the five rhabdomeres (a sixth retinular cell is small, has no axon or perirhabdomal vacuole and is located distally in the retinula) are so organized that their microvilli are aligned in only two perpendicular directions.

After keeping the *Artemia* 3 months in the dark, these rhabdoms were marked abnormal (Plate 7, *b*). The regular pattern of tubule arrangement had been virtually destroyed, vacuoles had appeared and the tubules had shortened 20–40%. In spite of this, other cytoplasmic components appear normal in our electron micrographs. As in *Procambarus* this means that the rhabdom is especially sensitive to light lack. Again initial effects of prolonged darkness could be seen already in brine shrimp kept only 1 month in the dark. Since our animals had been raised in darkness from the resting egg, normal eye development was possible in the dark but not long time maintenance of full rhabdom differentiation.

DISCUSSION

Several aspects of the comparative fine structure of crustacean rhabdoms deserve further comment. To begin with, the type pattern is striking for two reasons. First, the regular alignment of microvilli in two mutually perpendicular directions normal to the optic axis is a prominent characteristic. Such an arrangement suggests that there are at least two kinds of cells in each retina, one comprising cells 1, 4 and 5, the other 2, 3, 6 and 7 (Fig. 1).

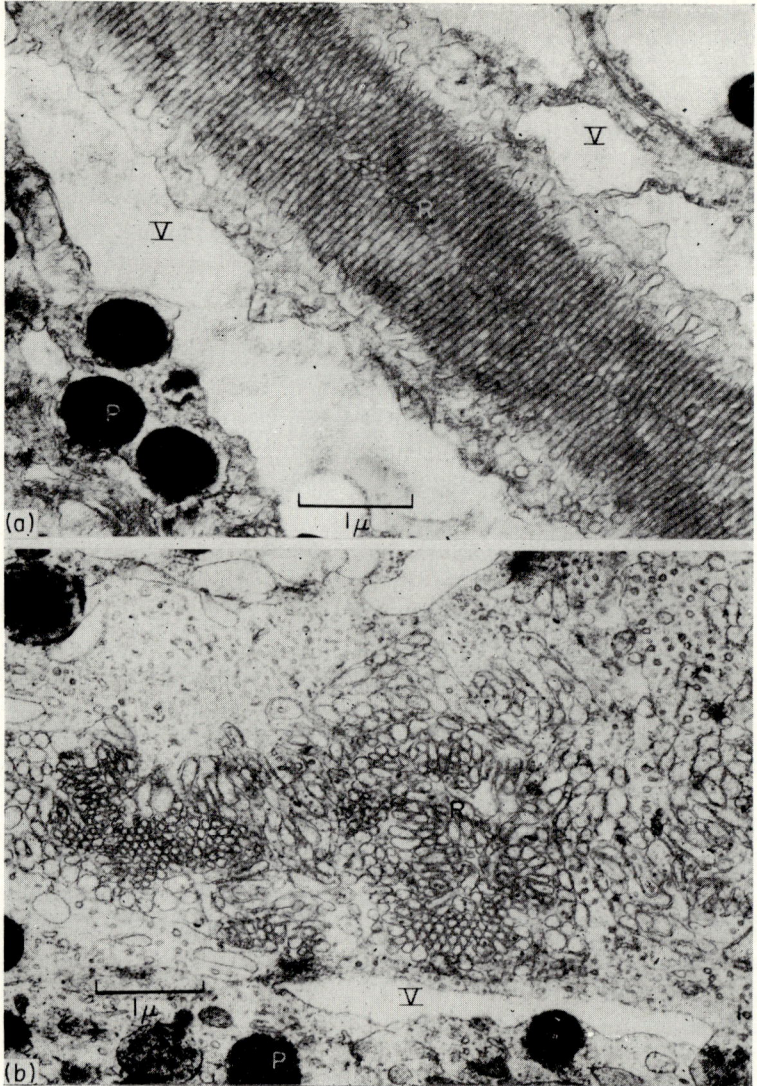

PLATE 7

a, Longitudinal section through the distal part of the rhabdom (R) in a normal *Artemia* compound eye. Many closely packed and parallel microvilli are visible in this rhabdom which lacks layering. V, large vacuoles; P, pigment granules × 14,800. b, Longitudinal section through the same ommatidial region as that shown in Plate 7, a of an *Artemia* which was kept in the dark for 3 months. The former could serve as the control for any dark induced changes. The fine regular arrangement of microvilli is seriously upset, and the normally orderly pattern has become irregular. Some of the microvilli had swollen so that their diameters had increased. Lettering as in a. × 14,800.

Similar binary systems are present not only in typical decapod crustacean rhabdoms but also in *Daphnia* (Eguchi and Waterman, 1965, in preparation) and *Leptodora* (Wolken and Gallik, 1965), among branchiopods, in addition to *Artemia* reported above; in *Mysidium*; probably in Euphausiacea; in a number of insects (for review see Goldsmith, 1964) and in cephalopod molluscs both octapod and decapod (for review see Moody, 1964).

Because of the geometry of such systems the most intriguing possibility is in the present context that these two oriented microvillus groups provide the input of two neurosensory channels for the analysis of polarized light (Waterman, 1965a, 1965b). This idea is consonant with the fact that all the animal groups concerned are capable of perceiving the *e*-vector of linearly polarized light (Waterman, 1965c).

The possibility is also consistent with the most plausible hypothesis for polarized light analysis by arthropods and cephalopods (Jander and Waterman, 1960; Jander, Daumer and Waterman, 1963) and is directly supported by electrophysiological experiments on the crab *Cardisoma* (Waterman and Horch, 1965, in preparation) and on *Octopus* (Tasaki, 1965).

A second point about the type rhabdom pattern in decapod crustaceans is the layered arrangement of the microvilli (Plates 1, 4, *a*, 6, *a*). This is not known to occur in insect or cephalopod rhabdoms and is absent in the branchiopods studied. Such a layered rhabdom pattern divides each single rhabdomere into a number of isolated sections; yet at the same time it brings into more intimate contact the rhabdomeres of all seven retinular cells. This directs attention to an important lacuna in our knowledge of compound eye function, namely, whether each neurosensory cell in a retinula can be excited independently and conduct the resulting information to the lamina ganglionaris via its proximal axon. This is almost universally assumed to be so but has never been directly demonstrated.

The occurrence of two part rhabdoms with one portion having no layering of its microvilli, and with the other having a typical microvillus orientation, may provide an experimental clue to rhabdom function. This disproportion of tubules in the two perpendicular directions might be expected to affect polarized light orientation. But if the dark material inside the tubules of the proximal part of the rhabdom is visual pigment and the distal rhabdom lacks it, the functional significance of the latter is dubious. However, the wavy shape of the distal rhabdom villi could be due to their release from a long-term morphogenetic influence of visual pigment necessary to maintain the highly regular rhabdomere pattern.

In *Panulirus* the larger part of the retinula (proximal) has microvilli aligned in many directions even within a single retinular cell. This would mean that *e*-vector perception of the sort which apparently prevails typically would not be possible unless the small distal rhabdom is adequate to provide the necessary discrimination. Electrophysiological and behavioral correlates of the fine structural pattern should be sought in this case as in others where the basic type is modified.

Recently, the idea that light is required for the normal maintenance of fine structure in the outer segment of vertebrate rods and cones has been challenged (Eakin, 1965). The supporting data showed that development and continuing maintenance of lamellar fine structure were normal in the retina of the tree frog *Hyla regilla* kept for 60 days in the dark. At least some previous evidence of lamellar disintegration and vacuole formation correlated with long periods in darkness was attributable to inadequate fixation. Such an explanation hardly could be valid for our work, however, since both control and dark maintained eyes were fixed and postfixed with glutaraldehyde and osmic acid as described above. Furthermore, in the case of *Hyla* longer periods of darkness may be required before exclusion of an effect of prolonged darkness. In *Drosophila*, for example, stocks had to be reared in the dark for 210 generations before rhabdom disintegration was marked (Eguchi, unpublished data). In the crustaceans at least the possibility of testing the electrophysiological and behavioral consequences of the disruption of regular microvillus arrangement, particularly on polarized light detection and polarotaxis, offers a stimulating challenge for future research.

SUMMARY

1. The typical rhabdom in the compound eye of decapod Crustacea is a multilayered structure built up of rhabdomeres contributed by seven retinular cells. The rhabdomeres are composed of many elongate microvilli all running in the same direction in one rhabdomere but in perpendicular directions in alternate layers of the whole rhabdom. Three retinular cells form one set of rhabdom layers whereas the remaining four form the alternate set. There is thus present a two-channel system suggestive of some functional discrimination, most specifically in relation to the perception of linearly polarized light by such eyes.

2. Comparative morphological study of rhabdom fine structure shows some interesting aberrations from typical form. In *Panulirus* the rhabdom is in two parts, having a small normally layered part and a large complex and peculiar part. In the latter layering is absent, the rhabdomeres are intracellular and the microvilli of a single retinular cell are oriented in many directions rather than the typical single one. The effect of this on the spiny lobster's capability of detecting the *e*-vector of polarized light would be a matter of considerable interest.

In *Mysidium* the two-part rhabdom shows an aberrant distal part and a more typical layered proximal part. The distal rhabdom shows no banding and has microvilli rather loosely aligned and oriented in only one direction.

Furthermore, these distal villi are much less electron dense than their proximal counterparts.

3. Experimentally induced fine structural changes in rhabdoms have been studied in *Procambarus* and in *Artemia*. After keeping these species in continuous darkness for 3 months, the microvilli are irregularly arranged so that their normal highly patterned array is destroyed. Even when such rhabdom changes are drastic, other cellular components remained normal. This suggests that rhabdom fine structure is the most sensitive in this regard and should therefore be one of the initial morphological changes in the evolutionary degeneration of compound eyes in continuous darkness.

ACKNOWLEDGEMENTS

The authors are grateful to Dr. William R. Adams and Dr. Joseph Gall for their generous cooperation in making electron microscopes and related facilities freely available for this work. We also wish to thank Mrs. Mabelita Campbell for her helpful assistance especially in preparing light microscopic sections of many kinds of eyes for comparative study. Acknowledgement should also be made to the Director and staff of the Bermuda Biological Station for their cooperation in obtaining some of the live material required. This research has been supported by NIH Grant NB-03076.

REFERENCES

DEBAISIEUX, P. 1944. Les yeux des crustacés. *La Cellule* **50**, 9–122.

EAKIN, R. M. 1963. Lines of evolution of photoreceptors. In *General Physiology of Cell Specialization* (D. Mazia and A. Tyler, eds.) pp. 393–425. McGraw-Hill, New York.

EAKIN, R. M. 1965. Differentiation of rods and cones in total darkness. *J. Cell Biol.* **25**, 162–5.

EGUCHI, E. 1964. The structure of rhabdom and action potentials of single retinula cells in crayfish. 25 pp. Ph.D. Thesis, Kyushu University.

EGUCHI, E. 1965. Rhabdom structure and receptor potentials in single crayfish retinular cells. *J. Cell. Comp. Physiol.*, **66**, 411–429.

GOLDSMITH, T. H. 1964. The visual system of insects. In *The Physiology of Insecta*, Vol. I (M. Rockstein, ed.) pp. 397–462. Academic, New York.

HORRIDGE, G. A. 1965. Arthropods: Receptors for light, and optic lobe. In *Structure and Function in the Nervous Systems of Invertebrates*, Vol. II (T. H. Bullock and G. A. Horridge) pp. 1063–113. W. H. Freeman, San Francisco.

HORRIDGE, G. A. and BARNARD, P. B. T. 1965. Movement of palisade in locust retinula cells when illuminated. *Quart. J. Micro. Sci.* **106**, 131–5.

JANDER, R. and WATERMAN, T. H. 1960. Sensory discrimination between polarized light and light intensity patterns by arthropods. *J. Cell. Comp. Physiol.* **56**, 137–59.

JANDER, R., DAUMER, K. and WATERMAN, T. H. 1963. Polarized light orientation by two Hawaiian decapod cephalopods. *Z. vergl. Physiol.* **46**, 383–94.

KLEINHOLZ, L. H. 1961. Pigmentary effectors. In *The Physiology of Crustacea*, Vol. II (T. H. Waterman, ed.) pp. 133–69. Academic Press, New York.

LUFT, J. H. 1961. Improvements in epoxy resin embedding methods. *J. Biophys. Biochem. Cytol.* **9**, 409.

Moody, M. F. 1964. Photoreceptor organelles in animals. *Biol. Rev. Cambridge Phil. Soc.* **39**, 43–86.

Reynolds, E. S. 1963. The use of lead citrate at high pH as an electron-opaque stain in electron microscopy. *J. Cell Biol.* **17**, 208–12.

Rutherford, D. J. and Horridge, G. A. 1965. The rhabdom of the lobster eye. *Quart. J. Micro. Sci.* **106**, 119–30.

Sabatini, D. D., Bensch, K. and Barrnett, R. J. 1963. Cytochemistry and electron microscopy: The preservation of cellular ultrastructure and enzymatic activity by aldehyde fixation. *J. Cell Biol.* **17**, 19–58.

Tasaki, K. 1965. The octopus retina as an analyser for polarized light. (Abstr.) *Symposium on Comparative Neurophysiology*, Tokyo, Japan, p. 7.

Viallanes, M. H. 1892. Contribution a l'histologie du systeme nerveux des Invertébrés. La lame ganglionaire de la langouste. *Ann. Sci. Nat., Ser. 7*, **13**, 385–400.

Waterman, T. H. 1961. Light sensitivity and vision. In *The Physiology of Crustacea*, Vol. II (T. H. Waterman, ed.) pp. 1–64. Academic Press, New York.

Waterman, T. H. 1965a. Visual information processing in crustaceans. (Abstr.) *Symposium on Comparative Neurophysiology*, Tokyo, Japan, p. 17.

Waterman, T. H. 1965b. Systems analysis and the visual orientation of animals. *Amer. Sci.* (in press).

Waterman, T. H. 1965c. Specific effects of polarized light on organisms. In *Handbook of Environmental Biology*. Fed. Amer. Soc. Exptl. Biol. (In press).

Wolken, J. J. and Gallik, G. J. 1965. The compound eye of a crustacean *Leptodora kindtii. J. Cell Biol.* **26**, 968–73.

SOME PHOTOCHEMICAL AND PHYSIOLOGICAL
ASPECTS OF VISUAL EXCITATION
IN COMPOUND EYES*

T. H. GOLDSMITH and H. R. FERNANDEZ

Department of Biology, Yale University, New Haven, Connecticut, U.S.A.

RETINAL, RETINOL, AND THE VISUAL SYSTEM OF INSECTS

ASIDE from *Limulus*, all work with intracellular micropipette electrodes on primary photoreceptor cells has been done on insects. Despite this fact, the visual pigments of insects are poorly characterized chemically. There are a number of phenomena encountered in insects which are not well developed in vertebrate retinas and which are not yet adequately accounted for in molecular terms. Among these are ultraviolet sensitivity, polarized light responses, and the double-peaked sensitivity curves described by Burkhardt (1962) which appear to indicate visual pigments with two absorption maxima. One of our interests in New Haven for the past several years has been simply to demonstrate that carotenoid derivatives are involved in visual excitation. One can conclude with some certainty that the visual pigments of insects are conjugated proteins in which retinal (retinaldehyde, retinene$_1$, vitamin A aldehyde) is the chromophore, and it is now profitable to summarize the results of several different kinds of experiment.

Reports of retinal in insects have been accumulating from several laboratories (see Goldsmith, 1964, for references), and in Hymenoptera retinal was shown to be bound to protein to form a pigment with peak of absorption at 440 mμ (Goldsmith, 1958). This pigment bleaches in the light, liberating retinal. It is curiously unlike vertebrate rhodopsin in that it is readily soluble in buffered solutions without the aid of such agents as digitonin. Although there are still difficulties in relating its absorption spectrum to the spectral sensitivity of worker bees, on balance the evidence suggests that it is a visual pigment.

The demonstration that the concentration of retinal falls during light adaptation also implicates this substance in the visual excitation of insects.

* The work of the first author was supported in part by a grant (NB-03333) from the Insitute of Neurological Diseases and Blindness, U.S. Public Health Service. Dr. Fernandez is a postdoctoral Fellow of the U.S. Public Health Service; his experiments reported here were done as a doctoral candidate in the Cellular and Molecular Biology Training Program, University of Miami, Florida.

125

Our original extracts of bees seemed not to contain any retinol (vitamin A), and this in turn prompted us to wonder whether in insects retinol occurs as a normal part of the visual cycle. To examine this question, the C_{20} carotenoids of light- and dark-adapted bees were compared. Acetone extracts of heads were chromatographed from petroleum ether on columns of aluminum oxide, and retinol and retinal were identified by the characteristic transient absorption bands which appear when these molecular species are mixed with saturated solutions of antimony trichloride in chloroform (Goldsmith and Warner, 1964).

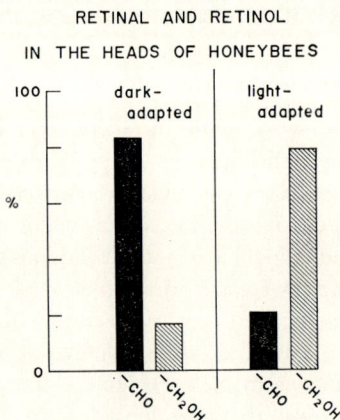

RETINAL AND RETINOL

IN THE HEADS OF HONEYBEES

FIG. 1

The proportions of retinal (-CHO) and retinol (-CH$_2$OH) in the heads of dark- and light-adapted honeybees (*Apis mellifera*), based on an experiment of Goldsmith and Warner (1964). More than 20,000 eyes were used for each extract; the total recovery of C_{20} carotenoid was 0·20 μg per g fresh weight of heads from dark-adapted bees and 0·125 μg per g from light-adapted animals.

Figure 1 shows the results of a large experiment involving several kilograms of bees. In dark-adapted animals very little retinol is present, but following several hours' exposure of the living animals to light, the retinol increases. At the same time the retinal decreases, suggesting an interconversion. The reduction of retinal to retinol was demonstrated *in vitro* with an enzyme extract of heads.

The light-induced fall in the concentration of retinal is a very good indication that this substance is directly involved in photoreception. At the same time, this experiment is the only evidence from an invertebrate of retinol being produced during light adaptation. It is interesting that in the bee there is no reserve of retinol; most, perhaps all, is converted in the dark to the aldehyde and presumably bound in visual pigments. This parsimonious occurrence of retinol stands in sharp contrast to the situation in crustacea, where, in many marine forms, the eyestalks are laden with retinol, chiefly as the neo-b isomer (see Fisher and Kon, 1959, for references).

A third line of attack has been to manipulate the sensitivity of the photoreceptors by rearing the animals in the absence of retinol, retinal, or any carotenoids which might serve as precursors of these substances. Under such conditions the ability of the sense cells to respond to light is greatly diminished. It is not easy to control the diet of honeybees, so in this work we have turned to the housefly (*Musca domestica*) for an experimental animal. Flies were grown in three ways. A control stock was maintained on a fermenting mixture of alfalfa meal, brewer's grain, wheat bran, and yeast, or in some experiments, dog food. In the case of experimental animals, eggs were surface-sterilized in hypochlorite solutions and placed on a previously autoclaved, carotenoid-free medium devised by Monroe (1960, 1962). Other experimental animals were handled in the same way, except that Monroe's diet was supplemented with β-carotene. For a measure of the responsiveness of the photoreceptors we wished a method that permitted a large number of cells to be tested in a relatively short time with as little damage as possible to the animal and with a minimum of uncertainty introduced by the geometrical relation of optical stimulator and receptor. Moreover, we wished to avoid any added complexities which might be introduced by the central nervous system in a behavioral experiment. The retinal action potential, the mass response, fits these requirements, for by giving test flashes of 0.5–1.0 sec duration one can separate the slow potential, which arises largely if not entirely in the cell bodies of the retinular cells, from the on and off responses. (The off responses come from unidentified higher order cells, and the origins of the on transients are even less well understood.) Further details of the method and some results of this work have been published (Goldsmith, Barker and Cohen, 1964).

Figure 2 is an example of the kind of records which are made by this technique. This experiment shows that the eyes of animals reared in the absence of carotenoid are less sensitive to light than normal, and furthermore, that the effect can be prevented by the inclusion of β-carotene in the larval food.

This carotenoid deficiency has a very simple feature (Fig. 3). Within the limits of experimental error, the response–energy curves of depleted animals are parallel to those of controls. The displacement along the abscissa is a measure of the decrease in sensitivity; this is the amount by which the energy of the test flash would have to be increased to obtain a response of normal size. It is as though the absence of carotenoid simply decreases the probability that an incident photon will be absorbed by the visual pigment. One can readily suppose that this is because there is less visual pigment present.

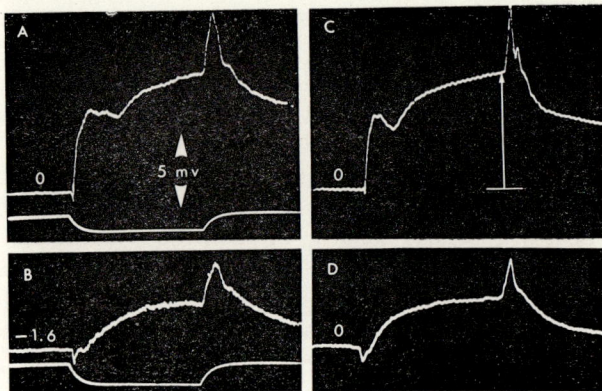

Fig. 2

Retinal action potentials of normal and carotenoid-depleted houseflies. Relative intensity of the stimulus is given in log units at the beginning of each trace. A, B, (control diet; C, Monroe's diet plus β-carotene; D, Monroe's diet (carotenoid-free). The animal raised in the absence of retinol or its provitamins (D) is only 2·5% as sensitive as the control (A,B), but normal sensitivity is maintained by β-carotene (C). Most carotenoid-deficient flies are less sensitive than the example in D. The photocell response (lower trace, A and B) is 0·5 sec. Stimulating light was 500 mμ; log I=0 corresponds to an energy flux at the cornea of 5×10^3 ergs sec^{-1} cm^{-2}. Negativity of the illuminated eye is indicated by an upward deflection; the 5 mV voltage calibration in A applies to all frames. The arrow in C indicates the component of the response on which determinations of sensitivity were based. This sustained negativity arises in the layer of sense cells. (From Goldsmith, Barker, and Cohen, 1964.)

Figure 4 shows some average sensitivities of carotenoid-deficient and control flies. This experiment shows that the threshold of deficient animals rises in both the visible and near ultraviolet regions of the spectrum. Curiously, the change seems to be somewhat larger at the shorter wavelength, an observation that has been made repeatedly. The primary conclusion, however, is that the visual pigment absorbing in the near ultraviolet, like that absorbing in the visible region of the spectrum, has a chromophore derived from carotenoid.

We were very surprised to find that flies which had been grown on Monroe's diet for twelve and fifteen generations had about the same receptor sensitivity as the F_1. We considered the possibility that carotenoid might be deposited in the egg and prevent complete blindness in the first generation. It seemed to us, however, that if this were the only source of carotenoid, in the following generations it should rapidly be diluted to insignificant levels. To account for the experimental result, however, one must suppose that small amounts of carotenoid were made available to successive generations.

A likely source of trace contamination is the synthetic activity of microorganisms which either survived the hypochlorite treatment of the eggs or

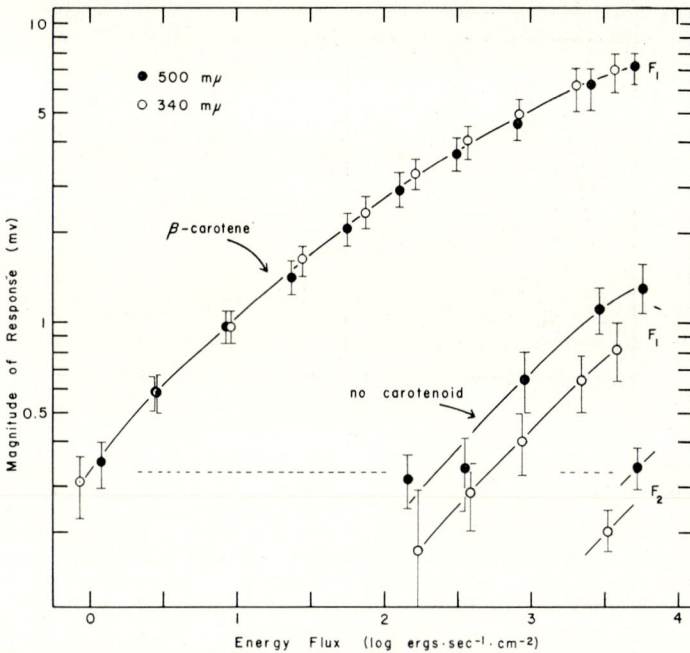

FIG. 3

Response–energy curves for the receptor component of the retinal action potential of flies grown on Monroe's diet, with and without β-carotene. Open circles, 340 mμ; filled circles, 500 mμ. Each point is the average of 8–12 animals; standard errors are indicated by vertical lines through the experimental points. The F_2 flies were reared as described for Fig. 5.

reinfected the adults prior to laying of eggs. The latter seemed very likely, for in the experiments shown in Fig. 4 no effort was made to keep the animals under sterile conditions during adult life.

A simple and direct way to test this hypothesis is to keep the bottle stoppered until the second or third generation has emerged from their puparia. Figure 5 shows that when microbial recontamination is prevented in this manner, the threshold continues to rise in successive generations. The changes in threshold at 340 mμ parallel closely those at 500 mμ, at least after the first generation; and by the F_3, threshold at both wavelengths is more than 4 log units above normal. In the eye of the fly, therefore, somewhat more than four log units is the minimum range of sensitivity that can be controlled by the concentration of visual pigment.

An attempt was made to reverse the deficiency by providing β-carotene to the F_2 larvae. Recovery was good, although not complete. Numerous attempts to produce recovery of deficient flies by feeding carotenoids

C.E.—K

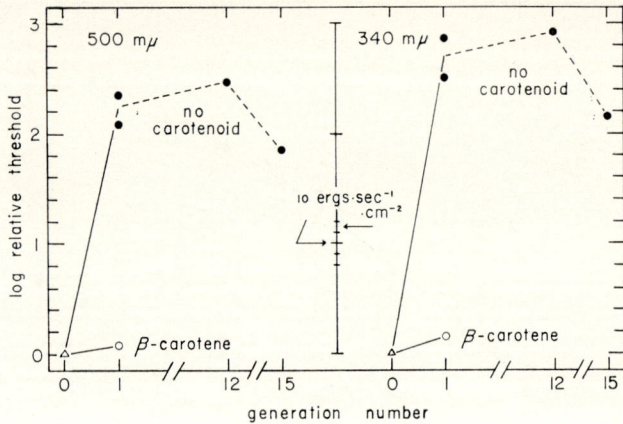

FIG. 4

Log relative threshold of flies reared on a normal control diet (open triangles), Monroe's diet with no carotenoid (filled circles), and Monroe's diet supplemented with β-carotene (open circles). In the breeding stock from which the F_{12} and F_{15} were obtained, adults were not kept under sterile conditions, although eggs and larvae were. The relative energies necessary for a response of about 300 μV to a 0·5 second flash of light (Fig. 2) are given on the ordinate. In the case of the 500 mμ test light, the energy flux (log ergs sec^{-1} cm^{-2}) required for the criterion response can be read directly along the left margin of the figure. The control flies were about 40% more sensitive to ultraviolet than to green light, however, and in order that the curves on each side of the figure might start at zero on the ordinate, the scale for the 340 mμ test light has been shifted up 0·15 log unit, as shown in the center of the figure. Each point represents an average of about six animals. (From Goldsmith, Barker, and Cohen, 1964.)

(unpublished work) suggest that the incomplete recovery shown in Fig. 5 is not necessarily evidence for irreversible damage.

It is perhaps worth remarking that the F_2 and F_3 flies in Fig. 5 behaved as though they were virtually blind; one could pick them off the sides of a screen cage with great ease. Aside from this apparent blindness, which one might reasonably expect in animals having little visual pigment, there was no other obvious indication of a vitamin A deficiency. It appears most likely that flies do not require retinol for growth.

If carotenoid-depleted flies are able to utilize small amounts of carotenoid obtained from micro-organisms, one might expect that deficient adults kept under non-sterile conditions should show some measure of recovery. Figure 6 compares the sensitivities of young (0–2) and old (7–14-day) flies. In the first column are the relative thresholds of normal controls. In the second column are flies grown on Monroe's carotenoid-free diet; the old flies were kept in plugged bottles until removed for testing; thus they were not subject to recontamination by bacteria. In both cases—normal and deficient—old flies have about the same sensitivity as young animals.

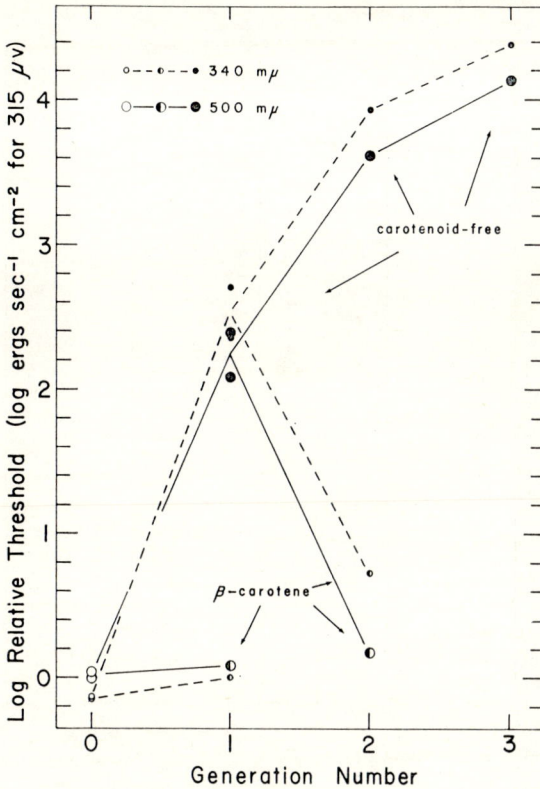

FIG. 5

Filled circles: log relative threshold of *Musca* reared for three successive generations on a carotenoid-free diet under conditions designed to minimize microbial
contamination. Half-filled circles: the effect of supplementing the larval diets of
F_1 and F_2 flies with β-carotene. Open circles: control flies. Small circles and
broken curve show sensitivities to 340 mμ; large circles and solid curve, 500 mμ.
Each point represents an average of 6–12 animals. Unlike the results in Fig. 4, the
threshold continues to rise when adults in successive generations are kept from
adventitious contact with micro-organisms.

The results of allowing deficient adults to live in screen cages open to the
room where they are fed sugar and tap water are shown in the last two
columns. There is a small fall in threshold of F_1 flies, but in the case of very
deficient animals which had been carried for three generations on Monroe's
diet without permitting recontamination, the recovery of non-sterile adults
was larger, nearly 1·5 log units. This, like the experiment shown in Fig. 5,
is further evidence that in a deficient state houseflies may receive marginal
benefit from carotenoid supplied by micro-organisms.

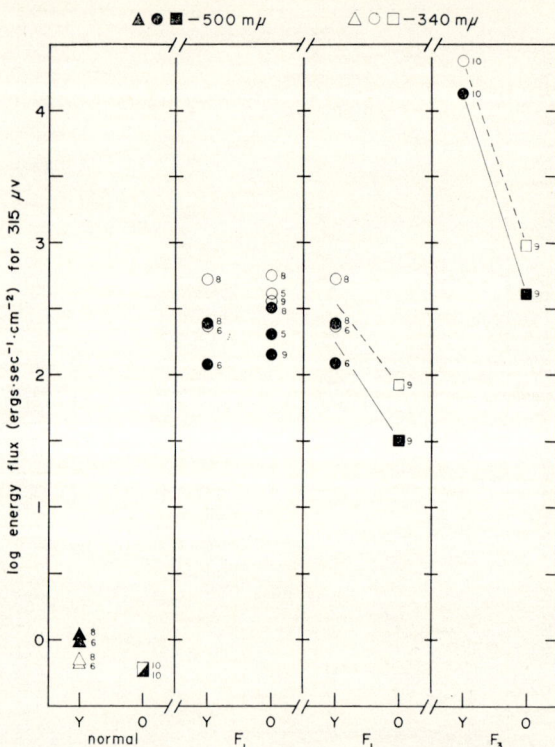

FIG. 6

Log relative threshold of young (Y, 0–2 days) and old (O, 7–14 days) flies. Open symbols, 340 mμ; closed symbols, 500 mμ. Each point represents an average obtained with animals from a single batch of eggs. The numeral by each point indicates the number of animals which enter the average. All adults were maintained on sugar and water. Triangles: Larvae reared on dog food; no attempt to maintain aseptic conditions. Circles: carotenoid-free larval diet; aseptic conditions; adults kept in closed flasks on sterile sugar and water. Squares: adults kept in open cages from 0–2 days after emergence until tested.

CRUSTACEAN VISUAL PIGMENTS

Principally because crustaceans and *Limulus* yield visual pigments to the same preparative procedures which have been developed for the extraction of vertebrate rhodopsins, more numerous direct measurements of absorption have been obtained from these animals than from insects. Figure 7 shows an experiment which is typical in several respects of what can be obtained from crustaceans. Fifty-four eyes of the spiny lobster, *Panulirus argus*, obtained from dark-adapted animals, were macerated in cold 45% sucrose, layered under neutral phosphate buffer (M/15) and centrifuged. The pellet was resuspended and the floatation repeated. The interfacial material from

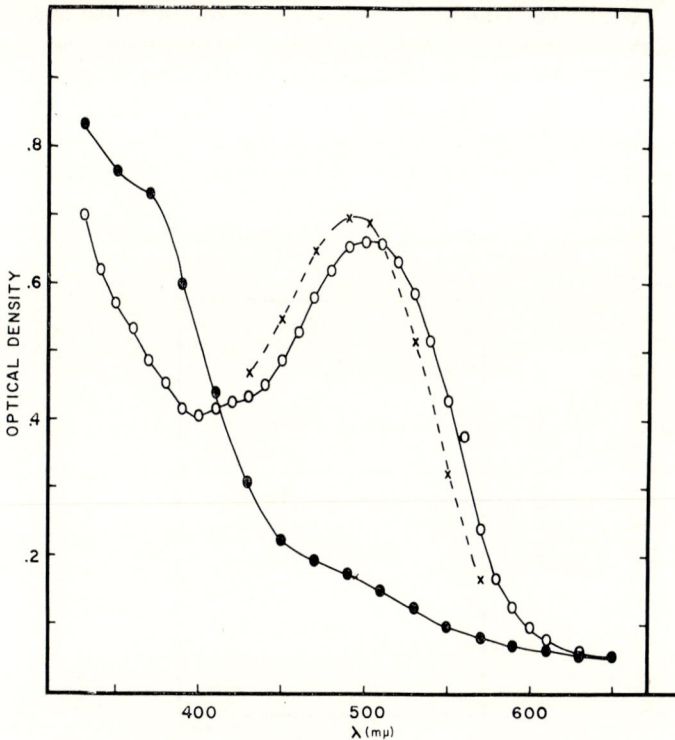

FIG. 7

A digitonin extract from the eyes of *Panulirus argus*. Open circles, initial measurement; crosses and dashed line, after an exposure to light; filled circles, after 180 min in the dark. See the text for further description.

three successive flotations was pooled, diluted with buffer, and sedimented. The precipitate was washed repeatedly with cold buffer until the supernatant was colorless, then lyophilized. Free carotenoids were removed from the dry residue by several extractions with petroleum ether. Following three additional washes in cold buffer, the sediment was suspended in 2 % aqueous digitonin overnight at 7°C. The final extract was cleared by centrifugation and the supernatant brought to pH 8·4 with a small volume of saturated sodium borate.

The absorption spectrum of this solution is shown in Fig. 7 by the open circles. After 3 min exposure to white light from a 30 watt tungsten lamp (Leybold assembly, model 45060A) at 25°C, the maximal extinction had increased slightly and the absorption peak shifted about 8 mμ to shorter wavelengths (*x*'s, broken curve). This represents the formation of a meta-rhodopsin. The metarhodopsin subsequently decayed slowly in the dark so that after 180 min the extract had the absorption shown by the filled circles. The difference spectrum for the bleaching of the parent photopigment indicates a λ_{max} at 504 mμ and coincides exactly over the rest of its spectrum with a rhodopsin based on Dartnall's (1953) nomogram (Fig. 8). The difference spectrum for the decay of the metarhodopsin indicates that the λ_{max} of metarhodopsin lies at 495 mμ. The product of bleaching is retinal (retinene$_1$), judging by the 370 mμ peak in the difference spectrum (not shown). This conclusion is confirmed by antimony trichloride tests.

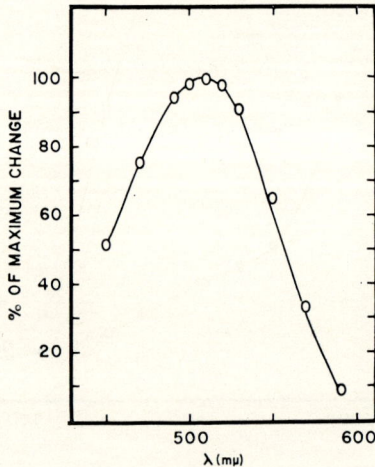

FIG. 8

Comparison of the difference spectrum of the visual pigment of *Panulirus argus* (open circles) with the spectrum of a 504 mμ visual pigment (solid line) from Dartnall's nomogram.

Other experiments showed that extracts of *Panulirus* contain only a single visual pigment, as demonstrated by the method of partial bleaching. A metarhodopsin absorbing in the blue–green also forms when bleaching occurs at pH 6·6. Further details of this and other experiments will appear elsewhere (Fernandez, in preparation).

Table 1 summarizes the available information on the properties of crustacean visual pigments. In many cases the available data are scanty. Moreover, for reasons which are not yet clear the standard methods of extraction give much larger and cleaner yields with Macrurans (lobsters, crayfish) than Brachyurans (crabs).

The data summarized in Table 1 allow several tentative generalizations. There is no correlation between the λ_{max} of the visual pigment and the presence of photopic (apposition) or scotopic (superposition) eyes. The morphological type of eye seems to be fairly constant within certain major

TABLE 1

VISUAL PIGMENTS OF CRUSTACEA

Species	Morphology[1]	Habits	λ_{max} of pigment(s) (mμ)	Metarhodopsin (λ_{max}, mμ) appears as intermediate of bleaching at room temperature	Chromophore	Author
Order Isopoda						
Porcellio scaber (woodlouse)	(A)	Terrestrial	480	?	ret.$_1$[3]	Briggs, 1961a
Order Euphausiacea						
Euphausia pacifica	S	Deep sea	462	?	probably ret.$_1$[3]	Kampa, 1955
Meganyctiphanes norvegica	S	Deep sea	460–465	no	ret.$_1$[4]	Fisher and Goldie, 1960[2]
Nematoscelis megalops	(S)	Deep sea	465	no	ret.$_1$[4]	Fisher and Goldie, 1960[2]
Stylocheiron maximum	(S)	Deep sea	470	no	ret.$_1$[4]	Fisher and Goldie, 1960[2]
Thysanoessa raschii	(S)	Deep sea	460–465	no	ret.$_1$[4]	Fisher and Goldie, 1960[2]
Thysanopoda acutifrons	(S)	Deep sea	480	no	ret.$_1$[4]	Fisher and Goldie, 1960[2]
Order Decapoda						
Suborder Natantia						
Acanthephyra haeckeli (bathypelagic shrimp)	(S)	Deep sea	480	yes	ret.$_1$[4]	Fisher and Goldie, 1960[2]
Sergestes arcticus (penaeid shrimp)	(S)	Deep sea	475	yes	ret.$_1$[4]	Fisher and Goldie, 1960[2]
Sergestes robustus (penaeid shrimp)	(S)	Deep sea	470	yes	ret.$_1$[4]	Fisher and Goldie, 1960[2]
Palaemonetes palludosus (fresh water prawn)	S	Fresh water, arhythmic	539 and 512	497 and possibly not	ret.$_1$[3,4]	Fernandez, 1965
Penaeus duorarum (pink shrimp)	S	Marine, nocturnal	516	475	ret.$_1$[3]	Fernandez, 1965
Suborder Reptantia						
Section Macrura						
Homarus americanus (American lobster)	S	Marine	515	490	ret.$_1$[3,4]	Wald and Hubbard, 1957
Procambarus alleni (Everglades crayfish)	S	Fresh water, apparently arhythmic	(540–560) and 506	yes and possibly yes	ret.$_1$[3] [4]	Fernandez, 1965
Orconectes virilis (northern crayfish)	(S)	Fresh water	562 and 508	530 and no	ret.$_1$[3]	Wald, 1962 (abstract)
Panulirus argus (spiny lobster)	S	Marine, nocturnal	504	495	ret.$_1$[3,4]	Fernandez, 1965
Section Brachyura						
Callinectes ornatus (blue crab)	A	Marine or brackish water	484	possibly not	ret.$_1$[3,4]	Fernandez, 1965
Callinectes sapidus (blue crab)	A	Marine or brackish water	476; 480	possibly not	ret.$_1$[3,4]	Fernandez, 1965
Hemigrapsus edwardsii (mud crab)	(A)	Marine	513	495	ret.$_1$[3,4]	Fernandez, 1965; Goldsmith and Waterman, unpublished
Leptograpsus variegatus (rock crab)	(A)	Adults terrestrial, active at low tide	513	495	ret.$_1$[3,4]	Briggs, 1961b
Ocypode quadrata (ghost crab)	A	Marine	478	?	ret.$_1$[3,4]	Briggs, 1961b / Fernandez, 1965
Uca pugnax and *U. pugilator* (fiddler crabs)	A	Marine beaches, active at low tide	480	possibly not	ret.$_1$[4]	Goldsmith and Purple, unpublished

[1] A = "apposition" or photopic morphology; S = "superposition" or scotopic morphology. Where the letter is placed in parentheses we were unable to examine histological sections of the eye or to locate an adequate description, and our designation of the morphological type is based on knowledge of near relatives of the species. We are grateful to Prof. T. H. Waterman and Mrs. Mabelita Campbell for making available to us their slides of crustacean eyes.

[2] Only absorption maxima are cited; absorption or difference spectra are not published.

[3] Determined in the Carr–Price reaction.

[4] Determined by the absorptio maximum of the product of bleaching.

subgroups of crustacea, but the absorption properties of the visual pigments are not. Fisher and Goldie (1960) have pointed out that the euphausiids and decapods which they examined all inhabit depths at which the incident light has its dominant wavelengths between 470 and 480 mμ. Interestingly, all the pigments they reported have their λ_{max} in the region 462–480 mμ. A number of crustacea living in shallower waters or in the littoral zone where the wavelengths of maximal transmission are longer have visual pigments with λ_{max} between 500 and 515 mμ. There are enough exceptions to this latter category in the crabs *Callinectes*, *Uca*, and *Ocypode*, however, to suggest that in many species other factors can be more important in determining the wavelengths of maximum sensitivity.

In some species there is more than one pigment present, and this suggests the presence of color vision. Wald (1963) has indicated some discrepancies between the wavelengths of maximum sensitivity as determined electrophysiologically and the absorption spectra of extracted pigments: in the crayfish *Orconectes* there is physiological evidence for pigments at 435 and 570 mμ, rather than 508 and 562 mμ as observed in extracts. Daumer and Waterman (cited in Waterman, 1966) have shown that in *Daphnia* the spectral sensitivity of orientation to polarized light is maximal at 440 mμ, and a peak of sensitivity at 450 mμ has been reported for the electroretinogram of the spider crab *Libinia* (Wald, 1963). No pigments yet extracted from crustacea absorb maximally at these short wavelengths.

In no instance has 3-dehydro retinal (retinene)$_2$ been demonstrated in an invertebrate. Although 3-dehydro retinal is the chromophore in certain freshwater vertebrates, this is not true for freshwater arthropods. The crayfish *Orconectes* and *Procambarus* as well as the freshwater prawn *Palaemonetes palludosus* all employ retinal.

There is no direct demonstration that retinal assumes the 11-*cis* (neo-b) configuration in arthropod visual pigments. On the other hand, it is probably significant that most of the excess stores of retinol in the eyes of a number of species of crustacea seem to be the 11-*cis* isomer (cf. Fisher and Kon, 1959).

A final feature of many of the visual pigments of decapod crustacea is that the metarhodopsin which is formed on irradiation is much more stable thermally than vertebrate metarhodopsins, requiring many minutes at room temperature to hydrolyze to retinal and opsin. If this is also true *in vivo* it may mean that retinol is not a regular participant in the visual cycle.

AN INFLUENCE OF SPATIAL SUMMATION ON SPECTRAL SENSITIVITY

Practically everything that is known about the absorption spectra of insect visual pigments has been deduced from physiological measurements of spectral sensitivity. Similar but less extensive measurements have been made on crustacea (cf. Waterman, 1961). The technique is very useful, but has its pitfalls. For example, in the study of Diptera there recently developed the following perplexing situation. The spectral sensitivity curves of *Calliphora* and *Musca* have maxima in the red, and long wavelengths evoke larger on and off effects in the retinal action potential than green or blue lights (Fig. 9). Moreover, by an ingenious marriage of colorimetric principles with the recording of transient electrical responses to rapid color substitutions,

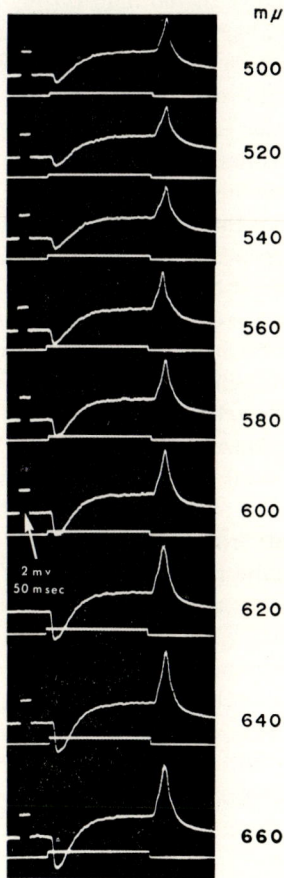

FIG. 9

Dependence of the retinal action potential of a wild type housefly on the wave-length of the stimulus. Energies of the stimulating lights were adjusted to evoke approximately equal receptor components; however, the relative prominence of the on and off effects clearly increases with wavelength. Negativity of the subcor-neal electrode is indicated by an upward deflection. Photocell response (lower trace of each pair) is about 0·5 sec and indicates the time of stimulation. (From Goldsmith, 1965.)

Mazokhin-Porshnjakov (1960a, 1960b) has produced an argument for the presence of a red receptor, and indeed described its spectral sensitivity. The difficulty has been that Autrum (1955) and Hoffmann and Langer (1961e were unable to find the red maximum in white eye mutants which lack th) red ommochrome screening pigments; or Burkhardt (1962), in single retinular cells of red-eyed flies except when the cells seemed to be illuminated only weakly by stray light which had been filtered through the pigment sleeves. These observations led the Munich group to the view that a peak of red sensitivity is caused by leakage of red light through the red pigment sleeves to distant parts of the eye which would otherwise not be stimulated.

One of us has recently reinvestigated this problem in the housefly (Goldsmith, 1965), coming to the conclusion that the screening hypothesis is correct, and, moreover, that the results of color substitution or flicker experiments, as well as qualitative wavelength–dependent differences in the retinal action potential, are natural consequences of this hypothesis. The essence of the matter is this: the size of the on and off transients relative to the receptor component depends critically on the *number* of receptors stimulated. Thus a red enhancement of on and off effects indicates spatial summation of receptors rather than excitation of different *kinds* of receptors. These results are in agreement with the work of Burkhardt (1964).

There are two reasons for believing that the long wavelength enhancement of the on and off effects in the retinal action potential is another manifestation of the phenomenon which Mazokhin-Porshnjakov has studied in color substitution experiments: (1) at all levels of stimulation except perhaps the very lowest, the on and off transients are larger for red light than for green, so it becomes impossible to shift from one wavelength to the other without an electrical response; and (2) the spectral sensitivity of the on and off responses follows closely the sensitivity of Mazokhin-Porshnjakov's calculated "red receptor" (Goldsmith, 1965).

The 620 mμ sensitivity maximum in the receptor component of the retinal action potential can be enhanced by selective adaptation to a violet background light (Fig. 10). This is classical evidence for a receptor maximally sensitive in the red, but in this case it has another explanation. Peripheral ommatidia, whose axes are oriented at a large angle to the light sources, are not strongly adapted by the violet light but are stimulated by red test wavelengths.

If cells in the optic ganglion responsible for on and off effects received excitatory and inhibitory inputs from receptors with different spectral sensitivities, the spectral sensitivity of the higher order cell could differ greatly from that of either of its inputs. It is conceivable, for example, that a 620 mμ maximum might arise through the interplay of an excitatory input with peak sensitivity in the green and an inhibitory unit maximally responsive in the blue. Receptors with these spectral sensitivities have been reported (e.g.

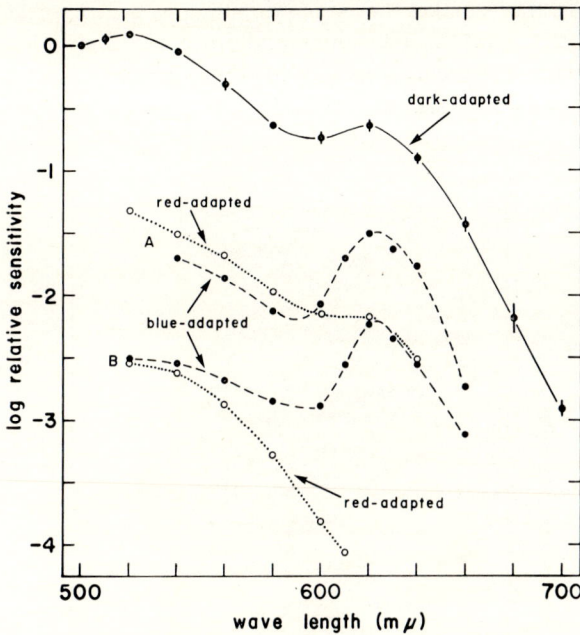

FIG. 10

Spectral sensitivity of the receptor component of the retinal action potential of dark-adapted, red-eyed *Musca* (filled circles, solid line). Points represent averages of eight animals; standard errors, when larger than the points, are indicated by vertical lines. The effects of red and violet adapting lights are shown for two animals (A and B). Blue light enhances the 620 mμ peak. Ordinate: log reciprocal photons for a constant receptor component. Abscissa: wavelength of the stimulus, in millimicrons. (From Goldsmith, 1965.)

Buckhardt, 1962). The experiment in Fig. 10, however, seems to rule out this kind of neural interaction as the explanation for the red peak. If quiescence in the inhibitory pathway were required for the appearance of a 620 mμ peak, a violet adapting light which activates the inhibitory mechanism should depress rather than enhance the relative prominence of the red maximum. This conclusion is not changed by supposing the inhibitory mechanism is fatigued by the violet adapting light employed in the experiment of Fig. 10, for in that case the red peak should shift to shorter wavelengths, and, with complete fatigue of the inhibitory system, vanish entirely.

The spectral sensitivity of normal red-eyed flies is compared with that of white eye mutants in Fig. 11. This mutant has no screening pigment between the ommatidia. It lacks the peak of sensitivity in the red, even when adapted to a violet background light. Moreover, it is much more sensitive to green light than the wild type, and in this respect it is reminiscent of *Calliphora*

(Autrum, 1955). If one makes the assumption that the gene *w* affects screening pigments but not receptor pigments—and for reasons detailed elsewhere (Goldsmith, 1965) this seems reasonable—this experiment is strong support for the screening hypothesis.

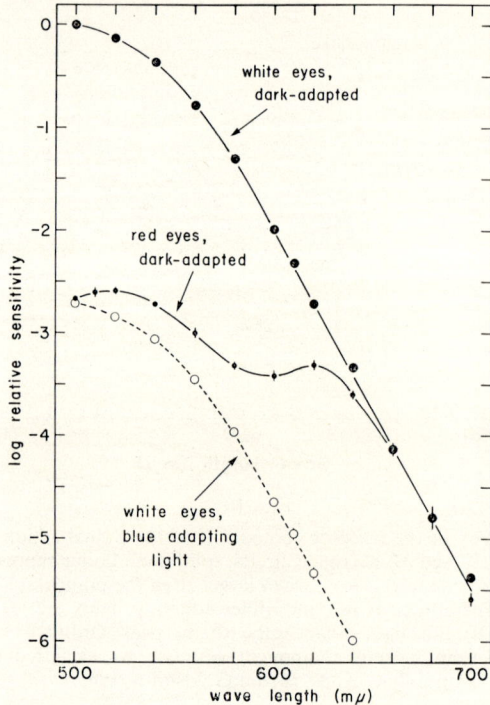

Fig. 11

Average spectral sensitivity of nine dark-adapted, white-eyed flies (large filled circles, solid curve) compared with normal red-eyed flies (small filled circles, solid curve) and the average sensitivity of the nine white-eyed flies in the presence of a violet adapting light (open circles, dashed curve). Axes as in Fig. 10. On an absolute energy basis, the sensitivities of red- and white-eyed flies are the same at 660 mμ and longer wavelengths but are very different in the yellow and green regions of the spectrum.

There are three additional features of the electric responses of red- and white-eyed flies which reinforce the case for the screening hypothesis. In the white eye mutant the wavelength dependence of the shape of the retinal action potential is absent; responses at 500 mμ can be matched at 620 mμ by a suitable adjustment of the intensity. Furthermore, these responses have large on and off effects and are similar to the responses of red-eyed animals to long wavelengths. Large on and off transients are therefore found under conditions where the stimulus penetrates throughout the eye.

Secondly, in wild-type flies the curve which describes the magnitude of the receptor component as a function of incident energy rises more steeply for red light than for shorter wavelengths. This is to be expected if red light passes through the accessory pigment more readily than green light (Goldsmith, 1965). As predicted by the screening hypothesis, this difference in slopes is not seen in the white eye mutant.

Finally, one can demonstrate potentiation of the on and off effects through spatial summation of receptors by a method which requires no assumptions about the absorbance of the accessory pigment screens. Figure 12 compares

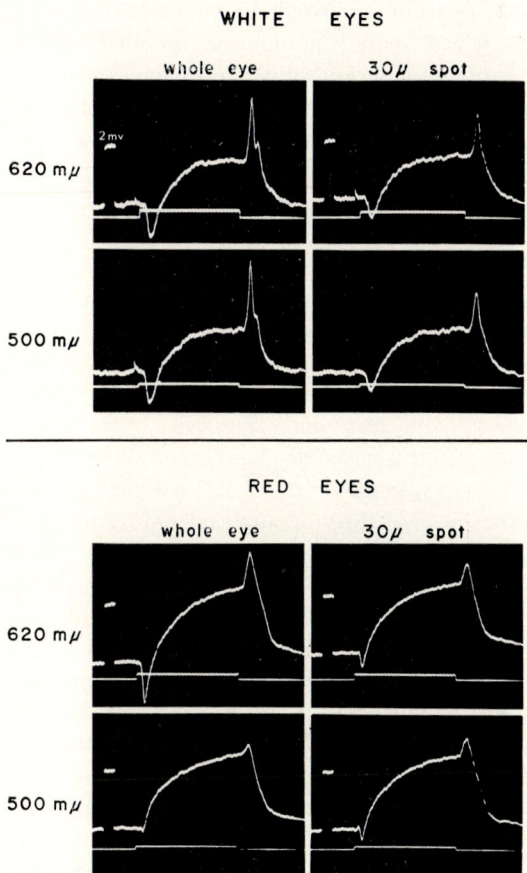

FIG. 12

The effect of the size of the test spot on the relative prominence of the on and off effects in two animals, white- and red-eyed. In each animal, energies were adjusted for approximately equal receptor components. Test flashes were 0·5 sec and calibration pulses 2 mV throughout. An upward deflection indicates negativity of the illuminated eye. (From Goldsmith, 1965.)

the electrical responses when the whole surface of the eye is illuminated from one direction and when the beam is focused on a small patch of five or six facets. The energies have been adjusted to evoke equal receptor components, and in the white-eyed fly the on and off effects are obviously more prominent when the number of ommatidia excited is great. Furthermore, the effect is independent of wavelength. In red-eyed flies (lower half of the figure) the enhancement of the on and off effects by recruitment of additional ommatidia can be seen with red light but not blue–green. This is to be expected, for at short wavelengths increasing the size of the 500 mμ test spot fails to bring in additional ommatidia whose axes are oriented more than about 8° (de Vries and Kuiper, 1958; Autrum and Wiedemann, 1962) from the stimulus.

The extent to which spatial summation in other arthropods produces effects suggestive of color receptors is a problem which must be faced in each case (Goldsmith, 1965). The occurrence of this phenomenon in flies is interesting in its own right, but its demonstration should also influence the design of future experiments on color vision in arthropod eyes.

SUMMARY

1. Retinal is the chromophore of insect visual pigments. In the honeybee retinal is reduced to retinol during light adaptation. In houseflies it has been possible to induce a condition analogous to the "nutritional night blindness" of mammals by withholding retinal, retinol, and carotenoids from the diet. In the most deficient animals studied to date, sensitivity of the receptor cells to both near ultraviolet and visible wavelengths has been lowered more than 4 log units.

2. The spiny lobster (*Panulirus argus*) has a visual pigment with λ_{max} at 504 mμ. It bleaches in the light, liberating retinal (retinene$_1$). Present knowledge of the visual pigments of crustaceans is briefly reviewed: (a) Some correlations of λ_{max} of pigment with the principal wavelengths present in the environment are possible, but such patterns are not adhered to rigorously; (b) 3-dehydro retinal (retinene$_2$) has not been found in arthropods—marine, freshwater or terrestrial; (c) some crustacean visual pigments form relatively stable metarhodopsins on irradiation; (d) heterogeneity of pigment extracts of several freshwater decapods suggests the presence of systems for color vision.

3. A possible complication in the interpretation of spectral sensitivity functions is discussed. The conclusion of Autrum and Burkhardt that in flies the peak of sensitivity at 620 mμ is an artifact caused by the transparency of the accessory screening pigment to long wavelengths is confirmed. The wavelength specific effects on the retinal action potential and the results of color substitution experiments can both be explained in the same manner. Therefore in flies, at least, evidence that has heretofore been interpreted as signifying the presence of different *kinds* of receptors in reality means only that different *numbers* are stimulated.

REFERENCES

AUTRUM, H. 1955. Die spektrale Empfindlichkeit der Augenmutation white-apricot von *Calliphora erythrocephala*. *Biol. Zbl.* **74**, 515–24.

AUTRUM, H. and WIEDEMANN, I. 1962. Versuche über den Strahlengang im Insektenauge (Appositionsauge). *Z. Naturf.* **17b**, 480–2.

BRIGGS, M. H. 1961a. The visual pigment of an isopod crustacean. *Aust. J. Biol. Sci.* **14**, 487–8.

BRIGGS, M. H. 1961b. Visual pigment of grapsoid crabs. *Nature* **190**, 784–6.

BURKHARDT, D. 1962. Spectral sensitivity and other response characteristics of single visual cells in the arthropod eye. *Symp. Soc. Exp. Biol.* **XVI**, 86–109.

BURKHARDT, D. 1964. Colour discrimination in insects. In *Advances in Insect Physiology* (J. W. L. Beament, J. W. Treherne, and V. B. Wigglesworth, eds.) Vol. 2, pp. 131–73. Academic Press, New York.

DARTNALL, H. J. A. 1953. The interpretation of spectral sensitivity curves. *Brit. Med. Bull.* **9**, 24–30.

DAUMER, K. and WATERMAN, T. H. 1965. Personal communication.

DE VRIES, H. and KUIPER, J. W. 1958. Optics of the insect eye. *Ann. N.Y. Acad. Sci.* **74**, 196–203.

FERNANDEZ, H. R. 1965. A survey of the visual pigments of Decapod Crustacea of South Florida. Ph.D. Thesis, University of Miami, Coral Gables, Florida.

FISHER, L. R. and GOLDIE, E. H. 1959. The eye pigments of a euphausiid crustacean, *Meganyctiphanes norvegica* (M. Sars). *XVth Internat. Congr. Zool.* 533–4.

FISHER, L. R. and GOLDIE, E. H. 1960. Pigments of compound eyes. *Progress in Photobiology, Proc. 3rd Internat. Congr. Photobiol.* 153–4.

FISHER, L. R. and KON, S. K. 1959. Vitamin A in the invertebrates. *Camb. Phil. Soc. Biol. Rev.* **34**, 1–36.

GOLDSMITH, T. H. 1958. The visual system of the honeybee. *Proc. Nat. Acad. Sci.* **44**, 123–6.

GOLDSMITH, T. H. 1964. The visual system of insects. In *The Physiology of Insecta* (M. Rockstein, ed.) Vol. 1, pp. 397–462. Academic Press, New York.

GOLDSMITH, T. H. 1965. Do flies have a red receptor? *J. Gen. Physiol.* **49**, 265–87.

GOLDSMITH, T. H. and WARNER, L. T. 1964. Vitamin A in the vision of insects. *J. Gen. Physiol.* **47**, 433–41.

GOLDSMITH, T. H., BARKER, R. J. and COHEN, C. F. 1964. Sensitivity of visual receptors of carotenoid-depleted flies: a vitamin A deficiency in an invertebrate. *Science* **146**, 65–7.

HOFFMANN, C. and LANGER, H. 1961. Die spektrale Augenempfindlichkeit der Mutante "chalky" von *Calliphora erythrocephala*. *Naturwissenschaften* **48**, 605.

KAMPA, E. M. 1955. Euphausiopsin, a new photosensitive pigment from the eyes of euphausiid crustaceans. *Nature* **175**, 996–8.

MAZOKHIN-PORSHNJAKOV, G. A. 1960a. Colorimetric study of the properties of colour vision of insects as exemplified by the housefly. *Biophys.* **5**, 340–9.

MAZOKHIN-PORSHNJAKOV, G. A. 1960b. System of colour vision of the fly, *Calliphora*. *Biophys.* **5**, 790–7.

MONROE, R. E. 1960. Effect of dietary cholesterol on housefly reproduction. *Ann. Entomol. Soc. Amer.* **53**, 821–4.

MONROE, R. E. 1962. A method for rearing housefly larvae aseptically on a synthetic medium. *Ann. Entomol. Soc. Amer.* **55**, 140.

WALD, G. 1962. Visual pigments of the fresh-water crayfish. *Fed. Amer. Soc. Exp. Biol.* **21**, 344.

WALD, G. 1963. Single and multiple visual systems in arthropods. *Fed. Amer. Soc. Exp. Biol.* **22**, 519.

WALD, G. and HUBBARD, R. 1957. Visual pigment of a decapod crustacean: the lobster. *Nature* **180**, 278–80.

WATERMAN, T. H. 1961. Light sensitivity and vision. In *The Physiology of Crustacea*, (T. H. Waterman, ed.) Vol. II, pp. 1–64. Academic Press, New York.

WATERMAN, T. H. 1966. Polarotaxis and primary photoreceptor events in crustacea. In *Functional Organization of the Compound Eye* (C. G. Bernhard, ed.) Pergamon, Oxford.

MICROSPECTROPHOTOMETRIC ASSAY OF VISUAL PIGMENTS IN SINGLE RHABDOMERES OF THE INSECT EYE

H. LANGER and B. THORELL

Department of Pathology, Karolinska Institutet, Stockholm, Sweden

RETINENE$_1$ was extracted by Goldsmith (1958) from the eyes of honeybees, and it has been assumed that the visual pigments in insect eyes are similar to the rhodopsins in vertebrates and cephalopods. However, the concentrations of these pigments in the retinula of the insect eye are in general too small for the photometrical assay in the total eye. The great amounts of "screening" pigments—the ommochromes and pteridines—further complicate light absorption analysis of the visual pigment *in situ*.

The rhabdomeres of the visual cells in the ommatidium represent only about 3–5 % of the total volume of the insect eye. Since it can be assumed that the visual pigments are located within the rhabdomeres, the local concentrations of pigments can be calculated to be of such an order of magnitude that rhodopsin absorption would be detectable microphotometrically, if the *single* rhabdomere is measured exclusively (Hamdorf and Langer, 1965). The eyes of Diptera are preferred for such measurements, since the rhabdomeres of the seven visual cells in one ommatidium are situated around a central space and are thus morphologically separated from each other.

The blowfly, *Calliphora erythrocephala* Meigen, is red-eyed in the wild type, but has a mutant "chalky" (Langer, 1962), which lacks all screening pigments in the eyes so that these appear bright white. For this reason visual pigments can be more easily detected by absorption microspectrophotometry. The rhabdomeres are about 1 μ in diameter and are separated by at least 3 μ within the ommatidium. Because the calculated spectral absorption was small, measurements had to be made along the long axis of the rhabdomere which is about 200 times larger than the diameter. In most of the ommatidia the rhabdomeres are inflected; they receive the stimulating light from the dioptric apparatus and conduct it along their length. The rhabdomeres, therefore, were kept *in situ* and illumination in the microspectrophotometer was introduced in the natural direction via the dioptric apparatus.

The microspectrophotometer was similar to the type described previously (Thorell and Chance, 1960) for assay of intracellular respiratory pigments.

In the present investigations the instrument was equipped with a Zeiss "Ultrafluar" objective 100×, N.A. 0·85, and Zeiss "UV-Achromat" condensor. The measurement and reference beams were both 1 μ in diameter. The output of the measurement amplifier was obtained as the extinction-linear voltage, i.e. the extinction vs. wavelength was directly recorded. An essential feature of the microspectrophotometer is the possibility of expanding the extinction scale, so that small changes in absorption can be recorded upon high levels of non-specific light losses due to scatter, etc. The baseline was controlled in every recording by placing the measurement beam outside the rhabdomere before and after the actual measurement of visual pigment.

Slices were cut from the eyes of freshly decapitated flies with a razor blade in such a manner that in one part of each slice the ommatidia maintained their normal relationship but were largely freed from the adjacent first optical ganglion. The specimens were mounted in Jones' salt solution (Jones, 1956) between two quartz cover slips without pressing. The whole preparation procedure was carried out in dim red light. If a part of the slice of the proper thickness (i.e. undamaged ommatidia covered by a minimum amount of ganglion material) was put in the optical axis of the microspectrophotometer, light was conducted to the rhabdomeres and they became bright (Fig. 1).

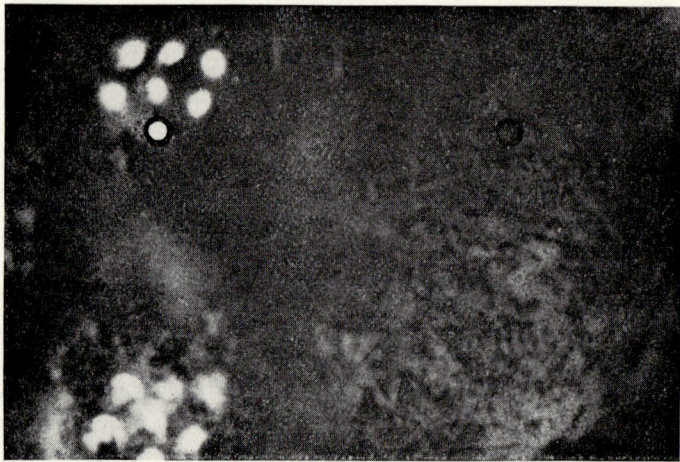

Fig. 1

Photomicrograph of a slice from a mutant "chalky" eye about 300 μ thick. The rhabdomeres of one ommatidium are well illuminated. Position and diameter of measurement and reference beam are marked by black circles. Distance between the two beams is 25 μ.

One of the rhabdomeres was put in the measurement beam, and the reference beam passed between visual and pigment cells at a distance of 25 μ from the measurement beam. The material in the reference beam had no specific absorption. At wavelengths longer than 330 nm, the extinction curve for the reference beam was found to agree completely with the baseline for the "empty" instrument. Since only the variation in extinction dependent on wavelength was of interest here, the zero point of the instrument was suppressed electrically so that the whole width of the recorder could be utilized for $\triangle E = 0{\cdot}1$.

Most of the extinction curves for a single rhabdomere show maxima at about 500 nm, and between 350 and 380 nm (Fig. 2). They are similar to the

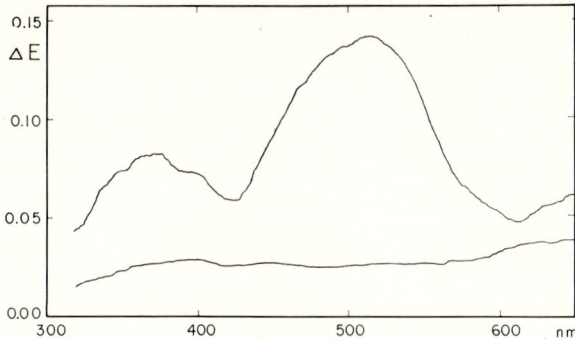

FIG. 2

Extinction curve of rhabdomere No. 6 and the baseline taken outside this rhabdomere.

absorption curves for rhodopsins in solution and fit well with the theoretical curves calculated according to Dartnall (1957). In fresh preparations the maximum of absorption around 360 nm is small, but in older (illuminated) specimens it is larger than that of pure rhodopsin. The curves agree with those of partially bleached extracts from the retina of cattle and squid.

Because the seven rhabdomeres have a characteristic position within the ommatidium, it is possible to label them for comparison one with another. Corresponding rhabdomeres from different ommatidia and different eyes show very similar absorption spectra. Mean curves can be obtained by calculating the mean values of analogous points of "normalized" curves. For rhabdomeres 1–6, such mean curves, obtained by a computer, show maxima at 510 and 380 nm (Langer and Thorell, 1965).

It was possible to differentiate between the absorption characteristics of the rhabdomeres. Two types were evident. In the central rhabdomere—No. 7 in the nomenclature of Dietrich (1909)—the main maximum appears consistently at shorter wavelengths (about 470 nm) than in the other six (Langer and Thorell, 1965).

Measurements of extinction curves with linear polarized light, after introducing a polarizing filter into the illuminating beam at different positions, give evidence for dichroism in the rhabdomere, indicating an orientated pattern of the pigment molecules (Fig. 3). Measurements at the maximum of around 500 nm mostly show a dichroic ratio of about 4:3. The position of the plane of maximal absorption varies among the rhabdomeres of an ommatidium; this may be of importance in the perception of polarization patterns.

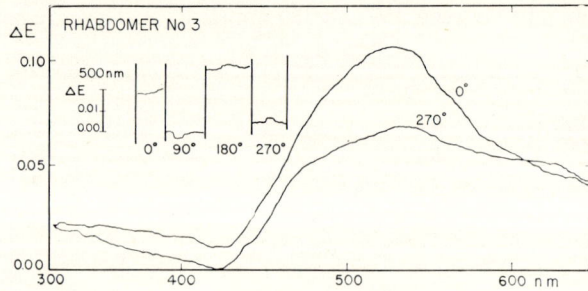

FIG. 3

Extinction curves of rhabdomere No. 3 obtained with linear polarized light in two different planes of polarization (0° and 270°). Insert shows changes in extinction at 500 nm when four planes of polarization are used (intervals of 90°).

The spectral absorption measurements show a photosensitive pigment in the rhabdomeres which has absorption characteristics similar to those of rhodopsins. We might conclude that these substances are the visual pigments of the fly, all of them containing retinene$_1$ as the prosthetic group, but differing in the protein part of the molecule in at least one of the seven rhabdomeres in any ommatidium (No. 7). The curves of spectral efficiency of quantum-like light stimuli on the intact eyes of the mutant "chalky", as measured by the electroretinogram (Hoffmann and Langer, 1961), and the extinction curves of their rhabdomeres are nearly identical. They also are very similar to the spectral sensitivity curves which were obtained by Burkhardt (1962) from single visual cells of the wild-type eyes in experiments with intracellular microelectrodes. The extinction curves of the rhabdomeres 1-6 fit well with the sensitivity characteristics of his "green-receptor". Rhabdomere No. 7 probably represents his "blue-receptor". Within each ommatidium this seems to have a fixed position. The presence of different visual pigments within particular cells of the same ommatidium is undoubtedly important for colour vision in the insect.

ACKNOWLEDGEMENTS

This investigation was supported by the Swedish Medical Research Council (B.T.) and the Deutsche Forschungsgemeinschaft (H.L.).

REFERENCES

BURKHARDT, D. 1962. Spectral sensitivity and other response characteristics of single visual cells in the arthropod eye. *Sympos. Soc. Exp. Biol.* **16**, 86.

DARTNALL, H. J. A. 1957. *The Visual Pigments*. London.

DIETRICH, W. 1909. Die Facettenaugen der Dipterien. *Ztschr. wiss. Zool.* **92**, 465.

GOLDSMITH, T. H. 1958. On the visual system of the bee (*Apis mellifera*). *Proc. Nat. Acad. Sci.* **44**, 123.

HAMDORF, K. and LANGER, H. 1965. *Ztschr. vgl. Physiol.* In press.

HOFFMANN, C. and LANGER, H. 1961. Die spektrale Augenempfindlichkeit der Mutante "chalky" von *Calliphora erythrocephala. Naturwissenschaften* **48**, 605.

JONES, B. M. 1956. Endocrine activity during insect embryogenesis. Function of the ventral head glands in locust embryos (*Locustana pardalina* and *Locusta migratoria orthoptera*). *J. Exp. Biol.* **33**, 174.

LANGER, H. 1962. A new eye colour mutation in *Calliphora erythrocephala* Meig. *Nature* **194**, 111.

LANGER, H. and THORELL, B. 1965. Microspectrophotometry of single rhabdomeres in the insect eye. *Exp. Cell Res.* In press.

THORELL, B. and CHANCE, B. 1960. Microspectrography of respiratory enzymes within the single, mammalian cell under different metabolic conditions. *Exp. Cell Res.* **20**, 43.

THE RÔLE OF SULPHYDRYL GROUPS IN THE VISUAL EXCITATION OF THE COMPOUND EYE IN DIPTERA

L. Giulio*

Istituto di Fisiologia Veterinaria, Università di Perugia, Italia

In the sequence of events which lead to visual excitation, geometrical configuration modifications of the chromophore of photosensitive pigment for the absorption of a single quantum of light (*cis–trans* isomerism) seem most likely to be the first in order of time. As Wald (1961) said, "The only thing that light does in any visual system we know is to isomerize retinene." Events occurring afterward, in fact, come into the category of thermal ("dark") reactions.†

The isomerization of the chromophore from 11-*cis* to all-*trans* eliminates the steric correspondence between the chromophore itself and the protein fraction of the photosensitive pigment, joined together by a "Schiff base linkage" between the terminal aldehyde group and the amino group. In this way the close "lock and key" relationship between retinene (or retinal, according to the Commission on the Nomenclature of Biological Chemistry, *J. Am. Chem. Soc.* 1960, **82**, 5575) and protein ends and the process begins which will lead, at least in the unstable meta-rhodopsin of vertebrates, to the hydrolysis in opsin and all-*trans* retinal (process of bleaching).

The steric configuration of the 11-*cis* retinal is of the greatest importance. In fact, it allows, by the "sufficiently intimate approach" between the isoprenoid side chain and the chromophore ring on one side, and protein fraction on the other, intervention of van der Waals' attraction forces and

---

* Impresa di Elettrofisiologia del C.N.R., gruppo di Torino.

† The energy transfer from the molecule of photosensitive pigment to the cell membrane, and thus over considerable distances compared to molecular dimensions, might occur by means of "exciton" or "radiationless migration" mechanism: the absorption of photons might lead to the formation of excitons at the level of photosensitive molecules, that is, excited states capable of propagating to a distance carrying energy without at the same time carrying charge. The exciton as we know (see Davydov, 1962) is formed by an electron and by a hole in joined configuration, usually at the lowest energy. The migration velocity of the excitons can be of the order of 10^7 cm/s. It should be noted that microspectrophotometric studies carried out on the pigments of single retinal rods have not shown the existence of a "spread of bleaching changes from an illuminated to an unilluminated part of the same outer segment" at distances greater than 2μ from the stimulated area (Liebman, 1962).

some degree of charge displacement (Hubbard, 1958). The effect of the absorption of one quantum, and therefore of the following isomerization, is at least twofold: the electric tension between chromophore and protein disappears and the parts of the protein which were covered by the chromophore are now revealed. This second process exposes two to three sulphydryl groups per molecule, and a "proton-binding" group with a pK of about 6·6 (in the molecule of the photosensitive pigment the Schiff base linkage is protonated, i.e. has attached an H^+, and the opsin, moreover, assumes a negative charge which, in intimate association with the retinal isoprenoid side chain, draws the positive charge up into the conjugated system; all of which enhances the resonance forms and shifts the absorption spectrum towards the red (Wald, 1961; see also Hara, 1963)).

The exposition of the sulphydryl groups could have, even more than cis–trans isomerization, a considerable importance on visual excitation (Hubbard and Kropf, 1959; Wald, Brown and Gibbons, 1962). Wald and Brown (1952) have shown that the resynthesis of rhodopsin (cattle) from retinal and opsin in vitro after bleaching is completely inhibited by low concentrations of p-chloromercuribencoate (PCMB*), a well-known reagent of the –SH groups.

In the isolated retina of the frog and rabbit a rapid extinction of the electroretinogram (ERG) is brought about by adding a mercurial compound [salicyl-(3-hydroxymercuri-2-methoxypropyl)-amido-O-sodium acetate, Uragan] at a concentration of 10^{-6} or 10^{-5} M; and this happens more quickly in photopic than scotopic conditions. The addition of cysteine, 10^{-4} or 10^{-5} M, completely re-establishes the ERG (Sickel and Demirtschoglian, 1961, 1962; Demirtschoglian, 1962). This seems to indicate that the mechanism which is based on cis–trans isomerism, with a subsequent thermal physical rearrangement of the protein fraction so as to expose two (or three) –SH groups and one proton-binding group per molecule, is a pre-visual (photochemical) process of general validity.

With respect to the compound eye, Wald and Burg (1957) isolated vitamin A (or retinol) from the head of Drosophila. Retinal (i.e. the aldehyde of retinol) conjugated with a soluble protein has been identified in the head of Apis mellifica L. This complex is photosensitive, bleaches partly in the light and presents an absorption peak of about 440 nm (Goldsmith, 1958). Later research by Goldsmith and Warner (1962) has confirmed the presence of retinol in the head of Apis, and has shown that the ratio of retinol to retinal, which is 4:1 in photopic conditions, becomes 1:4 in the scotopic state. So during light adaptation the quantity of retinol increases at the expense of retinal.

---

* PCMB reacts with the –SH groups of opsin. Among all the ions of heavy metals, Hg^{II} has the highest association constant ($K_{RSM} > 10^{20}$: Edsall and Wyman, 1958). The organic compounds of mercury (of the R Hg X type) react with the thiols to form mercaptides (see Cecil and McPhee, 1959): $R\ Hg\ X + R'\ SH \leftrightharpoons R\ Hg\ SR' + HX$. PCMB penetrates very slowly through the diffusion barrier of cells (Vansteveninck, Weed and Rothstein, 1965).

Wolken (1957) and Wolken, Mellon and Contis (1957) have not found photosensitive pigments in the head of *Drosophila*. These results were obtained with *Musca domestica* L. by Bowness and Wolken (1959) who were able to isolate a yellow, photosensitive pigment with an absorption peak of 437 nm, of unknown chemical nature and, in any case, not containing retinal. In more recent research Wolken, Bowness and Scheer (1960) have found retinal in *Musca domestica* L.; results were confirmed by Briggs (1961) in several species of insects of the orders Odonata, Hymenoptera, Lepidoptera, Coleoptera and Orthoptera. Fisher and Goldie (1961) and Cohen and Barker (1963) have found retinal in the bodies of insects. Flies kept for generations on a diet lacking carotenoids showed a marked loss of visual sensitivity (Goldsmith, Barker and Cohen, 1964). During light adaptation the retinol in the head of *Apis* increases at the expense of the retinal which decreases (Goldsmith and Warner, 1964).

With regard to –SH group blocking agents, the compound eye behaves similarly to the retina of vertebrates. The micro-injection of PCMB 10^{-5} M in the compound eye, intact or surgically operated (Fig. 1), of the blowfly

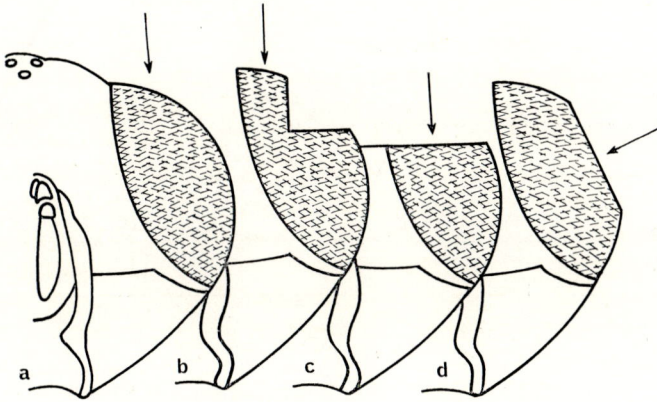

FIG. 1

Schematic illustration showing various experimental arrangements. Arrow indicates light stimulus.

Calliphora erythrocephala Meigen, has no appreciable action on the shape and size of the ERG recorded monopolarly in the conventional way (active subcorneal electrode) with preparation in scotopic conditions ($<$ 0·1 lumen/m²); the stimulus tests have a negligible effect.

The ERG is not modified if the preparation is irradiated with infrared rays $>$ 700 $<$ 3000 nm (with local increase in temperature of about 1·5°C). In photopic conditions, however ("white " light lacking infrared rays, corneal illumination intensity about 1000 lumen/m², energy content referred to infra-red radiation used in the preceding experiment equal to 57%), the electro-retinographic response is gradually reduced in amplitude, influencing both the "on" and the "off" effects until they almost completely disappear.

When the electroretinographic response to light stimulus was greatly decreased or eliminated, a small quantity of cysteine hydrochloride 10^{-4} M

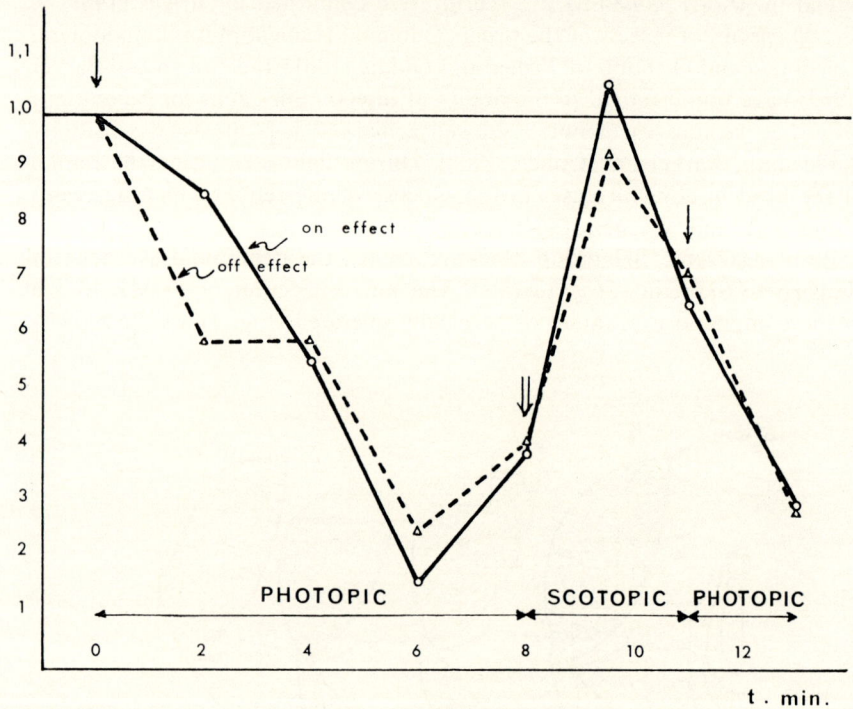

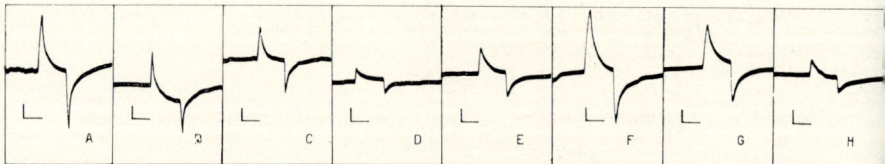

FIG. 2

The graph shows the changes of the mass response of the compound eye (receptor area exposed) to a single flash (505 nm) of about 300 msec duration, occurring in scotopic and photopic states (as indicated) and under the action of PCMB or L-cysteine hydrochloride. Ordinate: amplitude of "on" (circles connected with solid line) and "off" (triangles connected with broken line) effects in percent of respective normal (control) value. Abscissa: time in minutes. ↓ application of PCMB 10^{-4} M. ⇓ application of L-cysteine hydrochloride 10^{-4} M. Single records (inserted below) correspond, left to right, to the upper tracings. Calibrations: 1 mV, 200 msec.

was added to the preparation (in order to increase appreciably the concentration of sulphydryl groups) and a return to normal conditions was rapidly obtained (Giulio, 1964a). The succession of events is illustrated in the graphs of Figs. 2 and 3.

The demonstration of a pronounced inhibitory action on the formation of illumination potentials in the compound eye of *Calliphora* by an agent

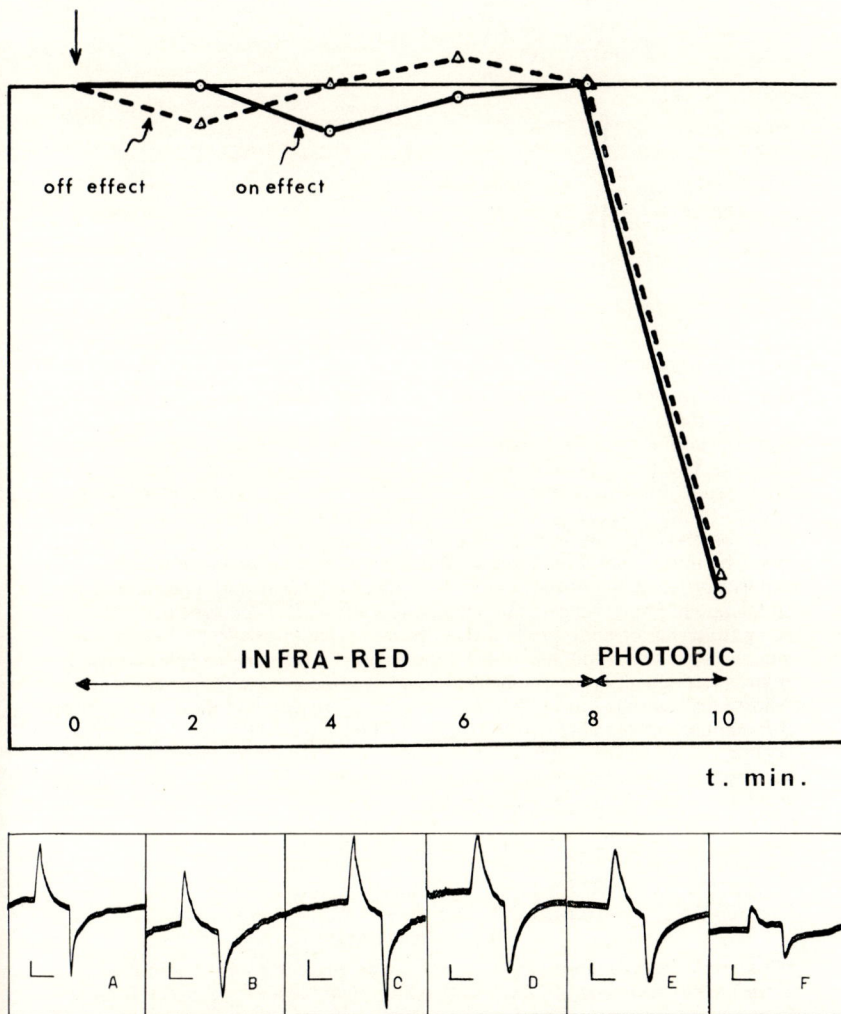

FIG. 3

Changes of the mass response of the compound eye (receptor area exposed) to a single flash (505 nm, 300 msec) occurring during infrared stimulation and in photopic state. Other explanations, see Fig. 2.

blocking the –SH groups *exclusively under photopic conditions* (and therefore
when the absorption of photons by the prosthetic fractions of the photosensitive pigments presumably exposes two or three sulphydryl groups per
molecule), and the complete, or almost complete, recovery of the response

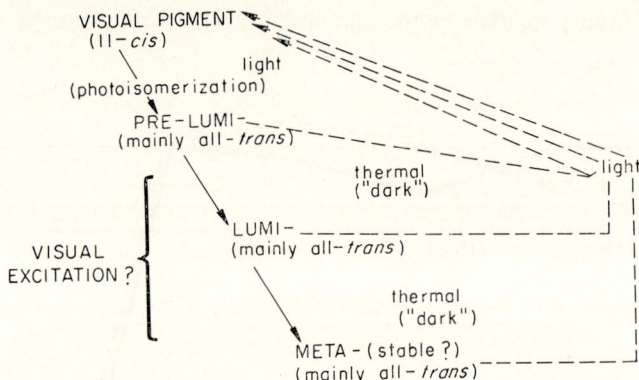

FIG. 4

Hypothetical action of light on visual pigments of "invertebrates" (from Pitt and
Morton, 1960, modif.). Visual excitation should begin after the photo-stereo-
isomerization of the chromophore, i.e. after the formation of the pre-lumi-
pigment. The first electrical response to light ("early receptor potential"; see
Brown and Murakami, 1964, a, b; Cone, 1964; Pak and Cone, 1964) shows a
"rate of formation of the positive peak, as indicated by the reciprocal of the peak
time" which varies "by a factor of about 3 in a temperature variation of 10° C".
Since the initial photoexcitation of rhodopsin requires photons of several eV, a
temperature variation of 10° C (about 10^{-3} eV) should have only a negligible effect
on the rate of photo-isomerization. Pak and Ebrey (1965) conclude that "the step
going from rhodopsin to pre-lumirhodopsin . . . is not likely to be the rate-deter-
mining step in the production of the positive peak". An "early receptor potential"
anyway has not yet been demonstrated in the compound eye. With regard to the
"short cuts" outlined in the figure, the light "by isomerizing the 11-*cis* retinene
chromophore to the all-*trans* form, presses the trigger which results in the production of the nervous impulse; it can also, by putting energy into the all-*trans*
chromophore, isomerize it back to the 11-*cis* isomer, which is at a higher energy
level" (Pitt and Morton, *loc. cit.*; see also Adams, Kennedy, Wulff and Zonana,
1958).

FIG. 5 *opposite*

Mass responses (corneo-negative wave and "on effect") from the compound eye
of the blowfly stimulated by flashes of "white" light (40 joules, 1 msec). From top
to bottom: 1. Intact eye (the electrodes were placed in the ommatidial layer and
in the vertex of the head; DC amplif.). 2. Receptor area exposed (the electrodes
were placed in the ommatidial layer and in the lamina ganglionaris; AC amplif.).
3. "Isolated" retina (the electrodes were placed in the ommatidial layer and in the
lamina ganglionaris; AC amplif.). Negativity downwards in all records. Other
explanations, see Fig. 6. Vertical bar, 1 mV; horizontal bar 10 msec.

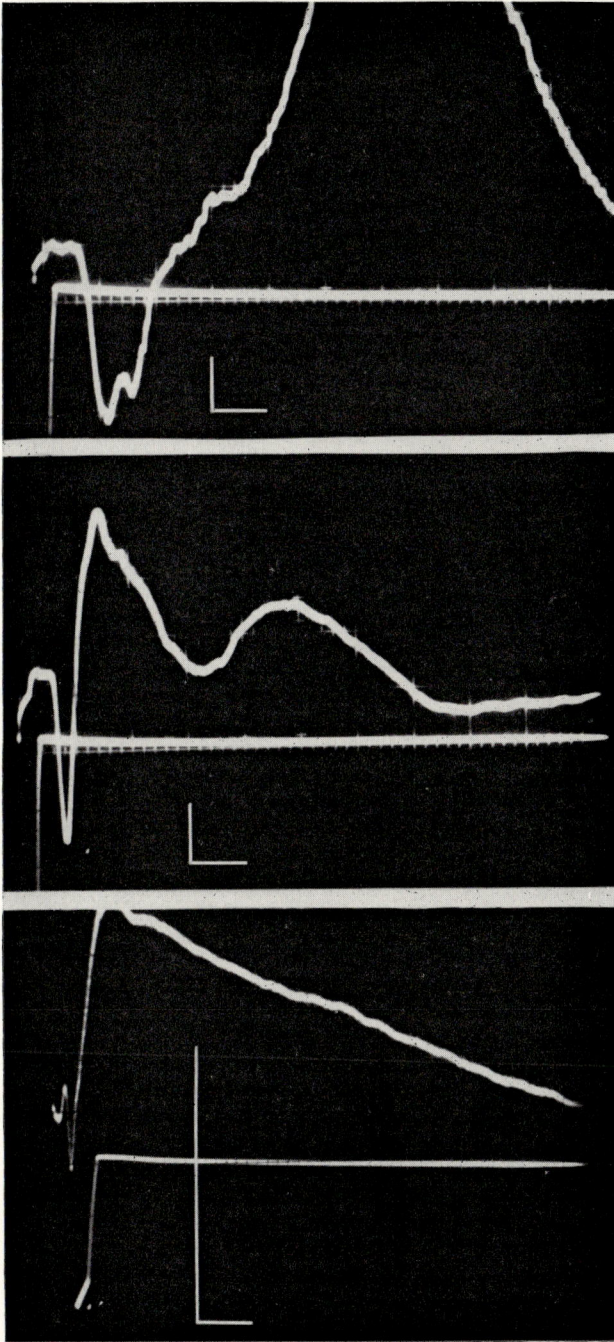

FIG. 5

to light by the subsequent action of cysteine, seems to indicate analogous mechanisms, at least in the first photochemical stages, in the compound eye and the vertebrate retina. This may suggest that the PCMB, blocking the –SH groups of the protein fraction of the pre-lumi, lumi- and meta-pigment, opposes the resynthesis of visual pigment (and therefore *trans–cis* re-isomerization) by steric hindrance, thus interrupting the "short cuts" put forward by Pitt and Morton (1960) and leading finally to the accumulation of stable photoproducts (see Fig. 4).

As the size of the mass response (ERG) depends also on the number of active "elements", the reduction to disappearance of the ERG, tested with stimuli of constant energetic content, by the action of PCMB can probably be brought back by gradually reducing the number of such elements (Giulio, 1964b).

Even more demonstrative results may be obtained by using the preparation "isolated compound eye". The compound eye of *Calliphora* may be isolated surgically, *preserving the optic ganglion*. The preparation is put, at room temperature, in a perspex cell filled with "blowfly physiological saline"* so that the convex surface of the cornea lens is turned towards the light source. The stimulus is provided by flashes of intense "white" light of short duration (160 joules, about 1 msec) transmitted through a rod of perspex and focused with quartz lenses. A portion of the stimulating light flash activates a vacuum photocell (delay about 0.1 μsec), the output of which leads to the lower beam of the oscilloscope. The illumination potential, monopolarly recorded with stainless steel electrodes, is led to the upper beam of the scope (different subcorneal electrode).

The electroretinographic response of the preparation of the isolated compound eye is analogous to that obtained in the compound eye *in situ*: a polyphasic electroretinogram is used with a cornea-negative component (component 1 of Ruck, 1961). As the optic ganglion lies between the recording

* Of the following composition: H_2O 1 l.; NaCl 6.5 g; KCl 0.14 g; $CaCl_2$ 0.12 g; NaH_2PO_4 0.01 g; $NaHCO_3$ 0.1 g.

FIG. 6 *opposite*

Effects of PCMB 10^{-4} M on the illumination potential of the "isolated" compound eye of the blowfly when passing from the scotopic (A) to photopic (B, C) states, and incomplete recovery after washing and successive application of L-cysteine hydrochloride 10^{-4} M (D). The stimulus flashes were produced by a 160 joule photographic lamp having about 1 msec flash duration. A, Control. B, After 60 sec of "white" light (10^4 lumen/m²), stimulus superimposed to the "background" illumination: the mass response is markedly decreased. C, 20 min later, scotopic state: the responsiveness is almost totally abolished. D, 9 min after cysteine was applied: incomplete recovery of ERG. AC amplification; negativity downwards. A trace in the lower part of each record indicates the end of the stimulus; arrow indicates stimulus artifact. Vertical bar 1 mV; horizontal bar 10 msec.

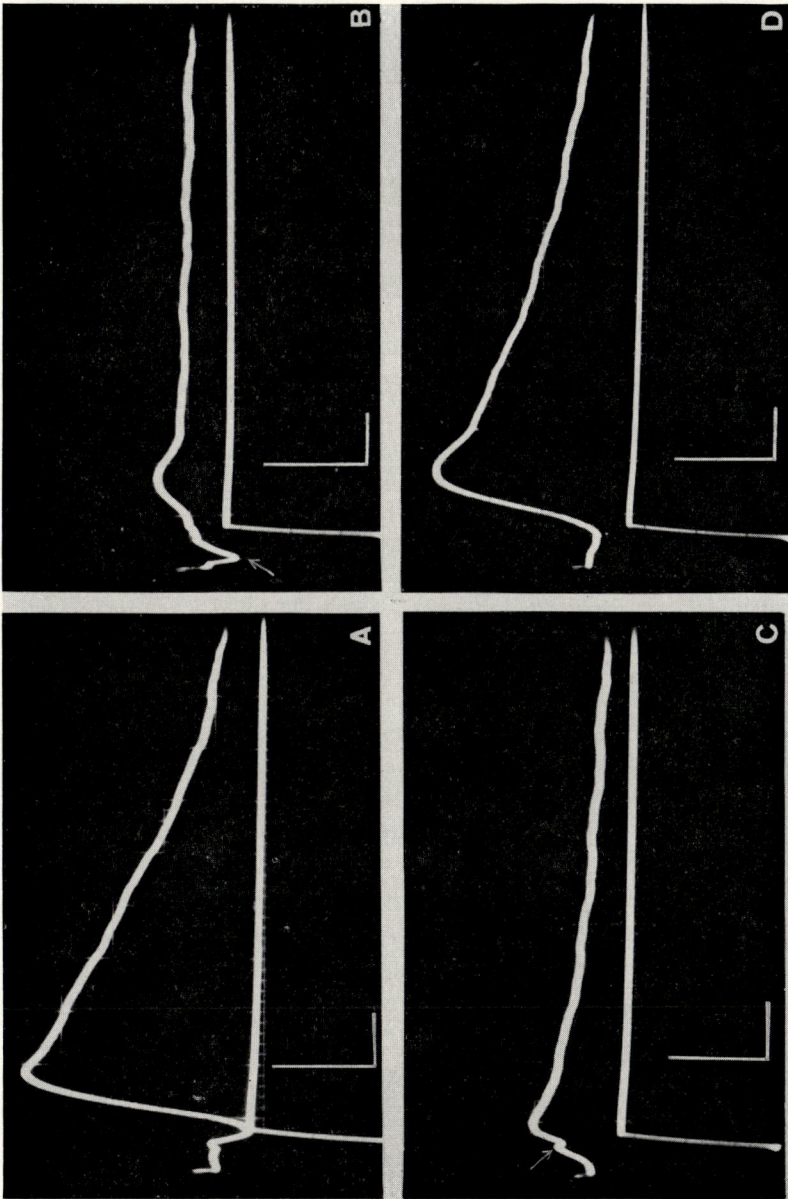

Fig. 6

electrodes, there is usually a predominant cornea-positive component ("on effect") easily obtainable (component 3 of Ruck, *loc. cit.*). The cornea-positive component is preceded, in several electroretinograms, by a spike-like negative wave (component 1; see also Autrum, 1958, and Autrum, Autrum and Hoffmann, 1961).

According to Ruck's interpretation component 1 is thought to originate in the photoreceptor cells, component 3 (which is added algebraically to the preceding one) in the nervous structure of the optic ganglion.*

Since the PCMB penetrates very slowly through the diffusion barrier of the cells, it is added to the physiological solution in scotopic conditions at the beginning of every experiment. The electroretinographic response of the isolated compound eye in these conditions is exactly the same as that obtained without the addition of PCMB to the medium. The flashes, provided they are not too many, do not seem to have any appreciable effect. Illumination with "white" light (10^4 lumen/m^2) for a short time (see Fig. 6) causes a reduction of both components (1 and 3) of the ERG until they totally disappear.

Subsequent washing with a physiological saline to which has been added cysteine hydrochloride returns the preparation to its former conditions of reactivity (with quicker and more complete recovery than component 3).

It is possible to obtain a regular alternation of absence and presence of normal electroretinographic responses using the PCMB in photopic conditions and subsequently washing with a physiological solution to which has been added cysteine (Giulio, Lucaroni and Messina, 1965).

A further argument in favour of the hypothesis that the –SH groups (which, when blocked, lead to the disappearance of ERG), are closely related to the first photochemical events of vision is the fact that prolonged electric stimulation of the isolated compound eye immersed in a physiological solution containing PCMB 10^{-4} M does not eliminate or reduce its response to light. Therefore, in order to obtain this effect, light seems to be indispensable, and, to be more precise, light from high energy photons is (several eV) suitable for the initial excitation of the photopigment.

---

* The very distinct "off" effect in the ERG has not been a subject of particular investigations here.

REFERENCES

ADAMS, R. G., KENNEDY, D., WULFF, V. J. and ZONANA, H. W. 1958. Rhodopsin bleaching in the presence of hydroxylamine. *Arch. Bioch. Biophys.* **75**, 534–6.

AUTRUM, H. 1958. Electrophysiological analysis of the visual system in insects. *Exp. Cell Res.*, Suppl. **5**, 426–39.

AUTRUM, H., AUTRUM, I. and HOFFMANN, C. 1961. Komponenten in Retinogramm von Calliphora und ihre Abhängigkeit von der Spektralfarbe. *Biol. Zbl.* **80**, 513–47.

BOWNESS, J. M. and WOLKEN, J. J. 1959. A light-sensitive yellow pigment from the housefly. *J. Gen. Physiol.* **42**, 779–92.

BRIGGS, M. H. 1961. Retinene₁, in insect tissues. *Nature* **192**, 874–5.

BROWN, K. T. and MURAKAMI, M. 1964a. A new receptor potential of the monkey retina with no detectable latency. *Nature* **201**, 626–8.

BROWN, K. T. and MURAKAMI, M. 1964b. Biphasic form of the early receptor potential of the monkey retina. *Nature* **204**, 739–40.

CECIL, R. and McPHEE, J. R. 1959. The sulfur chemistry of proteins. In *Advances in Protein Chemistry* (Anfinsen, Anson, Bailey and Edsall, eds.) Vol. XIV, pp. 255–389. Academic Press, New York.

COHEN, C. F. and BARKER, R. J. 1963. Vitamin A content and spectral response of house-flies reared on diets with and without a vitamin A source. *J. Cell. Comp. Physiol.* **62**, 43–7.

CONE, R. A. 1964. Early receptor potential of the vertebrate retina. *Nature* **204**, 736–9.

DAVYDOV, A. S. 1962. *Theory of Molecular Excitons.* McGraw-Hill, New York.

DEMIRTSCHOGLIAN, G. G. 1962. The molecular basis of the origin of the ERG of animals and man. *Proc. of the Int. Union of Physiol. Sciences.* Vol. I, XXII Int. Congress Leiden. Lectures and Symposia, Part I, p. 481.

EDSALL, J. T. and WYMAN, J. 1958. *Biophysical Chemistry*, Vol. I, p. 644 and following. Academic Press, New York.

FISHER, L. R. and GOLDIE, E. H. 1961. Pigments of compound eyes. Progress in photobiology. *Proc. 3rd Internat. Congr. Photobiol.* pp. 153–4.

GIULIO, L. 1964a. Importanza dei gruppi sulfidrilici per la formazione de potenziale di illuminazione nell'occhio composto dei Ditteri. *Boll. Soc. It. Biol. Sper.* **40**, 214–5.

GIULIO, L. 1964b. Il ciclo visivo nell'occhio composto di Calliphora erythrocephala Meigen. *Boll. Soc. It. Biol. Sper.* **40**, 215–6.

GIULIO, L., LUCARONI, A. and MESSINA, F. 1965. Effetti del blocco dei gruppi -SH sull' elettroretinogramma dell'occhio composito di Calliphora. *Boll. Soc. It. Biol. Sper.* **41**, 996–8.

GOLDSMITH, T. H. 1958. The visual system of the honeybee. *Proc. Nat. Acad. Sci. Wash.* **44**, 123–6.

GOLDSMITH, T. H. and WARNER, L. T. 1962. The role of vitamin A in the visual cycle of an insect. Seventeenth Annual Meeting of the Society of General Physiologists. Oregon State University, Corvallis, Oregon, August 26–29, 1962: *J. Gen. Physiol.* **46**, 360 A.

GOLDSMITH, T. H. and WARNER, L. T. 1964. Vitamin A in the vision of insects. *J. Gen. Physiol.* **47**, 433–41.

GOLDSMITH, T. H., BARKER, R. J. and COHEN, C. F. 1964. Sensitivity of visual receptors of carotenoid-depleted flies: a vitamin A deficiency in an invertebrate. *Science* **146**, 65–7.

HARA, R. 1963. Changes in electrical conductance of rhodopsin on photolysis. *J. Gen. Physiol.* **47**, 241–64.

HUBBARD, R. 1958. In *Visual Problems of Colour*, Nat. Phys. Lab. Symposium 8, H. M. Stationery Office, London.

HUBBARD, R. and KROPF, A. 1959. The mechanism of bleaching rhodopsin. *Ann. N.Y. Acad. Sci.* **81**, 388–98.

LIEBMAN, P. A. 1962. *In situ* microspectrophotometric studies on the pigments of single retinal rods. *Biophys. J.* **2**, 161–78.

PAK, W. L. and CONE, R. A. 1964. Isolation and identification of the initial peak of the early receptor potential. *Nature* **204**, 836–8.

PAK, W. L. and EBREY, T. G. 1965. Visual receptor potential observed at sub-zero temperatures. *Nature* **205**, 484–6.

PITT, G. A. J. and MORTON, R. A. 1960. *Cis-trans* isomers of retinene in visual processes. In *Steric Aspects of the Chemistry and Biochemistry of Natural Products*, pp. 67–89. Cambridge University Press.

RUCK, P. 1961. Photoreceptor cell response and flicker fusion frequency in the compound eye of the fly, *Lucilia sericata* (Meigen). *Biol. Bull.* **120**, 375–83.

SICKEL, W. and DEMIRTSCHOGLIAN, G. G. 1961. Elektroretinographische Sulphydryl-Titration an der umströmten Netzhaut. *Naturwiss.* **48**, 647.

SICKEL, W. and DEMIRTSCHOGLIAN, G. G. 1962. About the importance of sulphydryl groups in the origin of electrical reaction of man and animal isolated retina. *Biofizika* 7, 225–6.

VANSTEVENINCK, J., WEED, R. I. and ROTHSTEIN, A. 1965. Localization of erythrocyte membrane sulhydryl groups essential for glucose transport. *J. Gen. Physiol.* **48**, 617–32.

WALD, G. 1961. The molecular organization of visual systems. In *A Symposium of Light and Life* (W. D. McElroy and Bentley Glass, eds.) pp. 724–53. John Hopkins Press, Baltimore.

WALD, G. and BROWN, P. K. 1952. The role of sulfhydryl groups in the bleaching and synthesis of rhodopsin. *J. Gen. Physiol.* **35**, 797–821.

WALD, G. and BURG, S. P. 1957. The vitamin A of the lobster. *J. Gen. Physiol.* **40**, 609–25 (see p. 622).

WALD, G., BROWN, P. K. and GIBBONS, I. R. 1962. Visual excitation: a chemo-anatomical study. In *Biological Receptor Mechanisms* pp. 32–57. Cambridge University Press.

WOLKEN, J. J. 1957. *Trans. N.Y. Acad. Sci.* Ser. II, **19**, 315.

WOLKEN, J. J., BOWNESS, J. M. and SCHEER, I. J. 1960. The visual complex of the insect: retinene in the housefly. *Biochim. Biophys. Acta* **43**, 531–7.

WOLKEN, J. J., MELLON, A. D. and CONTIS, G. 1957. Photoreceptor structures. II. *Drosophila melanogaster. J. Exp. Zool.* **134**, 383.

RECOGNITION OF COLOURED OBJECTS
BY INSECTS

G. A. Mazokhin-Porshnjakov

Institute of Problems of Information Communication, USSR Academy of Sciences, Moscow

In MODERN physiology of insect sense organs, non-behavioural, particularly electrophysiological investigations are in vogue, for such experiments hold out the possibility of giving insights into the mechanism of action of the receptors, which attracts great attention at present. However, even a good knowledge of the structure and physiology of the receptors does not allow one to determine the extent to which sensory information is used by the animal in its life. Only on the basis of behavioural experiments is it possible to judge the ability of the whole organism to respond to some stimuli and, moreover, to recognize one stimulus among others. This presentation deals with behavioural experiments concerning recognition of pigment stimuli and combinations of such stimuli by insects.

I

The works of Daumer (1956, 1958) and my own (1956, 1959, 1960, 1962, 1964, 1965a, 1965b) demonstrated that Apidae such as the honey bee *Apis mellifera* and the bumble bee *Bombus* distinguish a vast number of colours, their eyes possessing a high (from 1%) contrast sensitivity and trichromatic colour vision.

It is evident that colour vision appeared in animals in order to distinguish objects by their pigmentation, i.e. by the spectral composition of the light reflected by them. Almost all the objects in nature which insects and other animals are dealing with do not emit their own light but merely reflect the light falling on them. Under natural conditions, however, illumination varies so that at different times the same object may reflect light of different spectral composition. For example, when the sky is cloudless, a white object in the shade reflects mainly blue–violet rays, for it is illuminated only by the blue light of the sky; under trees the same object reflects many green rays, since green reflections from leaves fall on it. Therefore, the physical composition of the light reflected by an object under different conditions depends upon the characteristics of the illumination, and in order to avoid error when recognizing the colour of objects under different conditions of illumination, it is necessary to be able to introduce a "correction for illumination" (Helmholtz) to the visible colour of objects. Man has a special mechanism for a complex treatment of visual information which automatically introduces the necessary correction; this provides the constancy of perception of pigmented objects. We subconsciously distinguish the colour of an object from the colour of illumination, which is why we usually do not make errors recognizing colours under different conditions of illumination (Nyberg, 1960). One of the possible mechanisms in attaining this is a correction for illumination based on the colour of white, i.e. the lightest, objects. The colour of light can be also recognized by colour of reflections, of the shade and by other characteristics.

Experiments with honey bees have shown that insects possess a mechanism for maintaining the constancy of perception of an object's colour (Mazokhin-Porshnjakov, 1965a, b). This fact was established in experiments reproducing one of the typical situations encountered by the insect in nature. The problem to be solved was whether bees are able to recognize the yellow dandelion (*Taraxacum officinale*) by its colour under different conditions of illumination, in the shade and in the sunshine. The dandelion in the shade reflects mainly

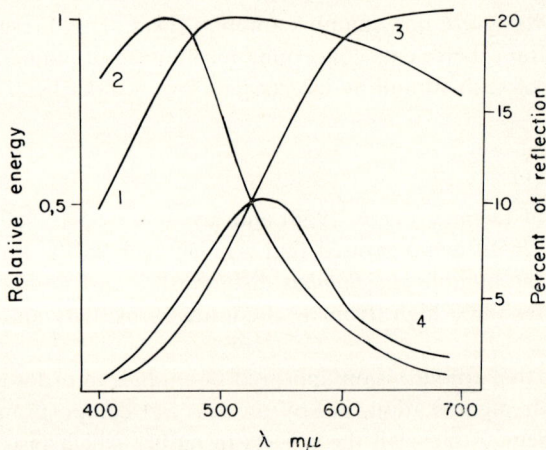

FIG. 1

The approximative curves of relative distribution of energy in a solar spectrum (1) and in blue sky-light (2) and the curves of the spectral reflection of sunlight by yellow (3) and green (4) papers.

green rays since the dispersed light from the blue sky—illumination in the shade—contains few yellow–red rays (Fig. 1, 2), while in an open place the dandelion reflects many more yellow–red rays than green ones. In other words, the dandelion in the shade is objectively green, reflecting light of almost the same spectral composition as the lighter green leaves in the sun.

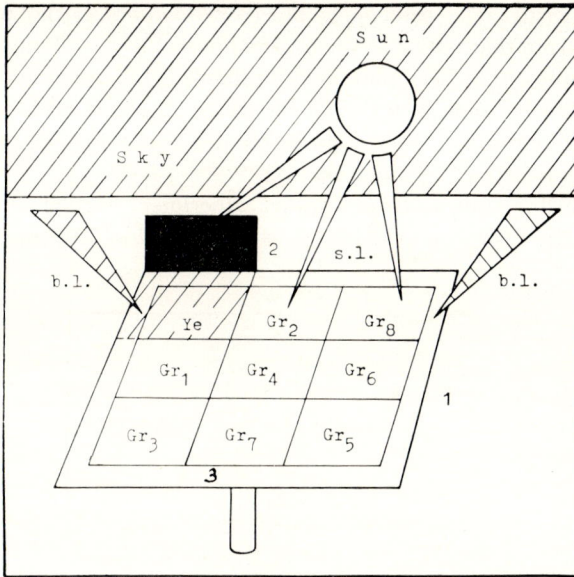

FIG. 2

A plan of an experiment demonstrating the existence of constancy of colour reception in bees (*Apis mellifera*). 1. The green papers of different brightness (Gr$_{1-8}$) and yellow paper (Ye) on the rotating table. 2. An opaque screen casting a shadow on the yellow pattern, which becomes objectively green in these conditions (Ye in blue sky-light = Gr). 3. The light border b.l., blue sky-light; s.l., sun-light.

In the experiment a set of nine square pieces of coloured paper was placed on a rotating table designed for bee training. Eight of the pieces were greens of different brightness, while one was yellow (Fig. 2, 1). This yellow piece, when illuminated only by the blue light of the sky, reflected light of practically the same physical composition as of the green papers in the sunshine. This can easily be demonstrated by comparing the product of the ordinates of curves 1 and 4, with 2 and 3 plotted in Graph 1. The set of nine papers was surrounded by a light border of paper and covered with glass. A dish with sugar-syrup was placed on the yellow paper, dishes with water being placed on the green papers. In the course of training, the yellow paper with the bait was periodically replaced, the whole table being rotated around its axis.

Starting at 9 o'clock on cloudless days the table was placed in the sunshine and the bees were trained to find the yellow paper among the green ones. About noon, when the bees began to find the yellow paper accurately, the shade of a quadrangular opaque screen was thrown on it before each new arrival of the bee (Fig. 2, 2). Although the shaded yellow paper became objectively green, resembling one of the green papers, the bees continued to recognize it easily. The percentage of erroneous choices did not increase significantly from that obtained when the whole table was illuminated by the sun. This implies that bees possess a mechanism for maintaining the constancy of colour perception: they may recognize objects by their colour under different illumination, i.e. they seem to be able to distinguish the colour of the object regardless of the illumination.

This conclusion follows from another experiment carried out by myself and Mrs. T. M. Vishnevskaya. In this experiment (Fig. 3) bees easily recog-

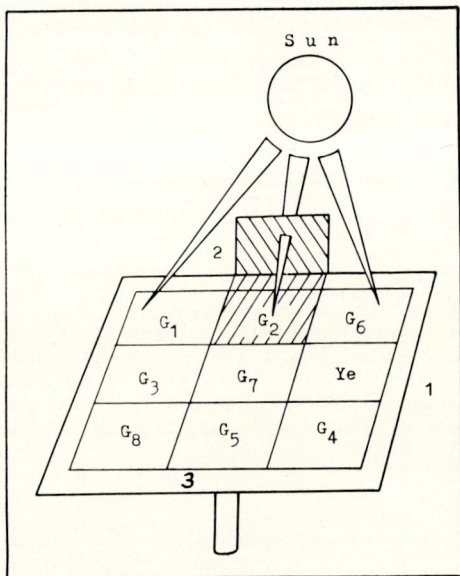

FIG. 3

A plan of an experiment demonstrating the ability of bees to discriminate between a yellow paper and a white one illuminated by yellow rays. 1. The grey papers of different brightness (G_{1-8}) and yellow paper (Ye) on the rotating table. 2. Yellow filter through which the straight sunbeams fall on one of the pieces (G_2) of grey paper; in this case Ye + sun-light = G_2 + yellow light. 3. The light border. The bees trained to detect the yellow paper (Ye) among the grey papers of different brightness (G_{1-8}) did not sit down on the grey paper (G_2) illuminated by the yellow light through filter (2), although this grey paper reflected light of the same spectral composition as the yellow paper.

nized yellow paper illuminated with "white" sunlight from grey paper illuminated with yellow rays. The illumination was selected in such a manner that both types of paper reflected light of the same physical composition. Nevertheless the bees were able to distinguish these papers. The local colour illumination could have been distinguished by the bees in this experiment either by a yellow patch of light on the glass filter or by a yellow patch on the light edge of the table.

There are some grounds for the suggestion that not only bees but also other insects closely connected with flowering plants, such as bumble bees, butterflies and flies, make such correction for illumination. Without such an ability to make a correction for illumination, these insects would not have such a great ability to recognize objects by their colour under different conditions of illumination.

II

It is well known now that insects are able to distinguish objects by their colour, i.e. insects possess the ability to recognize pigments under different conditions of illumination. Yet the objects with which insects are dealing in nature often show patterns of several colours: two, three and more. For example, patterns of two colours are common in flowering plants such as *Leucanthemum vulgare* and *Melampyrum nemorosa*, while *Galeopsis speciosa* and some violets (*Viola*) are tricoloured. Multicoloured patterns are typical of many insects, e.g. butterflies. Man can recognize objects by means of their patterns of coloration, but are insects able to memorize combinations of colour and use them to recognize flowering plants?

Experiments were carried out in which bees had to memorize combinations of two or three colours (Mazokhin-Porshnjakov, 1965a, b). A conditioned feeding reflex was developed in response to different combinations, for example, to Blue (Bl) and Green (Gr) placed among paired combinations of the same colours with some others, namely Orange (Or) + Bl, Or + Gr, Bl + Yellow (Ye) and Or + Ye (Fig. 4). The Bl + Gr combination cannot be distinguished in such surroundings by one character only, e.g. "is Orange

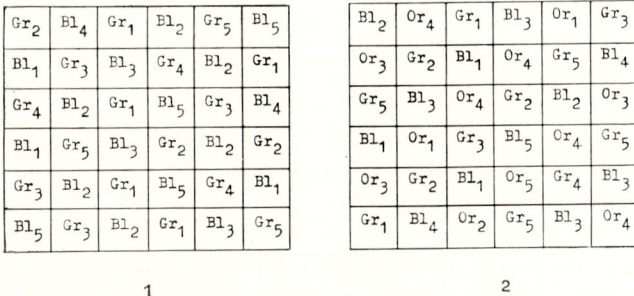

Gr_2	Bl_4	Gr_1	Bl_2	Gr_5	Bl_5
Bl_1	Gr_3	Bl_3	Gr_4	Bl_2	Gr_1
Gr_4	Bl_2	Gr_1	Bl_5	Gr_3	Bl_4
Bl_1	Gr_5	Bl_3	Gr_2	Bl_2	Gr_2
Gr_3	Bl_2	Gr_1	Bl_5	Gr_4	Bl_1
Bl_5	Gr_3	Bl_2	Gr_1	Bl_3	Gr_5

1

Bl_2	Or_4	Gr_1	Bl_3	Or_1	Gr_3
Or_3	Gr_2	Bl_1	Or_4	Gr_5	Bl_4
Gr_5	Bl_3	Or_4	Gr_2	Bl_2	Or_3
Bl_1	Or_1	Gr_3	Bl_5	Or_4	Gr_5
Or_3	Gr_2	Bl_1	Or_5	Gr_4	Bl_3
Gr_1	Bl_4	Or_2	Gr_5	Bl_3	Or_4

2

FIG. 4

Examples of two-coloured (green + blue) (1) and three-coloured (blue + orange + green) (2) patterns which bees can remember. Bl_{1-5}, Gr_{1-5} and Or_{1-5}, blue, green and orange papers of five different degrees of brightness.

present" or "is Orange absent", since Gr without blue is also present in Gr + Or combination, while Or is also absent in Bl + Ye combination. The Bl + Gr combination can be memorized only by a dual character: "both Gr and Bl present" or "neither Or nor Ye present". In order to rule out the possibility of recognition by brightness, each colour was represented by several variants of different brightness.

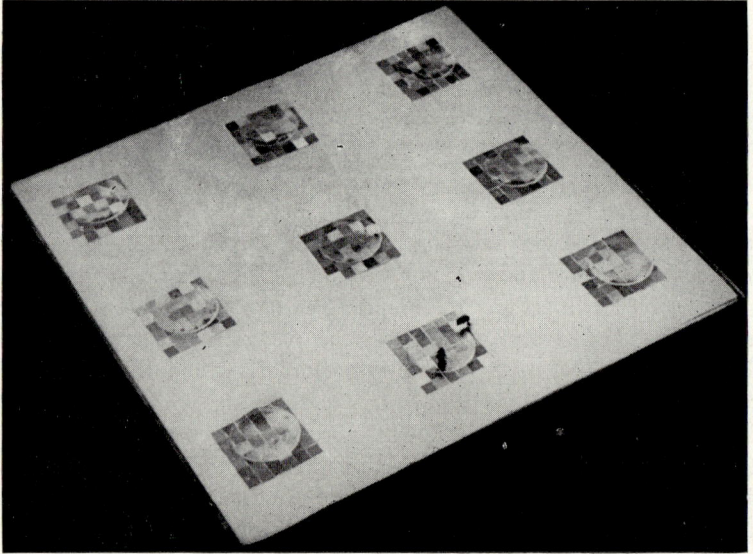

Fig. 5

The arrangement of two-coloured patterns on the rotating table in the course of training bees to recognize green + blue among eight other two-coloured combinations. Two bees are seen on the cup of sugar solution situated on the green + blue pattern.

The experiment was carried out in the manner as follows (Fig. 5). Nine chromatic patterns built up of square pieces of paper of two colours (of various degrees of brightness) were placed on the same rotating table under glass. Three-coloured patterns were also used (Fig. 4, 2). A dish with sugar-syrup was put on the training pattern, e.g. Gr + Bl, while dishes with water were placed on the other patterns (two Gr + Or, two Bl + Ye, two Gr + Ye and Bl + Or). After training, an attempt of a bee to feed from the dish over the training pattern, in this case Gr + Bl, was considered as the correct choice, while an attempt on other patterns was evaluated as an erroneous choice.

After the training period the observation of many feeding visits showed that the bees made almost no errors in the choice of the training pattern

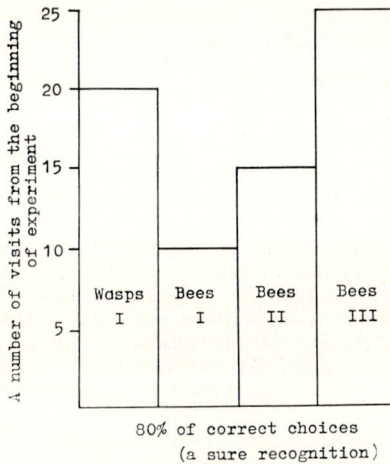

FIG. 6

A comparison of the rate of formation of conditioned reflexes for discrimination of colours and combinations of colours by bees (*Apis mellifera*) and wasps (*Vespula vulgaris*). I. The recognition of one colour (these experiments are not described here; see Mazokhin-Porshnjakov, 1959, 1960). II. The recognition of a combination of two colours. III. The recognition of a combination of three colours.

(Fig. 6). The same was observed in the control, when the training pattern was replaced by one with the same combination of colours but of different degrees of brightness, and all the dishes were removed from the table. Therefore, bees can recognize combinations of two and even three colours. On the contrary, wasps of the genus *Vespula*, whose mode of life is not so closely related to flowering plants as that of the bees, could not be trained to find even combinations of two colours, although a reflex for the distinction of one colour from another could be elicited rather easily.

SUMMARY

The results of the field experiments described here show that the information about coloured objects obtained by insects through their compound eyes is actually used in their behaviour. In particular, bees are able to recognize objects by their colour under illumination conditions which differ in spectral composition; that is, they can distinguish the colour of the object from the colour of illumination. Moreover, bees can memorize combinations of two and three different colours.

ACKNOWLEDGEMENT

I would like to thank Dr. T. Goldsmith for his help in correcting the English translation.

REFERENCES

DAUMER, K. 1956. Reizmetrische Untersuchung des Farbensehens der Bienen. *Z. vergl. Physiol.* **38**, 413–78.

DAUMER, K. 1958. Blumenfarben, wie sie die Bienen sehen. *Z. vergl. Physiol.* **41**, 49–110.

MAZOKHIN-PORSHNJAKOV, G. A. 1956. On the colour vision of insects. *Biophysica* **1**, 98–105 (In Russian).

MAZOKHIN-PORSHNJAKOV, G. A. 1959. Discrimination by bees between green, yellow and orange paints. *Biophysica* **4**, 48–54 (In Russian).

MAZOKHIN-PORSHNJAKOV, G. A. 1960. Demonstration of the existence of the colour vision in wasps (Vespidae). *Zool. Journ.* (*Moscow*) **34**, 553–7. (In Russian).

MAZOKHIN-PORSHNJAKOV, G. A. 1962. Colorimetrical evidence of the trichromatic vision of Apidae (on bumblebees example). *Biophysica* **7**, 211–17 (In Russian).

MAZOKHIN-PORSHNJAKOV, G. A. 1964. Methods and recent state of knowledge of the colour vision of insects. *Entomologich. obosrenie* **43**, 503–23 (In Russian).

MAZOKHIN-PORSHNJAKOV, G. A. 1965a. Insects and colours. *Priroda* No. 6, 58–62 (In Russian).

MAZOKHIN-PORSHNJAKOV, G. A. 1965b. *Vision of Insects.* Moscow (In Russian).

NYBERG, N. D. 1960. Paradoxes of colour vision. *Priroda* No. 8, 53–9 (In Russian).

ANALYSIS OF POLARIZED LIGHT IN WOLF-SPIDERS*

F. Magni

Istituto di Fisiologia dell'Università di Pisa, Centro di Neurologia e
Gruppo d'Elettrofisiologia del C.N.R., Sezione di Pisa, Italia

I. ANATOMICAL INTRODUCTION

The visual system of spiders consists of four pairs of eyes, all of which are provided with a dioptric apparatus (cornea, lens and vitreous body) and a receptive apparatus, the retina.

The four pairs of eyes can be subdivided into two groups on the basis of structure and embryological development (Bertkau, 1886; Widmann, 1907). The anterior median pair are called the principal eyes and the other three pairs (anterior lateral, posterior median and posterior lateral) are called secondary eyes. The former differ from the latter in the following ways: (i) the rhabdoms are distal to the retinal cell bodies, (ii) they have ocular muscles, and (iii) they lack a highly reflective crystal layer, the tapetum.

The structure of the eyes of the wolf-spider *Arctosa variana* has been studied in detail by Baccetti and Bedini (1964) by means of light and electron microscopy. Figure 1 shows a section of the principal eye cut parallel to the optic axis and Fig. 2 shows a similar section of a secondary eye. The gross anatomic relationships of the ocular structures can be clearly seen. The nerve fibres, which constitute the optic nerves, originate from the retinal cells, and terminate in the optic lobes. Electron micrographs of the rhabdoms show microtubular structures surrounding the retinal cells (the microvilli), which is in agreement with findings obtained on other arthropods (Goldsmith and Philpott, 1958; Wolken *et al.*, 1958; Fernandez-Morán, 1958).

A difference in the organization of the rhabdoms in the various pairs of eyes has been reported, but Baccetti and Bedini (1964) were unable to find any feature in the anatomy which could be related to a differential sensitivity to polarized light. These results of Baccetti and Bedini (1964) were recently confirmed and extended by Melamed and Trujillo-Cenóz (1965), who discovered a plexus of nerve fibres in the retina of the secondary eye. The fibres of this plexus originate from peripherally located retinal cells and make synaptic contacts with other retinal cells.

* The research reported in this paper has been sponsored by the Air Force Office of Scientific Research under Grant AF EOAR 64–37 through the European Office of Aerospace Research (OAR), United States Air Force.

171

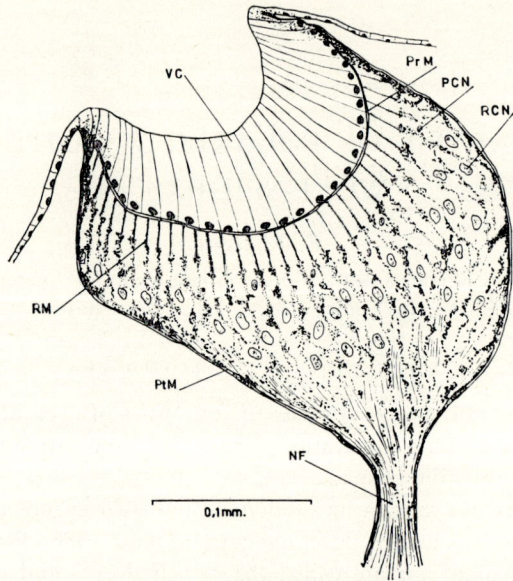

FIG. 1

Section of a principal eye of *Arctosa variana*, parallel to the optic axis. *VC*, vitreous body cells; *PrM*, preretinal membrane; *RCN*, nuclei of the retinal cells; *PCN*, nuclei of the pigment cells; *NF*, nerve fibres; *PtM*, postretinal membrane; *RM*, rhabdoms. (From Baccetti and Bedini, 1964.)

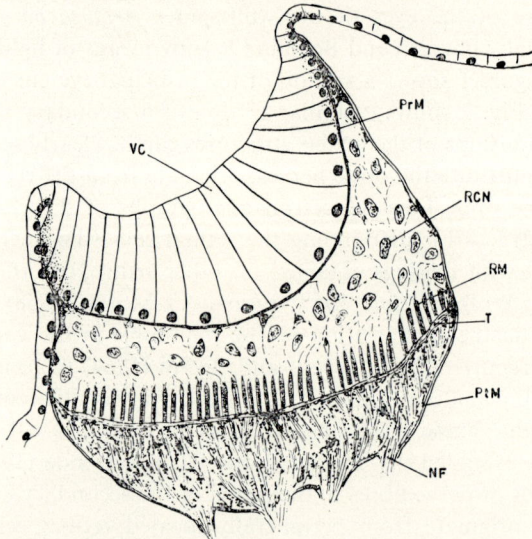

FIG. 2

Section of a secondary eye (posterior lateral) of *Arctosa variana*, parallel to the optic axis. Abbreviations as in Fig. 1. *T*, tapetum. (From Baccetti and Bedini, 1964.)

II. BEHAVIOURAL STUDIES

The rôle played by principal and secondary eyes has been investigated primarily by means of orientation experiments, both short-range and astronomical. In Salticidae, which have been more intensively investigated from this point of view, a different function has been recognized for principal and secondary eyes (Homann, 1928; Dzimirski, 1959). Secondary eyes are important in the perception of moving objects and for vision at short distances. Perception of a moving object elicits an attempt at orientation, i.e. movements of the spider's body aimed at bringing the object into the visual field of the principal eyes. These have a greater resolving power than the secondary eyes and are well suited to the perception of images, to vision at relatively great distances, and to the fixation of objects. In Thomisidae and Lycosidae the secondary eyes are of importance in alerting responses, whereas principal eyes are necessary to direct the animal's attack on the prey (Homann, 1931, 1934). Of particular interest are the findings of Görner (1958, 1962) on the orientation of *Agelena labyrinthica* (Cl.). This spider orients itself on its web by responding to several stimuli, among which are the position of the light source and the plane of polarization of the light. When only the principal eyes are left to the animal, it can still orient itself according to the plane of vibration of polarized light, whereas with the secondary eyes alone visual orientation is only possible on the basis of the position of the light sources.

As far as the Lycosid spider *Arctosa variana* is concerned, considerable data on its astronomical orientation have been collected (Papi, 1955a, 1955b, 1959; Papi *et al.*, 1957). Under a clear sky these spiders can direct themselves towards home at any time of the day, using only sky light as the stimulus for orientation. When *A. variana*, which lives on the shores of rivers, is placed on the water, it returns to its home shore along a route perpendicular to the shore line. The same heading is taken by spiders placed in a dish of water, with only a view of the sky. The importance of the position of the sun as a factor in orientation has been conclusively demonstrated (Papi, 1955b). However, the animals are also capable of correct orientation when in the shade of a small screen, provided that their vision of the clear sky is not completely obstructed, or when the sun is below the horizon. In this latter situation it is difficult to decide whether the animal orients itself on the basis of the distribution of light intensity in the sky, or the pattern of polarized light in the sky, or a combination of both. It has been shown that it is possible to change the direction of movement by interposing a polaroid sheet between the animal and the sky (Papi, 1955b).

The principal and secondary eyes of *A. variana* have different rôles in orientation. This may be demonstrated when one or more pairs of eyes are covered with a light-proof paste (Magni *et al.*, 1964). When only the principal eyes are uncovered, the animals, although less active, are still capable of correct orientation, both in sun and in shade. On the other hand, when the principal eyes alone are covered and all the secondary eyes are uncovered, the orientation capability of the animals is severely reduced. When only one pair of secondary eyes is left uncovered, the headings taken by the animals become completely erratic.

As pointed out above, the orientation experiments clearly indicate that astronomical signs other than the actual position of the sun can be used by the animal in choosing the direction of flight, i.e. intensity distribution of light in the sky and distribution pattern of polarized light at any time of the day. However, these factors are dependent on solar position. After the discovery made by von Frisch (1948, 1949, 1950, 1956) that the orientation of bees depends on the plane of vibration of polarized light, considerable work has been devoted to the importance of this phenomenon in other species and to investigating the underlying physiological mechanisms (Stockhammer, 1956; see Stockhammer, 1959 for ref.). There seems to be general agreement that the probable site for polarized light analysis is the rhabdom of the compound eye (Autrum and Stumpff, 1950; Stockhammer, 1956; Lüdtke, 1957; Kuwabara and Naka, 1959; von Frisch et al., 1960; Burkhardt and Wendler, 1960; Moody and Parris, 1961; Autrum and Zwehl, 1962). In particular, Moody and Parris (1961) suggest that the analysis of polarized light is performed at the level of the microvilli (Goldsmith and Philpott, 1958; Wolken et al., 1958; Fernandez-Morán, 1958; Baccetti and Bedini, 1964; Melamed and Trujillo-Cenóz, 1965).

It has also been suggested (Baylor and Kennedy, 1958; Baylor and Smith, 1958; Kalmus, 1959; Smith and Baylor, 1960; Kennedy and Baylor, 1961) that the orientation to polarized light is not accomplished through the direct analysis of the plane of polarization, but rather by an evaluation of the intensity pattern elicited by polarized light on the background. The general application of this attractive hypothesis is limited, in my opinion, by two main lines of evidence. First of all, electrophysiological experiments (Lüdtke, 1957; Kuwabara and Naka, 1959; Burkhardt and Wendler, 1960; Autrum and Zwehl, 1962; Giulio, 1963) show that different responses can be recorded from retinula cells to direct stimulation of the eye with light polarized in different planes; second, orientation to polarized light has been shown to be present in an experimental situation in which contamination with reflection pattern has been largely reduced or eliminated (von Frisch et al., 1960; Bainbridge and Waterman, 1957; Waterman, 1960; Görner, 1962).

On the basis of indications obtained by behavioural results, electro-physiological experiments have been performed with the following aims: (i) to ascertain whether or not the eyes of lycosid spiders show a different response to light polarized in different planes, and (ii) to analyse the mechanisms involved (Magni et al., 1962, 1965; Magni and Strata, 1966). These experiments have also yielded information concerning the functional organization of principal and secondary eyes of the Lycosids and will be reported in brief (Magni and Strata, 1965).

III. ELECTROPHYSIOLOGICAL STUDIES

1. *Analysis of Polarized Light in the Eyes of* Arctosa variana (*C. L. Koch*)

Adult and subadult spiders were collected on the banks of the River Arno, near Pisa. Under light chloroform anaesthesia, the animals were secured to a small board by means of adhesive tape, and all the eyes, except that to be investigated, were covered with a lightproof paste made of a mixture of shellac and lampblack. The completeness of this covering was routinely checked at the end of each experiment.

The light of a projector lamp was passed down a bundle of glass fibres (American Optical Company) in order to eliminate stray polarizations. The beam of light was then focused on the eye by means of a microscope objective, taking care to have the axis of the beam coincident, as nearly as possible, with the optical axis of the eye. A polaroid filter was interposed between the microscope objective and the eye. No variation in the light intensity was observed by rotating the polaroid filter. Calibrated neutral density filters were interposed in the path of the rays in order to control the intensity of the light. Flashes of 100 msec duration were used at a repetition rate of 0·1/sec.

A silver–silver chloride electrode of approximately 100 μ diameter was introduced in the cephalothorax, near the eye; an "indifferent" electrode was placed on the abdomen. The potentials were amplified by AC or DC amplifiers and displayed on the screen of a cathode-ray oscilloscope.

Before beginning the experiment, the animals were dark-adapted for at least 30 min.

Following stimulation with a light flash, a negative potential is recorded from the electrode placed near the eye. This potential deflection, which has a latency of about 8 msec, rises to a peak in about 50 msec and then declines in amplitude. At the cessation of the stimulus the potential declines to zero. If the stimulus is longer than 250 msec, then at the cessation of the stimulus the potential shows a positive overshoot before returning to zero (Fig. 3). The polarity and the time course of the potential are the same for all eyes. The amplitude of the potential decays considerably when the electrode is moved away from the eye. Figure 4 shows the extent of this decay for displacements of 1 and 2 mm. The response always disappears when the eye is covered with black varnish.

These experiments show that the responses are generated within the eye. They will henceforth be referred to as the electroretinogram (ERG).

The amplitude of the ERG is linearly proportional to the log of the light intensity over a range of 5–100 lux (Fig. 5) and is reduced by light adaptation.

Only few experiments were devoted to the flicker fusion; the critical frequency was found not to exceed 30/sec.

The ERG recorded in *Arctosa variana* is closely similar to that recorded by Autrum (1958) in *Dixippus*, by De Voe (1962) in *Lycosa baltimoriana* and

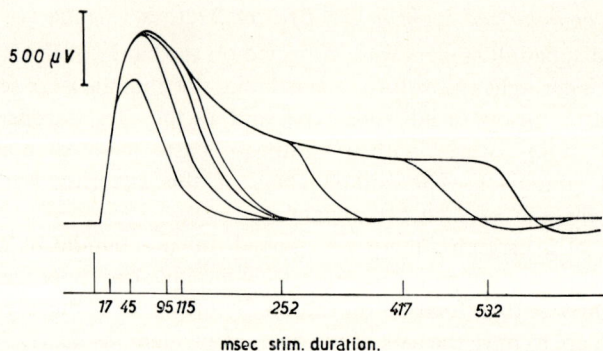

FIG. 3

Waveform and time course of the ERG of *Arctosa variana* to light stimulation of constant intensity and increasing duration. Superimposed drawings from actual records from posterior median eye of *A. variana*. DC amplification, non-polarized light. Stimulus duration in msec on the abscissa. (From Magni *et al.*, 1965.)

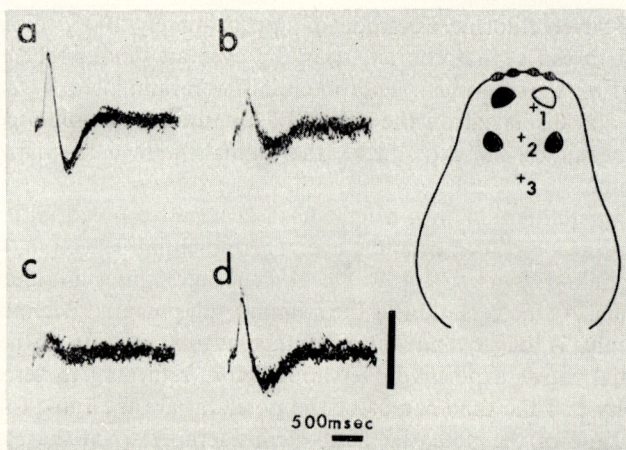

FIG. 4

ERG responses from the posterior median eye of *Arctosa variana* recorded at different distances from the eye. a, b and c show the responses led from an electrode placed in positions 1, 2 and 3 respectively. d, response obtained after replacement of electrode at position 1. AC amplification, negatively upwards. Voltage calibration: 100 μV. Black circles in the diagram represent the blinded eyes; the open circle represents the eye being investigated. (From Magni *et al.*, 1965.)

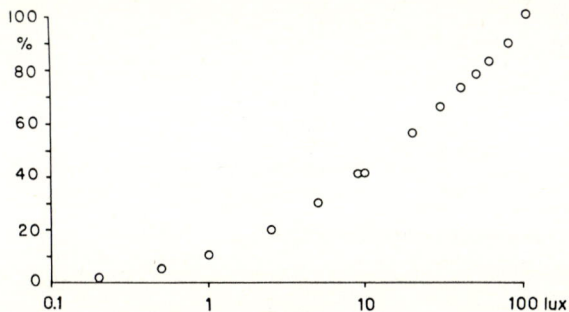

FIG. 5

Relationship between response amplitude and stimulus intensity in *Arctosa variana*. Dark-adapted anterior median eye. The response amplitude as percentage of maximum (ordinate) is plotted against the log of the stimulus intensity (abscissa) values. (From Magni *et al.*, 1965.)

by Giulio (1962) in *Tegenaria*. Also, the fact that this potential originates from elements located within or in close proximity to the eye, and the linear relationship between response amplitude and the log of the stimulus intensity, suggest that the ERG of *A. variana* represents, at least in part, the summed generator potentials of the retinal receptors. Of course, it is not possible with our technique to exclude the possibility that impulse activity in retinal cells and optic nerve fibres contribute to the recorded potential.

When the anterior median (principal) and the posterior median (secondary) eyes are stimulated with flashes of linearly polarized light of constant intensity, the amplitude of the ERG varies according to the plane of vibration of the polarized light. Over a 360° turn of the plane of polarization, two maxima and two minima in response amplitude are recorded (Fig. 6). The ERG amplitude is at a minimum when the *ĕ* vector lies in a plane normal to the frontal plane of the animal; in this situation the position of the polaroid filter is referred to as 0°. The response attains a maximum when the polaroid filter is rotated 90° from the 0° position; intermediate positions of the polaroid filter evoke responses of intermediate amplitude. The difference in amplitude between maxima and minima is of the same order as that produced by a 40 % increase in light intensity. As shown in the records of Fig. 6, C, the amplitude of the ERG of posterior lateral and anterior lateral eyes is unaffected by varying the plane of polarization of the light.

Since in our experimental conditions the rôle of reflection patterns can be excluded, the observed differences in the ERG to light polarized in different planes might be explained by one of the following hypotheses: (1) the analysis is performed at the level of the dioptric media; (2) the ratio of reflected to refracted light at the corneal surface varies with the plane of polarization of the light as a consequence of asymmetries in the radius of

C.E.—N

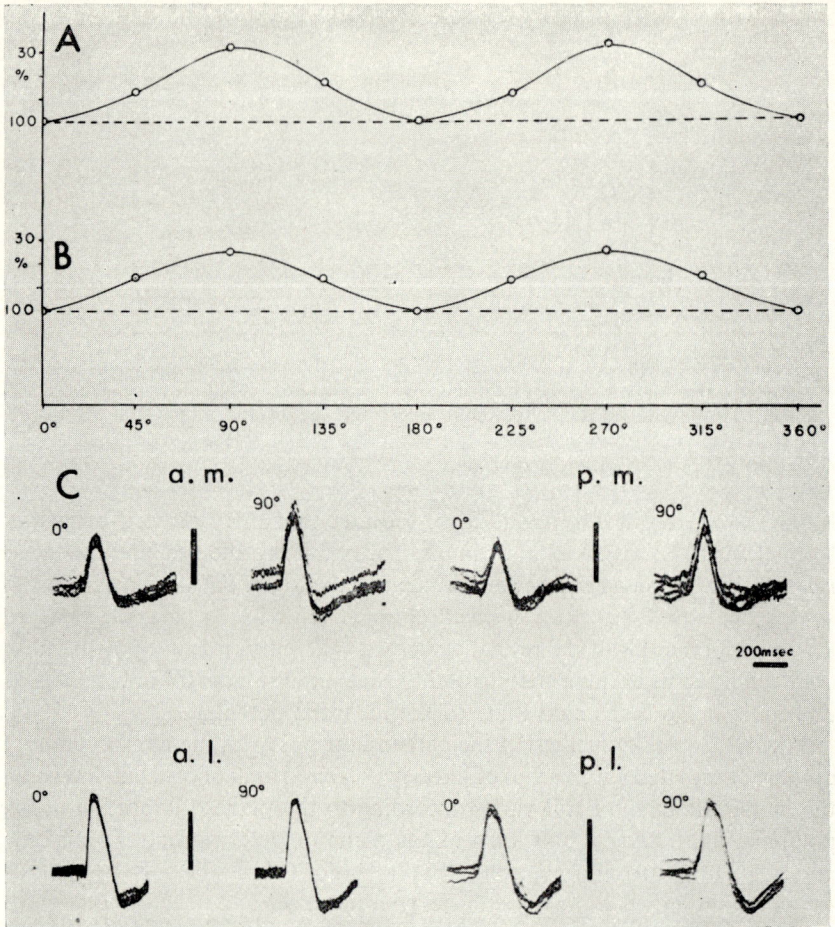

FIG. 6

Effect of the rotation of the plane of vibration of polarized light on the electroretinographic response in *Arctosa variana*. A, Anterior median eye. Average variations in response amplitude (as per cent of the response at 0°) obtained during a 360° turn of the polaroid filter, in 10 separate experiments. B, Posterior median eye, same as A. C, Specimen records, from all four pairs of eyes at 0° and 90° polaroid position; *a.m.*, anterior median eyes; *p.m.*, posterior median eyes; *a.l.*, anterior lateral eyes; *p.l.*, posterior lateral eyes. AC amplification; negativity upwards. Voltage calibration 100 μV for *a.m.* and *p.m.*, 200 μV for *a.l.* and *p.l.*
(From Magni *et al.*, 1965.)

curvature of the cornea or of a misalignment of the light beam with respect to the optic axis; (3) the analysis takes place at the level of the receptors.

The first hypothesis is ruled out by the fact that observations with a polarization microscope have shown that the dioptric media of all eyes of *A. variana* are isotropic (see also Stockhammer, 1956).

As far as the second hypothesis is concerned, several considerations make it unlikely. First of all, no difference in the amplitude of the ERG upon rotation of the plane of polarized light has been observed in anterior lateral and posterior lateral eyes. Also, the consistency of the results can be taken to indicate that random misalignments of the light beam do not play any significant rôle. Crucial evidence against this hypothesis is provided by the effect of light adaptation on the differential responses to polarized light. As already pointed out, the eye of this spider shows the phenomenon of light adaptation. As the eye is adapted to light of increasing intensity, the difference in the response to test flashes of polarized light at 0° and 90° becomes smaller and smaller, until it disappears when the eye is adapted to a strong light. Figure 7 illustrates this phenomenon. Rotation of the polaroid filter from 90° to 0° (Fig. 7, e, f) produces a large difference in the ERG of the dark-adapted eye. This difference is the same as that produced by decreasing the light intensity of non-polarized light by 40% (Fig. 7, a, b); Fig. 7, g and h,

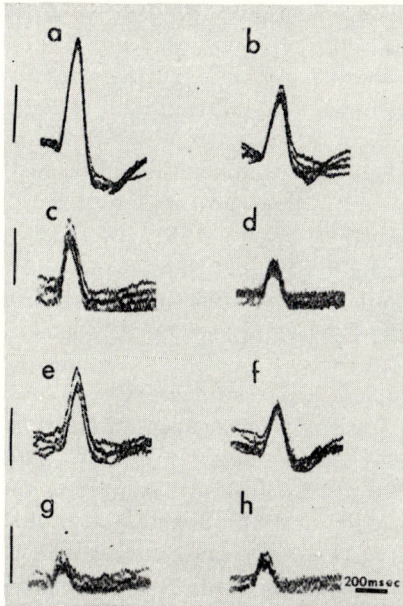

FIG. 7

Effect of light adaptation on the response to polarized light in *Arctosa variana*. Anterior median eye; a and b: effect of changing the intensity of non-polarized light on the response of the dark-adapted eye (in b the stimulus is 60% of that in a); c and d: same as a and b, but in the light-adapted eye; e and f: effect of the rotation of the polaroid filter ($e = 90°$; $f = 0°$) on the response of the dark-adapted eye; g and h: same as e and f, but in the light-adapted eye. AC amplification; negativity upwards. Voltage calibrations: 200 μV for a, b, e, f; 100 μV for c, d, g, h. (From Magni *et al.*, 1965.)

show equal responses to light polarized at 90° and 0° in the light-adapted eye, while panels *d* and *e* show the marked response difference which is still obtained in the light-adapted eye by decreasing the intensity of non-polarized light by 40%.

It is thus possible to conclude that light adaptation selectively abolishes the effect of rotation of the plane of polarized light on the ERG while the retina is still sensitive to intensity variations of 40%. The nature of this effect is not obvious at present. Were the difference in the responses to light polarized at 0° and 90° to be ascribed to variations in the intensity of the light impinging upon the retina, they could be abolished by the overall decrease in retinal sensitivity following light adaptation. This, however, is not the case. The light-adapted eye is still sensitive to a variation in stimulus intensity of the same order of magnitude as that needed to produce a difference in response comparable to that obtained by a 90° turn of the polaroid filter in conditions of dark adaptation. On these grounds the second hypothesis can be discounted.

It is necessary, therefore, to postulate that the analysis of polarized light takes place at the level of the retinal elements of the anterior median and posterior median eyes of *A. variana*, and that these elements are spatially arranged in such a way that they are activated by light polarized in a given plane.

Our results are in full agreement with those obtained on other arthropods (Autrum and Zwehl, 1962; Burkhardt and Wendler, 1960; Kuwabara and Naka, 1959; Lüdtke, 1957; Giulio, 1963). Of particular relevance are the results of Autrum and Zwehl (1962) who found by recording intracellularly that 50% of the retinula cells of *Calliphora* are sensitive to variations of the plane of polarization of the light, and 50% are sensitive only to variations of light intensity.

Electron microscopical investigations (Baccetti and Bedini, 1964) show that there are three types of arrangements in the rhabdoms of *A. variana*. It is interesting to note that the posterior median and posterior lateral eyes, although they have the same structural organization, differ in their ability to respond to light polarized in different planes. It is clear, therefore, that the distinctive structural features of the elements capable of analysing polarized light are beyond the capabilities of the present electron microscopical techniques. The different behaviour of posterior lateral and posterior median eyes can be accounted for by two alternative hypotheses, namely: (i) that the retina of posterior lateral eyes (as well as that of anterior median ones) is devoid of elements capable of analysing polarized light, or (ii) the elements are so distributed that for any given plane of polarization an equal number is activated. The latter hypothesis has been found adequate to explain the failure of macroelectrode recording to show differential responses to polarized light in *Apis* (Autrum and Stumpff, 1950). As in the case of *Apis* (Burkhardt and Wendler, 1960), where microelectrode recording from single retinal cells has shown different responses to polarized light, the unitary approach is the only method which will permit a decision between the two hypotheses.

The function of the different pairs of eyes in astronomical orientation deserves some comment in this context. As indicated previously, the anterior median (principal) eyes play a predominant rôle in astronomical orientation (Magni *et al.*, 1964). The fact that the same eyes are also capable of analysing the plane of polarized light is in keeping with the behavioural results. Although the posterior median and anterior median eyes both possess the capability of analysing the plane of polarized light, and have extensively overlapping visual fields, the posterior median pair seem to play only a minor rôle in astronomical orientation, and then only when the other secondary eyes are not blinded (Magni *et al.*, 1964). It is possible that the sensory message transmitted by posterior median eyes when stimulated by polarized light is used for something other than astronomical orientation.

2 *Analysis of Polarized Light in the Eyes of* Lycosa tarentula (*Rossi*)

Unlike *Arctosa variana*, very little is known about the visual functions of *Lysoca tarentula*, particularly with respect to its orienting ability. H. E. Savely has begun a series of field investigations in order to collect data about the behaviour of this spider.

The electrophysiological investigations were started primarily with the aim of determining whether the ability to analyse polarized light is present in Lycosids other than *A. variana*. A further reason for studying these spiders is their large size (relative to that of *A. variana*), a fact that could possibly help in attempts to record at unitary levels.

The technique used was essentially the same as that described above.

The response of all eyes to brief flashes of light (100 msec) consists of a negative monophasic wave, similar to that described in *A. variana* (Magni *et al.*, 1962, 1965). The amplitude of this potential is linearly proportional to the log of the stimulus intensity. When stimuli of longer duration are used, differences in the ERG of primary and secondary eyes appear. In the secondary eyes a positive potential is recorded, which can be abolished by several procedures (Magni and Strata, 1965). It is tentatively suggested that the positive component of the ERG of secondary eyes may be of synaptic origin, since in these eyes a nerve network interconnecting the receptor cells has recently been described (Melamed and Trujillo-Cenóz, 1965; for further details see Magni and Strata, 1965).

The effect of polarized light on the ERG of the eyes of *L. tarentula* has been tested so far only with flashes of 100 msec duration. The amplitude of the responses recorded from the posterior median and posterior lateral (all secondary) eyes show two maxima and two minima when the plane of polarization of the light is rotated through 360°. The minimum is at 0° and the maximum at 90° (see above). This phenomenon is absent in the ERG of the anterior lateral (secondary) eyes. From the anterior median (principal) eyes inconsistent results have been obtained.

The record in Fig. 8 is typical of those obtained from a dark-adapted posterior median eye in response to light polarized at 0° and 90°. The difference in response amplitude between 0° and 90° remains approximately constant over the range of stimulus intensities used (6–40 lux). Thus, the percentage difference decreases as the stimulus intensity (and hence the response size) increases.

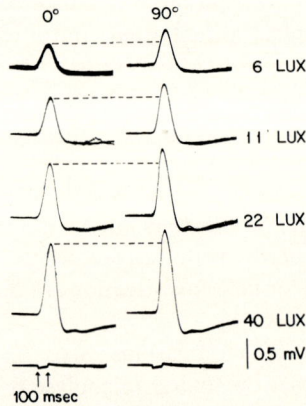

Fig. 8

Effect of the rotation of the polaroid filter on the response of the posterior median eye of *Lycosa tarentula*. Dark-adapted eye. Stimulation with 100 msec flashes of light of the indicated intensity, polarized at 0° and at 90°. AC amplification, negativity upwards. On the bottom trace is the stimulus signal. (From Magni and Strata, 1966.)

The fact that response differences to light polarized at 0° and at 90° are present only in two pairs of eyes, as well as the consistency of the results, can be taken, as discussed for *A. variana*, to indicate the presence of an intraretinal analysing system. On the other hand, when the experiment is repeated under conditions of light adaptation, the difference in response amplitude to polarized light at 0° and 90° becomes proportional to the stimulus intensity (Fig. 9). If we compare the magnitudes of the responses elicited in the darkadapted eye by flashes of light of equal intensities, but polarized at 0° and 90°, to those elicited by flashes of non-polarized light having the same intensity, we see that the responses to light polarized at 0° and 90° are, respectively, smaller and larger than those evoked by non-polarized light (Fig. 10).

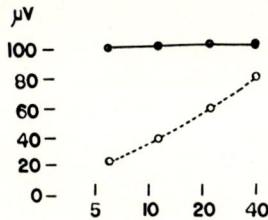

FIG. 9

Difference in response amplitude elicited by stimulation with light polarized at 0°
and 90° in the dark- and light-adapted eye in *Lycosa tarentula*. Posterior median
eye. Difference in response amplitude (μV) to light polarized at 0° and 90°
plotted against stimulus intensity (lux, log scale, abscissa). Filled circles: dark-
adapted eye. Open circles: light-adapted eye. (From Magni and Strata, 1966.)

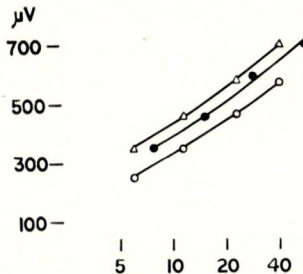

FIG. 10

Comparison of the effects of non-polarized and polarized light on the dark-
adapted eye of *Lycosa tarentula*. Posterior median eye. Response amplitude (μV)
plotted against stimulus intensity (lux, log scale, abscissa). Filled circles: non-
polarized light; triangles: light polarized at 90°; open circles: light polarized at 0°.
(From Magni and Strata, 1966.)

When the eye is stimulated with light polarized at 0°, a linear increase in
the response amplitude is observed. When the light is polarized at 90° the
responses are also linearly related to the log of the stimulus intensity, but
with a fixed increment above those recorded with 0° stimulation. When
non-polarized light is used (which is assumed to be 50% polarized at 90°)
the amplitudes of the responses are approximately half-way between the
values of the responses evoked by 0° and 90° stimulation. It is possible that
the experimental data can be explained in terms of the non-linearity of the
response. Experiments are being performed in order to verify this hypothesis.
Should this prove not to be the case, then the data would indicate that,
under these experimental conditions, the responses are composed of two
components, one involving the intensity of the light stimulus, and the
other the amount of light polarized at 90°. The intensity component would
be proportional to the log of the intensity of the light stimulus, whereas

the polarization component would seem to have the same value over the entire range of stimulus intensities used. This latter component could best be characterized, in terms of the experimental data, as being a function of the fraction of the total amount of light impinging upon the eye which is polarized at 90°.

In the light-adapted eye (Fig. 11), the absolute levels of the responses to polarized and non-polarized light stimulation are lower than those recorded from the dark-adapted eye. The responses to non-polarized light are, how-

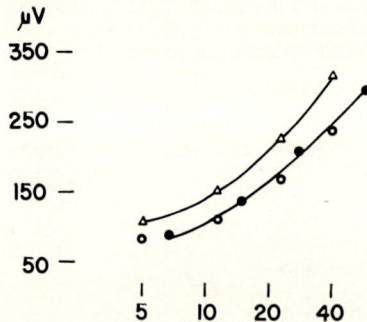

FIG. 11

Comparison of the effect of non-polarized and polarized light on the light-adapted eye of *Lycosa tarentula*. Posterior median eye. Coordinates same as Fig. 10. Filled circles: non-polarized light; triangles: light polarized at 90°; open circles; light polarized at 0°. (From Magni and Strata, 1966.)

ever, approximately of the same amplitude as those elicited by 0° polarized light. Both of these groups of responses are lower than those elicited by stimulation with 90° polarized light, in a manner which is proportional to the log of the intensity of the stimulus.

Microelectrode recording from single units and the effect of selective adaptation to light polarized in different planes will be essential in furthering our understanding of some of the retinal neural mechanisms. These experiments are at present under way in our laboratory. The analysing system of *L. tarentula* seems to have certain properties in common with *A. variana* (i.e. preferential plane of polarization of light and susceptibility to light adaptation). The major differences seem to be concerned with the topography since the response to polarized light is located in two pairs of secondary eyes in *L. tarentula*, and in the principal and one pair of secondary eyes in *A. variana*. Behavioural studies, which are also under way, will be of great interest in indicating the rôle of the different pairs of eyes in the integrated behaviour of the animals.

SUMMARY

In two species of wolf-spider, *A. variana* (C. L. Koch) and *L. tarentula* (Rossi), the electroretinographic responses to flashes of light polarized in different planes have been recorded.

In *A. variana* the amplitude of the response led from anterior median and posterior median eyes showed two maxima and two minima over a 360° rotation of the plane of polarization of the light. When the eyes are stimulated with polarized light, so that the *ĕ* vector lies in a plane normal to the frontal plane of the animal (0°), the response is at a minimum. The response is at a maximum when the plane of polarization is rotated by 90° from the 0° position. In *L. tarentula* the same response pattern is observed in posterior median and posterior lateral eyes. Several lines of evidence are presented to indicate that the mechanism for the analysis of polarized light is located at the level of the retina in both species.

The physiological significance of these findings is discussed in relation to the behaviour of *A. variana*.

REFERENCES

AUTRUM, H. 1958. Electrophysiological analysis of the visual system of insects. *Exp. Cell Research*, Suppl. 5, 426–39.

AUTRUM, H. and STUMPFF, H. 1950. Das Bienenauge als Analysator für polarisiertes Licht. *Z. Naturforsch.* **5b**, 116–22.

AUTRUM, H. and VON ZWEHL, V. 1962. Die Sehzellen der Insekten als Analysatoren für polarisiertes Licht. *Z. vergl. Physiol.* **46**, 1–17.

BACCETTI, B. and BEDINI, C. 1964. Research on the structure and physiology of the eyes of a Lycosid spider. I—Microscopic and ultramicroscopic structure. *Arch. ital. Biol.* **102**, 97–122.

BAINBRIDGE, R. and WATERMAN, T. H. 1957. Polarized light and the orientation of two marine crustacea. *J. Exp. Biol.* **34**, 342–64.

BAYLOR, E. R. and KENNEDY, D. 1958. Evidence against a polarizing analyzer in the bee's eye. *Anat. Rec.* **132**, 411.

BAYLOR, E. R. and SMITH, F. E. 1958. Extraocular polarization analysis in the honey-bee. *Anat. Rec.* **132**, 411–412.

BERTKAU, P. 1886. Beiträge zur Kentniss der Sinnesorgan der Spinnen I: Die Augen der Spinnen. *Arch. mikr. Anat.* **27**, 589–631.

BURKHARDT, D. and WENDLER, L. 1960. Ein direkter Beweis für die Fähigkeit einzelner Sehzellen des Insektenauges, die Schwingungsrichtung polarisierten Lichtes zu analysieren. *Z. vergl. Physiol.* **43**, 687–92.

DE VOE, R. D. 1962. Linear superposition of retinal action potentials to predict electrical flicker responses from the eye of the wolf-spider *Lycosa baltimoriana* (Keiserling). *J. Gen. Physiol.* **46**, 75–96.

DZIMIRSKI, I. 1959. Untersuchungen über Bewegungssehen und Optomotorik bei Springspinnen (Salticidae). *Z. Tierpsychol.* **16**, 385–402.

FERNANDEZ-MORAN, H. 1958. Fine structure of the light receptors in the compound eye of insects. *Exp. Cell Research*, Suppl. 5, 586–644.

FRISCH, K. VON. 1948. Gelöste und ungelöste Rätsel der Bienensprache, *Naturwissenschaften*, **35**, 38–43.

FRISCH, K. VON. 1949. Die Polarization des Himmellichtes als orientierenden Faktor bei den Tänzen der Bienen. *Experientia* **5**, 142–8.

FRISCH, K. VON. 1950. Die Sonne als Kompass im Leben der Bienen. *Experientia* **6**, 210–21.

FRISCH, K. VON. 1956. The language and orientation of the bees. *Proc. Amer. Philosoph. Soc.* **100**, 515–9.

FRISCH, K. VON, LINDAUER, M. and DAUMER, K. 1960. Über die Wahrnehmung polarisierten Lichtes durch das Bienenauge. *Experientia* **16**, 289–301.

GIULIO, L. 1962. L'elettroretinogramma ocellare in *Tegenaria* (Aranenae Agelenidae) I. Caratteristiche del potenziale d'illuminazione. *Boll. Soc. it. Biol. sper.* **38**, 910–12.

GIULIO, L. 1963. Elektroretinographische Beweisführung dicroitischer Eigenschaften des Komplexauges bei Zweiflüglern. *Z. vergl. Physiol.* **46**, 491–5.

GOLDSMITH, T. H., and PHILPOTT, D. E. 1958. The microstructure of the compound eye of insects. *J. Biophys. Biochem. Cytol.* **3**, 429–40.

GÖRNER, P. 1958. Die optische und kinästhetische Orientierung der Trichterspinne *Agelena labyrinthica* (Cl.). *Z. vergl. Physiol.* **41**, 11–153.

GÖRNER, P. 1962. Die Orientierung der Trichterspinne nach polarisiertem Licht. *Z. vergl. Physiol.* **45**, 307–14.

HOMANN, H. 1928. Beiträge zur Physiologie der Spinnenaugen. I: Untersuchungsmethoden. II: Das Sehvermögen der Salticiden. *Z. vergl. Physiol.* **7**, 201–68.

HOMANN, H. 1931. Beiträge zur Physiologie der Spinnenaugen. III: Das Sehvermögen der Lycosiden. *Z. vergl. Physiol.* **14**, 40–67.

HOMANN, H. 1934. Beiträge zur Physiologie der Spinnenaugen. IV: Das Sehvermögen der Thomisiden. *Z. vergl. Physiol.* **20**, 420–9.

KALMUS, H. 1959. Orientation of animals to polarized light. *Nature* **184**, 228–30.

KENNEDY, D. and BAYLOR, E. R. 1961. Analysis of polarized light by the bee's eye. *Nature* **191**, 34–7.

KUWABARA, M. and NAKA, K. 1959. Responses of a single retinula cell to polarized light. *Nature*, **184**, 455–6.

LÜDTKF, H. 1957. Beziehungen des Feinbaues im Rückenschwimmerauge zu seiner Fähigkeit polarisierte Licht zu analyzieren. *Z. vergl. Physiol.* **40**, 329–44.

MAGNI, F. and STRATA, P. 1965. Electroretinographic responses from the eyes of the wolfspider *Lycosa tarentula* (Rossi). *Arch. ital. Biol.* (in press).

MAGNI, F. and STRATA, P. 1966. *Arch. ital. Biol.* (in press).

MAGNI, F., PAPI, F., SAVELY, H. E. and TONGIORGI, P. 1962. Electroretinographic responses to polarized light in the wolf-spider *Arctosa variana* (C. L. Koch). *Experientia*, **18**, 511–13.

MAGNI, F., PAPI, F., SAVELY, H. E. and TONGIORGI, P. 1964. Research on the structure and physiology of the eyes of a lycosid spider. II. The rôle of different pairs of eyes in astronomical orientation. *Arch. ital. Biol.* **102**, 123–36.

MAGNI, F., PAPI, F., SAVELY, H. E. and TONGIORGI, P. 1965. Research on the structure and physiology of the eyes of a Lycosid spider. III. Electroretinographic responses to polarized light. *Arch. ital. Biol.* **103**, 146–58.

MELAMED, J. and TRUJILLO-CENÓZ, O. 1965. Personal communication.

MOODY, M. F. and PARRIS, J. R. 1961. The discrimination of polarized light of *Octopus*: a behavioural and morphological study. *Z. vergl. Physiol.* **44**, 268–91.

PAPI, F. 1955a. Astronomische orientierung bei der wolfspinnen, *Arctosa perita* (Latr.). *Z. vergl. Physiol.* **37**, 230–3.

PAPI, F. 1955b. Ricerche sull'orientamento di *Arctosa perita* (Latr.) (Araneae Lycosidae). *Pubbl. Staz. zool. Napoli* **27**, 76–103.

PAPI, F. 1959. Sull'orientamento astronomico in specie del gen. *Arctosa* (Araneae Lycosidae). *Z. vergl. Physiol.* **41**, 481–9.

PAPI, F., SERRETTI, L. and PARRINI, S. 1957. Nuove ricerche sull'orientamento e il senso del tempo di *Arctosa perita* (Latr.) (Araneae Lycosidae). *Z. vergl. Physiol.* **39**, 531–61.

SMITH, F. E. and BAYLOR, E. R. 1960. Bees, *Daphnia* and polarized light. *Ecology* **41**, 360–3.

STOCKHAMMER, K. 1956. Zur Wahrnehmung der Schwingungsrichtung linear polarisierten Lichtes bei Insecten. *Z. vergl. Physiol.* **38**, 30–83.

STOCKHAMMER, K. 1959. Die Orientierung nach der Schwingungsrichtung linear polarisierten Lichtes und ihre sinnesphysiologische Grundlagen. *Ergebn. Biol.* **21**.

WATERMAN, T. H. 1960. Interaction of polarized light and turbidity in the orientation of *Daphnia* and *Mysidium*. *Z. vergl. Physiol.* **43**, 149–72.

WIDMANN, E. 1907. Der feinere Bau der Augen einiger Spinnen. *Zool. Anz.* **31**, 755–62.

WOLKEN, J. J., CAPENOS, J. and TURANO, A. 1958. Photoreceptor structures. III. *Drosophila melanogaster*. *J. Biophys. Cytol.* **3**, 441–7.

SELECTIVE ADAPTATION OF LOCAL REGIONS OF THE RHABDOM IN AN OMMATIDIUM OF THE COMPOUND EYE OF *LIMULUS**

F. Ratliff

The Rockefeller University, New York, U.S.A.

In the compound eye the mosaic formed by the ommatidia is relatively coarse, and the visual field of each ommatidium is so broad that it overlaps that of its near neighbors. Therefore, according to Johannes Müller's "mosaic theory"—in which the ommatidia are regarded as the limiting receptor units—the resolution of fine detail by the compound eye should be rather poor. The validity of the mosaic theory has been questioned from time to time, however, and the alternative theory that the limiting receptor unit is the retinular cell, rather than the ommatidium as a whole, has often been advanced. The issue has yet to be resolved. For recent studies both *pro* and *con* (in addition to the relevant work reported in this Symposium) see Kuiper (1962), Burtt and Catton (1962), Götz (1965), Palka (1965), and Barlow (1965).

The following experiment on an ommatidium in the compound eye of *Limulus* lends support to the view that the retinular cells—or, at least, local regions of the retinula—may function independently of one another. In this experiment I used to advantage the extremely wide visual field of the *Limulus* ommatidium (half-width of the spatial sensitivity distribution about 8°). First, I dissected apart a small bundle of fibers from the optic nerve until only one active eccentric cell axon remained on the recording electrodes. Next, I focused two independently controlled beams of light, each coming from a different direction in the visual field, on the corneal facet of the ommatidium containing that eccentric cell (Fig. 1). Finally, by switching from one beam to the other, I alternately illuminated the ommatidium from these two different directions (thus presumably illuminating two different, but possibly overlapping, local regions of the photosensitive rhabdom). At the same time, I recorded the discharge of impulses in the axon of the eccentric cell (Fig. 2).

* This investigation was supported by a research grant (NB 00864) from the National Institute of Neurological Diseases and Blindness, U.S. Public Health Service, and by an Equipment Loan Contract (Nonr. 1442(00)) with the U.S. Office of Naval Research.

Light emitted from one side of a tungsten coil filament provided one beam; light from the opposite side, the other. In each beam an image of the filament was focused on the aperture of an electromagnetic shutter. The diverging beam beyond the shutter filled a field lens, which focused a second image of

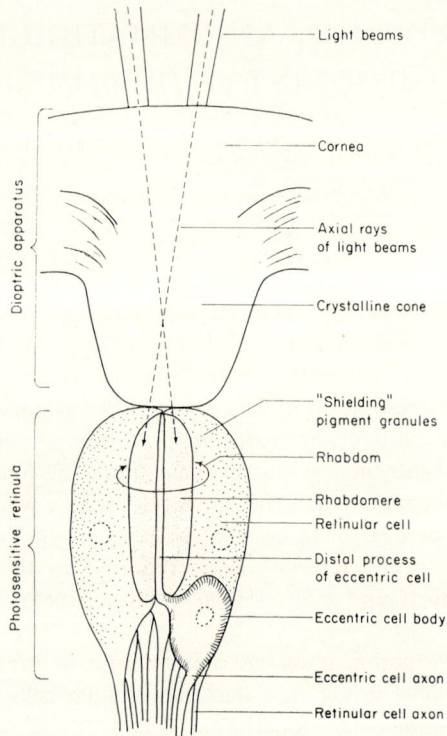

FIG. 1

Schematic drawing of longitudinal section through the optical axis of an ommatidium in the compound lateral eye of *Limulus*. The rhabdomeres are formed by microvillous outgrowths at and near the apexes of the wedge-shaped retinular cells (Miller, 1957) and in cross-section the rhabdom as a whole resembles the hub and spokes of a wheel, centered on the distal process of the eccentric cell. The section represented here passes near the margins of the retinular cells, and thus is in the plane of a pair of the spoke-like parts of the rhabdom. (The paths of the axial rays of the two light beams within the crystalline cone are conjectural.)

the filament in an objective lens, which in turn focused the stop of the field lens on the surface of the eye. Both beams passed through a combining prism just before they reached the objective lens, where the two images of the filament were then superimposed. By placing a mask over about two-thirds of the length of the image of the filament in the shutter aperture, I reduced the length of the corresponding image of the filament in the objective lens and confined the image to one side of the lens. Similarly, I reduced the image formed by the other beam and confined it to a small region in the opposite side of the objective lens (see inset in Fig. 2). By adjustments in the size and position of the two field stops, the two beams, coming from the two different directions, were focused on the same corneal facet.

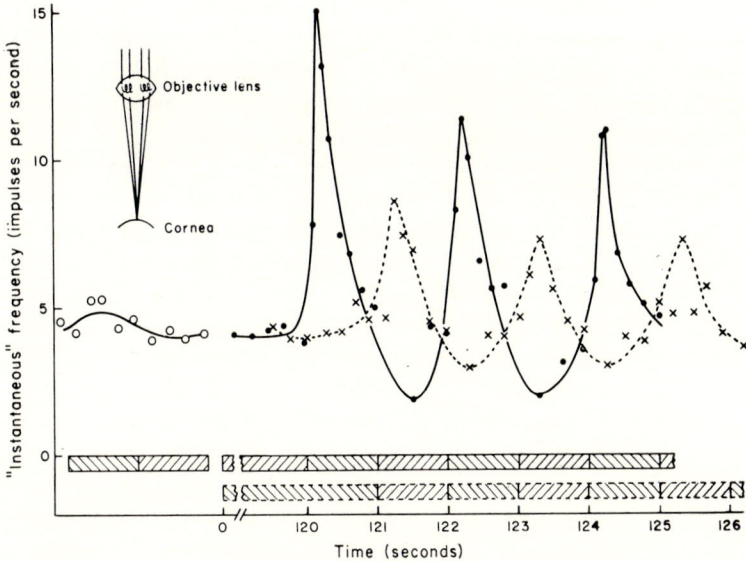

FIG. 2

Frequency of impulses discharged from the eccentric cell of an ommatidium in response to 1 sec flashes of light, the angles of incidence of which alternated from left to right of the optical axis. A schematic diagram of the final paths of the two beams is shown in the inset. The direction of the hatch marks in the bars at the bottom of the graph indicates the direction of the incident beam during the corresponding period. The bars outlined with solid lines correspond to the data points fitted with a solid curve; bars outlined with broken lines correspond to the data points fitted with a broken line.

Programed timers controlled the shutters. The first program turned the two beams on and off once a second and 180° out of phase, so that when one beam was on the other was off. By means of neutral density wedges, I adjusted the intensity of the two beams so that there was little or no change in the frequency of impulses discharged from the eccentric cell as the incident light changed direction. Sample data recorded during one cycle of this nearly perfect balance of responses to the 1 sec flashes of light incident from the two different angles are illustrated on the left of Fig. 2. I then changed the program of the timers so that the beam of light entering from one direction remained on for approximately 2 min. (The data obtained during most of the resulting steady discharge are not shown. The period omitted is indicated by the breaks in the graph.)

At the end of this 2 min period, the second by second alternation of the angle of incidence of the illumination resumed. Now the responses to illumination incident from the two different angles were quite different. There was a transient high frequency response to the flash of light in the beam that had not been turned on for 2 min and a transient low frequency response to the following flash from the other direction. As the alternation continued, the difference in response gradually decreased until after about 30 or 40 sec the difference was not much greater than it had been previous to the 2 min exposure to the beam of light from a single direction.

Leaving the light from the other direction on for approximately 2 min and then resuming the alternation reversed the maxima and minima in the frequency of discharge. As before, when the light was turned on from the direction which had not been on for 2 min, there was a vigorous response, then, when switched to the other side, there was a smaller response, and so on. Also, as before, the maxima and minima in the responses to the two directions of stimulation gradually diminished until they were barely perceptible. Note that the slight "preference" for illumination from the left, which can be seen in the single cycle shown at the left side of the figure, subsequently appears as a bias in the amplitude of the curves representing the responses following prolonged illumination from one side or the other. (The smooth curves through the data points were fitted by eye. Because of this smoothing, changes in the curves in some places appear to anticipate the corresponding changes in the direction of illumination, but changes in the actual data points always follow the changes in direction.)

These marked effects on the frequency of discharge of impulses from the eccentric cell, produced by changing the angle of incidence of the illumination on the ommatidium, must result from local changes of state within the retinula. It is uncertain, however, what these changes are and where they take place. One very likely possibility is that they are merely a local bleaching of photopigments in the rhabdom. Another possibility is a local depletion of some transmitter substance that provides the linkage between the retinular cells and the eccentric cell. A third possibility is a local migration of some of the "screening" pigments in the retinular cells. During exposure to light, these pigments migrate toward the axis, in between the rays of the rhabdom; during darkness, they migrate in the opposite direction, sometimes completely out of the rhabdom (Miller, 1958). Further experiments are required, of course, to elucidate these points.

Whatever the mechanisms underlying the observed effects, these results lend some support to the view that the structure and function of components of the rhabdom, rather than of the rhabdom as a whole, are limiting factors in the resolving power of the compound eye.

REFERENCES

BARLOW, H. B. 1965. Visual resolution and the diffraction limit. *Science* **149**, 553–5.

BURTT, E. T. and CATTON, W. T. 1962. Resolving power of the compound eye. Biological receptor mechanisms. *Symposia of the Society for Experimental Biology*, No. XVI, 72–85. Academic Press, New York.

GÖTZ, K. G. 1965. Die optische Übertragungseigenschaften der Komplexaugen von *Drosophila*. *Kybernetik* **2**, 215–21.

KUIPER, J. W. 1962. The optics of the compound eye. Biological receptor mechanisms. *Symposia of the Society for Experimental Biology*, No. XVI, 58–71. Academic Press, New York.

MILLER, W. H. 1957. Morphology of the ommatidia of the compound eye of *Limulus*. *Journal of Biophysical and Biochemical Cytology* **3**, 421–8.

MILLER, W. H. 1958. Fine structure of some invertebrate photoreceptors. *Annals of the New York Academy of Sciences* **74**, 204–9.

PALKA, J. 1965. Diffraction and visual acuity of insects. *Science* **149**, 551–3.

PART III

Receptor excitation. Quantum sensitivity

EXTRACELLULAR ASPECTS OF RECEPTOR EXCITATION IN THE DORSAL OCELLUS*

P. RUCK

Department of Zoology, University of Wisconsin, U.S.A.

IN A well-known study of the electroretinogram (ERG) of the compound eye in the water beetle *Dytiscus*, Bernhard (1942) showed that the action potential of the isolated ommatidial layer contains two negative components, a faster one, *R*, and a slower one, *S*. Both components survived the surgical removal of the optic ganglion and the application of cocaine. Bernhard surmised that if the two components could be isolated from one another they would appear as in Fig. 1 (top, right).

Autrum (1950) pointed out that the compound eyes of the walking stick, *Dixippus*, and the cricket, *Tachycines*, yield ERGs which contain the same two components.

Stieve (1960), working with the ERG of the isolated receptor layer of the compound eye in the hermit crab, *Eupagurus*, distinguished two negative components, *K* I and *K* II, and stated that they probably correspond to components *R* and *S* described by Bernhard. He suggested that *K* I is directly linked to a change in permeability of receptor membrane, whereas *K* II is a polarization phenomenon which arises secondarily as a consequence of the *K* I event.

Two components very similar to those just mentioned occur in ERGs of the dorsal ocelli in the cockroach, *Blaberus craniifer*, but the one corresponding to component *S* of Bernhard was overlooked completely in an analysis of the ocellar ERG which appeared several years ago (Ruck, 1961). A principal objective of this paper is to add the "missing" component to the ocellar ERG and to describe several of its properties.

The ocelli in *Blaberus* are relatively large organs, well suited for physiological studies. The axons of the photoreceptor cells make synaptic contact with dendrites of ocellar nerve fibers deep within the ocellar cup, and electrical contributions of receptor cells and postsynaptic units are recorded in the ERG of the normal, intact preparation. These ocelli lack colored shielding pigments altogether, and instead have a white tapetum.

* This work was begun in the Department of Biology, Tufts University, with support from NIH Grant E-547 and was continued at the University of Wisconsin with support from NSF Grant GB-127.

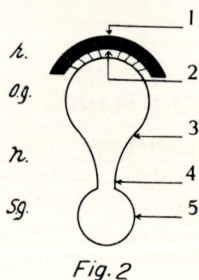

Fig. 2

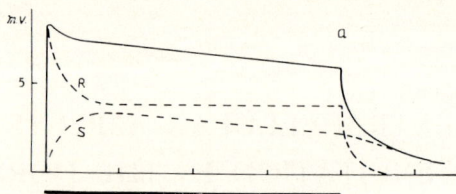

Fig. 13

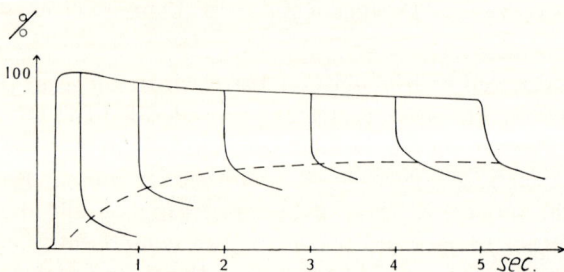

Fig. 8

FIG. 1

Includes Fig. 2, Fig. 8 and Fig. 13 from Bernhard (1942). Following are direct quotations of the legends of Bernhard's original figures. "Fig. 2. Schematic drawing of an eye prepared for an experiment with receptorial layer (r), optic ganglion (og), optic nerve (n), and supra-oesophageal ganglion (sg). The numbers 1–4 show the different loci used for the active electrode, whereas 5 is the constant locus of the reference electrode on the supra-oesophageal ganglion. Fig. 8. Diagram showing the course of fall of the retinal negativity towards the baseline after varying times of exposure. The dotted line shows the level to which the rapidly falling phase of the vanishing response drops at 'off'. The values are in per cent of the maximal amplitude of the retinal response. Fig. 13. a, analysis of the electroretinogram of the isolated compound eye (line drawn in full). Components drawn in broken lines, heavy black line indicates a stimulus of 20 sec."

In the work to be reported, an experimental preparation consists of an intact animal which is immobilized and positioned with the front of the head directed upward (Fig. 2). Two wax cups are built up on the front of the head, one around an ocellar cornea and the other around the base of an antenna. Each cup is connected through a saline-agar bridge with a well containing 3 M KCl and a Ag–AgCl electrode. When the antenna is cut off and a drop of insect saline is added to the wax cup, electrode E_3 (Fig. 2) makes electrical contact with the blood. When a portion of the ocellar cornea is excised and the ocellar cup is filled with saline, E_1 makes electrical contact with the distal surface of the receptor layer. (The basic insect saline which was used throughout had the following composition: NaCl, 140 mM; $CaCl_2$, 2 mM; $MgCl_2$ 2 mM; NaH_2PO_4, 6 mM; $KHCO_3$, 4 mM; sucrose, 134 mM.)

The ERG contains components which originate both in the receptor cell layer and in the postsynaptic units of the ocellar nerve (Ruck, 1961). In Fig. 3, the right column illustrates the ERGs obtained from an ocellus with its nerve intact. All response components characteristic of the normal preparation are present. In the left column of Fig. 3 appear responses from the ocellus of the opposite side of the same animal. The ocellar nerve on this side had been transected 3 days prior to the day of recording. (The cut had been made through a small slit in the exoskeleton of the front of the head, and then the

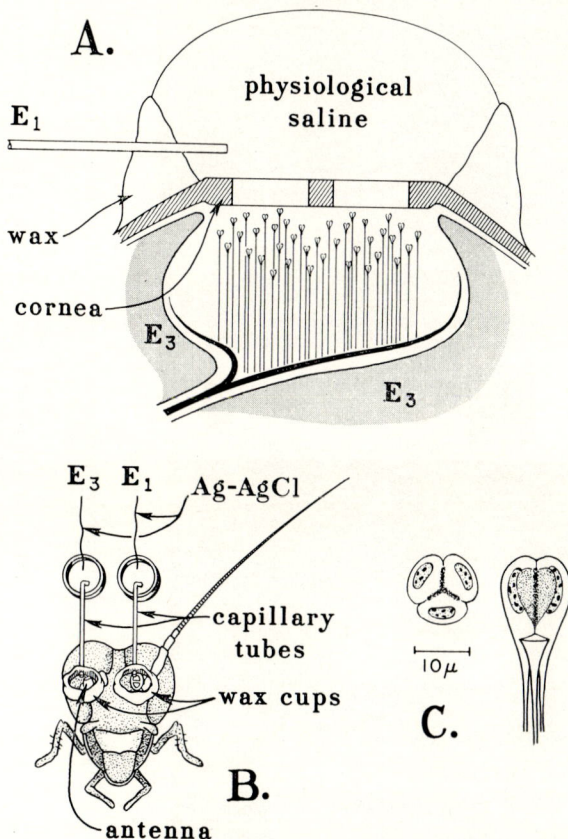

FIG. 2

A and B, Diagrams of ocellar preparation (*Blaberus*). E_1 and E_3 communicate with wax cups by way of capillary tubes filled with agar made up in physiological saline. Ag–AgCl wires extend from wells filled with 3 M KCl to input of DC preamplifier. Two pieces of cornea are removed; a bridge is left between them to help retain the soft parts of the ocellus. E_1 makes contact with the exposed surface of the receptor layer by way of the saline drop; E_3 makes contact with blood by way of the antennal stump. In A, receptor axons from several layers of retinulas extend downward to synapses with dendrites of ocellar nerve fibers. C, Cross and longitudinal sections of a retinula. Rhabdomeres stippled.

198 P. RUCK

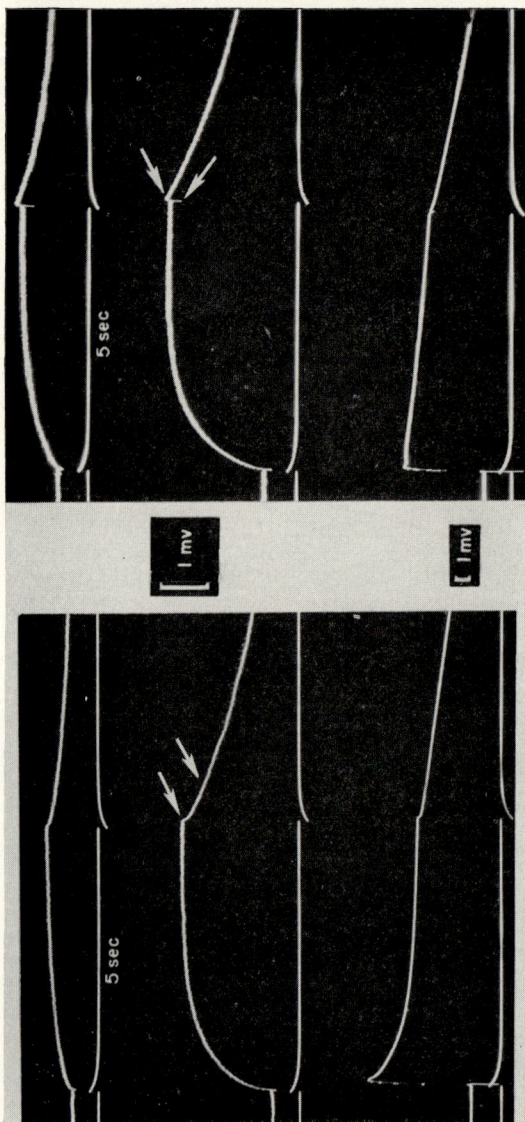

FIG. 3

ERGs from right ocellus (right column) and left ocellus (left column) of same animal (*Blaberus*). Right ocellar nerve intact; left ocellar nerve cut three days prior to recording. Recording situation similar to that in Fig. 2. Arrows in right column indicate postsynaptic off-components, which are absent in left column. Arrows in left column indicate fast and slow phases of the decline toward the baseline at "off". Negativity of E_1 (surface of receptor layer) gives upward deflection. Approximate corneal illumination (white light from tungsten lamp) for both columns: top, 0·07 footcandle; middle, 1 footcandle; bottom, 1000 footcandles. DC recording.

slit had been sealed with wax.) The responses of the right column contain off-components of postsynaptic origin (arrows), while the responses of the left column do not. In all other respects the two columns of responses are quite similar.

Cutting the ocellar nerve abolishes postsynaptic off-components and reveals two underlying phases in the descent of the ERG to baseline potential at "off", a rapid and a slow phase (arrows, left column). The responses of the left column are considered to originate solely in the summated activity of the retinula cells. The responses differ from those of the deganglionated compound eye of *Dytiscus* (Fig. 1) principally in that they have prominent cornea-positive on-effects. These on-effects (component 2 in the nomenclature of Ruck, 1961) are presumed to be an extracellulary recorded sign of depolarization of retinula cell axons.

The slow phase of the descent at "off" to baseline potential can be eliminated from the ERG by appropriate placement of the recording electrodes. This placement is shown in Fig. 4. A microelectrode (glass micropipette, tip diameter less than 1 μ, filled with 3 M KCl) is introduced through a small hole in the cornea and advanced to a deep position in the ocellar cup. The lead, E_1 vs. E_2, is the one in which the slow phase is eliminated (Figs. 5 and 6). The slow phase is present whenever a reference electrode (E_3) in the blood is used. It is present in leads E_1 vs. E_3 and E_2 vs. E_3, and it has the same electrical sign in both of these leads, i.e. the extracellular spaces inside the ocellar cup are negative with respect to the blood. The slow phase is eliminated in lead E_1 vs. E_2 because the extracellular spaces and the saline pool are isopotential with respect to the slow phase.

Extracellular spaces and saline pool are also isopotential, or nearly so, with respect to a large fraction of the sustained negativity during illumination, and also with respect to postsynaptic off-components. The latter, however, are removed by ocellar nerve section, whereas the former is not (Fig. 3). The slow phase at "off" is the concluding phase of a component whose wave-form is similar to that of Bernhard's component S in *Dytiscus* (Fig. 1). An estimate of the time course of this component may be obtained by subtracting in Fig. 5 and Fig. 6 a response in lead E_1 vs. E_2 from a corresponding response in lead E_1 vs. E_3.

The rapid phase at "off" is isolated in lead E_1 vs. E_2. It is the concluding phase of a component (similar to component R of Bernhard) which exists as an electrical dipole in the extracellular spaces together with their extension into the saline pool. This component, presumably the extracellularly recorded primary receptor potential of the retinula cells, is negative toward the cornea, but positive deep in the ocellar cup (Ruck, 1961). It is isolated together with a sharp on-effect whose dipolar field in the extracellular spaces is positive toward the cornea and negative deep in the ocellar cup, i.e. the reverse of the situation for the primary receptor potential. This on-effect, to reiterate, is

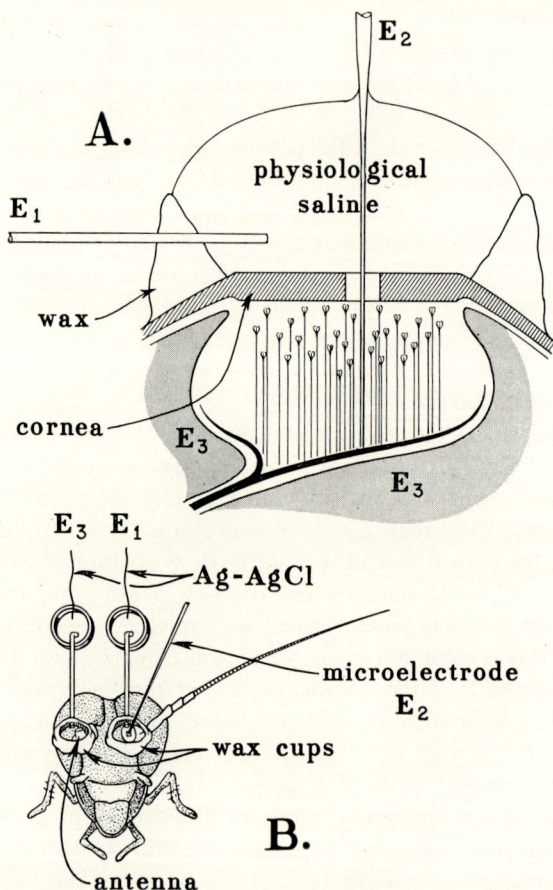

Fig. 4

Like Fig. 2 except that a third electrode, the micropipette E_2, has been added, and that a single, smaller hole has been cut through the cornea.

presumed to be an extracellularly recorded depolarization of the retinula cell axons (Ruck, 1961).

The component responsible for the slow decay at "off" remains after cutting the ocellar nerve in *Blaberus* (Fig. 3), after removing the optic ganglion from the compound eye in *Dytiscus* (Bernhard, 1942), and after isolating the layer of retinula cells in *Eupagurus* (Stieve, 1960). It remains also after applying cocaine to the optic ganglion in *Dytiscus* (Bernhard, 1942). Here it will be shown that it remains also in the ocellus of *Blaberus* after tetrodotoxin, from the puffer fish, has abolished the cornea-positive on-effect (of the retinula cell axons), and all postsynaptic activity. Tetrodotoxin has been shown to abolish selectively the increase in membrane sodium conductance associated with electrically excitable electrogenesis in a number of preparations (for references see Hagiwara and Nakajima, 1965).

A preparation similar to that of Fig. 2 was used in the tetrodotoxin experiments. Using lead E_1 vs. E_3, control responses in the basic saline (above) were obtained. Then the control saline was replaced by another which was identical except for containing either 10^{-5} gm/ml or 10^{-4} gm/ml of tetrodotoxin. After a suitable period of exposure to tetrodotoxin, recovery was followed in the control saline.

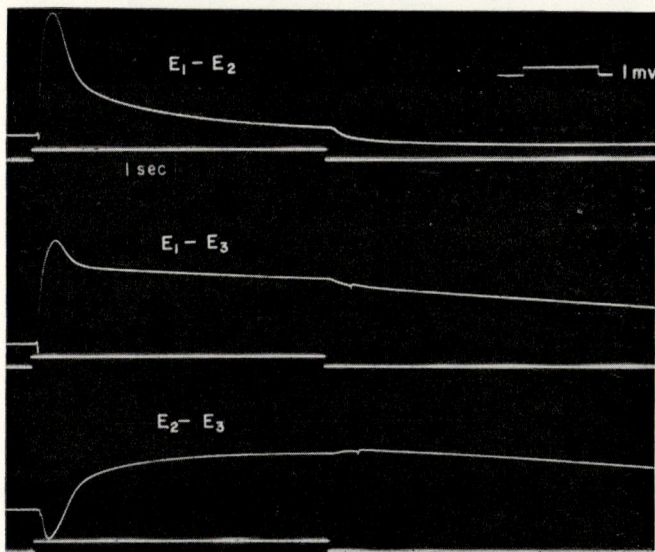

FIG. 5

ERGs of *Blaberus* ocellus recorded with electrodes placed as shown in Fig. 4. Approximate corneal illumination was 1000 footcandles, the same for all three records. Recordings were made one at a time, allowing sufficient time for recovery to the same state of adaptation following each stimulus. DC recording. In E_1 vs. E_2 and in E_1 vs. E_3, negativity of E_1 gives upward deflection. In E_2 vs. E_3, negativity of E_2 gives upward deflection. See text.

Figure 7 records features of a tetrodotoxin experiment. In the concentration range, 10^{-5} to 10^{-4} gm/ml, tetrodotoxin abolishes all components of the ERG except for cornea-negative components which originate in the layer of retinula cells.

One may conclude that the component responsible for the slow decay at "off" is not dependent upon either the postsynaptic elements of the ocellus or the elements (retinula cell axons) responsible for the cornea-positive on-effect. Whenever it is present, this component is accompanied by the primary receptor potential, i.e. the cornea-negative component which can be isolated in lead E_1 vs. E_2.

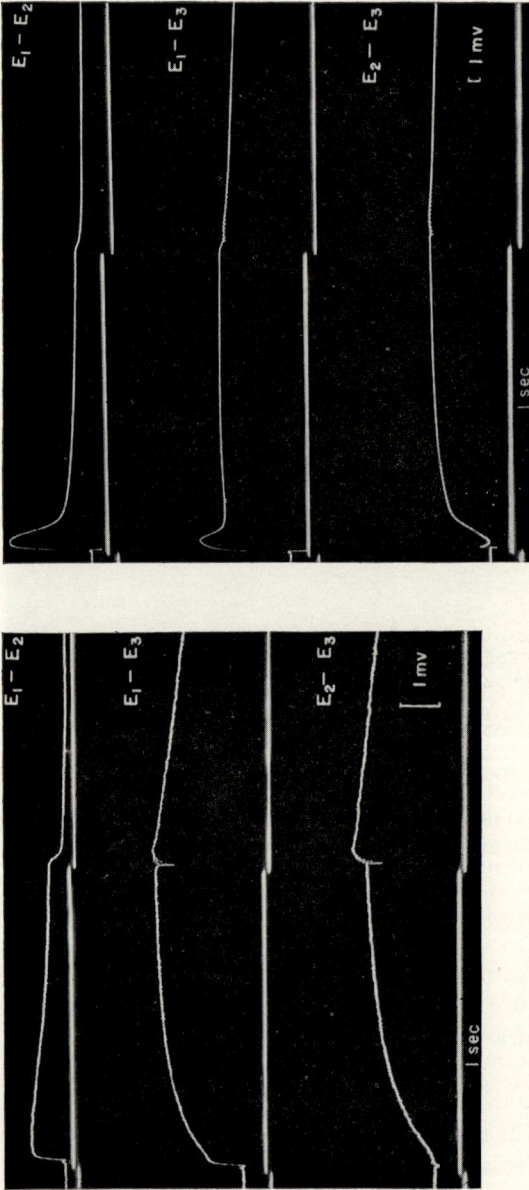

Fig. 6

ERGs of *Blaberus* ocellus with electrodes placed as shown in Fig. 4. Approximate corneal illuminations for left column, 0·1 footcandle, and for right column, 1000 footcandles. DC recording; polarity conventions as in Fig. 5. See text.

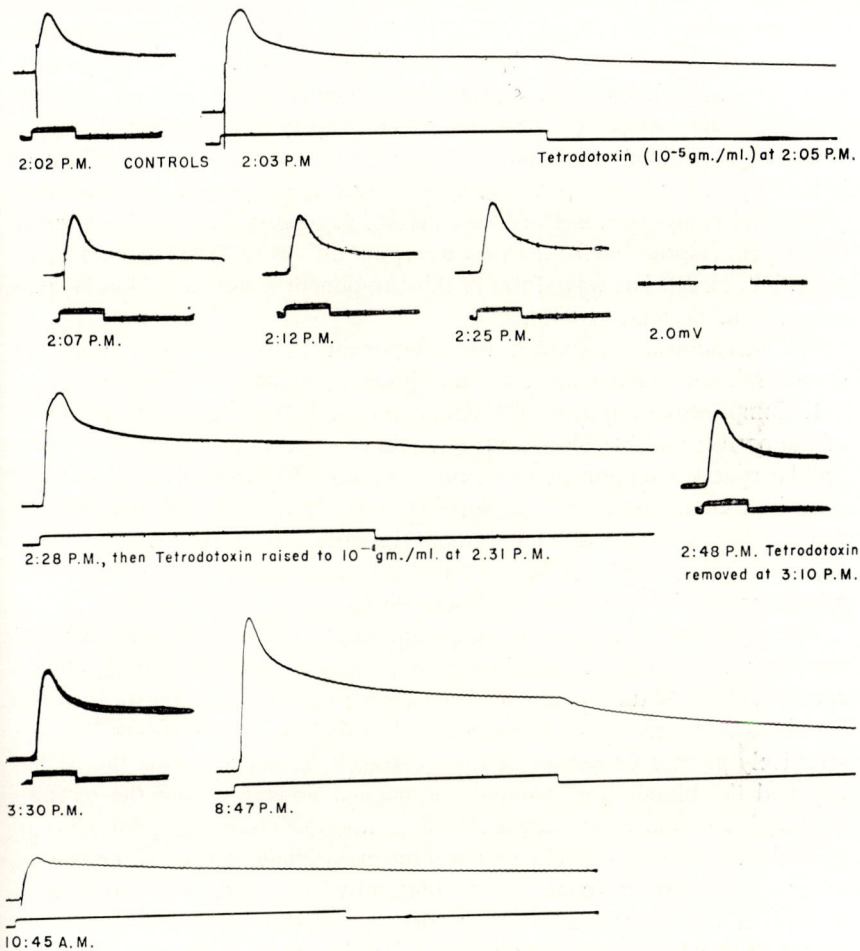

FIG. 7

Effect of tetrodotoxin on ocellar ERG of *Blaberus*. Preparation as in Fig. 2. Responses to stimuli of 1/8 sec duration (2:02, 2:07 p.m., etc.) were recorded as steady state responses with a stimulus repetition rate of one flash per 5 sec. Responses to stimuli of 1 sec duration (2:03, 2:28 p.m., etc.) were recorded after 1 min of dark-adaptation. Corneal illumination approximately 1000 footcandles for all stimuli. Control records at 2:02 and 2:03 p.m. were obtained with the basic physiological saline in the wax cup over the exposed receptor layer. After application of tetrodotoxin (2:05 p.m.) the cornea-positive on-effect quickly decreased in amplitude, whereas the cornea-negative components of the retinula cell layer response were little changed. After removal of tetrodotoxin and restoration of the control saline (3:10 p.m.), recovery was slow and incomplete. The last record shows, however, a partial return of the cornea-positive on-effect.

DISCUSSION

In an earlier study (Ruck, 1961) the dual nature of the cornea-negative responses of the retinula cell layer was not appreciated, and two components were subsumed under the designation component 1. The two components may be accommodated by subdividing the category of component 1 into 1a and 1b. Component 1a will refer to the cornea-negative component isolated in lead E_1 vs. E_2; it very probably corresponds to component R of Bernhard (1942) and component K I of Stieve (1960). Component 1b will refer to the component responsible for the slow decay at "off" as recorded in leads E_1 vs. E_3 and E_2 vs. E_3. The wave-form of this component is similar to that of component S of Bernhard (1942).

The mechanism responsible for component 1b is not understood, but several relevant statements concerning it can be made.

1. Component 1b appears as a potential drop between extracellular spaces of the ocellus and the blood, but not between two points within the extracellular spaces. Component 1b cannot, therefore, be explained as a potential drop in a circuit involving current flow into the retinula cells distally, out through their axons, and back through the extracellular spaces. Component 1a, on the other hand, can be attributed to a potential drop across the extracellular spaces in such a circuit (Ruck, 1961).

2. Component 1b appears to be a trans-sheath potential dependent somehow upon the events associated with component 1a. A number of hypotheses concerning the nature of this dependence is possible. Component 1b might be a kind of concentration cell potential in which the neural sheath acts as a selectively permeable barrier between extracellular spaces inside the ocellar cup and the blood. For example, the current flowing during the receptor potential, component 1a, might include a fraction representing an efflux of potassium ions from retinula cells into the extracellular spaces. If the volume of the extracellular spaces were sufficiently restricted, the extracellular potassium ion concentration might rise appreciably. Associated with this would go an increase in potassium concentration gradient directed across the ocellar sheath from extracellular spaces toward the blood. Given a relatively greater restraint upon anion movements than upon those of potassium, a trans-sheath potential with extracellular spaces negative to the blood could result. An hypothesis of this general type may be implicit in Stieve's (1960) comments with respect to component K II of the isolated *Eupagurus* retina. Thus far no tests of such an hypothesis have been reported.

Component 1b could be associated with the active transport of anion. For example, illumination might initiate the transport of a species of anion from the blood across the ocellar sheath into the extracellular spaces. Once again there has been no test of this kind of hypothesis.

It would be of great interest to observe the intracellular counterpart, if any, of component 1b in the ocellar retinula cells, but attempts to do so in our laboratory have been unsuccessful thus far. Also, the role of component 1b in sensory functions such as light and dark adaptation remains to be evaluated.

In conclusion, it is interesting to point out the virtual absence of a tetrodotoxin effect on the receptor potential, component 1a. It is certain that the toxin diffuses to points deeper than the distal ends of the retinulas, for all components which originate in the deep layers of the ocellus are abolished by tetrodotoxin.

ACKNOWLEDGEMENT

The assistance of Dr. H. David Potter in the experiments with tetrodotoxin is gratefully acknowledged.

REFERENCES

AUTRUM, H. 1950. Die Belichtungspotentiale und das Sehen der Insekten (Untersuchungen an Calliphora und Dixippus). *Z. vergleich. Physiol.* **32**, 176–227.

BERNHARD, C. G. 1942. Isolation of retinal and optic ganglion response in the eye of *Dytiscus. J. Neurophysiol.* **5**, 32–48.

HAGIWARA, S. and NAKAJIMA, S. 1965. Tetrodotoxin and manganese ion: Effects on action potential of the frog heart. *Science* **149**, 1254–5.

RUCK, P. 1961. Electrophysiology of the insect dorsal ocellus. I. Origin of the components of the electroretinogram. *J. Gen. Physiol.* **44**, 605–27.

STIEVE, A. 1960. Elektrophysiologische Untersuchungen des Auges von *Eupagurus bernhardus* L. *Helgeländer Wissenschaftliche Meeresuntersuchungen,* **7**, 149–88.

ORIGIN OF ELECTRICAL RESPONSES IN THE EYE OF *PERIPLANETA AMERICANA**

M. L. WOLBARSHT, H. G. WAGNER†

U.S. Naval Medical Research Institute, Bethesda, Maryland, U.S.A.

and

D. BODENSTEIN

Department of Biology, University of Virginia, Charlottesville, Virginia, U.S.A.

INTRODUCTION

WHEN the electroretinogram (ERG) was first discovered a century ago by Holmgren (1865–6), it was thought to represent activity in the optic nerve only. However, the years that followed have made plain that it was more likely a summed potential reflecting the activities of several different types of cells present in the retina, the optic nerve, and adjacent structures. Workers on the vertebrate eye have directed their efforts towards isolation of the various components of this compound ERG. The assignment of components to particular sites of generation within the visual system has been a particular subject of long debate. Indeed, the recent review by Tomita (1963) indicates the lack of any precise knowledge about what any particular intraretinal potential contributes to the vertebrate ERG. In invertebrate eyes, and in particular in insect compound eyes, there is possibly a better chance for success since there are fewer cell types and those cell types are relatively more isolated spatially one from the other.

The compound eyes of some insects show a relatively simple corneal negativity when illuminated, while others have a complex multiphasic response. The variations among species are great. However, Autrum (1958) has suggested that most insects can be separated into two divisions. One division, primarily the jumping, crawling insects like *Periplaneta* and *Tachycines*, has a relatively simple negative potential which maintains itself more or less and returns to the baseline after the light is extinguished. The other

* This article was prepared at Bethesda, Maryland, with the sponsorship of the U.S. Navy. Reproduction for the purpose of the United States Government is permitted from the Bureau of Medicine and Surgery, Navy Department, Research Task MR-005.13-1500.05. Part of the work reported here was supported by the National Science Foundation: grant no. G 21759. The opinions or assertions expressed herein are the private ones of the author and are not to be construed as official or reflecting the views of the Navy Department or the naval service at large.

† Dr. Wagner's present address is: Director, Aerospace Crew Equipment Laboratory, Naval Air Engineering Center, Philadelphia, Pennsylvania, 19112, U.S.A.

group is made up of fast flying insects, examples of which are *Calliphora* and *Apis*. The eyes of these when illuminated give rise to a complex waveform with striking positive-going spikes both at onset and extinction of light. Autrum (1958) also claimed that the two groups are separable on the basis of their flicker fusion frequencies. The members of the first group had flicker fusion frequencies (FFF) below 60 c/s, while the second group could resolve flicker above 200 c/s. It has become convenient to term these groups as slow and fast eyes, respectively. Autrum was struck by the observation that in the fast eyes the optic lobes were well developed and anatomically close to the retinal cell layer; while in the slow eyes the ganglion layers were either smaller or further removed from the retinal eye cells. He proposed that this relationship might be the key to the differences in FFF and the other features of the ERG.

The significance of the ganglionic layers to the generation of the ERG has been a subject of speculation since Adrian's work (1937). A number of studies (reviewed by Dethier, 1963) have been focused on just what happens if the ganglion layers are removed surgically or blocked by the use of some pharmacological agent, or if the electrodes are placed so that the recording system is able to ignore currents arising from the ganglion layers.

Bernhard (1942) in his work on the fast eye of the water beetle, *Dytiscus*, used several methods for isolating the components of the ERG. First, he placed his recording electrodes in various locations within the optic pathway in such a way as to most favorably record the electrical activity of the different structures. He excised the optic lobe (a technique used previously with inconclusive results by Roeder, 1940), and finally he used cocaine as an anesthetic to block the operation of the post-receptor elements. With each of these methods he found a relatively simple negative wave arising in the retinula layer, similar to that observed in the slow eyes lacking the ganglionic masses close to the retina.

Autrum and Hoffman (1960) found that the multiphasic ERG in the fast eye of *Calliphora* lost its steep "on" and "off" responses and became a simple negative wave when the insect was made anoxic. They reasoned that the component of the ERG most resistant to anoxia would be that arising from the retinula cells. In the same series of experiments they observed that the effects of nicotine applied to the optic ganglion, or excision of this structure, were equivalent to the effects of anoxia. Also, Hartline and his co-workers in 1952 reported approximately the same results from their optic lobe ablation experiments in *Musca*. It might be wondered why uncertainty persists in spite of these generally consistent results.

In each of these experiments it has always been possible that the changes were traceable to the injury rather than truly significant of the role of the optic lobe. It is difficult to conceive of an experimental approach which is completely free of objections of this sort. The simplicity of the intraretinal responses to light compared to the complexity of the ERG suggests that some of the complexities in the latter arise as a result of changes in the conductive pathways during the course of stimulation rather than in changes in the generating waveform. Confidence in our conclusions may have to rest on a number of approaches which differ in principle but lead to a similar conclusion.

Our experiments (previously presented in abstract form, Wagner and Wolbarsht, 1963) took advantage of the ability to graft an excised adult eye, devoid of optic ganglia, to another part of the body, where, after a period of some months acceptance of the graft and recovery of the animal was complete, the ERG could be re-examined and compared with that from the normal compound eye. Also, we used an anesthetic (CO_2) that could be applied without any surgical manipulations. The eyes during the experiment had normal circulation and adequate intact tracheation for respiration. These experiments on the "slow" eye of the cockroach provided additional data consistent with previous conclusions about the role of the optic ganglion and its effect upon the form of the ERG.

METHODS

All experiments were performed on the lateral (compound) eyes of the adult American cockroach, *Periplaneta americana*. In certain of the experiments the eyes examined had been previously transplanted onto the legs of younger nymphs and allowed to molt in synchrony with their new host several times. In these animals the eyes of adult individuals were transplanted into the ventral coxal surfaces of the third thoracic legs of 7th or 8th stage nymphs in the following manner. The eye was excised from the donor animal with as little of the optic ganglion as possible by cutting the eye from the optic stalk as close to the retinula cells as possible. The eye was then placed into its new position on the leg (Fig. 1E), after a portion of the ventral coxal skin and some of the underlying leg muscles were removed. A ring of wax held the eye in its new location. Care was taken to insure that all surfaces to which the wax had to adhere were dry and that no air remained in the wound between transplant and the host tissue. After transplantation, the hosts were allowed to molt twice, at which time they usually became adults. Only adult animals, about 2 months after the initial operation, were used for the electrophysiological experiments.

For recording purposes the animal was immobilized in a mount made of Tacky wax. The electrodes were cotton wicks soaked in insect Ringer's solution in contact with silver-chloride-coated silver rods. The indifferent electrode was placed on the mouth parts or adjacent to the cornea of the eye from which the recordings were made. The recording electrode was placed on the cornea of the eye which had been previously shaved slightly to remove the waxy coat and insure good electrical contact. A direct-coupled cathode follower input stage was used with an input impedance of approximately 500 megohms. This input stage (as shown in Fig. 2) was designed for us by

C.E.—P

Professor E. F. MacNichol, Jr. to be operated with a high-gain DC transistor amplifier (MacNichol and Bickart, 1958). It is quite stable and non-microphonic. The rest of the system was direct-coupled throughout and conventional recording techniques were used. The optical stimulator has been described in detail previously (Wagner *et al.*, 1960).

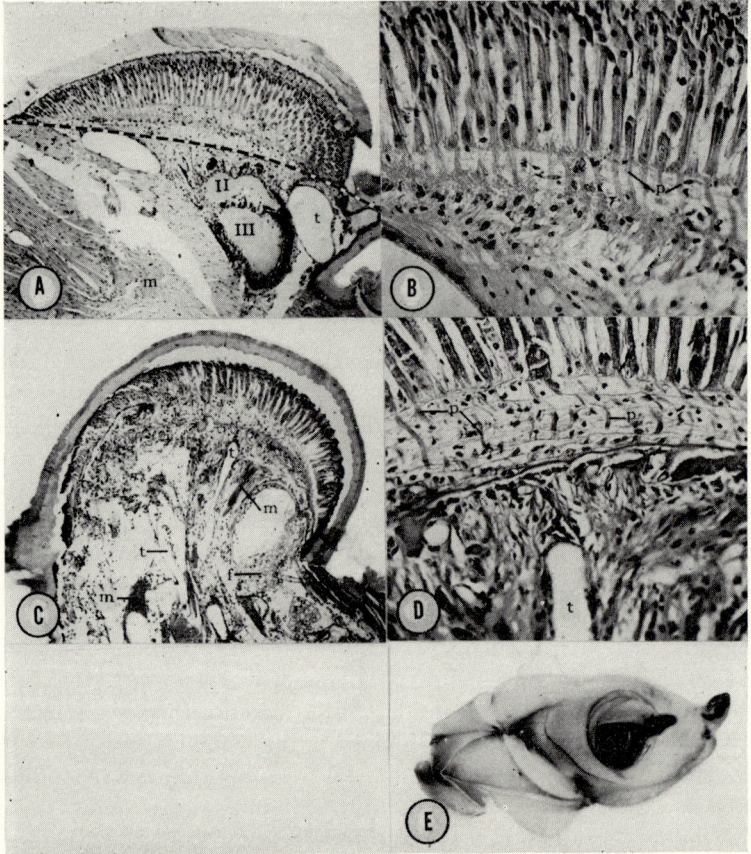

FIG. 1

Various views of the compound eye of *Periplaneta americana*. A, Cross-section of the normal eye. B, Enlargement of A in the region of the basement membrane. C, A cross-section through a transplanted eye approximately two months after the operation. D, Enlargement of C in the region of the basement membrane (compare with B). E, Photograph of the whole mount of an eye transplanted into the ventral coxal surface of a third thoracic leg after two post-operative molts. This is the same eye whose histological sections are shown in C and D. Note the distal parts of this leg (femur, tibia and tarsus) are missing. Roman numerals, II and III, the second and third optic ganglia. *F*, fat body. *M*, muscles. *P*, post-retinal fibers. *T*, trachea. See text for other details.

The CO_2 gas used for anesthesia was administered either from a tank of dry CO_2 or by placing solid CO_2 ice in water and allowing the resultant gas to flow onto the animal. The responses resulting from the two types of CO_2 administration were not noticeably different.

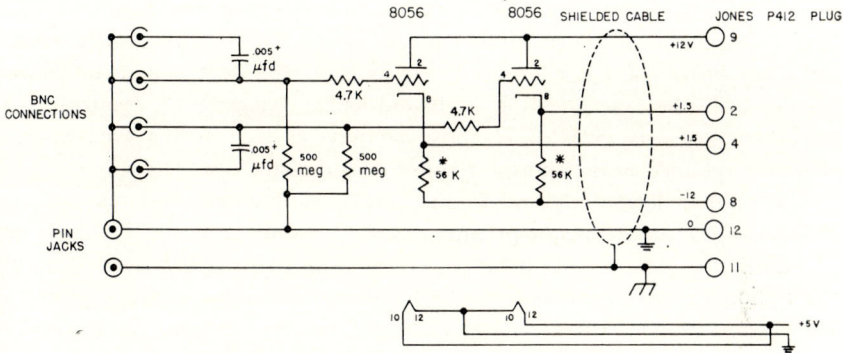

NOTES

+ Polystyrene or similar low leakage capacitor.

* Metal film resistor.

Circuit ($\perp$) and chassis grounds should be isolated, they should be connected through the pin jacks, if recording conditions require it.

FIG. 2

Cathode follower probe for transistor preamplifier (MacNichol and Bickart, 1958). One modification must be made to the original amplifier circuit. The two bias batteries must be reversed so that the negative terminals are connected to pins 1 and 3 (instead of 2 and 4 as shown in the original circuit diagram). In constructing this probe, care should be taken to mount all components on a plastic card which is loosely connected to the input and output leads. Limp paper packing material should be used to support the card to insulate it against low frequency shocks. The nuvister tubes (type 8056) themselves are quite resistant to noise in the audio range. The filament voltage should be about 5 V and one side of the supply must be grounded. The 4·7 K resistor in the grid circuit is to reduce television interference as discussed in Wolbarsht and Dethier (1958). It should be a low noise, low capacitance composition type.

After completion of the electrophysiological experiments, the eyes were fixed in alcoholic Bouin's solution, embedded in paraffin, and cut in sections $7\,\mu$ thick. The sections were stained with hematoxylin and eosin, and examined to correlate their histological appearance with the electrophysiological findings.

NATURE OF THE TRANSPLANTED EYES

Figure 1A illustrates the histology of the normal eye. The dashed line passing through the section marks the plane of the cut used in preparing the transplant. This plane passes through the outer layers of the lamina ganglionaris proximal to the fenestrated basement membrane. Figure 1B (the same section at higher magnification) gives greater detail in the region of the lamina ganglionaris. These should be compared with Fig. 1C and D which show the histological appearance of equivalent sections through the transplanted eye. The exact location of the cut which separated the eye from the ganglionic mass is revealed in those sections as well as the type of eye structure retained in the transplant after its removal from the donor.

The cellular structure distal to the lamina ganglionaris has retained its normal appearance while the proximal tissues are quite different. It should be noted that the graft is well tracheated. There is no evidence of regeneration of the optic ganglia. In the same section one can see some apparently newly regenerated muscles and an aggregation of fat cells. The latter are normally found in the coxal region of the legs. In preparing the transplantation site many coxal muscles were cut, but the muscle fragments which were left at this time in the wound region are no longer found. Apparently all wound debris has been absorbed.

One can also see in the experimental eye (Fig. 1D), the proximal processes of the retinula cells (post-retinal fibers) as they pass through the region normally occupied by the lamina ganglionaris. Here a majority of these fibers would have synapsed. The remainder of the fibers normally synapse at the second optic ganglion. However, in the absence of the lamina ganglionaris and the second optic ganglion, the retinula cell fibers have continued growing until they merge with the leg nerve. At present, we are not certain where these retinula fibers, which now grow into the leg nerve, do end.

ELECTROPHYSIOLOGICAL RESPONSES OF NORMAL EYES

The electrical response of the normal eye to light is shown in the top record of Fig. 3. The response is primarily a sustained negative potential. After an initial rapidly rising negative peak ("on" effect), the potential settles to a lower level and maintains itself throughout the stimulus duration. Upon the extinction of light there is a small "off" effect consisting of a negative spike somewhat similar to the initial "on" peak. This is followed by an exponential-like return to the resting level. The spike-like background noise was present in the record in light and dark and did not seem to be correlated with the light stimulus. A small initial positive spike present at the beginning of the stimulus may also be part of the "on" response. It was not present in every record, possibly because of masking from the spike-like background. For the present, we have treated it as an artifact; more study may reveal that there is indeed a positive wave that is part of the "on" response.

The ERG described above differs somewhat from the responses mentioned by Walther (1958) and Ruck (1958). Neither author reported a distinct "on" or "off" response. This may have resulted from their use of somewhat lower light intensities and shorter stimuli. It is possible that our "on" response corresponds to the peak seen in some of the records obtained by Walther when he stimulated with red light under a light adapted condition. His conditions were similar to ours in that our animals were light adapted and the stimulus was from a tungsten lamp with a color temperature of 2900° K. The short stimuli used by both of them in comparison with ours may account for the absence of the "off" effect in their records.

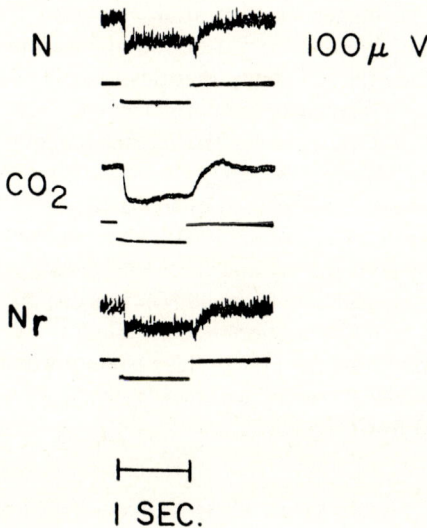

Fig. 3

Normal electrical responses from a normal compound eye, *Periplaneta americana*, to light stimulus. N is the normal response; CO_2, the response of the same eye during anesthesia with carbon dioxide gas; and NR is the recovery following the return of the normal atmosphere. The light stimulus is indicated by the downward pulse in the lower trace of each recording. Stimulus intensity is 3500 $\mu W/cm^2$. Voltage calibrations apply to the magnitude of the step in the light stimulus trace.

Following the lead used by Autrum and Hoffman (1960), we attempted to alter the ERG by changing the gaseous environment of the insect. This can be done without changing the other experimental conditions radically. We selected CO_2, which is used frequently as insect anesthetic, as an alternative to simple anoxia (100% N_2), since the CO_2 acts more quickly and has a specific nervous action. The effects of CO_2 anesthesia are shown in Fig. 3, middle recording. Both the "on" and "off" responses have disappeared. The absence of background activity suggests a muscular or nervous origin for it. The "on" and "off" responses apparently arise in portions of the optic pathway that are susceptible to anesthesia. They may represent conducted impulses from the retinal cells or activity in the lamina ganglionaris and optic lobe. During anesthesia the ERG has a much slower rise time but the potential is still maintained during illumination. The response following the cessation of illumination lacks the "off" response but has a similar exponential return to the baseline. The recovery of the normal response, shown in the lower trace, rapidly follows restoration of the normal atmosphere.

The action of CO_2 as a general anesthetic in insects has been studied extensively by Boistel (1960). He showed that its activity is different from simple anoxia because, at low concentration (less than 15%), it produces hyperexcitability. At higher concentrations narcosis results. The action potentials disappear about 30 sec after the application of CO_2. Boistel's work seems to exclude the possibility that this is a pH effect. Upon removal to a CO_2 free atmosphere, recovery to normal activity occurs within a minute. During the period of CO_2 narcosis the resting potential of the neuron is depressed from 68 mV to 55 mV.

Carbon dioxide anesthesia was used by Leutscher-Hazelhoff and Kuiper in their study of the eye of *Calliphora* (1964). They reported a cessation of all spike activity almost immediately and the ERG underwent a drastic change. In particular, the waveform in the ganglion opticus disappeared and what was left was reversed in sign and monophasic although the waveform across the sense cells was hardly impaired at all. This response which they identified as "the peripheral response" resembled closely the response we observed in *Periplaneta* exposed to CO_2 gas.

ELECTROPHYSIOLOGICAL RESPONSES OF TRANSPLANTED EYES

The ERG of the transplanted eye seems to be of a lower amplitude than that seen in the normal eye. A typical record is shown in the lower trace of Fig. 4. For comparison, responses of the normal eye and the normal eye under the influence of CO_2 anesthesia are shown in the top and middle records of this figure.

The ERG of the transplanted eye resembles that of the normal eye in that it is a sustained negative potential but in detail it is even closer to the ERG of the anesthetized eye. The most obvious differences from the normal ERG are the more sluggish rise time and the absence of both "on" and "off" peaks.

Since in these transplants histological examination discloses the absence of the lamina ganglionaris and the optic ganglia, it is not unreasonable to assume that the disappearance of these features in the ERG can be directly correlated with the loss of these structures.

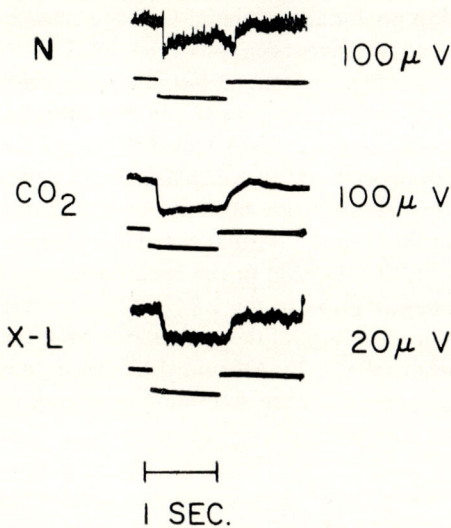

FIG. 4

Electrophysiological responses of normal and transplanted eyes, *Periplaneta americana*, to light stimulus. N is the response of the normal eye. CO_2, the same eye while under carbon dioxide anesthesia. X-L indicates the electrical response of the transplanted eye. The duration of light stimulus is indicated by the downward pulse of the lower trace in each set of records. Stimulus intensity is 4260 $\mu W/cm^2$ for X-L, and 3500 $\mu W/cm^2$ for N and CO_2. Voltage calibrations apply to the magnitude of the step in the light stimulus trace.

The similarity of the ERG of the transplant to that of the anesthetized eye suggests that CO_2 suppressed functional activity in a ganglion comparable to the removal of the ganglia.

The surgical extirpation of the optic ganglion in other species produces similar changes in the response waveform (Bernhard, 1942; Hartline *et al.*, 1952; Autrum and Hoffman, 1960). From this it would seem to follow that the "on" and "off" responses were simple additions to a fundamental potential and had their origin in the ganglia themselves. It may be safe to assume that the simple potential remaining after these various procedures was related to activity in the retinula cells. It is less valid to assume that the simple potential observed is identical to the fundamental component contributed by the retinula cells to the ERG. We can not be sure that the retinula cells were otherwise unchanged by these procedures, nor can we be sure that the retinula cells were only responsible for the simple or fundamental components observed. We are confident that more than one event is taking place in the retinula cells when excited by light. The large intracellular slow potential change has been studied extensively (Burkhardt, 1962) and is thought to be directly related to at least a part of the ERG. We can not be certain that there is a conducted action potential associated with the retinula cell of the cockroach. Action potentials have been observed in *Apis* (Naka, 1961). The possibility should be excluded that a retinula cell component capable of affecting the electrodes was so sensitive to the procedures that it degenerated quickly and completely without disturbing the remainder of the response. The axons of the retinula cells of the transplanted eyes appeared to be healthy. Their function, if any, should have been as good or better (because of their greater length) than those in the normal eye. This suggests that the impulses from the retinula cells (if produced in the cockroach eyes as in *Apis*) do not make a significant contribution to the ERG of the normal eye. As has been mentioned earlier, the waveform of the normal eye is not that of a typical slow eye. But the conclusions drawn by Autrum (1958) seem to be valid in that the extraretinal elements present are the determinants of additional complications in the ERG.

DISCUSSION

It is generally accepted that the retinula cells have a primary role in the visual process and that it begins with the absorption of light by the photopigment concentrated in the rhabdom. The sequence of events thus initiated includes local currents in the retinula cells and their surroundings which are ultimately picked up by the recording electrodes as well as conducted changes along axons, synapses to other neurons which also set up currents to add to the potentials observed by the recording electrodes. The action of light in some way leads to a change in membrane permeability, probably the membrane of the rhabdom itself. The increase in ionic current flow away from this surface follows conducting pathways which are dependent upon the location of the sink and the conductances present in the media. It is unlikely that all the conductance pathways are purely passive. Since the extracellular volume is quite limited, it must be assumed that an appreciable current passes through cells and across membranes. The glia already are suspected of active participation (Svaetichin *et al.*, 1961). The recording electrodes are at some distance from the respective sources and sinks. They see only a small fraction of the total current but it is important to recognize that they may detect changes in the conductance pathways as well as changes in the generator potentials. Under these circumstances the potential at the electrodes may not be a miniature copy of a simple potential developed in a retinula cell.

As seen by an external electrode, the slowest components are those produced in the primary cells. This is rather strange and perhaps it indicates the electroretinogram does not truly reflect the intracellular transmission of information through the primary sense cells in the retina. Perhaps further investigations with intracellular micropipettes on transplanted eyes will tell us what the contribution of each cell type is with more certainty.

REFERENCES

ADRIAN, E. D. 1937. Synchronized reactions in the optic lobe of *Dytiscus. J. Physiol.* **91**, 66–89.

AUTRUM, H. 1958. Electrophysiological analysis of the visual system in insects. *Exp. Cell Res.* Suppl. **5**, 426–39.

AUTRUM, H. and HOFFMAN, C. 1960. Diphasic and monophasic responses in the compound eye of *Calliphora. J. Insect Physiol.* **4**, 122–7.

BERNHARD, G. G. 1942. Isolation of retinal and optic ganglion response in the eye of *Dytiscus. J. Neurophysiol.* **5**, 32–48.

BODENSTEIN, D. 1962. Humoral conditions and cellular interactions in the development of the insect eye. In *Insect Physiology* (V. Brooks, Ed.). Oregon State Univ. Press, Corvallis, 110 pp.

BOISTEL, J. 1960. *Charactéristiques fonctionnelles des fibres nerveuses et des récepteurs tactiles ou olfactifs des Insectes.* Librarie Arnette, Paris, 147 pp.

BURKHARDT, D. 1962. Spectral sensitivity and other response characteristics of single visual cells. *Symp. Soc. Exp. Biol.* **16**, 86–109.

DETHIER, V. G. 1963. *The Physiology of Insect Senses.* Methuen, London, 266 pp.

HARTLINE, H. K., WAGNER, H. G. and MACNICHOL, E. F., Jr. 1952. The peripheral origin of nervous activity in the visual system. *Cold Spring Harbor Symp. Quant. Biol.* **17**, 125–41.

HOLMGREN, Fr. 1865–6. Method att objektivera effecten af ljusintryck på retina. *Upsala läkaref. förh.* **1**, 177–91.

LEUTSCHER-HAZELHOFF, J. T. and KUIPER, J. 1964. Responses of the blow fly (*Calliphora erythrocephala*) to light flashes and to sinusoidally modulated light. In *Flicker* (H. E. Henkes and L. H. van der Tweel, Eds.). Dr. W. Junk Publishers, The Hague, 540 pp.

MACNICHOL, E. F., Jr. and BICKART, T. 1958. The use of transistors in physiological amplifiers. *I.R.E. Trans. on Med. Elect.* **PGME-10**, 15–24.

NAKA, K. 1961. Recording of retinal action potentials from single cells in the insect compound eye. *J. Gen. Physiol.* **44**, 571–84.

ROEDER, K. D. 1940. The origin of visual rhythms in the grasshopper, *Melanoplus femurrubrum. J. Cell. Comp. Physiol.* **16**, 399–401.

RUCK, P. 1958. A comparison of the electrical responses of compound eyes and dorsal ocelli in four insect species. *J. Insect Physiol.* **2**, 261–74.

SVAETICHIN, G., LAUFER, M., MITARAI, G., FATEHCHAND, R., VALLECALLE, E. and VILLEGAS, J. 1961. Glial control of neuronal networks and receptors. In *The Visual System: Neurophysiology and Psychophysics* (R. Jung and H. Kornhuber, Eds.). Springer-Verlag, Berlin, 524 pp.

TOMITA, T. 1963. Electrical activity in the vertebrate retina. *J. Opt. Soc. Amer.* **53**, 49–57.

WAGNER, H. G., MACNICHOL, E. F., JR. and WOLBARSHT, M. L. 1960. The response properties of single ganglion cells in the goldfish retina. *J. Gen. Physiol.* **43** (6): (supplement) 45–62.

WAGNER, H. G. and WOLBARSHT, M. L. 1963. Electrical responses from transplanted insect eyes. *Fed. Proc.* **22** (2), Pt. 1, 519.

WALTHER, J. B. 1958. Changes induced in spectral sensitivity and form of retinal action potential of the cockroach eye by selective adaptation. *J. Imsect Physiol.* **2**, 142–51.

WOLBARSHT, M. L. and DETHIER, V. G. 1958. Electrical activity in the chemoreceptors of the blow fly. I. Responses to chemical and mechanical stimulation. *J. Gen. Physiol.* **42**, 393–412.

ELECTRICAL POTENTIAL FIELD IN EYE AND OPTIC LOBE OF LOCUST: POTENTIAL VARIATIONS AND CHANGES IN VISUAL THRESHOLD DURING LIGHT- AND DARK-ADAPTATION

E. T. Burtt, W. T. Catton and D. J. Cosens

Departments of Zoology and Physiology, University of Newcastle upon Tyne, England

Many previous studies of electrical changes in insect eyes in response to illumination have been made. These have been reviewed recently by Ruck (1962, 1964), and will be referred to only in the course of the following brief description of recent work by the three authors named above.

I. ELECTRICAL POTENTIAL FIELD IN EYE AND OPTIC LOBE: EFFECTS OF LIGHT- AND DARK-ADAPTATION

Using glass micropipette electrodes of 1–5 MΩ resistance, the profile of steady d.c. potential along the axis of the eye and optic lobe of the locust and several other insect species was recorded (Burtt and Catton, 1964a).

The Potential Profile of the Eye and Optic Lobe

With a large indifferent electrode in the body of the insect the micro-pipette was inserted through a hole in the centre of the cornea and advanced by micrometer along the axis of the eye. The characteristic profile of potential (Fig. 1) showed negativity near the cornea and positivity in the zone of retinula cells (10–15 mV) followed by a rapid negative swing to reach a peak of negativity (60–70 mV) coincident with the first region of synapses (lamina ganglionaris). Further negative peaks were found to be associated with the second and third synaptic regions in the optic lobes of *Locusta*, *Schistocerca*, *Aeschna*, *Periplaneta* and *Phormia*. Brief interruption of the light falling on the eye evoked transient off-deflexions, which were positive in the ommatidial zone and negative at points deeper than the basement membrane. No transient deflexions could be obtained in the vicinity of the basement membrane itself. The negative peaks could be eliminated by crushing the optic lobe or by subjecting it to anoxia (tracheal blockage, nitrogen atmosphere), or by treatment with 0·2 % sodium azide solution (cf. Fig. 2). When this was done the transient deflexions were abolished. Dark-adaptation increased the positivity in the ommatidial zone, but had little effect on the peak potential. Transition from steady state light-adaptation to steady state dark-adaptation increased the p.d. between ommatidial zone and negative peak by 20–40%. The possibility was considered that the photoreceptor cells in insect eyes are subjected to a strong d.c. bias, which enhances their sensitivity in a manner analogous to that of the standing potential in the mammalian cochlea (discussed in Burtt and Catton, 1964a).

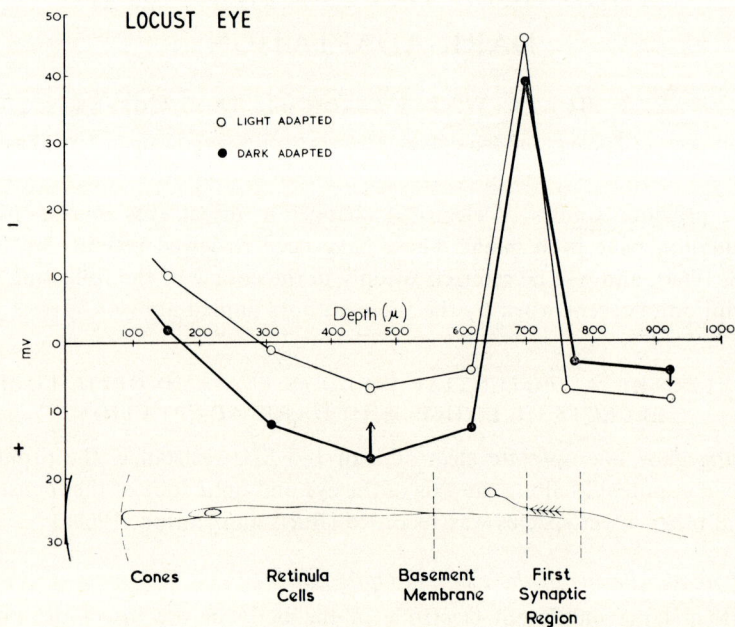

FIG. 1

Potential profiles of locust eye and optic lobe taken to a depth of 1000 μ. A schematic diagram of the optical, photoreceptor and neural elements along the axis of penetration appears below. The arrows show the direction of the on-transient in response to sudden illumination.

The origin of the negative peak in the lamina ganglionaris was considered to be due most likely to penetration by the electrode of large glial cells, such as have been shown to occur in the ganglia of certain insect species, e.g. *Rhodnius* (Wigglesworth, 1959). Large glial cells in some fish eyes are implicated in the production of slow potentials related to the level of illumination (*S*-potentials of Svaetichin (1952)). No specific function could be allocated to the negative peaks in the second and third synaptic layers.

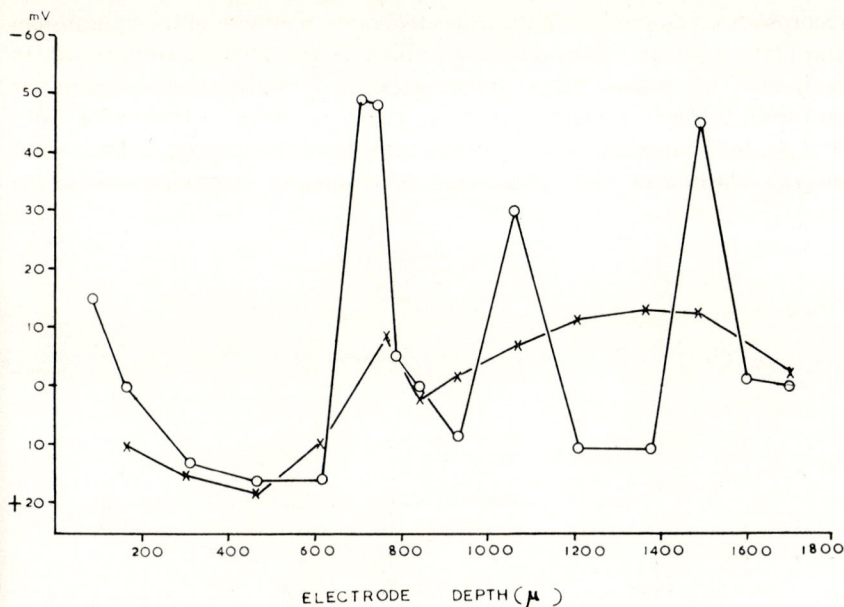

FIG. 2

Potential profiles of locust eye and optic lobe to a depth of 1800 μ. $\bigcirc$, normal; $\times$, after injection of 0·2% sodium azide solution. Each negative peak corresponds to a synaptic region.

II. POTENTIAL VARIATIONS ASSOCIATED WITH LIGHT- AND DARK-ADAPTATION

These were investigated over periods of time (5–10 min) long enough to ensure fairly complete adaptation, at different depths in the eye and optic lobe, and with and without subjecting the optic lobe to trauma or anoxia. Recording was extracellular and readings were taken directly from a high-impedance millivoltmeter (Burtt and Catton, 1964b).

Illumination was by tungsten filament bulb, giving an intensity of about 100 lux at the eye. Figure 3 shows potential variations in the ommatidial zone of a locust in response to 5 min light-adaptation followed by 5 min dark-adaptation. Although the recording was extracellular the main features (on-transient and plateau phase) of the light-adaptation response closely resemble the response of individual retinula cells obtained by microelectrode recordings in other insect species (e.g. Naka and Eguchi (1962) on honeybee drone; Burkhardt (1962) and Washizu et al. (1964) on Calliphora), as also the typical Limulus eye response recorded by many authors. Our records simply differ in extending the time of observation from the order of seconds to that of minutes. Another respect in which the extra- and intracellular records are comparable is in the respective rates of growth of the on-transient and plateau phases of the response to light as the intensity is increased. In both cases the plateau phase soon reaches a saturation level, whereas the on-transient goes on increasing for a further range of at least 3 log units (Fig. 4). Burkhardt and Autrum (1960) considered that the appearance of the on-transient in their intracellular records was due to superimposition of the

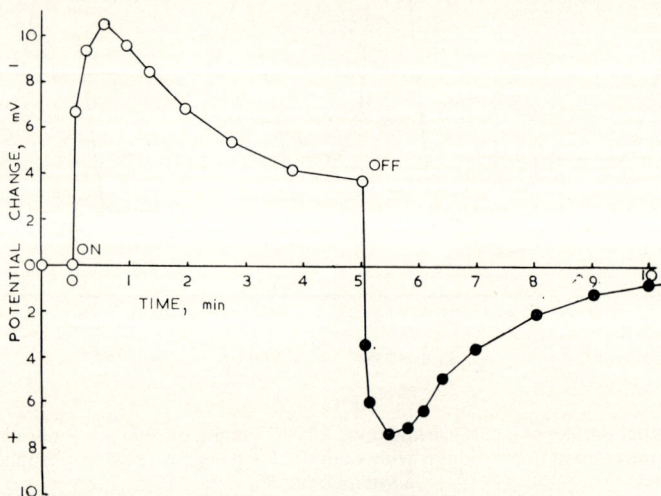

Fig. 3

Variation of potential in retinula cell zone of locust eye during light-adaptation (○) and dark-adaptation (●). The baseline in this and other figures is the steady potential associated with full dark-adaptation.

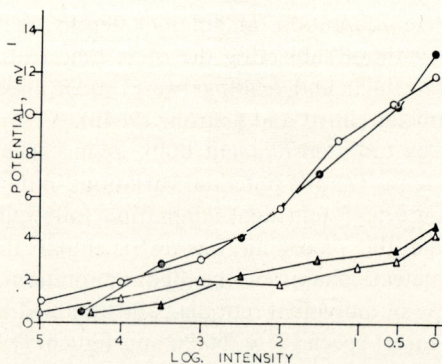

Fig. 4

Amplitudes of (a) maximum negative potential change (○, ●) and (b) potential after 5 min light-adaptation (△, ▲) plotted over a range of 5 log units of intensity. The results are from two different locusts (○, △ and ●, ▲).

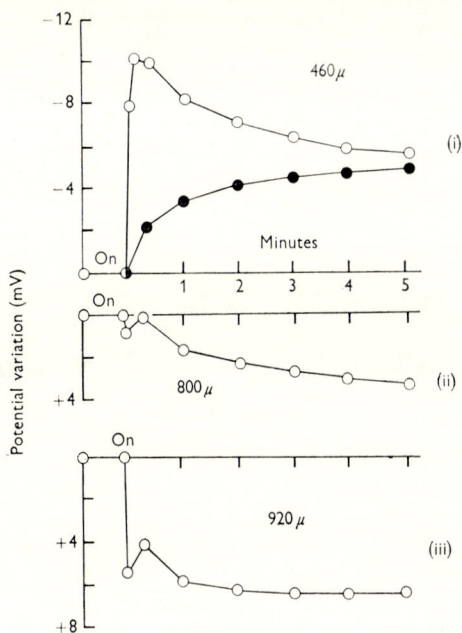

FIG. 5

Potential changes in locust eye during light-adaptation. For explanation, see text.

mass ERG response, owing to the decreased membrane resistance of the retinula cell during illumination. Ruck (1964) has criticized this interpretation, and regards the initial transient as the response of the retinula cell axons; the plateau component he terms the generator potential of the retinula cell, which is developed in the cell soma and evokes the axonal response at the higher intensities.

Extracellular recordings in *Calliphora* eye by Autrum and co-workers differ from ours in *Locusta* and in *Phormia* (Fig. 6) in showing no sustained negative phase in the intact eye.

Several of our observations suggest that the on- and off-transient responses have an origin different from that of the plateau phase of the adaptation responses we record. Thus the value of the on-transient rises at a greater rate, with increase in intensity, than does the plateau phase and does not saturate at low intensity levels (Fig. 4). Both the on- and off-transients reverse in sign across the basement membrane (Fig. 5), and they are both eliminated when the optic lobe is crushed or subjected to anoxia (Burtt and Catton, 1964b; Autrum and Hoffmann, 1960), as also when the optic lobe is severed from the eye (Bernhard (1942) on *Dytiscus*; Autrum and Gallwitz (1951) on *Calliphora*). The slow component, although displaced due to the fact that it takes off from

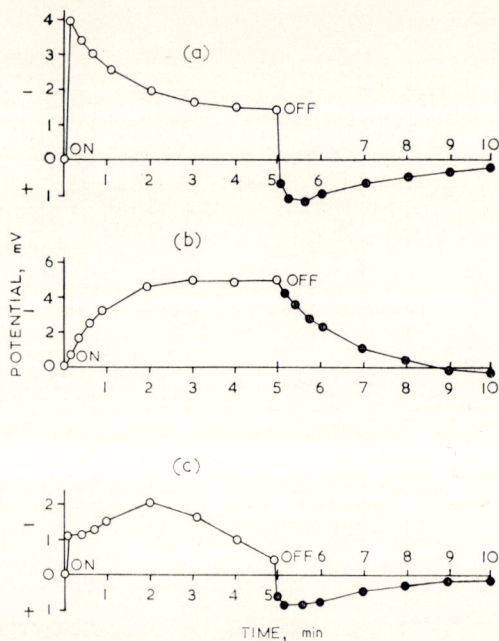

FIG. 6

Potential changes accompanying light-adaptation (○) and dark adaptation (●) in the retinula cell zones of (a) *Phormia*, (b) a larva of *Aeschna*, and (c) adult *Periplaneta*.

the peak of the on-transient, follows a similar time-course in both superficial and deep zones. The transient and slow components thus appear to sum algebraically.

When the optic lobe was crushed, repeatedly transfixed, subjected to anoxia or treated with sodium azide, the transient components of the ommatidial zone response were eliminated, leaving only the slow component (Fig. 5 (i)). Prolonged anoxia would eventually attenuate this response also, but it was much more resistant to anoxia than the fast components. Sensitivity to anoxia is a characteristic of nervous elements, whereas photoreceptor cells themselves are relatively resistant.

We suggest from the above findings that the transient components are dependent on nervous activity, the slow component on events restricted to the photoreceptor elements themselves. With our method of recording the two summate algebraically.

It would be attractive to consider that the on-transient represents activity in the retinula cell axon, the region from which, according to evidence supplied by a number of authors (e.g. Tomita (1956), Fuortes (1959) on *Limulus*; Naka and Eguchi (1962) on honeybee drone), spike discharges may originate. As recorded intracellularly this initial transient can carry the membrane potential to zero (e.g. in *Calliphora* (Burkhardt and Autrum, 1960), and in *Limulus* (Fuortes and Poggio, 1963), or even at high intensities reverse the membrane potential (Benolken, 1961). The progressive increase in amplitude of the on-transient in extracellular records can clearly be explained by recruitment of additional active units by internal scattering of light, but it is just as definitely a graded response in intracellular studies, i.e. it is not all-or-none and does not, in our experiments on *Locusta*, show a clear threshold. On present evidence it cannot be assumed to be a propagated response, but is to be regarded as one of the two main components of the receptor potential. The case of *Aeschna* larva is of particular interest. In this species (Burtt and Catton, 1964b) the transient components are absent in the ommatidial zone (Fig. 6 (b)), but are found only in the optic lobe. In this larval form the post-retinal fibres are very much longer than in the adult of this and other species, and the optic lobe is widely separated from the eye. Autrum and Gallwitz (1951) first drew attention to this feature and its correlation with the change in form of the electroretinogram during development, in which the transient phases appeared only in the adult eye, when the optic lobe was in close apposition to it.

III. ORIGIN OF THE OFF-RESPONSE

There is evidence that the off-transient may have an origin distinct from that of the on-transient. Experiments in this laboratory (Cosens, unpublished) in which two microelectrodes were inserted into the eye (one just within the cornea which was earthed and a second roving electrode), revealed that the off-transient first appeared when the roving electrode penetrated the basement membrane. With both electrodes in the ommatidial region only the on-transient and plateau phase were recorded. With our original method of recording the adaptational responses, using an indifferent electrode in the body and a roving electrode in the eye, electrical events would be recorded in series, so that an off-response appears in ommatidial zone records, although it may truly originate in the optic lobe.

The off-deflexion is notably absent in all intracellular recordings so far made from retinula cells of various species, and in the few cases where spikes have been recorded from retinula cells (e.g. Naka and Eguchi, 1962) there was no discharge at light off.

Off-spike discharges do not occur in optic nerve fibres of *Limulus*, but arise in the centrally situated synaptic layers (Wilska and Hartline, 1941). Off-spike discharges in the optic lobe of the locust were found in association only with single units which were inhibited by light (Burtt and Catton, 1960), suggesting an origin due to release from inhibition. In many ocelli a spike discharge occurs only at light-off, post-synaptic hyperpolarization occurring at light-on (Ruck, 1961 a, b).

IV. ADAPTATIONAL CHANGES IN VISUAL THRESHOLD; CORRELATION WITH POTENTIAL VARIATIONS

Visual threshold changes in the locust eye have been studied in this laboratory, using the ventral nerve cord spike response as an indication of threshold (Burtt, Catton and Cosens, 1964). The eye was initially dark-adapted for $\frac{1}{2}$ hr, during which time repeated tests of visual threshold were made, using an illuminated test spot projected very briefly on to a screen placed in the visual field. When the threshold was steady the whole eye was illuminated with an intensity of 100 lux. The visual threshold rose very sharply in the first few seconds, followed by a rapid but incomplete recovery, so that a plateau was reached, representing the light-adapted threshold. When the light was switched off the threshold fell at first sharply, then more slowly to reach the original dark-adapted baseline (Fig. 7).

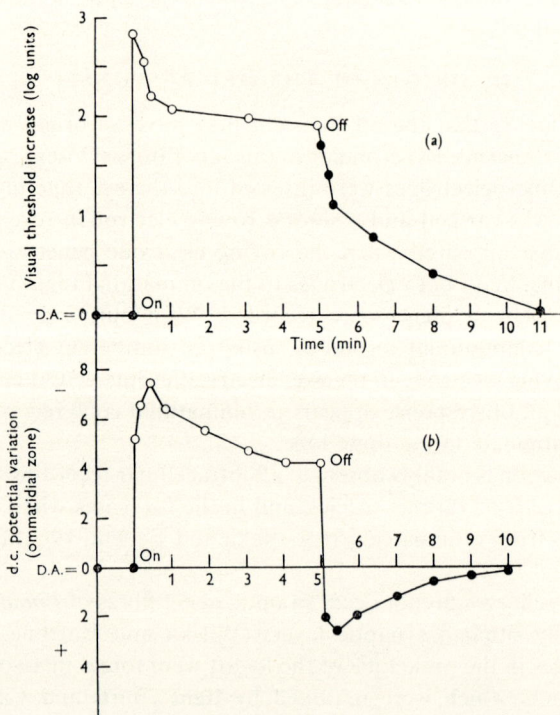

FIG. 7

Changes in (a) visual threshold, (b) potential in ommatidial region, for the locust compound eye during light- and dark-adaptation.

It was not possible to perform both visual threshold and potential measurements on the same eye, but a comparison of the time-courses of the two phenomena, recorded in different eyes, is made in Fig. 7. The two curves are seen to be closely similar, differing essentially at light-off, where the potential overshoots the dark-adapted baseline, but the visual threshold simply falls back to its original level. Later experiments, in which the ommatidial zone response alone was recorded by using two electrodes in the eye, have shown a much closer correspondence between potential change and visual threshold (Cosens, unpublished).

V. CORRELATION OF POTENTIAL WAVES IN EYE AND OPTIC LOBE, WITH SPIKE DISCHARGES IN OPTIC LOBE AND VENTRAL NERVE CORD

Recording of single unit activity at the level of the second synaptic region of the optic lobe (Burtt and Catton, 1960) revealed that the most common type of unit (*D*-unit) gave a brief high-frequency spike train at light-on and light-off only. These units showed a spontaneous dark discharge and this was partially inhibited during the period of illumination. Far less common were units (*L*-units) which were silent in darkness, but gave a discharge at constant frequency during illumination; frequency of discharge was a logarithmic function of light intensity. Recordings from the ventral nerve cord using external electrodes showed only on- and off-bursts with no trace of tonic light responses. More recent work, in which single-fibre responses in the ventral nerve cord connectives have been studied with the use of microelectrodes, has revealed the presence of tonically light-responding units here also.

The on- and off-spike discharges recorded from both optic lobe and nerve cord were similar in duration to the fast transient components of the potential waves recorded in the eye, and are presumably in some way "keyed" in to the transient responses. In a species (*Periplaneta*) showing weak transients (Fig. 6 (c)) no spike responses were present in the nerve cord. Similarly, one may suppose that the optic lobe *L*-units are keyed in to the plateau phase of the wave response. No units were found to give a pure off-response.

Single unit responses could not be obtained from the first synaptic layer, although large cell bodies (giant monopolar cells of Cajal) are found here. Failure to record from this region could have been due to limitations of technique, in particular the use of electrodes of tip diameter 5–15 μ. One would expect that responses from the first synaptic layer would bear the simplest relation to the potential waves, and a reinvestigation of this layer with improved technique is called for. That synaptic delay across this region occurs was shown earlier (Burtt and Catton, 1959).

VI. POSSIBLE DUAL SYSTEM IN VISUAL PATHWAY

Morphological duality may be inherent in the ommatidium, in that in many insect retinulae one, or more rarely two, retinula cells differ in form or position from the rest. One may regard these as the morphological homologues of the eccentric cell in the *Limulus* ommatidum, although they differ in one important respect, in that they often possess a striated rhabdomere, while the *Limulus* eccentric cell does not. Thus considered functionally the *Limulus* cell is not a primary photoreceptor, but is activated by junctional contact with the surrounding retinula cells, serving in this way as a second order neurone. All the information passing down the "optic nerve" of *Limulus* is represented as coded signals in eccentric cell fibres. Nonetheless, the eccentric cell is so closely coupled to the retinula cells that responses to light recorded intracellularly from the two types of cell are not easily distinguished. In view of the primitive and specialized features shown by *Limulus* one may be justified in regarding the eccentric cell mechanism of the eye as peculiar to the species and off the main line of arthropod evolution.

Early investigators of the neurohistology of the insect optic lobe (e.g. Cajal and Sanchez, 1915; Hanström, 1927) described a system of retinula cell fibres which passed straight through the first synaptic region and synapsed in the second region. In *Calliphora* one can recognize one especially thick post-retinal fibre arising from each ommatidium (Burtt and Catton, 1962). Such a morphological differentiation was not seen in *Locusta*, but may be revealed with further study in other species.

The theory of functional duality may be expressed as follows. Normal retinula cells project by means of thin post-retinal fibres on to the first synaptic region, and here lateral inhibition is effective (cf. basal synaptic layer of *Limulus* eye). There is marked overlapping of this fibre distribution. Chiasmatal fibres from the first region make synaptic junctions with neurones in the second region. These show the behaviour of *D*-units (Burtt and Catton, 1960), i.e. they have a dark discharge inhibited by light, and predominantly respond by spike bursts to stepwise changes of light intensity (on–off).

"Eccentric cells" project by fibres which pass through the first synaptic layer and terminate in the second. They have no dark discharge, are not subject to lateral inhibition, and give a discharge frequency proportional to light intensity (*L*-units of Burtt and Catton, 1960). Due to the absence of inhibition they give no off-response (essentially a rebound phenomenon). In the locust the ratio of *D*-units to *L*-units was about equal to the ratio of retinula cells to eccentric cells, i.e. 6 or 7 to 1.

The respective functions of the two systems are envisaged as follows. Normal retinula cell fibres mediate responses to rapidly-changing light contours crossing the visual field and are perhaps primarily activated by movement stimuli. The final common pathway is the large fibre system (largely crossed) in the ventral nerve cord, in which the responses are almost entirely phasic (on–off). This system is capable of a high degree of pattern resolution, which is assisted by lateral inhibitory action in the synaptic regions serving to increase the effective image contrast. Eccentric cell fibres (not morphologically distinguishable in all species) mediate the response to ambient light intensity and form a coarse mosaic imaging system based on the ommatidium as a unit. Here lateral inhibition plays no part, and would indeed be inimical to the function of the system in its role as quantitative indicator of light intensity. Lacking the assistance of adjacent channel inhibition to sharpen the image, and based on a much coarser mosaic than that of independently functioning retinula cells, the overall resolution of this system would be expected to be limited to an angle at best not less than the inter-ommatidial inclination. Nonetheless, it could provide a basis for a crude form of imaging of stationary objects and recognition of shape.

Clearly we are dealing here largely with speculation, but such a dual theory may serve as a useful guide to further experimental approaches to problems of compound eye function.

REFERENCES

AUTRUM, H. and GALLWITZ, U. 1951. Zur Analyse der Belichtungspotentiale des Insekten auges. *Z. vergl. Physiol.* **33**, 407–35.
AUTRUM, H. and HOFFMANN, C. 1960. Diphasic and monophasic responses in the compound eye of *Drosophila, J. Insect Physiol.* **4**, 122–7.
BENOLKEN, R. M. 1961. Reversal of photoreceptor polarity recorded during the graded receptor potential response to light in the eye of *Limulus. Biophys. J.* **1**, 551–64.
BERNHARD, C. G. 1942. Isolation of the retinal and optic ganglion response in the eye of *Dytiscus. J. Neurophysiol.* **5**, 32–48.
BURKHARDT, D. 1962. Spectral sensitivity and other response characteristics of single visual cells in the arthropod eye. *Symp. Soc. Exp. Biol.* **16**, 86–109.
BURKHARDT, D. and AUTRUM, H. 1960. Die Belichtungspotentiale einzelner Sehzellen von *Calliphora erythrocephala* Meig. *Z. Naturf.* **15b**, 612–6.
BURTT, E. T. and CATTON, W. T. 1959. Transmission of visual impulses in the nervous system of the locust. *J. Physiol.* **146**, 492–515.
BURTT, E. T. and CATTON, W. T. 1960. The properties of single unit discharges in the optic lobe of the locust. *J. Physiol.* **154**, 479–90.
BURTT, E. T. and CATTON, W. T. 1962. A diffraction theory of insect vision. Pt I. An experimental study of visual acuity in certain insects. *Proc. Roy. Soc.* B **157**, 53–82.
BURTT, E. T. and CATTON, W. T. 1964a. The potential profile of the insect compound eye and optic lobe. *J. Insect Physiol.* **10**, 689–710.
BURTT, E. T. and CATTON, W. T. 1964b. Potential changes in the eye and optic lobe of certain insects during light- and dark-adaptation. *J. Insect Physiol.* **10**, 865–86.
BURTT, E. T., CATTON, W. T. and COSENS, D. J. 1964. Correlation between electrical potential and visual threshold changes in an insect eye. *J. Physiol.* **170**, 57–8P.
CAJAL, RAMON Y and SANCHEZ, D. 1915. Contribucion al conocimiento de los centros nerviosos de los insectos. *Trab. lab. invest. biol. Univ. Madrid.* **13**, 1–164.
FUORTES, M. G. F. 1959. Initiation of visual impulses in visual cells of *Limulus. J. Physiol.* **148**, 14–28.
FUORTES, M. G. F. and POGGIO, G. F. 1963. Transient responses to sudden illumination in cells of the eye of *Limulus. J. Gen. Physiol.* **46**, 435–52.

230   E. T. BURTT, W. T. CATTON AND D. J. COSENS

HANSTRÖM, B. 1927. Über die Frage, ob funktionell verschiedene zapfen- und stäb-chenartige Sehzellen im Komplexauge der Arthropoda vorkommen. *Z. vergl. Physiol.* **6**, 566–97.

NAKA, K. I. and EGUCHI, E. 1962. Spike potentials recorded from the insect photo-receptor. *J. Gen. Physiol.* **45**, 663–80.

RUCK, P. 1961a. Electrophysiology of the insect dorsal ocellus. I. Origin of components of the electroretinogram. *J. Gen. Physiol.* **44**, 605–27.

RUCK, P. 1961b. Electrophysiology of the insect dorsal ocellus. II. Mechanisms of genera-tion and inhibition of impulses in the ocellar nerve of dragonflies. *J. Gen. Physiol.* **44**, 629–39.

RUCK, P. 1962. On photoreceptor mechanisms of retinula cells. *Biol. Bull. Mar. Biol. Lab. Wood's Hole.* **123**, 618–34.

RUCK, P. 1964. Retinal structure and photoreception. *Ann. Rev. Ent.* **9**, 83–102.

SVAETICHIN, G. 1952. The cone action potential. *Acta Physiol. Scand.* (Suppl.) **29**, 565–600.

TOMITA, T. 1956. The nature of action potentials in the lateral eye of the horseshoe crab as revealed by simultaneous intra- and extracellular recording. *Jap. J. Physiol.* **6**, 327–40.

WASHIZU, Y., BURKHARDT, D. and STRECK, P. 1964. Visual field of single retinula cells and interommatidial inclination in the compound eye of the blowfly *Calliphora erythroce-phala. Z. vergl. Physiol.* **48**, 413–28.

WIGGLESWORTH, V. B. 1959. The histology of the nervous system of an insect. *Rhodnius prolixus* (Hemiptera). II. The central ganglia. *Quart. J. Micr. Sci.* **100**, 299–312.

WILSKA, A. and HARTLINE, H. K. 1941. The origin of "off-responses" in the optic pathway. *Amer. J. Physiol.* **133**, 491P.

DISSECTION OF A GRADED VISUAL
RESPONSE WITH TETRODOTOXIN*

R. M. BENOLKEN and C. J. RUSSELL

Zoology Department, University of Minnesota, Minneapolis, Minnesota, U.S.A.

INTRODUCTION

THE *Limulus* eye has proved advantageous for intracellular studies because of the relatively large size of the visual cells (Miller, 1957) and because of the characteristic isolation of visual units in a compound eye. A further dividend has been provided by the relative ease with which both the graded generator potential and optic nerve activity can be monitored in a single preparation. The latter property has been especially useful for asking how the generator potential controls optic nerve activity, and this question has been approached with considerable experimental success (Hartline, Wagner and MacNichol, 1952; MacNichol, 1956; Fuortes, 1959; Behrens and Wulff, 1965; and others). A second question might be phrased as follows: How do the light reactions control the generator potential response? Experimental approaches to the latter problem have emphasized the properties of the generator potential itself, although these properties establish only one set of boundary conditions for the general problem.

A model of the generator response system is shown in Fig. 1 (Benolken, 1961). If the light reactions adjust R_2 "properly", the transient and steady-state components of the generator potential could be produced as shown. This model and other available models are probably an oversimplification. The data to be presented here suggested that the light reactions control at least two electrical parameters of the model, for example, R_1 and R_2. A further complication was also indicated by the data. It appears likely that the light reactions provide two independent inputs to the generator potential process as well as exerting control at two independent electrical points.

The transient ("initial") component of the response is affected differently than the steady-state ("final") component of the generator potential by calcium deprivation, by potassium concentration changes, and by probe withdrawal (Yeandle, 1957). Further chemical dissection of the generator potential response would be especially useful if this could be accomplished with agents of defined pharmacological specificity. Tetrodotoxin, a poison

* This work was supported by U.S. Public Health Service grant NB-02660 from the National Institute of Neurological Diseases and Blindness.

INSIDE

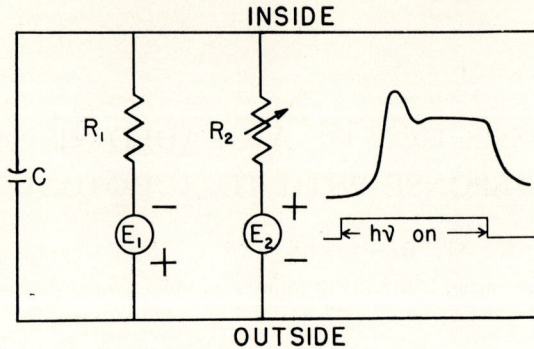

OUTSIDE

FIG. 1

Oversimplified electrical model of the generator potential response.

extracted from puffer fish, has been shown to block impulse activity in muscle and nerve (Furukawa, Sasaoka, and Hosoya, 1959; Narahashi, Moore and Scott, 1964; Nakamura, Nakajima and Grundfest, 1965; and others). In nerve, the drug appears to act specifically by inhibiting the ionic processes which are associated with the regenerative sodium conductance changes of a propagated impulse.

Loewenstein, Terzuolo and Washizu (1963) applied tetrodotoxin to two sensory systems, (a) the crustacean stretch receptor and (b) the mammalian pacinian corpuscle. In both cases these authors reported that the drug selectively blocked the propagated nerve impulses of the sense organs but that it had *no* effect on the graded generator potential. Results to be reported here indicate that such is not the case for the *Limulus* eye. Perhaps it should be pointed out that a different result for *Limulus* was not altogether unexpected. The graded generator potential of *Limulus* exhibits two properties which appear to be somewhat unusual in sensory systems: (1) the graded response can "reverse" the resting level of the visual cell (Benolken, 1961) and (2) a portion of the graded response domain may show regenerative transducing properties (Fuortes and Poggio, 1963; Adolph, 1964; Benolken, 1965a; and Benolken, 1965b).

METHODS

A lateral eye of *Limulus* was excised and cut transversely to expose the ommatidia. Solutions were exchanged in two ways: (1) when analyzing the effect of drug concentration, the whole eye was mounted in a clamp and solutions were exchanged with an infusion-withdrawal pump; (2) when multiple exchanges of drug and sea water were desired, thin sections of the eye were mounted in a small chamber as suggested by Adolph (1965), and tetrodotoxin was added to the chamber via a small capillary during continuous (or intermittent) chase with sea water. Without exception crystalline tetrodo-toxin was dissolved in sea water, and percentage concentration refers to weight in grams dissolved in 100 ml of sea water.

Micropipettes, filled with 2M KCl, were probed through an ommatidium until a light response could be recorded intracellularly. The micropipette provided a salt bridge between the preparation and an Ag–AgCl electrode connected to a negative capacitance preamp (MacNichol and Wagner, 1954). The circuit was completed through an Ag–AgCl electrode placed in the sea water surrounding the eye. The amplified output of the preamp was monitored by an oscilloscope and a high-speed ink writer. A Grass camera provided records of the scope traces.

Stimuli were provided by a tungsten source and an optical bench. Inten-sities were controlled by attenuating a constant source intensity with neutral density wedges. Scattered light was visually apparent at the air–solution interface of the preparation. If percentage scatter was reasonably constant for a given preparation, the experimental results should be independent of the scatter because of the experimental controls. Stimulus durations and stimulus cycles were programmed with an estimated reproducibility of ± 200 μsec, and flash waveforms were flat with rise times less than or equal to 500 μsec.

RESULTS

Physiological properties of a drug are not independent of dosage character-istics. However, it will be convenient to begin by considering tetrodotoxin as an "effective" dissecting tool and to defer a definition of effective dosage until later. The simplest way to analyze the generator potential response as a function of tetrodotoxin is to make all other parameters of the system as invariant as possible. A closely controlled stimulus program was set up to maintain constant stimulus conditions for the experiments unless otherwise noted. A stimulus of constant duration and intensity was presented to the eye every 20 sec for a period of some hours preceding the records of Fig. 2, and the same program was continued throughout the experimental period of the preparation. Before the first record the preparation had been presented with a continuous chase of sea water. After record 1 the chase was stopped and tetrodotoxin was injected into the system. Within 60 sec the transient component of the generator potential had been reduced as shown in record 4; then the sea water chase was started, and the effect of the drug was reversed in less than 60 sec as shown in records 7 and 8.

Prior to the records of Fig. 2 the preparation had been subjected to several injections of tetrodotoxin. Although the primary effects of the drug had been reversed by sea water, the responses appear to be "noisy" when compared to responses observed before exposure to the drug. A noisy response as shown in Fig. 2 was characteristic of preparations which had been subjected to tetrodo-toxin.

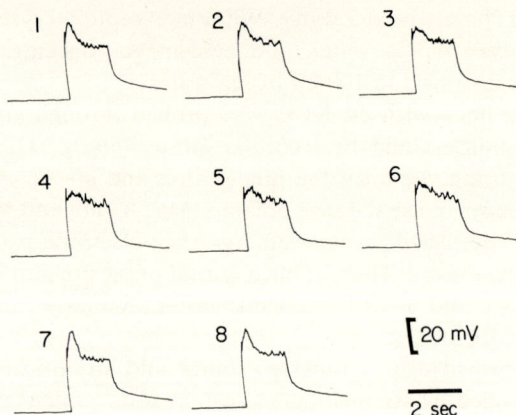

Fig. 2

Intracellular responses recorded when tetrodotoxin was added to the solution bathing the eye. Response 1 is a control recorded in sea water. Tetrodotoxin was added to the bathing solution after record 1. The drug was washed out by a sea water chase initiated after record 4. The "noisy" properties of the response are discussed in the text. The numbers above each record correspond to the numbered data points of Fig. 3. Stimuli were repeated every 20 sec. Each stimulus was of 2 sec duration and constant intensity. The recording baseline was established by the resting level of the cell. Positive polarity increases in an upward direction, and the curvilinear recording arc is defined for the voltage calibration.

Three response parameters were measured from the records of Fig. 2: (1) amplitude of "initial pulse", (2) maximum amplitude of the transient component, and (3) amplitude of the steady-state component at the end of the stimulus period. The initial pulse, or notch, occurs on all records of Fig. 2, but is especially obvious when the transient component is suppressed, e.g. on records 3 through 6. The initial pulse is not observed in all preparations, a point which will come up again later in the discussion of latency.

Figure 3 is a plot of the three response parameters vs. time. The numbered data points of the plot were derived from correspondingly numbered records of Fig. 2. A few general comments on the plot itself might be helpful. Although the points are not equidistantly spaced along the time axis, the preparation was controlled with a constant stimulus program, but only every third response was plotted when parameters were invariant in order to reduce congestion on the plot. The size of the symbols on the plot is a measure of the magnitude of uncertainty in reading a parameter from the records. The upward arrow indicates the end of a sea water chase and a short-term injection of tetrodotoxin, the downward arrow indicates when the sea water chase was started again, and the double arrow indicates that tetrodotoxin was injected for about 60 sec *while* a sea water chase was operating continuously. Thus the plot summarizes the response of one preparation to two injections

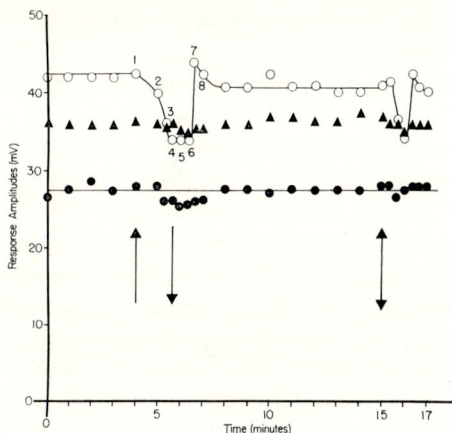

FIG. 3

The plot of response amplitude vs. time includes points derived from correspondingly numbered records of Fig. 2. The maximum amplitude of the transient component is represented by open circles, the peak of the initial pulse is represented by filled triangles, and the filled circles represent the amplitude of the steady-state component which was measured just before the light was switched off. All parameters were measured relative to the resting level of the cell before the stimulus was switched on. The uncertainty of reading amplitudes from the records is indicated by the magnitude of the symbols. The flow of sea water was stopped and tetrodotoxin was injected into the bathing solution at the upward arrow, sea water chase was resumed at the downward arrow, and the double arrow indicates a brief injection of tetrodotoxin *during* continuous sea water chase.

of tetrodotoxin, one injection with intermittent sea water chase and the other with continuous chase.

It is apparent from Fig. 3 that the transient component of the generator potential was inhibited selectively by tetrodotoxin, that the initial pulse and steady-state components were almost unaffected by the drug, and that the effect of the drug was reversed more rapidly under conditions of continuous rather than intermittent sea water chase. To anticipate the discussion on drug variability, it should be pointed out that the preparation of Figs. 2 and 3 was selected as an example of one extreme observed in the data. In the first place, the effect of the drug could be initiated and reversed rapidly. Under conditions of continuous chase the drug was delivered, the transient component reduced, and the effects were reversed in an interval of less than 80 sec. Secondly, the initial pulse and the steady-state component were almost invariant; the standard deviation of the mean for these two parameters was respectively less than or equal to the magnitude of uncertainty of measurement where calculations of standard deviation and mean value were based on the twenty-six responses shown in Fig. 3. Also the amplitude of the transient component was reduced markedly by tetrodotoxin, but it was not eliminated. Finally, the amplitude of the transient component of the generator potential completely recovered in sea water.

The curve of open circles in Fig. 3 corresponds to the maximum amplitude of the transient component of the response. There was a suggestion of overshoot in this parameter when the effect of the drug was reversed. This is an interesting observation. Presumably the light reactions and the photopigment were controlled by a constant quantum flux density during the time that the drug inhibited the transient component, a fact indicated both by the stimulus conditions and by the constant amplitude of the steady-state component of the generator potential. To phrase the situation differently, the transient component of the response appears to dark adapt when blocked by tetrodotoxin even though flux density and the amplitude of the steady-state component of the response appear to be constant throughout the experiment. The overshoot is not spectacular in Fig. 3, probably (a) because of the extremely rapid reversal of the drug and correspondingly short time for selective adaptation, (b) because the relatively lengthy stimulus cycle of 20 sec permitted appreciable dark adaptation between stimuli even in the absence of the drug, and (c) the stimulus intensity was at a nearly saturating level for the response mechanisms. The question of selective adaptation will be examined again under more favourable conditions.

Stimuli of constant intensity and duration were presented to the preparation of Figs. 4 and 5. The stimuli were carefully programmed to repeat every 10 sec. The reduced amplitude of the transient component relative to the amplitude of the steady-state component in the control records of Fig. 4

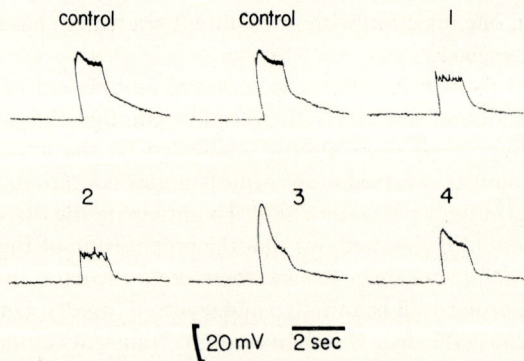

FIG. 4

Intracellular records. The two sea water controls were recorded immediately before tetrodotoxin was injected into the bathing solution. After about 5 min, response 1 was recorded. Sea water chase was started after record 1 in order to wash out the drug. The stimulus cycle was repeated every 10 sec, and the stimuli were of constant intensity and were of 1·3 sec duration. The numbers above each record correspond to numbered data points of Fig. 5. Other general recording features were similar to those of Fig. 2.

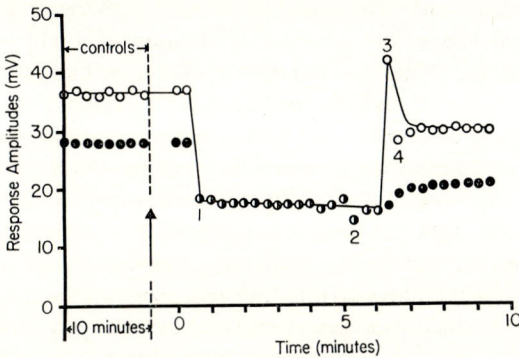

FIG. 5

Data points include amplitudes measured from correspondingly numbered records of Fig. 4. Open circles represent amplitudes of the transient component of the generator potential, and filled circles represent amplitudes of the steady-state component. The half-filled circles indicate responses for which there was no measurable transient component and only the steady-state component was observable on the records. The size of the symbols is a measure of reading precision. The flow of sea water was stopped and tetrodotoxin was injected into the bathing solution at the arrow. About 5 min elapsed from the arrow until time $t = 0$. No effect of the drug was observed until after $t = 0$. Sea water chase was started to wash out tetrodotoxin after the point numbered 1. Other general features of the plot were similar to Fig. 3.

indicates that the preparation was light adapted significantly by this shorter stimulus cycle. The general comments directed toward Fig. 3 also apply to the plot of Fig. 5. The numbered data points of Fig. 5 were derived from numbered records of Fig. 4, and the size of the symbols is a measure of precision. The arrow indicates that tetrodotoxin was presented to the preparation about 5 min before $t = 0$. At record 1, the sea water chase was resumed. The half-filled circles indicate that the transient component and the steady-state component were indistinguishable.

The effect of tetrodotoxin on the preparation of Fig. 5 should be compared to its effect on the earlier preparation of Fig. 3. For Fig. 5 the drug required considerable time to produce an effect and at least 5 min were required for its effect to be reversed in sea water. The amplitude of the steady-state component was reduced to about two-thirds of its control level after the preparation had been exposed to tetrodotoxin. The transient component was eliminated by the drug, that is, it was completely inhibited. Except for response record 3, the amplitudes of the transient and steady-state components never completely recovered their control value when returned to sea water. However, the *difference* in amplitude between the transient and steady-state component closely approached the control level. Thus it seems likely that the irreversible effect of the drug could be explained by an irreversible loss of amplitude of the steady-state component with almost complete recovery of the transient component. Experience with the drug would suggest that this unusual loss of the steady-state component might be explained by some unknown clumsiness in exchanging solutions, but convenience is the only merit which can be claimed for this type of explanation.

The overshoot of response 3 in Fig. 5 is striking, especially since thereafter in sea water the amplitude of the generator potential never again achieved the control value. The amplitude of the response suggests that the transient processes had been dark adapting selectively while completely inhibited for a period of 5 min. An even more compelling argument is presented by record 3 in Fig. 4. The waveshape of this transient response is characteristic of a dark adapted eye which has been stimulated by relatively intense light. (But the eye had been exposed to a constant flux density and stimulus program throughout the run.) Typically after dark adaptation, intense stimuli produce a transient component which is prolonged in duration as well as of large amplitude. In other words dark adaptation is accompanied by waveshape changes as well as amplitude changes in the transient component of the generator potential.

Latency

Is the latency of the generator potential altered by tetrodotoxin? The data suggested that the answer to this question depends upon how it is asked. Unfortunately the light response of *Limulus* is complicated by at least two different types of intracellular recording situations, and this complication appeared to be crucial to the latency question.

The response of Fig. 6 exhibited a clearly defined "initial pulse". The record at 5:14 is a control. At 5:14 tetrodotoxin was presented to the prepara-

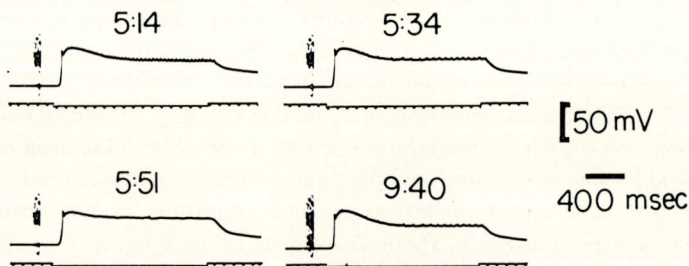

FIG. 6

The 5:14 record is a sea water control. Tetrodotoxin was injected immediately after 5:14, and the sea water chase was not resumed until after 5:51. A stimulus monitor deflected the lower scope trace of each record downward when the stimulus was on. A time base of 10 msec pulses repeated at 100 msec intervals was also recorded on the lower trace. A 1·6 sec stimulus of constant intensity was repeated on a 16 sec cycle. A ripple was observed especially on the upper trace of the 5:14 record and was almost absent from the 5:51 record. This was the result of nerve impulses which were poorly resolved at this writing speed.

tion and by 5:51 the drug had almost eliminated the transient component of the response. Sea water chase was started at 5:51 and by 9:40 the control amplitude of the transient response was almost recovered, although the nerve response did not completely reverse for this preparation. The preparation of Fig. 6 again demonstrated that the initial pulse of the generator potential was an almost invariant parameter in the presence of the drug. The latency of preparations showing an initial pulse probably was unaffected by tetrodotoxin.

Nerve impulses were not recorded from the preparation of Fig. 7, and the generator potential did not exhibit an initial pulse. (However, these two

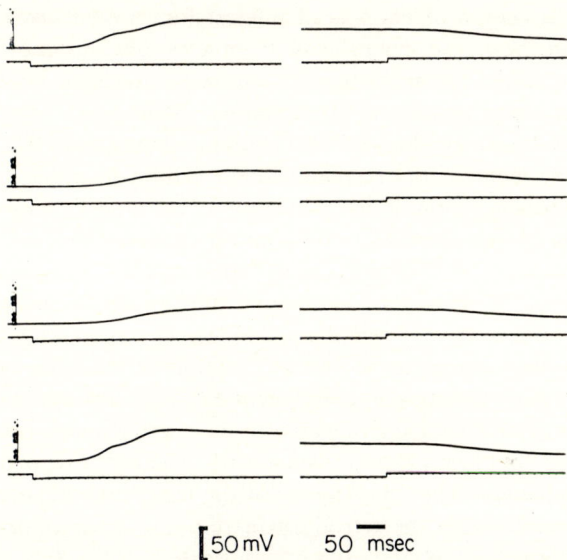

[50 mV   50 msec

FIG. 7

Records of responses to 4 consecutive stimuli of a 16 sec stimulus cycle. The upper record is a sea water control. Tetrodotoxin was injected after the upper record. The sea water chase was resumed 32 sec later immediately after the third record. Again, a downward deflection of the lower scope trace in each record indicated when the light was on. The timing pulses on the lower trace were separated by an interval of 10 msec. Notice the absence of an initial pulse and optic nerve activity in the control and other records. The break in the records was convenient because of the expanded time scale.

conditions are not necessarily correlated.) The responses were recorded in consecutive 16 sec intervals. The upper record was a control. Tetrodotoxin was injected after the first response and exerted considerable effect on the second response 16 sec later. The transient component was eliminated by the third record, and sea water reversed the effect of the drug with some transient overshoot in the bottom record. The lower trace of the records in Fig. 7 indicates when a light flash was switched on, and the timing pulses on the lower trace are separated by 10 msec. It would appear that the latency was increased by about 30 msec when the transient component was inhibited by tetrodotoxin. The latency change here is contrary to what was observed when the generator potential exhibited an initial pulse.

The initial pulse, when it occurred, was affected by tetrodotoxin in the same fashion as the steady-state component of the response. It is possible that there are three separable components of the generator potential, but for simplicity it will be assumed that there are only two until the data demand further complication. On these assumptions, the initial pulse seemed to be a part of the steady-state component.

While the latency problem was of interest for its own sake, the primary motivation for these experiments arose from a less obvious question. Perhaps the transient component of the graded response arises from activity near the distal process of the unique eccentric cell (see Miller, 1957, for an excellent description of the morphology of the *Limulus* ommatidium), and possibly the transient component of the response might exhibit a propagation velocity which would be a function of probe location in the ommatidium. The steady-state component was assumed to be a non-propagated process. One way to test the question of propagation was to follow latency changes as the probe proceeded from the transient electrogenic site toward the neural generator (recording sites 1 and 2 of Benolken, 1965a). The latency of the transient component would change as the probe position varied from one recording site to the other if the transient component exhibited a propagation velocity, while the steady-state component would provide a time reference. The steady-state reference could be precisely defined when tetrodotoxin eliminated the transient component. Then the latency of the transient component could be followed by subtracting the tetrodotoxin response from control sea water responses recorded before and after administration of the drug. In short, the time of appearance of a "difference" response should define the desired latency time. However, the "difference test" failed because of uncertainties in resolution of time and/or space. It quickly became obvious that the initial pulse, when present, always preceded the transient component. Therefore the transient component became bracketed in time-space by an initial pulse and the remainder of the steady-state component, and both bracketing parameters became noisy though relatively invariant in the presence of the drug (the noise problems associated with the drug were discussed in reference to Fig. 2). To the noise uncertainty must be added another uncertainty. Why do preparations presumably close to the transient electrogenic site exhibit or not exhibit an initial pulse? (Fig. 7). For that matter why do preparations presumably closer to the neural generator (Fig. 6) usually exhibit an initial pulse? It is the authors' opinion that the propagation question will not be resolved by data such as that of Figs. 6 and 7 until the spatial properties of the recording situation have been more precisely defined.

Optic Nerve Response

As expected, optic nerve impulses could be eliminated with tetrodotoxin, and the effect was reversible if the eye was again bathed in sea water. In general, tetrodotoxin eliminated the optic nerve response before and/or at lower concentrations than it eliminated the transient component of the graded generator potential. Presumably the drug acts on the receptor neuron, as it does on other nerves, by eliminating the initial regenerative component of current or the so-called sodium activation. However, stimulation of the receptor neuron here occurred by way of light reactions which initiate an electrical generator potential rather than by direct electrical stimulation as is the usual case for nerve experiments. Perhaps the drug acted on the eye by uncoupling the neural processes from the preceding light reactions, which include the generator potential, rather than by acting directly upon the neural process itself. This possibility suggests at least three alternatives: (1) the drug acts in the usual way upon the neural process itself, (2) the drug acts by uncoupling the neural process from the preceding light reactions, and (3) the drug acts both upon the neural process and upon the coupling process. The last alternative is the most conservative interpretation of the three, but an experimental test can be devised which should discriminate between the first two by providing a basis for rejecting one of them. Slightly spontaneous preparations proved to be useful for this test. Preparations were selected which exhibited a relatively low nerve-impulse frequency in darkness and which showed a marked increase of firing rate when the eye was stimulated with intense light.

Assume for argument that the drug acts by uncoupling the neural processes from preceding light reactions. On this assumption the drug should eliminate the increased firing rate observed during illumination of a spontaneous preparation but should have no effect on the spontaneous neural activity observed in darkness, since in darkness no generator potential is observed. That is, the coupling processes would be inhibited by the drug but the spontaneous neural processes would be unaffected. On the alternate hypothesis that the drug would act directly on the neural process, the drug should eliminate the spontaneous neural activity as well as the neural activity associated with illumination.

Selected records from a spontaneous preparation are shown in Fig. 8. The preparation was not stimulated at constant intensity as was the case for all previous records. In this case stimulus intensities were varied in steps over several log units, but the various steps were repeated in identical fashion from run to run. The stimulus program had been carefully controlled at least an hour before the first record and was maintained thereafter. Two responses are shown in each record; the response at the left was elicited by a stimulus ten times as intense as that for the response on the right. The record at 6:28 is a

C.E.—R

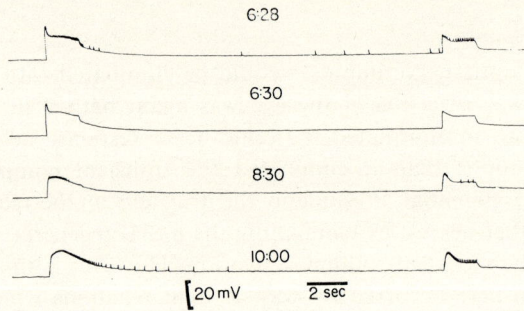

FIG. 8

Selected responses recorded from a spontaneous preparation. Light responses at the left were elicited by stimulus intensities which were 10 times greater than intensities at the right of each record. Tetrodotoxin was injected after the sea water control of 6:28. Sea water chase was resumed after the 6:30 record. During stimulation in some records impulses occurred at too high a frequency to be resolved with this time base; then the impulses appear only as a broadening of the generator potential trace.

control recorded in sea water. Spontaneous nerve impulses were observed on the record after the 2 sec stimulus had been switched off. Notice that the *spontaneous* neural activity occurs long after the generator potential had been recorded and the stimulus had been switched off. Tetrodotoxin was added to the bathing solution after the 6:28 record. The concentration of tetrodotoxin was sufficient to block nerve impulses but was too low to measurably affect the transient component of the generator potential. By 6:30 the drug had eliminated all nerve impulses, both those associated with illumination and the spontaneous impulses observed in darkness. From 6:30 to the end of the experiment the eye was subjected to a sea water chase. After 2 hr in sea water some neural activity was observed during periods of stimulation in the 8:30 record. Nerve impulses occurred both during stimulation and in darkness by 10:00.

If the 8:30 record of Fig. 8 is ignored, these data would seem to favor the hypothesis that the drug eliminates optic nerve impulses by acting on the neural process directly. The fact that tetrodotoxin eliminated spontaneous activity seems to demand at least, as a most conservative interpretation, that the drug acts both on the neural process itself *and* on the coupling processes.

Even the 8:30 record would support the argument that the drug acts directly on the neural process if the reasonable assumption is made that the drug acts in a quantitative rather than in an all-or-none fashion to inhibit sodium activation of the nerve. As the effect of the drug was slowly reversed during the sea water chase, the nerve threshold should be slowly decreased until the light reactions began to stimulate nerve activity although to a reduced extent relative to the control record. The data indicate that the threshold was considerably higher than the control value, because even during stimulation the number of impulses was considerably less during the 8:30 record than during the corresponding controls of 6:28 and 10:00. It is reasonable to suppose that the higher neural threshold indicated at 8:30 was above the spontaneous threshold. This would account for the observation that spontaneous activity was not reversed when a reduced neural activity was recorded during illumination even though tetrodotoxin was acting directly on the neural process in both situations.

For our discussion a stable preparation is defined as one which exhibits a constant response under a given set of conditions for the period of an experiment. This must be true whether the experiment requires a few minutes or several hours. Obviously reversing the effect of a drug has no quantitative meaning unless a control response can be repeated before and after the experimental run. It is also obvious that the 10:00 run of Fig. 8 did not reproduce the original control of 6:28. The spontaneous activity occupies a different portion of the time domain in the stimulus cycle and the generator potential at 10:00 has a dark adapted characteristic. The preparation of Fig. 8 was not stable as defined above, and indeed it was not expected to be so. Spontaneous activity appears to be a pathological symptom for the *Limulus* ommatidium. Except when useful for a specific experimental purpose, spontaneous preparations were routinely discarded as a sign of damage probably inflicted by the probing micropipette. Although a simple experiment in principle, tetrodotoxin was applied to only two spontaneous preparations which could be maintained in a state of "bad health" for 5 or 6 hr. (By contrast, non-spontaneous preparations such as those of Figs. 2 and 3 were stable for many hours.) It should be pointed out that these data indicated only that tetrodotoxin inhibited spontaneous neural activity as well as the neural activity associated with illumination. While both types of neural activity could be recovered in the same cell with a sea water chase, the response of a spontaneous preparation was not reversible in the sense that it could be reproduced quantitatively over a period of several hours. However, qualitatively the results were clear for the two successful spontaneous preparations: tetrodotoxin eliminated spontaneous neural activity as well as the neural activity associated with illumination.

Pharmacological Parameters

"Effective" concentrations of tetrodotoxin were assumed for the preceding discussions. Whenever effective, the general physiological effects of the drug were reasonably consistent. The data shown earlier were selected to provide examples of extremes in physiological variability, while variability in the time course of drug action is indicated by a comparison of Figs. 2–8. Variations observed in dosage values (effective concentrations) require further comment.

Dosage variations could arise from physiological differences between preparations, differences in the flow patterns during solution exchanges or additions, and differences from sample to sample in the drug itself. Deciding which was the most important source of variation is a risky business at best, but the data would seem to support the conclusion that the principal source of dosage variation was the variation between drug batches. This appeared to be true even though all of the drug was prepared by Sankyo Corporation, No. 1 Ginza-Nichome, Chuo-ku, Tokyo, Japan. The major variations observed in dosage characteristics correlated perfectly with batch differences of the drug, while physiological variations and the time course of drug action did not appear to correlate with known batch differences.

The dosage conclusions suggested here were based on samples from three batches of tetrodotoxin and about twenty "successful" preparations. The word "successful" has the following meaning: a stable preparation was successful if it could not be discarded because of obvious blunders in exchanging solutions, and the drug could be shown to have some effect on the eye. The latter qualification might appear to bias a consideration of dosage characteristics except for the fact that the drug always produced a physiological effect upon otherwise successful preparations unless it could be demonstrated that the drug had decomposed with time in solution. The potency of samples of tetrodotoxin declined monotonically with time in solution; as a rough rule of thumb, the drug became useless for our purposes about 2 weeks after a sample of the crystalline material had been dissolved in sea water.

The dosage characteristics of the drug were most carefully examined for the batch of highest potency. For drug samples of highest potency the optic nerve response was eliminated at concentrations less than or equal to $10^{-7}\%$ for freshly dissolved crystals. Concentrations of $10^{-7}\%$ had no measurable effect upon either component of the graded generator potential. The transient component of the graded receptor response was eliminated by drug solutions of about 100 times the above concentration, and these experiments were performed on the same preparations as those in which the neural response had been eliminated at concentrations of $10^{-7}\%$. That is, the transient component of the graded response could be eliminated by tetrodotoxin at concentrations equal to or less than $10^{-5}\%$. The discrimination between the neural process and the graded response as a function of drug concentration was useful for experiments such as that of Fig. 8.

The batch of intermediate potency eliminated the transient component of the generator potential at concentrations less than or equal to $10^{-3}\%$. The third batch of drug samples eliminated the optic nerve response at concentrations of about $10^{-3}\%$, but it did not affect the generator potential at maximum *practical* concentrations of about $5 \times 10^{-3}\%$. Experiments with the last drug batch did not contribute to the number of successful preparations.

DISCUSSION

Clearly tetrodotoxin eliminated the transient component of the graded generator potential as well as the neural impulses of the visual response. If (1) tetrodotoxin acts by inhibiting regenerative sodium conductance changes and if (2) the drug acts by inhibiting sodium sites whenever it produces an effect regardless of membrane origin, the data support the hypothesis that the transient component of the generator potential is controlled by a regenerative sodium process. In the absence of conflicting evidence and with the support of other lines of evidence (Benolken, 1961 and 1965a), this hypothesis and the explicit conditions of this hypothesis will be assumed for simplicity of argument. Notice that the second condition above is not necessarily contrary to the observation that the neural response and the graded transient response could be separated as a function of drug concentration. Again it is sufficient to invoke quantitative action by the drug, where the drug would be specific for a regenerative sodium process in both cases and where the neural process would be 100 times more sensitive to the drug than would be the graded response.

Independent of the question of drug specificity, tetrodotoxin did provide a precise chemical tool for selective dissection of the visual response. A schematic result of the dissection is summarized in Fig. 9. The three separable

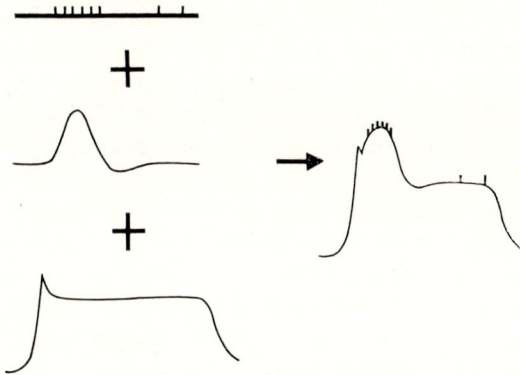

FIG. 9

The schematic light response at the right is represented as the sum of the three reversibly separable components at the left.

components are shown at the left, and the sum of the components—the intracellular light response of the *Limulus* eye—is shown at the right. The transient component of the total light response (right) shows characteristics of a slightly underdamped system. The response to a step function of light often exhibits an initial overshoot of the steady-state level *and* a subsequent undershoot before the steady-state level is established. The data indicated that when measurable the undershoot, as well as the overshoot, was eliminated by tetrodotoxin. However, the initial pulse of the response was not eliminated by tetrodotoxin. This point was discussed when latencies were considered, where it was assumed that the initial pulse was either a part of the steady-state graded process or a separate component of the response. Since the data did not demand the further complication of a third component of the graded response, the principle of parsimony was applied and the initial pulse was assumed to be a part of the steady-state response. This complicates terminology. If the initial pulse is part of the steady-state component, these data indicate that the steady-state component *usually* precedes the transient component in time. The earlier literature often refers to the transient component of the response as the "initial" component and to the steady-state component as the "second" component. But in fact the time sequence of events usually appears to be the reverse of that implied by earlier terminology, and usage of the terms "transient" and "steady-state" might avoid possible ambiguity.

The authors were encouraged to use tetrodotoxin as a dissection tool for the graded response of the *Limulus* eye by Terzuolo (1962) because of the presumed specificity of the drug in nerve tissue. The drug proved to be an especially fine and selective tool for the intracellular response of *Limulus*, often eliminating the transient component altogether but having no measurable effect upon the steady-state component. However, it should be emphasized that Yeandle (1957) had shown that especially Ca and perhaps K had preferential effects upon the two components of the graded response of the *Limulus* eye. While apparently these two physiological ions were not as precise or as well defined a dissection tool as tetrodotoxin, it seems unfortunate that Yeandle's earlier work has not been published where it would be more accessible.

The transient and steady-state components of the response were represented by an electrical model in Fig. 1. The resistive arm R_2 of the model was selected as the single variable (graded) component in the model "until such time as the data indicate the necessity of further complication". Further complication is indicated by these data, and a single variable component does not appear to be adequate to describe the response.

Because of the polarity of generator E_2 and because only the transient component of the generator potential has been demonstrated to reverse the resting level of the cell, the resistive arm R_2 of the model was related to the transient component of the response. Consequently, tetrodotoxin should act on the model either to open-circuit resistive arm R_2 or to fix R_2 to a constant value. Either action of the drug would be sufficient to remove the one variable electrical parameter of the model, and such cannot be the case since the steady-state component of the generator potential continues to be a graded function of light energy even in the presence of tetrodotoxin. With R_2 either fixed or eliminated (open-circuited) in the model, the response cannot be explained without a second variable electrical parameter. For example, the model would be inadequate unless, say, R_1 as well as R_2 were a variable parameter. It is possible to propose the not altogether trivial alternate hypothesis that the two variable components exist in the same arm of the model. Thus R_2 could be fixed at its maximum value by the drug, and a second variable resistor R_3, in the same arm E_2, could provide a graded steady-state function in the model. However, this alternative seems unlikely when considered from the perspective of the assumptions regarding drug action set forth in the beginning of this discussion section. The electrogenic source E_2 was presumably derived from membrane sites specific for a single ion, in this case sodium. If tetrodotoxin completely blocks these membrane sites, the entire arm E_2 would be open-circuited by the drug, and the variable component for the steady-state function could not occur in that same arm.

The transient processes appeared to dark adapt selectively when tetrodotoxin inhibited the transient component of the generator potential. The adaptation was selective for the transient response, since a controlled stimulus program was continued throughout the experiments and the steady-state component of the response was maintained at a constant state of adaptation. These observations provided the experimental basis for the earlier suggestion that the light reactions control the generator potential via two inputs to the electrical system. Notice that this statement is not equivalent to the proposition that the response mechanisms contain two variable electrical parameters; this hypothesis is stronger and demands two inputs into the electrical system as well as two variable parameters in the electrical system itself. By way of beginning consider another phenomenon which does not demand two independent processes. In the absence of drug the two components of the generator potential frequently light adapt at differing rates, the transient component being light adapted more rapidly than the steady-state component (see discussion of Fig. 4). This could be interpreted as indicating that a single light reaction step, which precedes the electrical event, inactivates the transient mechanism for a longer time than the steady-state processes. As an example suppose that a single chemical transmitter acts on both membrane sites, but after stimulation the transient receptor sites for the transmitter might be inactivated for a longer time than the steady-state sites. In the absence of evidence to the contrary, variations in the properties of membrane sites could account for the observed differences in the rate of light adaptation of the response components, and this interpretation is independent of whether or not the light reactions provide more than one kind of input into the electrical system. The same type of argument does not apply if selective adaptation occurs when one type of membrane site is inactivated by a light-independent agent.

A single input to the electrical process does not seem likely if the previous assumptions about drug action are correct, that is, if the drug simply acts on the receptor membrane to eliminate the specific permeability change of the transient process. When tetrodotoxin was applied, the stimulus program and the steady-state component remained constant while the transient process was inhibited. Apparently the transient electrical process was eliminated and the steady-state process continued without perturbation. Also the photochemical reactions were driven to the same state and at the same rate as they were before the drug was applied, and this must be the case if the photochemical reactions were entirely limited by light quanta. The simplest interpretation for selective adaptation of the transient component is that one product of the photochemical reactions accumulated when the transient process was eliminated by the drug. At the same time at least one other product of the light reactions proceeded at the usual rate with the steady-state process which remained invariant. True, this interpretation of the data is not conclusive (a common property of all positive scientific hypotheses). It is possible to explain the selective adaptation of the transient process on the basis of a "rebound" of the receptor membrane after removal of inhibiting drug. As a second of many possible alternatives it might be argued that there is an electrical–chemical transducer which senses the average electrical state of the receptor membrane and then acts on a feedback control to limit the photochemical reactions. However, until experimental evidence indicates otherwise the simplest hypothesis of two inputs to the electrical process will be assumed since it is consistent with these data.

An elegant analytical model has been proposed by Rushton (1965) which provides two points of electrical control for the visual process, one at the input of the electrical system and a second in a voltage feedback loop of an operational amplifier. The model is consistent with data which require two points of electrical control. The notion of two inputs to the electrical system was rejected by Rushton on the basis of human psychophysical data; the second control through the feedback loop was presented as an explicit function of the output voltage of the electrical network rather than as a function of a second input from the light reactions. If a common hypothesis is necessary here for psychophysical data and data on isolated receptor preparations, at least one of the two interpretations must be in error.

Spontaneous fluctuations or "quantum bumps" are observed when the *Limulus* eye dark adapts. What is the effect of tetrodotoxin on these fluctuations? Relatively unsystematic tests indicated that tetrodotoxin had no striking effect upon the fluctuations at concentrations which were physiologically significant for the light response. A more careful analysis would seem to be warranted, and the question should be examined further.

All of the physiological responses were measured intracellularly and hence, for completeness, a final remark should be directed toward the effect of tetrodotoxin upon the resting membrane potential of the cell. The resting level might be of more than usual interest here because of the characteristic recovery processes which occur after illumination of the eye. However, the data indicated that tetrodotoxin did not exhibit a marked effect upon the resting level of the cell. The changes often observed were not consistent; apparently the cell might be hyperpolarized slightly or depolarized slightly by the drug in an unpredictable fashion. Either tetrodotoxin has no significant effect upon the resting level of the cell or present data are inconclusive on this point.

SUMMARY

The transient component of the generator potential of the *Limulus* eye is selectively and reversibly inhibited by tetrodotoxin, while the steady-state component of this intracellular light response is either unaffected or only slightly affected by the drug. These data seem to support the hypothesis that the transient component of this graded response involves a regenerative sodium process. When inhibited by the drug the transient component selectively dark adapts under conditions of constant quantum flux density suggesting that the light reactions control at least two inputs to the generator potential process. Latency studies indicate that an initial portion of the steady-state component *usually* precedes the transient component of the response. At low concentrations tetrodotoxin inhibits only optic nerve activity. This inhibition appears to be specific for the neural mechanisms, and the drug does not appear to act as an uncoupling agent between the generator potential and the neural process.

REFERENCES

ADOLPH, A. R. 1964. Spontaneous slow potential fluctuations in the *Limulus* photoreceptor. *J. Gen. Physiol.* **48**, 297–322.

ADOLPH, A. R. 1965. Personal communication.

BEHRENS, M. E. and WULFF, V. J. 1965. Light-initiated responses of retinula and eccentric cells in the *Limulus* lateral eye. *J. Gen. Physiol.* **48**, 1081–93.

BENOLKEN, R. M. 1961. Reversal of photoreceptor polarity recorded during the graded receptor potential response to light in the eye of *Limulus*. *Biophys. J.* **1**, 551–64.

BENOLKEN, R. M. 1965a. Regenerative transducing properties of a graded visual response. *Cold Spring Harb. Symp. Quant. Biol.* **30** (in press).

BENOLKEN, R. M. 1965b. Light-independent component of a graded visual response. *Biophysical Society Abstracts* **9**, 78.

FUORTES, M. G. F. 1959. Initiation of impulses in visual cells of *Limulus*. *J. Physiol.* **148**, 14–28.

FUORTES, M. G. F. and POGGIO, G. F. 1963. Transient response to sudden illumination in cells of the eye of *Limulus*. *J. Gen. Physiol.* **46**, 435–52.

FURUKAWA, T., SASAOKA, T. and HOSOYA, Y. 1959. Effects of tetrodotoxin on the neuromuscular junction. *Jap. J. Physiol.* **9**, 143–52.

HARTLINE, H. K., WAGNER, H. G. and MACNICHOL, E. F. Jr. 1952. The peripheral origin of nervous activity in the visual systems. *Cold Spring Harb. Symp. Quant. Biol.* **17**, 125–41.

250   R. M. BENOLKEN AND C. J. RUSSELL

Loewenstein, W. R., Terzuolo, C. A. and Washizu, Y. 1963. Separation of transducer and impulse-generating processes in sensory receptors. *Science* **142**, 1180–1.

MacNichol, E. F., Jr. 1956. *Biological Transducers* in *Molecular Structure and Functional Activity of Nerve Cells* (R. G. Grenell and L. J. Mullins, eds.). AIBS pub. 1, pp. 34–53.

MacNichol, E. F., Jr. and Wagner, H. G. 1954. *A High-impedance Input Circuit Suitable for Electrophysiological Recording from Micropipette Electrodes.* Naval Med. Res. Rep. 12, 97–118.

Miller, W. H. 1957. Morphology of the ommatidia of the compound eye of *Limulus*. *J. Biophys. Biochem. Cytol.* **3**, 421–28.

Nakamura, Y., Nakajima, S. and Grundfest, H. 1965. The action of tetrodotoxin on electrogenic components of squid giant axons. *J. Gen. Physiol.* **48**, 985–96.

Narahashi, T., Moore, J. W. and Scott, W. R. 1964. Tetrodotoxin blockage of sodium conductance increase in lobster giant axons. *J. Gen. Physiol.* **47**, 965–74.

Rushton, W. A. H. 1965. Visual adaptation. *Proc. Roy. Soc. B.* **162**, 20–46.

Terzuolo, C. A. 1962. Personal communication. The authors are grateful also to Professor Terzuolo for providing two batches of tetrodotoxin.

Yeandle, S. 1957. Ph.D. dissertation. The Johns Hopkins University, Baltimore, Maryland, U.S.A.

RETINAL ACTION POTENTIALS DURING DARK AND LIGHT ADAPTATION

K. I. NAKA and K. KISHIDA

Neuropharmacology Division, Shionogi Research Laboratory, Osaka, Japan

RECENTLY several papers have appeared which described and analysed the wave form of the retinal action potentials during dark and light adaptation (DeVoe, 1962, 1963; Fuortes and Hodgkin, 1964). Fuortes and Hodgkin have made the most elaborate analysis of the results from the *Limulus* eye and have described the wave form of the action potentials. In this paper the assumption will be made that the light-induced reaction gives rise to a signal, possibly chemical in nature, which depolarizes the retinula cell membrane. Though lacking in experimental basis, this assumption is nevertheless a reasonable one. Based upon this assumption, changes in the sensitivity due to adaptation will be interpreted in terms of voltage vs. log light intensity curves or *V*–log *I* curves. Several authors have already observed the *V*–log *I* relation in the insect compound eye (Hartline, 1928; Goldsmith, 1960; Fuortes, 1963) and Bernhard and Ottoson (1960) have described the *V*–log *I* curve in light and dark adapted states in the Lepidoptera eye.

The *Apis* drone compound eye, which gives rise to clear spike potentials with slow depolarization, offers a very favourable preparation for the analysis of the retinal action potentials under various states of adaptation. It will be suggested that the decrease in sensitivity in the presence of a steady background light is not due to decrease in the signal from the light-induced reaction but is due to the properties of the retinula cell membrane, which cannot maintain the initial peak level induced by a large step input.

MATERIALS AND METHODS

The compound eyes of the *Apis* drone were used. The eye was prepared as described by Naka and Eguchi (1962). The electrodes used were of 2 M potassium citrate-filled glass pipettes having a d.c. resistance of a few hundred megohms. Amplification and recording were done with standard electrical equipment. A Bausch and Lomb 250 mm grating monochrometer combined with a 150 W Xenon lamp was the main light source. Wavelength of light used was of 440 nm and a mechanically driven shutter produced flashes of 50–100 msec. In one of the experiments, in which more light energy was required, the Xenon lamp was directly focused on the receptor layer through a heat-absorbing filter. Intensity of light was controlled by a Kodak 4 log neutral density wedge, the setting of which was measure on an oscilloscope by means of a potentiometer. Each frame of recording film usually contained information on the wave form of the response, log intensity and duration of flash. The pictures were enlarged and tracings were made from which V–log I curves were plotted. For steady illumination a 6 V car lamp (with a lens system) run at various voltages up to 10 V was used. The maximal intensity of this light was enough to bring the initial response to its ceiling (as defined in the Results). The duration and timing of the flash were monitored with a photodiode. The latency thus monitored depends on the relative position of the unit impaled and that of the diode in the optic pathway. However, measurement of change in the latency in a given unit was reliable irrespective of the position of the diode. As it was difficult to measure the earliest potential change the latency was measured at a given level of potential. The reference level of light energy was arbitrarily selected in each unit. No rigid control of the absolute energy of light was attempted. However, it seems reasonable to assume that in a given test run, which was completed within 30 min, the energy of light remained unchanged.

RESULTS

Components of the Response from Single Cells in the Drone Eye

As already described by Naka and Eguchi (1962) a photic stimulation gives rise to a slow depolarization of the retinula cell membrane and a spike potential takes off when the depolarization reaches a certain level (5–10 mV). As in other insect compound eyes, the slow potential induced by a longer flash is composed of an initial potential (described as a spike-like potential by Naka, 1961) followed by a sustained depolarization (cf. Burkhardt and Autrum, 1960). In a given cell, the threshold for firing a spike potential is nearly constant except during and after a strong illumination. Near the threshold the spike potential often destroys the rest of the slow potential as seen in other neurons (Figs. 1C and 2B, C); this might indicate some overlapping of the spike and slow-potential generating area. With stronger flashes it looks as if the slow potential overcomes the invasion of the spike potential (Fig. 1E, F). The spike potentials, except for the first one, become smaller as the slow potential becomes bigger (Fig. 1E, and Naka and Eguchi, 1962). This may be due to a decrease in the resistance of the retinula cell membrane as originally suggested (Naka and Eguchi, 1962) or may also be due to a possible shift of the spike generating area away from that of the slow potential. As seen in Fig. 1, a typical response to a high intensity flash is a spike potential followed by a slow potential with its peak coming far later than that of the spike.

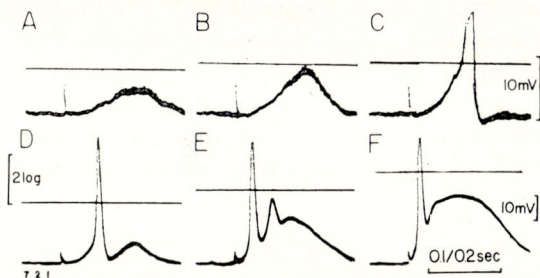

FIG. 1

Response of a single retinula cell to flash of 440 nm. Intensity of the flash was increased from A to F. A and B are subthreshold response. In E two spikes are seen. Note difference in the voltage and time scale for the upper and lower records.

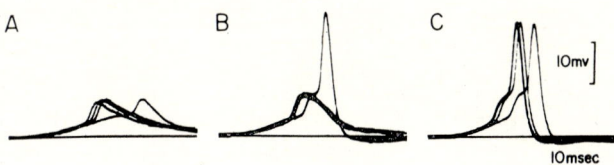

FIG. 2

Prepotential from the drone retinula cell. In each record four sweeps were superimposed. Note the notch on the rising phase of the spike potential in B and C.

Another feature of the potential from the drone retinula cell is a prepotential or local response seen superposed upon the slow depolarization (Fig. 2). The amplitude of the prepotential is usually a few mV and its time course is much faster than that of the slow potential. Near the threshold the spike potential takes off from the prepotential and a notch can be seen on the rising phase of the spike potential (Fig. 2B, C). Similar responses have been observed in neurons of the mammalian central nervous system (Spencer and Kandel, 1961; Naka, 1964). As can be seen in Fig. 2, at threshold the latency of the prepotential shows a considerable variation while the slow potential responds rather consistently to each flash. A patch of membrane may be responsible for this prepotential, but we cannot exclude the possibility that the potential may be an electrotonic spread of the spike potential from an adjoining retinula cell.

Voltage vs. Log I Curve

It is a well-known fact that many visual responses (i.e. incremental threshold, number of spikes or amplitude of the slow potential) plotted against log light intensity yield a straight line (Fechner line) with a tail which gradually comes down to the zero level (Rushton, 1961). Our first question is whether there is any change in the V–log I curve or in the slope of the Fechner line under various states of adaptation. Four curves in the left diagram of Fig. 3 were obtained in the dark (crosses), during (open and filled circles) and 3 min after (squares) termination of a moderate steady light. To see whether these four curves have the same shape all points in the left diagram were replotted in the right diagram with proper shift of the

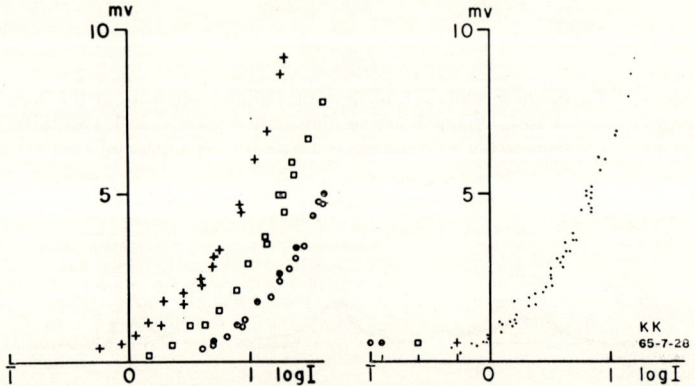

FIG. 3

V–log I curve obtained before (crosses), during (open and filled circles) and after (squares) a moderate light adaptation. In the left diagram curves were plotted on the log scale while in the right diagram these curves were displaced laterally so that all curves superposed. Amount of displacement for each curve is shown by corresponding sign.

log I axis. When properly displaced, all points fall on the same curve, the amount of lateral shift for each curve being shown with the corresponding sign. The sensitivity of a cell at a given moment can be defined as the amount of lateral shift to superpose a particular curve on a reference curve, i.e. the difference in sensitivity in the dark (crosses) and in the presence of a steady background light (filled circles) is about 0·8 log units. This observation suggests that the decrease in sensitivity by light adaptation is a shift of a template V–log I curve on the V–log I plane and is not associated with changes in the shape of the curve.

Figure 4 shows the relation between the sensitivity and spike threshold. In this experiment a drone was kept in the dark for 1 hr; both preparation of the eye and positioning of the electrode were done under red light to minimize light adaptation during these procedures. To begin with, a V–log I curve was obtained from this well dark adapted eye and the position of the curve was taken as the reference (marked A on the log I scale). Then the eye was given a steady adapting light during which another V–log I curve was obtained (the relative position of the curve is shown by *B*). This procedure was repeated to get *C* and *E* which were obtained in the dark and *D* with the same background light as in *B*. Altogether five *V*–log *I* curves were obtained and all points were plotted with proper shift of the log *I* axis, the amount of the shift being shown on the log *I* scale and marked as "sensitivity". All points fall on the same curve and a change in sensitivity of

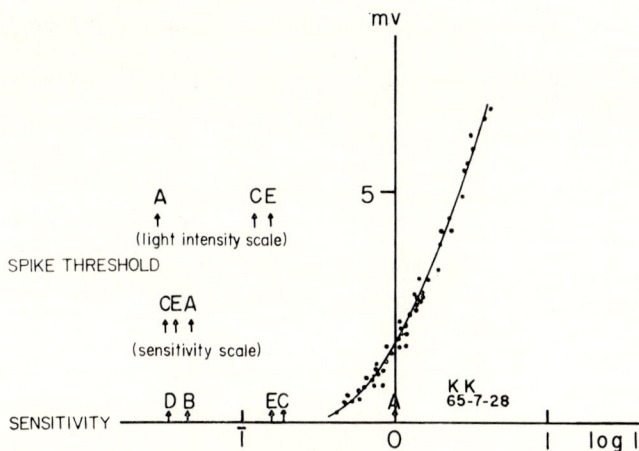

Fig. 4

Change in the sensitivity and spike threshold by light adaptation. All curves were laterally displaced so that they fall on the same position. Sequence of recording is as follows: *A* (well dark adapted)→*B* (with steady background)→*C* (in dark)→*D* (with steady background)→*E* (in dark). "Light intensity scale" is the log intensity of light just giving rise to a spike potential. "Sensitivity scale" is threshold range of the spike potential after three curves (*A*, *C* and *D*) were displaced to the position shown in this figure.

1·5 log units does not seem to cause any apparent change in the shape of the curve. It can be seen that the sensitivity of the cell in the dark decreased by 0·8 log units from a well dark adapted level *A–E* or *C* by light adaptation. In the present experiment no recovery of sensitivity to that of the well dark adapted level was obtained. It can be noted that in the diurnal Lepidoptera adaptation change did not cover more than 1–1·5 log units (Bernhard and Ottoson, 1960). The range of log light intensity for the spike threshold for each curve is shown above the " light intensity scale" and is about 0·72 while the range, when rescaled to account for the lateral shift of *V*–log *I* curve, decreased to 0·14 as shown above the sensitivity scale. If the spike threshold and d.c. level remained unchanged, all arrows on the "sensitivity scale" should coincide. The range of 0·14 log units may possibly be due to fractuation of threshold or to instability of the impaled cell.

V–Log I Curve During Steady Background Illumination

In Figs. 3 and 4 points were plotted as though the *V*–log *I* curve was displaced laterally by the steady background illumination. Change in sensitivity by background light was measured from the amount of lateral shift along the log *I* axis. However, this is not exactly appropriate because the steady background illumination shifts the d.c. level of the cell and curves in Figs. 3 and 4 were plotted without taking into account this "d.c. bias". In Fig. 5 circles and squares were obtained in the dark and triangles with a

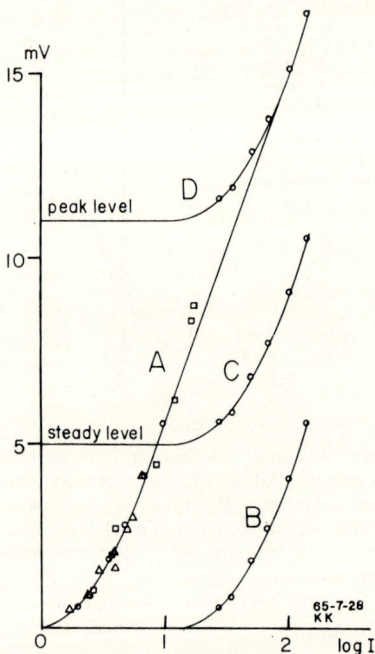

FIG. 5

V–log *I* curve in dark (squares and triangles) and in the presence of a steady background light (circles). In *A* all points were superposed. *B* is the position of *V*–log *I* curve in the presence of a steady background light plotted without any d.c. bias, *C* with a d.c. bias equal to the steady level and *D* with a d. c.bias equal to the peak level of the response by the steady illumination. All continuous curves are the same except the relative positions.

steady background light. These three runs were superposed in *A* and they all fall on the same curve. If the d.c. bias produced by the steady background light is not taken into account, the open circles which were obtained in the presence of the steady light move laterally to *B*, which is equivalent to a decrease in sensitivity by 1·2 log units. Figure 6 is the pen-writer recording of this experiment. The steady light or a step of light gave rise to an initial peak followed by a lower level which was maintained during illumination. As the test flash was put on this steady level, the curve B was actually on this level. To account for this d.c. bias B has to be moved vertically by 5 mV up to C in Fig. 5. By this manipulation the decrease in sensitivity by the background illumination is now 0·5 log units. Though this is what the results indicate, we can perform one more manipulation. As seen from the pen-writer record the steady light gave rise to an initial peak followed by a steady level. The V–log I curve in the presence of a steady background light is by using test flashes superposed on the background illumination. It is interesting to see what would happen if the test flash is added at the time of the initial peak. Though this cannot be done experimentally we can assume that the effect of the test flash is to add an extra potential to the original peak level of the response. To do this the curve B has to be displaced vertically by 12 mV to D or to the "peak level" in Figs. 5 and 6. When this is done the Fechner

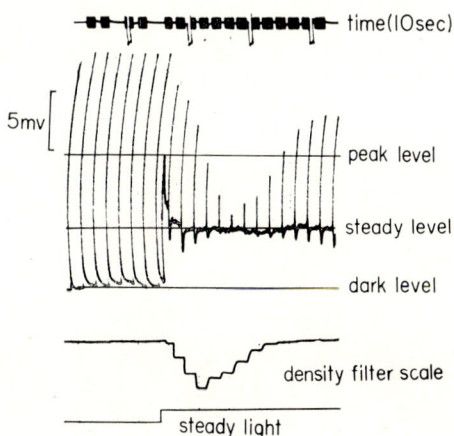

FIG. 6

Pen-writer record of the experiment shown in Fig. 5. The responses without steady illumination include the spike and slow potential. The measurement for Fig. 5 was done on the film record of the same run.

lines of the two curves A and D coincide. This is what one would expect if the relation between the voltage and light intensity is to be given by:

$$V = k \log (1 + I),$$

where V is the response amplitude and I is the sum of all actual light present (see Discussion for details of this equation). Thus the apparent decrease in the sensitivity by a steady background illumination is due to the fact that the response to a step input does not maintain its peak level but falls down to a lower steady level.

In Fig. 7 curves *A* and *B* in Fig. 5 are replotted on both log and linear scales. It is apparent that the lateral shift of a template *V*–log *I* curve is an extension of the linear range of the curve when plotted on a linear scale, i.e. when a cell is light adapted it looks as if the response becomes more linear to light intensity. This is in agreement with the results obtained in the wolf spider (DeVoe, 1963).

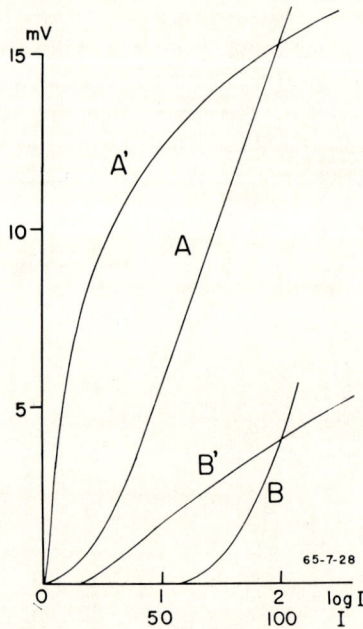

FIG. 7

Log and linear plot of the curves *A* and *B* in Fig. 5. *A* and *B* are on the log scale while *A'* and *B'* are on the linear scale.

In the results so far described it looks as though the Fechner line would go up indefinitely. However, it is obvious that this is physically impossible. To get the ceiling of the *V*–log *I* curve white light from the Xenon lamp was focused directly on the eye through a heat absorbing filter. Results shown in Fig. 8 are from six units and the maximal levels of each unit were normalized to a single unit to facilitate comparison. The heavy line drawn is $V = k \log (1 + I)$. Points from these six units seem to fall fairly well on this line and abruptly bend horizontally indicating that the response has reached its ceiling. Thus the Fechner line when extended (as shown by the thin line) covers a range of about 2·2 log units. It becomes interesting to see whether this ceiling is that of the signal from the photochemical reaction or that of the cell membrane.

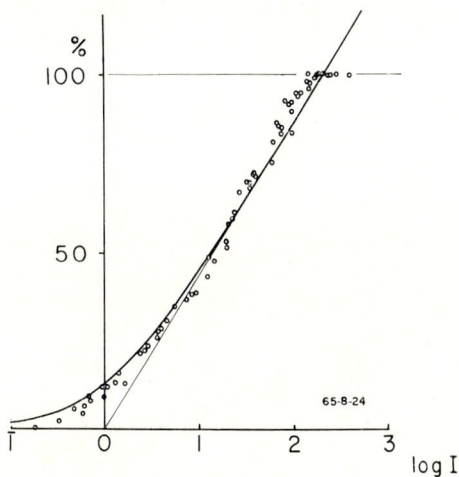

FIG. 8

Saturation of V–log I curve. Points are from six units. The curve drawn is $V = k$ log $(1 + I)$. Flashes used were from a Xenon lamp with a heat-absorbing filter.

In Fig. 9 responses were obtained without (white circles) and with (filled circles) steady background light. The saturation level of this cell was found to be at 45 mV and the steady light gave rise to an initial potential of about 40 mV. The three groups of filled circles are the same plot properly displaced and the three curves are also the same except for changes in I_d or I_b in the following equation:

$$V = k \log\left(1 + \frac{I + I_b}{I_d}\right).$$

When the d.c. bias due to the background illumination is neglected, the sensitivity of the cell decreases by 2 log units. In the displaced curve the maximal test flash was not strong enough to show any sign of a ceiling, though on the log I scale the displaced plot exceeded the saturation level obtained in the dark. As the range covered by the Fechner line in the dark was 2·2 log units, the steady background light apparently extended the "dynamic range" of the cell by nearly 1 log unit. When the curve was moved vertically to the level reached by the initial peak of the response to steady light, the Fechner line of the curve obtained in the dark coincides with that of the curve obtained with steady background light. Moreover, the vertical shift of the curve results in a hypothetical exceeding of the saturation level by 10 mV.

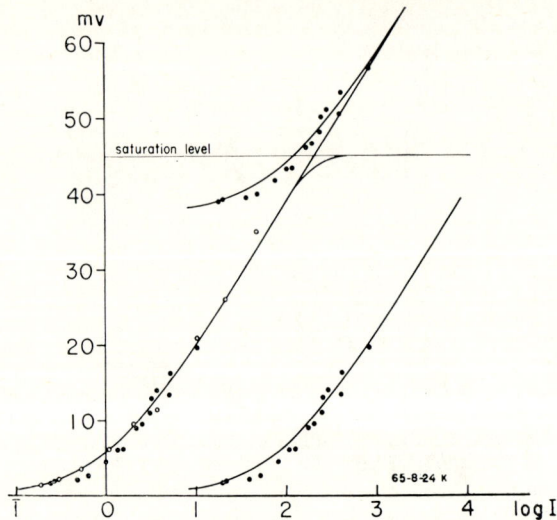

FIG. 9

V–log I curve without (open circles) and with (filled circles) a background light. Three groups of filled circles are the same plot displaced as in Fig. 5, i.e. one without any d.c. bias and the other with a d.c. bias equal to the peak level of the response by the steady light. Saturation level of this cell was obtained from the other test run which is included in Fig. 8. Three curves are the same:

$$\left[V = k \log \left(1 + \frac{I + I_b)}{I_d} \right) \right] \quad \text{except } I_b \text{ and } I_d.$$

Changes in both Sensitivity and Wave Form of the Response During and After a Strong Steady Illumination

In *Limulus* a steady light leaves the eye desensitized for several minutes after the light is "off" (cf. Benolken, 1962; Fuortes and Hodgkin, 1964). In the drone, however, it is extremely difficult to desensitize the retinula cell response by a steady illumination. Figure 10 illustrates a typical record in which a cell was subjected to a strong steady light for more than 2 min. Up to C the steady light was the same light used for the test flash. The steady light was momentarily replaced by a flash to test the change in the response amplitude (to a fixed intensity flash). The test flash was given immediately after the "off" of the steady light and then once in every 2 sec. Within 4–6 sec the response amplitude recovered to 90 % of the response obtained before the light adaptation. In D, E and F the steady background was obtained from another source and the test flash was added on the steady background (the intensity of the test flash was the same as the one used in A–C). When the d.c. shift was not taken into account the test flash gave rise to a response which was about 10 % of the response obtained in the dark. However, the

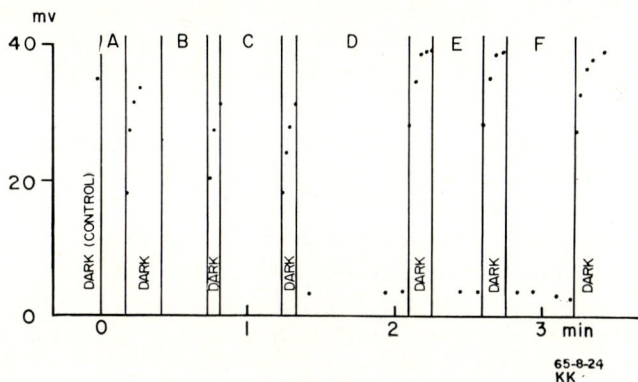

FIG. 10

Effects of prolonged steady illumination on the response by a fixed intensity flash. Points in "dark" are by flashes given once every 2 sec. In *A*, *B* and *C* the steady light was the same light used for the test flash while in *D*, *E* and *F* the steady light was from a 6 V car lamp run at 10 V. Test flashes were from a Xenon lamp with a heat absorbing filter.

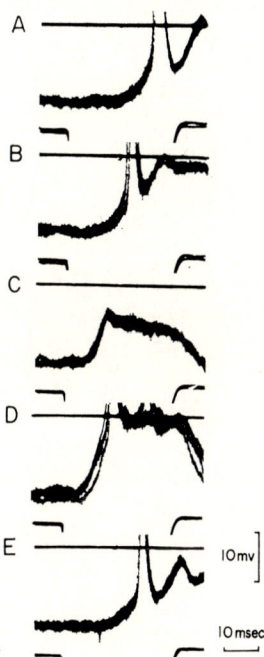

FIG. 11

Change in the wave form of the response caused by light adaptation. *A* in dark, *B* and *C* with a slight and a moderate background light, and *D* and *E* immediately after and one minute after "off" of the steady illumination. In each record four sweeps were superimposed. Flashes used were of 440 nm.

response quickly recovered on termination of the steady background light and it actually became bigger than the control obtained before steady light adaptation.

Time records of the response during and after "off" of the steady illumination are shown in Fig. 11 in which four sweeps were superimposed in each record to average any change in the latency and wave form of the response. *A* was recorded in dark, *B* with slight background, *C* with stronger background illumination, *D* immediately after and *E* 1 min after "off" of the background illumination. Except in *C*, one or two spikes are seen on the rising phase of the response. It is apparent from these records that the rising phase of the response becomes steeper and the latency of the response shorter with light adaptation.

Figure 12 illustrates changes in the latency and response amplitude after "off" of a steady light. Values in the dark are shown above "control". As seen from this figure, the latency which was one-third of the value obtained before light adaptation gradually returned to the original value within 20 sec. On the other hand, the amplitude of the response showed a transient increase followed by a period of depression. Thus the most conspicuous effect of light

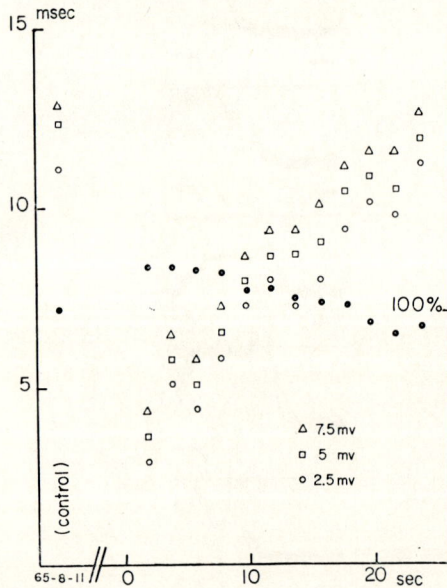

Fig. 12

Changes in the latency and amplitude of the response by a fixed intensity flash (440 nm) after "off" of a steady background illumination. Filled circles are amplitude and open circles, triangles and squares are the latency measured at 2·5, 5 and 7·5 mV. "Zero" indicates "off" of the steady adapting light.

adaptation is a decrease in the latency which is closely related to the change in the wave form but not to the response amplitude to a fixed intensity flash. The amplitude of the response to a flash of fixed intensity increased by 10% after "off" of the steady illumination and became smaller than the control at 20 sec after termination of the steady light.

DISCUSSION

Though the receptor layer of the insect compound eye apparently contains cells other than the retinula cell which may be able to give rise to potentials in response to photic stimulation as does the eccentric retinula cell (Eguchi, 1962), it seems reasonable to assume that the potentials described here have been recorded from single retinula cells which are primary sensory cells. As already described by Naka and Eguchi (1962), two types of response can be obtained from the receptor layer, one with and the other without any clear spike potentials. This does not necessarily mean presence of two different types of cells, but rather seems to indicate two states of one class of cells. It is interesting to note that in the *Limulus* eye similar responses have been observed, one usually attributed to the retinula cell and the other to the eccentric cell.

As fully discussed by Rushton (1965), many visual responses can be represented by the equation

$$V = k \log\left(1 + \frac{I + I_b}{I_d}\right),$$

where V is the response amplitude or increment threshold, I intensity of the test flash, I_b of the background light or field adapting light and I_d the "intrinsic light" of the eye. In the drone retinula cell the potential follows this equation up to the ceiling of the cell, though the slow approach to the base line is often steeper than the one predicted by the equation. Obviously change in I_b corresponds to sliding of the whole curve along the Fechner line and change of I_d to sliding of the curve upwards along the log I axis. In the dark adaptation experiment we could not obtain any clear indication of change in I_d except in cases where eyes were kept in the dark for several hours. Even in this case, change in the sensitivity was of the order of one log unit, and the shift was always towards a decrease in the sensitivity by light adaptation. It was not possible to bring the sensitivity back to the well dark adapted level. In intact diurnal Lepidoptera, Bernard and Ottoson (1960) obtained changes in the sensitivity of 1–1·5 log units. In these nocturnal species they showed that the further increase in the sensitivity is due to the movement of the screening pigment. This should be equivalent to increase in I_d.

Estimates of sensitivity change in the presence of a steady background light depend upon how the experiments are interpreted. If the d.c. bias caused by the background illumination is not taken into account or the response is monitored by an a.c. amplifier, it then looks as if the V–log I curve moved laterally, i.e. the I_d increased. If the steady level or d.c. bias caused by the background illumination is considered it looks as though both I_d and I_b have changed. A third interpretation is to assume that the test flash is to be added on to the initial transient potential but not on to the steady level produced by the background illumination. Though this could not be done experimentally, the V–log I curve can be shifted vertically to the peak level of the response. When this is done it becomes apparent that only I_b was changed by the background light. Steady adaptation does not change I_d or the slope of the Fechner line. This is what one could expect if there were no adaptation in the system; to add a steady background is equivalent to increasing in the intensity of the test flash. This leads to the interesting suggestion that we have this "apparent" decrease in the sensitivity because the response to a background light could not, or rather did not, maintain its initial peak level but fell off to a lower level. In this case the signal from the photochemical reaction is the sum of all actual light present.

The response of the retinula cell to a step of high intensity light is a transient peak (referred to as the spike-like potential by Naka, 1961) followed by a steady level (Burkhardt and Autrum, 1960; Naka, 1961). As shown in Fig. 8, the dynamic range of the drone retinula cell response (or the range of log light covered by the Fechner line) is a little more than 2 log units when measurements are done with flashes. If the peak level were to be maintained, a strong light could easily put the cell out of its dynamic range and a pulse of light superimposed on a steady light could not be detected. This levelling off from the peak level is therefore necessary to extend the dynamic range of the cell. Thus to overcome the limit set by the ceiling of the cell membrane voltage the retinula cell seems to have a mechanism which brings down the initial peak to a lower level even though the signal from the photochemical reaction(s) is to remain unchanged during a steady illumination. This levelling off is not due to any kind of desensitization because a pulse of light superposed on a steady background gives rise to a V–log I curve with no change in the slope or I_d if the V–log I curve is shifted up to the peak level. We favour a view that the levelling off is due to an active process or a kind of feedback in the retinula cell membrane. Fuortes and Hodgkin (1964) have suggested that there is a parametric feedback in the Limulus ommatidium which automatically gains control of the cell. In the drone retinula cell it was found that the sensitivity of the cell (measured by a fixed intensity flash) returned to the dark level or often exceeded the level a few seconds after termination of a strong adapting light. This is what one could expect if field adaptation is to have its effect in the retinula cell membrane and not in the photochemical part of the system. The transient decrease in the amplitude of the response immediately after the termination of adapting light may possibly be due to a time lag in the feedback system. It was mentioned that a decrease in sensitivity caused by a steady background light can be represented by an increase in I_d when the d.c. bias by the adapting light was not taken into account. Mathematical implications of the lateral shift of a V–log I curve along the log I axis corresponds to an extension of the pseudo-linear range when the curve is plotted on a linear scale, i.e. when the eye is light adapted it becomes more linear. In the wolf spider, DeVoe (1963) found that the condition producing linear responses was light adaptation of the eye. In Fig. 13 two time records, one obtained in the dark and the other in the presence of a steady illumination, are superposed to show differences in the wave form. When the eye is light adapted the peak at "on" appears as an undershoot at "off"; also under light adaptation "on" and "off" become symmetrical. This is what one expects in a linear system (cf. DeVoe, 1963). As seen in Fig. 13, the difference in the latency is very striking. A simple filter

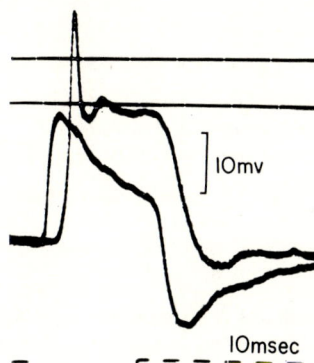

10mv

10msec

65-8-24

FIG. 13

Comparison of responses obtained in dark and in the presence of a steady background illumination. Records were selected for the similar slow potential amplitude. The response in dark gave rise to a spike potential.

network is not enough to account for the changes in the latency and wave form of the response under various states of adaptation (Fuortes and Hodgkin, 1964). A similar undershoot appears when a long steady illumination is turned off; this "sensory hyperpolarization" (cf. Granit, 1955) seems responsible for the bigger response after a strong light adaptation observed in Figs. 10 and 12.

The general scheme of the excitation process in the *Apis* drone retinula cell deduced from the results of this experiment is as follows: light gives rise to chemical reaction(s), probably in the rhabdomere, which produces a signal proportional to the logarithm of all actual light present at a given moment. It is extremely difficult to reduce the signal from the hypothetical photochemical reaction, even by an intense bleaching. The signal, which is probably chemical in nature, depolarizes the retinula cell membrane. The membrane incorporates a feedback system which reduces the potential level and prevents overloading of the cell by large step inputs. This feedback mechanism keeps the cell from saturating and also extends the dynamic range so that the signal from the photochemical reaction can be utilized fully. In the drone, the depolarization of the retinula cell membrane gives rise to spikes in the proximal portion of the cell.

ACKNOWLEDGEMENTS

We are grateful to Dr. Ryonosuke Kido for his generous support of this project. Our thanks are also due to Prof. Masutaro Kuwabara for his kind loan of some of the equipment used in the experiments.

REFERENCES

BENOLKEN, R. M. 1962. Effects of light- and dark-adaptation processes on the generator potential of the *Limulus* eye. *Vision Res.* **2**, 103–24.

BERNHARD, C. G. and OTTOSON, D. 1960. Comparative studies on dark adaptation in the compound eyes of nocturnal and diurnal Lepidoptera. *J. Gen. Physiol.* **44**, 195–203.

BURKHARDT, D. and AUTRUM, H. 1960. Die Belichtungs-Potentiale einzelner Sehzellen von *Calliphora erythrocephala*. *Z. Naturforsch.* **15b**, 612–6.

DEVOE, R. D. 1962. Linear superposition of retinal action potentials to predict electrical flicker responses from the eye of the wolf spider, *Lycosa baltimoriana* (Keyserling). *J. Gen. Physiol.* **46**, 75–96.

DEVOE, R. D. 1963. Linear relation between stimulus amplitudes and amplitudes of retinal action potentials from the eye of the wolf spider. *J. Gen. Physiol.* **47**, 13–32.

EGUCHI, E. 1962. The fine structure of the eccentric retinula cell in the insect compound eye (*Bombyx mori*). *J. Ultrastructure Research*, **7**, 328–38.

FUORTES, M. G. F. 1963. Visual responses in the eye of the dragonfly. *Science* **142**, 69–70.

FUORTES, M. G. F. and HODGKIN, A. L. 1964. Changes in time scale and sensitivity in the ommatidia of *Limulus*. *J. Physiol.* **172**, 239–63.

GOLDSMITH, T. H. 1960. The nature of the retinal action potential, and the spectral sensitivity of ultraviolet and green receptor systems of the compound eye of the worker honeybee. *J. Gen. Physiol.* **43**, 775–9.

GRANIT, R. 1955. *Receptors and Sensory Perception.* Yale University Press, New Haven.

HARTLINE, H. K. 1928. A quantitative and descriptive study of the electric response to illumination of the Arthropod eye. *Amer. J. Physiol.* **83**, 446–83.

NAKA, K. 1961. Recording of retinal action potentials from single cells in the insect compound eye. *J. Gen. Physiol.* **44**, 571–84.

NAKA, K. 1964. Electrophysiology of the fetal spinal cord. I. Action potentials of the motoneuron. *J. Gen. Physiol.* **47**, 1003–22.

NAKA, K. and EGUCHI, E. 1962. Spike potentials recorded from the insect photoreceptor. *J. gen. Physiol.* **45**, 663–80.

RUSHTON, W. A. H. 1961. The intensity factor in vision. In *Light and Life.* The Johns Hopkins Press, Baltimore.

RUSHTON, W. A. H. 1965. The Ferrier Lecture: Visual adaptation. *Proc. Roy. Soc., B* **162**, 20–46.

SPENCER, W. A. and KANDEL, E. R. 1961. Electrophysiology of hippocampal neurons. IV. Fast prepotentials. *J. Neurophysiol,* **24**, 272–85.

DETECTION OF SINGLE QUANTA BY THE COMPOUND EYE OF THE FLY *MUSCA*

W. E. Reichardt

Max-Planck-Institut für Biologie, Tübingen, Germany

INTRODUCTION

SOME twenty years ago Hecht, Shlaer and Pirenne (1942) found that the minimum energy required for threshold vision in the human eye yields values between 2·1 and 5·7 $\times$ 10^{-10} ergs at the cornea, which correspond to between 54 and 148 quanta of blue–green light. Taking into consideration the energy losses due to corneal reflection, absorption in the optic media, and retinal transmission, the range of 54 to 148 quanta at the cornea corresponds to an upper limit of 5 to 14 quanta actually absorbed by the retinal rods. Obviously the number of rods involved (500) precludes any significant two-quantum absorptions per rod. In order to trigger a visual effect, one quantum must be absorbed by each of 5 to 14 rods in the retina; i.e. a coincidence of 5 to 14 primary events is necessary for the elicitation of a visual effect. This finding might be due to the fact that several hundred rods are tied together in some kind of coincidence-detecting network summing the outputs of these primary elements.

More recently, this question has been taken up again by other investigators recording membrane potentials from visual cells in the invertebrate eye (see MacNichol, 1958). Yeandle (1957, 1958) has found in *Limulus* that an irregular succession of discrete depolarizing waves ("bumps") sometimes occur under conditions of dark adaptation. The average rate of occurrence of these waves is linearly related to the light intensity, as was reported by Fuortes and Yeandle (1964). They also found that the number of waves evoked by a light flash varies randomly, in approximately a Poisson distribution. The agreement of their data with the predictions based on the hypothesis that one, two, or three quanta of light are required for the elicitation of one wave is quite compatible with the one-quantum hypothesis. Similar experiments conducted by Scholes (1964) on the locust, and by Kirschfeld (1965a) on the fly's compound eye are not in conflict with these findings; they also strongly support the one-quantum receptor hypothesis.

During recent years an analysis of the optomotor reactions in insects has been worked out in this laboratory. These investigations are based on quantitative behavioral data (Götz, 1964; Hassenstein, 1951, 1958; Reichardt,

1957, 1961, 1962; Reichardt and Varjú, 1959; Varjú, 1959). It is essential for completion of the analysis of the optomotor reaction to clarify whether absorption of one light quantum by a photopigment molecule in the rhabdomere of the compound eye suffices to trigger a photochemical reaction, or whether absorption of more than one quantum within a critical time interval and molecular cross-section is necessary. Furthermore, one would especially like to know whether a temporal and/or spatial coincidence of physiological events elicited by the photochemical reactions takes place *before* perception of motion is carried out by the central nervous system.

THEORETICAL CONSIDERATIONS

Before turning to the methods and experimental results, the following theoretical argument can be put forward. We consider an area F, packed with N photopigment molecules, each molecule contributing to the area with a molecular cross-section q. It is assumed that in complete darkness all pigment molecules remain in their inactive state. If a light beam j, of n quanta per unit time, impinges on the area F, a pigment molecule may absorb one quantum. Let us first consider the case where the absorption of a quantum converts the inactive molecule into an activated molecule and where the photochemically activated molecule sets in train sequential reactions, which may culminate in a physiological event. In this case we may speak of a "one-quantum receptor" since absorption of one quantum sets off a physiological event with a finite probability. We may next consider the case where absorption of a first quantum converts the pigment molecule from the inactive state to a preactivated state and where absorption of a second quantum—during the life time τ of the preactivated state—is necessary for the conversion to the activated state. In this case, we may speak of a "two-quantum receptor", for here absorption of two quanta per molecular cross-section q and life time τ are required to elicit a physiological event with a finite probability. This two-quantum reaction may be formulated as follows:

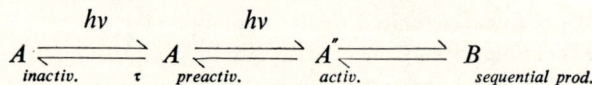

$$A \underset{inactiv.}{\overset{h\nu}{\rightleftharpoons}} \underset{\tau \quad preactiv.}{A} \overset{h\nu}{\rightleftharpoons} \underset{activ.}{A''} \rightleftharpoons \underset{sequential\ prod.}{B}$$

Based on these considerations one finds $\overline{m} = j \cdot (q/F)$ for the average number of quantum hits per molecular cross-section and unit time. The probability for one quantum hit per molecular cross-section q and per time τ is then given by $\overline{m} \cdot \tau$, and for z hits by the expression $(\overline{m} \cdot \tau)^z$, since the quanta are statistically independent from one another. Consequently $(1/\tau)(\overline{m} \cdot \tau)^z = \overline{m}(\overline{m} \cdot \tau)^{z-1}$ is the probability for z hits during unit time. The average number of photochemical reactions r for N molecules is then given by $r = N \cdot \overline{m}$ $(\overline{m} \cdot \tau)^{z-1} = j \ (N \cdot q/F) \ [j(q \cdot \tau/F)]^{z-1}$, and the average number of reactions per flux j by the expression $r/j = (N \cdot q/F) \ (j \ q \cdot \tau/F)^{z-1}$.

Two types of reactions may be considered:

(1) One-quantum reaction ($z = 1$). Here we find $r/j = N \cdot q/F$. The quantum yield does not depend on the flux j. The molecular cross-section is a constant.

(2) Two-quantum reaction ($z = 2$). Here we have $r/j = N \cdot Q/F$, where $Q = j \cdot q^2 \cdot \tau/F$. The quantum yield depends linearly on j, which amounts to saying that the effective molecular cross-section Q *changes* with the quantum flux j.

Various programs of light stimulation are conceivable to test whether the reaction depends on a one- or on a multi-quantum process. In the experiments to be described now, the following two light programs were selected.

Program type 1: the program consists of a light stimulus whose intensity is constant in time and equal to I_1 (see Fig. 1).

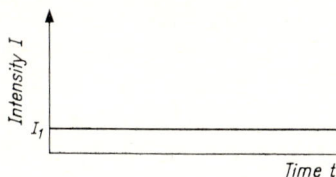

FIG. 1

Test program type 1.

Program type 2: the program consists of a sequence of short light pulses of width Δt, peak amplitude I_2, pulse frequency $1/T$ and average intensity I_1 (see Fig. 2). The average number of quanta applied per unit time evidently

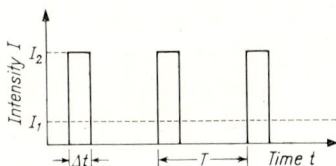

FIG. 2

Test program type 2.

is the same in both programs. Programs type 1 and 2 applied to a one-quantum receptor should result in the same average rate of photochemical reactions. If the programs are applied to a "multi-quantum receptor", program type 2 *may* trigger a greater photochemical reaction rate than program type 1. The maximum factor by which the reaction rates may differ is easily derived for the two-quantum case. Since I_2 is greater than I_1 by a factor $T/\Delta t$, the effective molecular cross-section Q is enlarged by this factor. Consequently, under program type 2 the two-quantum receptor is $T/\Delta t$ times more efficient than under program type 1 and conversely the rate of photochemical reactions is increased by the same factor. Whether the effect predicted for the two-quantum receptor is actually found depends on the magnitudes of τ, Δt and T. One expects to find the predicted effect if $\tau \leq \Delta t$; if, however, $\Delta t < \tau < T$ the individual pulse becomes integrated over the life time τ of the preactivated state and the expected increase of the rate of photochemical reaction must be smaller than $T/\Delta t$. The increase factor declines to unity when $\tau \geq T$, since in this case two or more pulses are integrated in time, and the expected effect disappears. Under these conditions, multi-quantum receptors behave like one-quantum receptors and do not respond differently to the two different light programs.

For any experimental test of the quantum efficiency it is of greatest importance that one operates near the visual threshold. Only under these conditions is the frequency of quanta incident per receptor sufficiently low that the rates of photochemical reaction elicited do not produce significant changes in the concentration of inactive receptor molecules. The kinetics of the photochemical reaction should then be determined entirely by the quantum flux and not by other processes.

The advantage of the experimental procedure described rests on the fact that no absolute light calibrations are necessary as they were, for instance, in some of the experiments by Hecht *et al.*

The theoretical argument developed here is based on photochemical considerations but is valid also for spatial or temporal nervous coincidence processes, if the terminology used here is adapted to that domain.

MATERIAL AND METHODS

The experiments to be described were carried out on females of a strain of *Musca* maintained in the laboratory. Flies were prepared for experiments by attaching a small cardboard tab between the head and thorax with a drop of a mixture of beeswax and resin. This served as a means of suspending the flies in the experimental apparatus, and prevented motion of the head relative to the thorax during measurement of the optomotor reaction. The ocelli were covered with a drop of lampblack suspended in beeswax, so that only the compound eyes could receive optical stimuli. During these operations the flies were anaesthetized with carbon dioxide in the earlier experiments, whereas in the later ones they were immobilized by cooling. After this preparation the flies were kept in individual cages provided with water and agar containing a mixture of sugar and yeast extract.

The torque exerted by *Musca* during fixed flight was utilized as the quantitative measure of the optomotor reaction of the insect to light programs of types 1 and 2. The principal components of the apparatus developed in this laboratory to measure the torque exerted by fixed flying insects are shown schematically in Fig. 3. A fly is clamped in a horizontal position, by means of the cardboard tab attached to its thorax, to a rigid double-coil system. The double-coil system is suspended from a fixed frame by tension bands that allow it to undergo angular displacement about an equilibrium position. The upper coil lies between the poles of a permanent magnet, while the lower coil lies in an alternating magnetic field produced by the high-frequency core of a coil fed with current from a 50 kc/s generator. The double-coil system

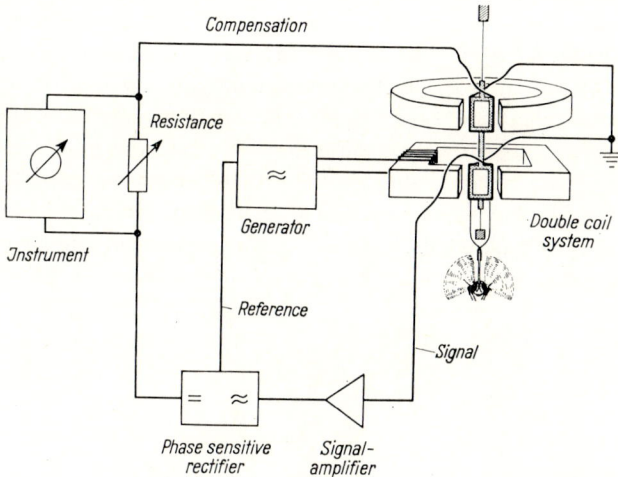

FIG. 3

Schematic representation of the torque-compensating apparatus for measurement of the optomotor reaction of *Musca*.

is at equilibrium when the lower coil is so oriented in the alternating magnetic field that no voltage is induced in it. When, under the influence of a torque exerted by the fly (optomotor reaction), the double-coil system is displaced from its equilibrium position, an alternating voltage is induced in the lower coil. The magnitude of the induced voltage is, for small displacements, proportional to the displacement angle. The induced voltage is amplified, undergoes phase-sensitive rectification with a reference voltage from the high-frequency generator, and is fed into the upper coil as a compensation current. Since the phase of the voltage induced in the lower coil shifts by 180° according to the direction of the displacement of the double-coil system, the compensation current changes sign with a change in the direction of the torque exerted by the fly. Interaction of the compensation current flowing through the upper coil with the field of the permanent magnet produces a torque on the double-coil system. The orientation of the magnetic field is such that this torque always opposes that exerted by the fly. The algebraic magnitude of the compensation current is then a linear measure of the torque exerted by the fly. When the amplification of the voltage induced in the lower coil is sufficiently large, then the double-coil system, and hence the attached fly, undergo only very small angular displacements under the influence of the torques developed by the fly.

Compensation current was recorded as a function of time with a Varian G-10 Graphic Recorder which had a time constant of 0·4 sec. The recorder was connected across an RC filter with a time constant of 1·6 sec. The relationship between applied torque and compensation current is linear, and the sensitivity of the instrument amounts to 0·27 mA/dyne cm. When a torque of magnitude 1·0 dyne/cm was applied to the double-coil system, which corresponds approximately to the maximum optomotor reaction of *Musca* observed in these experiments, the resulting angular displacement of the double-coil system was of the order of 1/100°, or about 1/200° of the angular separation between the optical axes of adjacent ommatidia in the eye of *Musca*. The arrangement used for eliciting optomotor reactions from *Musca* is shown schematically in Fig. 4. The experimental animal is clamped

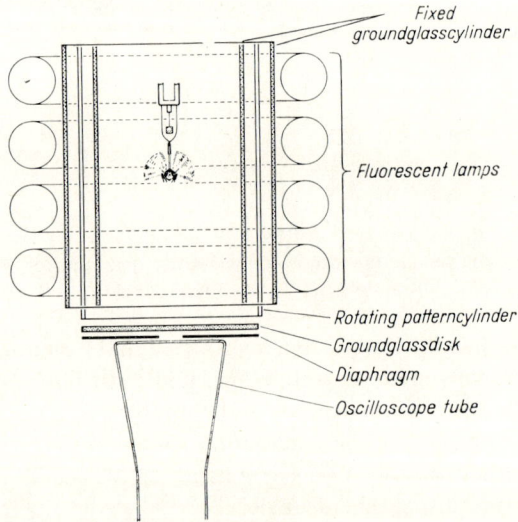

FIG. 4

Schematic representation of arrangements for eliciting optomotor reactions of *Musca*. The cylinder arrangement shown in the figure consists of three concentric cylinders. The outer and the inner ground-glass cylinders are stationary, whereas the cylinder located between the ground-glass cylinders carries the pattern and can be rotated by an AC motor through a planetary gear system. The three-cylinder arrangement shown in the figure was applied in the 1 c/s pulsed-light experiment whereas in the experiments with pulsed light frequencies above 20 c/s the inner ground-glass cylinder was removed. Outer illumination of patterned cylinder is provided by annular fluorescent lamps. During tests, constant or pulsed light illuminating the inner ground-glass or patterned cylinder from within is provided by means of an oscilloscope tube. The oscilloscope screen is covered by a diaphragm containing an optical window; the light from the screen is scattered in a ground-glass disk.

in the horizontal position to the torque-compensating instrument at the axis of a rotating patterned cylinder. The patterned cylinder was driven by an AC motor through a planetary gear system. Choice of gear settings allowed drum speeds in the range 0·04–1360°/sec. Patterns could be mounted on the rotating drum to provide stimuli for the optomotor reaction. In all the experiments reported here the pattern consisted of a sinusoidally changing transmittance or reflectance in the azimuthal direction with a spatial wave-length of 45°. The pattern was prepared in such a way that it transmitted or reflected light in approximate accordance with a Lambert surface. The radius of the sinusoidally-changing pattern was 5·75 cm. At the beginning of each experiment the rotating cylinder was illuminated through a fixed ground-glass cylinder from the outside with four Philips TLE 4OW/34 de Luxe annular fluorescent lamps. The lamps were powered from a regulated DC source. During the tests with constant intensity in time, or pulsed light intensity down to 20 c/s, the patterned cylinder was illuminated from within —the inner ground-glass cylinder removed—by means of an oscilloscope tube; the fluorescent lamps were switched off. During the experiments with 1 c/s frequency of pulsed light the three-cylinder arrangement shown in Fig. 4 was used; both the inner and outer illumination were switched on. The phosphor of the oscilloscope tube contained an activator with a decay time of 17 μsec to 1/10 of peak intensity value. The spectrum ranged from 320 to 620 mμ with a maximum at 430 mμ. In order to generate light program type 1 (constant intensity in time) the beam was defocused and centered in the axis of the oscilloscope tube. The light was scattered in a ground-glass disk and illuminated either the rotating patterned cylinder or the inner ground-glass cylinder. The light program type 2 (short light pulses at selected frequencies) was produced as follows. The electron beam was focused and the sweep of the oscilloscope turned on. Under these conditions the patterned cylinder or the inner ground-glass cylinder was illuminated with pulsed light. The pulse length was determined by the sweep speed of the electron beam and the diameter (1 cm) of the optical window. The following pulse-light programs were applied in our experiments.

Pulse frequency (c/s)	Pulse length (sec)	I_2/I_1
500	$1·50 \times 10^{-5}$	133
200	$1·25 \times 10^{-4}$	40
100	$2·50 \times 10^{-4}$	40
20	$2·50 \times 10^{-4}$	200
1	$5·00 \times 10^{-2}$	20

C.E.—T

Measurements of light intensity were made with a photomultiplier 1 P 28 having stabilized *dynode* voltages and a linear response to intensity. In order to provide linearity, the photomultiplier anode current was held below 5 μA and the *dynode* voltages at relatively high levels. The anode current was fed into a low-pass filter with a time constant of 5 sec, followed by feedback electronics. During the experiments the photomultiplier unit was mainly used for the equilibration of average quantum fluxes in the light programs of type 1 and type 2 (cf. Figs. 1 and 2). The contrast of the patterned cylinder used in the experiments was measured with a photomultiplier mounted in a slit system with an aperture of 1°. The contrast of the sinusoidal pattern is here defined to be $m = (a - b)/(a + b)$ where a is the maximal and b the minimal brightness of the pattern. Under oscilloscope illumination the patterned cylinder reflected a contrast of $m = 21\%$ if the inner ground-glass cylinder had been removed. In the three-cylinder arrangement a pattern contrast of $m = 50\%$ was measured from the fly's position if only the outer illumination, provided by the fluorescent lamps, was switched on. Mean brightness values at the surface of the patterned or inner ground-glass cylinders were measured with the photomultiplier, which had been calibrated with a flux-meter (Gossen Co., Erlangen, Germany). Mean brightness values are given in Apostilb (1 Apostilb $= 10^{-4}$ lambert).

Individual measurements of the optomotor reactions were made as follows. With a fly in the experimental apparatus, and with the selected light program, patterned cylinder and given drum speed, the cylinder was rotated first for one minute in one direction and then for another minute in the opposite direction. The reaction was evaluated as the quantity

$$\frac{1}{2} \left\{ \text{[average torque with cylinder rotating toward "right"]} - \text{[average torque with cylinder rotating toward "left"]} \right\}.$$

This measure of the reaction eliminates any possible asymmetries in the torques produced by the flies. Reactions (torques) following the direction of cylinder rotation are designated positive, those opposing the direction of cylinder rotation are designated negative. Averaging of the recorded torques was at first performed with the aid of a planimeter and later with an electronic integrator operating on line during the experiments.

The term reaction curve denotes here the optomotor reaction of *Musca* as a function of certain parameters (e.g. average brightness, cylinder speed, etc.). When possible, reaction curves were measured without interrupting the flight of the experimental animal. However, when alteration of the experimental parameters required appreciable time, then between measurements or during dark adaptation the animal was induced to interrupt its flight by giving it a small piece of paper to hold with its legs. Good specimens of *Musca* fly for 20–60 min without stopping, thus allowing 10–30 measurements during a single flight. In order to determine whether the magnitude of the optomotor reaction diminishes during the flight of the experimental animal, as might occur if the insect tires during its flight, the reactions of various flies were measured as a function of time with constant cylinder speed. The results of these measurements, published in an earlier paper (Fermi and Reichardt, 1963), show that the magnitude of the reaction remained relatively constant over a period of nearly an hour. All measurements of reaction curves were made with unsystematic alteration of the experimental parameters in order to minimize the small error arising from tiring of the fly.

Reaction curves presented in the experimental section are the averages obtained from several individual flies, unless stated otherwise. The points in the figures give the averages, $\bar{x}$, of the individual reactions, x_i; the vertical lines give the standard error $\pm\,\sigma$, where $\sigma^2 = (1/n - 1) \sum_{i=1}^{n} (x_i - \bar{x})^2$, with n being the number of measurements.

Room temperature was maintained between 19 and 21°C during all the experiments.

EXPERIMENTAL RESULTS

A. *Elicitation of an Optomotor Reaction*

Control Experiment I. At the beginning and at the end of the experimental procedure an optomotor reaction was elicited from every test fly under the following conditions. The annular fluorescent lamps were switched on and the oscilloscope tube was switched off. Under this illumination 1000 Apostilb average brightness was measured at the surface of the patterned or inner ground-glass cylinder. The angular velocity of the patterned cylinder amounted to $w = 49\cdot25°/\text{sec}$. With the rotating pattern used throughout these experiments a contrast frequency of $w/\lambda = 1\cdot09$ c/s was generated at an angular coordinate of the cylinder. This contrast frequency elicits the optimum optomotor reaction of *Musca*. The control experiments were carried out in order to test whether the flies reacted before and after the experimental procedure with the same torque. Only the results taken from flies whose reaction after the experimental procedure was within the limits of $\pm\,10\%$ of the torque measured at the beginning of the experiment were collected and are presented here.

B. *Dark Adaptation*

Control Experiment II. Every fly, after being checked on its optomotor reaction, was dark adapted for at least 30 min. In Fig. 5 a control experiment testing the time course of dark adaptation is shown. In this experiment the inner ground-glass cylinder was removed. At time $t = 0$ the outer illumination provided by the fluorescent lamps was switched off and the oscilloscope illumination switched on. This light program resulted in a decrease in the average brightness of the patterned cylinder from 1000 Apostilb to 1/100

Apostilb. Optomotor reaction was measured during a 35 min period after the decrease in intensity, applying a cylinder speed of $w = 49 \cdot 25°/\text{sec}$. The experiment shown in Fig. 5 and similar experiments—not presented here— indicate that dark adaptation to the level of 1/100 Apostilb is completed after 25 min.

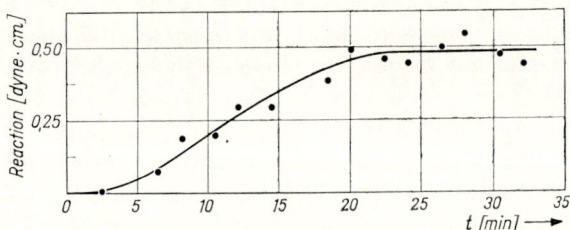

FIG. 5

Dark adaptation experiment. Light intensity switched down from 1000 Apostilb to 1/100 Apostilb at time $t = 0$. Optomotor reaction of test fly plotted versus time after step down of intensity. Cylinder speed $w = 49 \cdot 25°/\text{sec}$; spatial wavelength of sinusoidal pattern $\lambda = 45°$; pattern contrast $m = 21\%$. The individual points indicate optomotor reactions of one fly. In this experiment the inner ground-glass cylinder was removed.

C. *Tests of One- or Multi-quantum Reactions in Two-cylinder Arrangement*

The results of the critical tests for deciding between one- and multi-quantum reactions are plotted in Figs. 6–9. In order to compare optomotor reactions generated by the two different light programs, the average brightness at the surface of the rotating patterned cylinder had to be set to a very low quantum flux level. This condition is met if one operates near the threshold of reactions elicited by moving patterns of *high* contrast. In order to determine the associated average brightness range at the surface of the patterned cylinder, the strength of the optomotor reaction at various levels of brightness was measured with a group of dark adapted flies which had passed the control experiment I. All other parameters of the experiment (spatial wavelength of periodic pattern; pattern contrast; angular velocity of patterned cylinder) were kept unchanged. The measurements were carried out under constant illumination provided by the oscilloscope tube; the inner ground-glass cylinder was removed. The results are given by the solid curves in Figs. 6–9, which represent averages obtained from various individual flies. The averages and the standard errors of these measurements are *not* shown in the figures. The full and the open circles represent averages from other measurements which will be discussed later. In the experiments described here, the spatial wavelength of the sinusoidally patterned cylinder was $\lambda = 45°$ and the contrast amounted to $m = 21\%$. Reaction curves (solid lines) plotted in Figs. 6 and 7 were measured with a cylinder speed of $w = 49 \cdot 25°/\text{sec}$; those shown in Fig. 8 with a speed of $w = 24 \cdot 60°/\text{sec}$; and

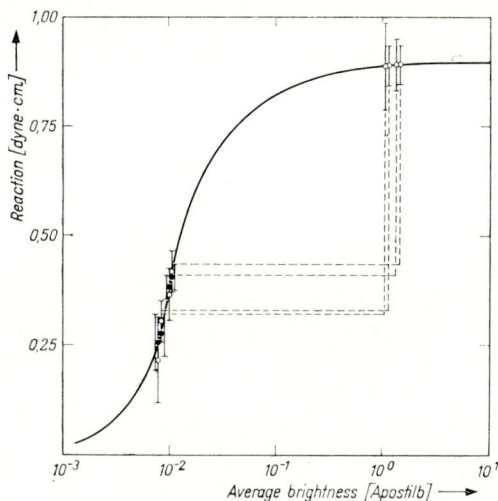

FIG. 6

Test of one- or multi-quantum reaction in two-cylinder arrangement. A, *Solid curve:* optomotor reaction versus average brightness of patterned cylinder. Illumination with light program type 1 (constant intensity in time) provided by oscilloscope tube. Spatial wavelength of patterned cylinder $\lambda = 45°$; pattern contrast $m = 21\%$; cylinder speed $w = 49·25°/sec$. Reaction curve represents the averages obtained from five individual flies. These averages and standard errors are *not* shown in the figure. Average standard error amounts to $\pm 0·15$ dyne/cm. B, *Full circles* and *open circles:* full circles represent averages obtained from four individual flies with light program type 1. The standard error $\pm \sigma$ of each average, indicated by vertical lines, is calculated from five measurements, each taken from one individual fly. The open circles near the abscissa value 10^{-2} Apostilb represent reaction averages obtained from the same flies under light program type 2. Pairs of full and open circles located at the *same* abscissa value were obtained from one and the same individual fly. Light program type 2 consisted of pulsed light with the same average quantum flux as in program of type 1. Pulse frequency 500 c/s; pulse length $1·5 \times 10^{-5}$ sec; ratio of peak intensity of pulse to average intensity: $I_2/I_1 = 133$. Open circles near abscissa value $10°$ Apostilb demonstrate optomotor reaction to be expected under light program type 2 for a two-quantum receptor if condition $\tau \leq 1·5 \times 10^{-5}$ sec is fulfilled. The abscissa values of these open circles are derived from the abscissa values of open circles actually measured and multiplied by the factor $I_2/I_1 = 133$. This factor determines the increase in effectiveness during program type 2, since the effective molecular cross-section of the two-quantum receptor changes by this factor. Horizontal dashed lines indicate these shifts of open circles, whereas vertical dashed lines give significant limits for one- versus two-quantum receptors. Experimental results plotted were obtained from oscilloscope illumination with the inner ground-glass cylinder removed. Spatial wavelength of patterned cylinder $\lambda = 45°$; pattern contrast $m = 21\%$; cylinder speed $w = 49·25°/sec$.

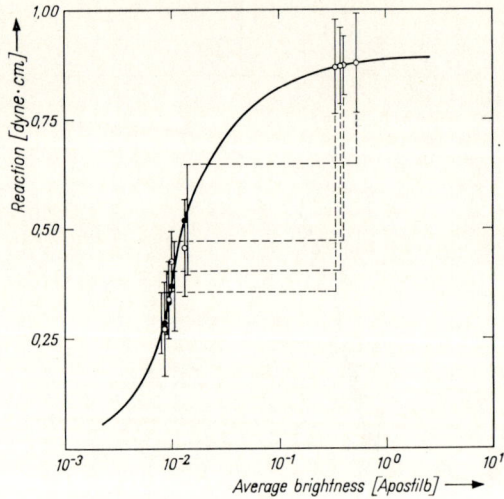

FIG. 7

Every detail as described and stated in the legend of Fig. 6 with the following exceptions. Pulse frequency in light program of type 2: 200 c/s; pulse length 1.25×10^{-4} sec; $I_2/I_1 = 40$. Dashed lines lead to expected reactions to pulsed light if the receptors are of two-quantum type and $\tau \leq 1.25 \times 10^{-4}$ sec.

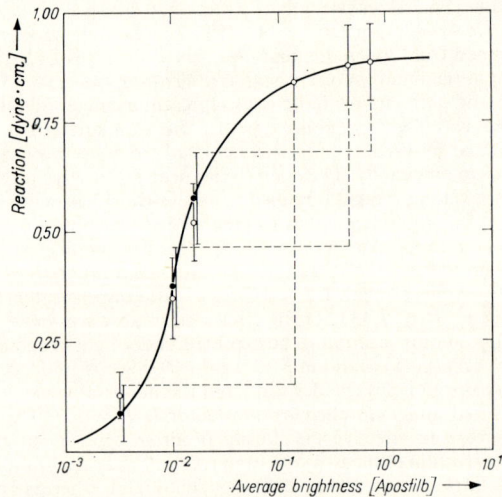

FIG. 8

Every detail as described and stated in the legend of Fig. 6 with the following exceptions. Speed of patterned cylinder $w = 24.6°/\text{sec}$. Pulse frequency in light program of type 2: 100 c/s; pulse length 2.5×10^{-4} sec; $I_2/I_1 = 40$. Dashed lines lead to expected reactions to pulsed light if receptors are of two quantum-type and $\tau \leq 2.5 \times 10^{-4}$ sec.

those in Fig. 9 with $w = 0.77°$/sec. The reasons for the selection of different speeds of the patterned cylinder will be discussed in section D. The reaction curves plotted in Figs. 6–8 do not differ, whereas the reaction curve shown in Fig. 9 has shifted to a higher level of brightness, which is due to the low angular speed of the pattern.

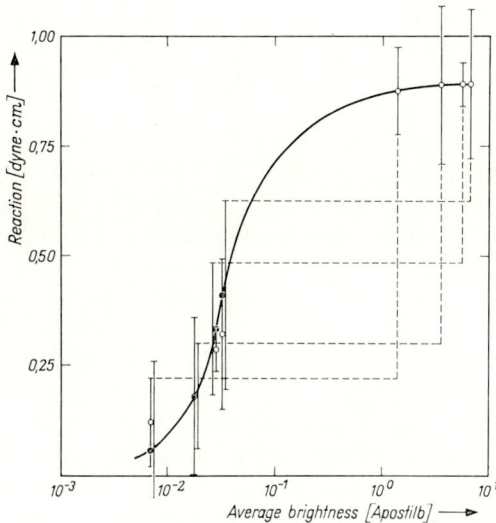

FIG. 9

Every detail as described and stated in the legend of Fig. 6 with the following exceptions. Speed of patterned cylinder $w = 0.77°$/sec. Note shift of solid curve to higher brightness values. Pulse frequency in light program of type 2: 20 c/s; pulse length 2.5×10^{-4} sec; $I_2/I_1 = 200$. Dashed lines lead to expected reactions to pulsed light if receptors are of two-quantum type and $\tau \leqq 2.5 \times 10^{-4}$ sec.

The reaction curves (solid lines) plotted in Figs. 6–9 show that the reaction depends most critically on changes in brightness in the neighbourhood of 10^{-2} Apostilb. This range was therefore selected for application of light programs of type 1 and type 2 in order to test whether the optomotor reaction reveals a requirement for absorption of two or more quanta. To apply this program the following procedure was selected. An individual fly was dark adapted and centered in the two-cylinder arrangement, which was illuminated with constant intensity by the oscilloscope tube. After the fly had adapted from complete darkness to this low-brightness level, the patterned cylinder (spatial wavelength of sinusoidal pattern $\lambda = 45°$, contrast $m = 21\%$) was rotated both clockwise and counter-clockwise, and the reaction elicited was measured. The light program was then switched to pulsed light of the same average intensity level, and the next measurement taken. The whole procedure was repeated five times. The average reactions to program type 1 are represented by full circles and the average reactions to program type 2 by open circles. Every pair of full and open circles located at the *same* brightness level are based on measurements made with one and the same individual fly. In Fig. 6 the light program type 2 consisted of pulses of length $1 \cdot 5 \times 10^{-5}$ sec, a pulse frequency of 500 c/s and an I_2 to I_1 ratio of 133. The near coincidence of the pairs of full and open circles at the same brightness levels near 10^{-2} Apostilb indicates that the reactions to the two different light programs do not differ significantly from each other. Hence in the perception of the special light program of type 2 applied here the receptors *behave* like one-quantum receptors.

One can easily estimate the strength of reaction which would be expected in the two-quantum receptor case if the coincidence time τ were of the same order of magnitude as, or smaller than, the length of the individual pulses ($\tau \leq 1 \cdot 5 \times 10^{-5}$ sec). Under these circumstances the effective molecular cross-section of the photopigment system would have been increased by the factor $I_2/I_1 = T/\Delta t = 133$. Consequently, the expected reaction can be estimated by shifting the open circles representing actually measured reactions to light program of type 2 along the abscissa by the factor 133 and raising them to the reaction values on the solid line corresponding to the reaction at that average brightness under constant illumination. These shifts are indicated by the horizontal and vertical dashed lines. The vertical dashed lines then represent the differences in reaction strength between the one- and the two-quantum receptor case under type 2 programs.

The results presented in Fig. 6 tell us that the receptors of the fly *Musca* behave like one-quantum receptors. In reality they may be of the two-quantum type, of course, since no difference would have been detectable between light programs of type 1 and 2 employed here if the coincidence time τ were equal to or greater than 1/500 sec, the time interval between successive light pulses. Further experiments were carried out, therefore, in which the pulse frequency in light programs of type 2 was reduced. First we applied a 200 c/s pulse frequency with a pulse length of $1 \cdot 25 \times 10^{-4}$ sec and a ratio of $I_2/I_1 = 40$. The results of measurements which were taken with four flies under this light program are plotted in Fig. 7. Again, no significant differences between the reactions to light programs of type 1 and 2 were observed. This implies that the receptors can be of the two-quantum type only if $\tau \geq 1/200$ sec. In the next set of experiments we therefore went down to a 100 c/s pulse frequency with a pulse length of $2 \cdot 5 \times 10^{-4}$ sec and a ratio $I_2/I_1 = 40$. Three flies were tested and the results plotted in Fig. 8. The receptors here too behave like one-quantum receptors. The effect expected in the two-quantum receptor case may still be hidden if $\tau \geq 1/100$ sec. The next group of experiments was undertaken with four flies at a pulse frequency of 20 c/s, pulse length $2 \cdot 5 \times 10^{-4}$ sec and an I_2 to I_1 ratio of 200. The averages of the reactions to light programs type 1 and type 2, which are plotted in Fig. 9, again show no significant differences. The dashed lines in Figs. 7–9 indicate, as was explained in connection with Fig. 6, the expected optimum differences between the reactions elicited by programs type 1 and type 2 for the two-quantum receptor case. Hence our conclusion is that the receptors of *Musca* behave like one-quantum receptors down to pulse programs of 20 c/s. Coincidences can only take place if the coincidence time τ is equal to or greater than 1/20 sec.

D. *Stroboscopic Effects*

Control Experiments III and IV. So far, we have not yet considered the stroboscopic effects which the pulsed light intensity generates when it illuminates the rotating pattern in the two-cylinder arrangement. A calculation (not presented here) of the moving interference patterns produced by the rotating cylinder and the pulsed light illumination leads to the following conclusions. If the moving pattern consists of a sinusoidally changing contrast with spatial wavelength λ, and is rotated with an angular speed w, the pulsed light with frequency v then generates two groups of interference patterns, one moving against and one moving in the direction of rotation of the patterned cylinder. The calculation shows that the interference group moving against the direction of the rotating cylinder rotates with angular velocities $(n \cdot \lambda \cdot v - w)$ and the interference group moving in the direction of the rotating cylinder moves with angular velocities $(n \cdot \lambda \cdot v + w)$; n being 1,2,3.... The spatial wavelength of the interference patterns do not differ, and are the same as the wavelength λ of the pattern fixed on the rotating cylinder.

In order to test whether the interference patterns influence the optomotor reactions measured under various pulsed light conditions, reactions versus angular velocity of the patterned cylinder (spatial wavelength $\lambda = 45°$, contrast $m = 21\%$) were measured under constant illumination at an average brightness level of 2×10^{-2} Apostilb. The result of these measurements is plotted in Fig. 10. The optomotor reaction rises above threshold at

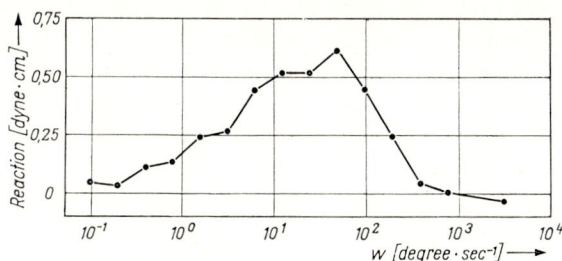

FIG. 10

Optomotor reaction versus angular velocity w of rotating, sinusoidally patterned cylinder. In this experiment the inner ground-glass cylinder was removed. Spatial wavelength of pattern $\lambda = 45°$; pattern contrast $m = 21\%$. Average brightness level of pattern 2×10^{-2} Apostilb. Illumination constant in time. Full circles represent averages taken from six flies. Average standard deviation amounts to ± 0.2 dyne/cm.

around 0·2°/sec and falls off to zero at 800°/sec angular cylinder velocity. If we inspect the velocities of the interference patterns, we find for first order interference ($n = 1$) at the different pulse frequencies:

Pulse frequency (c/s)	Velocities (degree/sec^{-1}) of first order interference patterns moving	
	"against"	"with"
500	$2·24 \times 10^{+4}$	$2·25 \times 10^{+4}$
200	$8·95 \times 10^{+3}$	$9·05 \times 10^{+3}$
100	$4·48 \times 10^{+3}$	$4·53 \times 10^{+3}$
20	$8·99 \times 10^{+2}$	$9·01 \times 10^{+2}$

At this brightness level the velocities of the first order interference patterns, and therefore also those of higher order interference patterns, are beyond the perceptional range of the optomotor reaction system and therefore do not influence the results presented in section C. This is due to the fact that a pulse frequency lower than 20 c/s was not applied in these experiments, and that the rotations of the patterned cylinder were switched to low angular velocities.

In addition to the experiments presented in Fig. 10, and the considerations given above, we have carried out various other control experiments, especially at 20 c/s pulse frequency, to test for possible influences of the interference patterns. One of these control experiments is shown in Fig. 11. The full circles represent measurements under constant illumination and the open circles show measurements under pulsed light conditions. Reactions are plotted versus velocity of the patterned cylinder. It is obvious from the results that the reactions to both light programs do not differ, at least up to $w \sim 10°$/sec. This rules out a possible influence of the interference patterns at $w = 0·77°$/sec, the velocity at which the measurements presented in Fig. 9 of section C were taken.

E. *Test of One- or Multi-quantum Reactions in Three-cylinder Arrangement*

The method (two-cylinder technique) so far described in this paper is applicable to light-pulse frequencies down to 20 c/s. At pulse frequencies below 20 c/s, rotating stroboscopic patterns begin to influence the optomotor reaction. This influence can be compensated for neither by lowering the velocity w of the rotating patterned cylinder nor by changing the spatial wavelength λ of the pattern, since the ratio w/λ determines the strength of the optomotor reaction (other parameters such as brightness and contrast being kept constant). Therefore a new method was recently introduced which makes use of two types of quantum fluxes: one type carrying motion information, the other determining the levels of average brightness and pattern contrast. The new method enables us to apply frequencies of light pulses below 20 c/s.

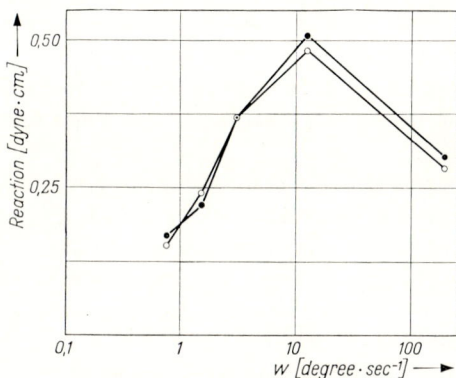

FIG. 11

Optomotor reaction versus angular velocity measured with one fly at an average brightness level of 3×10^{-2} Apostilb. Spatial wavelength of pattern $\lambda = 45°$; contrast $m = 21\%$. In this experiment the inner ground-glass cylinder was removed. Full circles represent reactions to constant illumination in time provided by the oscilloscope tube; open circles represent measurements to pulsed light program with the same average quantum flux. Pulse frequency 20 c/s; pulse length $2 \cdot 5 \times 10^{-4}$ sec. The reactions to both programs indicate that the interference patterns do not influence the reaction to pulsed light up to angular velocities of about $w = 10°/\text{sec}$.

This method makes use of a three-cylinder arrangement which is schematically shown in Fig. 4. The fluorescent lamps illuminate the outer stationary ground-glass cylinder, which in turn provides a homogeneous illumination of the rotating patterned cylinder and the inner stationary ground-glass cylinder. The inner ground-glass cylinder can in addition be illuminated from within by the oscilloscope screen. If only the fluorescent lamps are switched on and the patterned cylinder is rotated, a contrast frequency of w/λ c/s is generated at an angular coordinate of the inner ground-glass cylinder. The moving contrast at the inner surface of the inner stationary ground-glass cylinder then amounts to 50% sinusoidal modulation. However, if only the oscilloscope illumination is switched on and set to program type 1 operation, the moving contrast measured at the inner surface of the inner ground-glass cylinder is below 0·5%. This is due to the fact that only a small percentage of the light flux illuminating the inner ground-glass cylinder is reflected from the rotating patterned cylinder. Control experiments carried out under oscilloscope illumination with various flies have shown that optomotor reactions are not elicited by this contrast. Therefore, for the fly's eye only the light flux provided by the fluorescent lamps carries information of pattern motion whereas the light flux provided by the oscilloscope tube does not. Hence oscilloscope illumination under program type 2 does not generate stroboscopic effects which are perceived by the fly. These findings enable us to apply light program type 2 with pulse frequencies below 20 c/s. In the three-cylinder arrangement the combination of outer and inner illumination permits independent variation of two parameters: average brightness and pattern contrast, measured at the inner surface of the inner ground-glass cylinder.

To apply this new method the following experimental procedure was selected: an individual fly was dark adapted and centered in the three-cylinder arrangement, which was illuminated by the fluorescent lamps only. The intensity of the fluorescent lamps was dimmed by neutral filters so that a brightness density of $1 \cdot 5 \times 10^{-2}$ Apostilb was measured at the inner surface of the inner ground-glass cylinder. After the fly had adapted from complete darkness to this low-brightness level, the patterned cylinder (spatial wavelength of sinusoidal pattern $\lambda = 45°$; cylinder speed $w = 49 \cdot 25°/\text{sec}$; contrast measured from fly's position $m = 50\%$) was rotated in the clockwise and counter-clockwise directions and the reaction elicited was measured. Oscilloscope illumination set to program type 1 was then added and reaction measurements at various intensity levels of the oscilloscope were taken. The fly was adapted to each of these levels. The average reactions of an individual fly elicited under this program are indicated in Fig. 12 by crosses at the abscissa values of $1 \cdot 5 \times 10^{-2}$; $1 \cdot 86 \times 10^{-2}$; $5 \cdot 03 \times 10^{-2}$; $15 \cdot 6 \times 10^{-2}$ Apostilb (50%; $40 \cdot 3\%$; $14 \cdot 9\%$; $4 \cdot 8\%$ sinusoidal contrast respectively). The results plotted in Fig. 12 show that the strength of optomotor reaction diminishes with an increasing average brightness since the increase in brightness is accompanied by a strong decrease in pattern contrast at the inner surface of the inner ground-glass cylinder.

The steepest descent of the reaction curve is located at an average brightness level of $2 \cdot 36 \times 10^{-2}$ Apostilb, which corresponds to a pattern contrast of $m = 31 \cdot 4\%$. At this level the same fly was tested under programs of type 1 and type 2 in order to test whether the optomotor reaction reveals a requirement for absorption of two or more quanta. In this experiment the light-pulse frequency of program type 2 was set to 1 c/s operation. The length of the light pulses amounted to 5×10^{-2} sec with an I_2 to I_1 ratio of 20. In Fig. 12 the average reaction to program type 1 is represented by a full circle and the average reaction to program type 2 by an open circle. The coincidence of the pair of full and open circles at the same brightness or contrast level, respectively, indicates that the reactions of the fly to the two different light programs do not differ significantly from each other. Hence in the perception of the light program of type 2 applied here, the receptors *behave* like one-quantum receptors.

Again, we can easily estimate the strength of the optomotor reaction which would be expected in the two-quantum receptor case if the coincidence

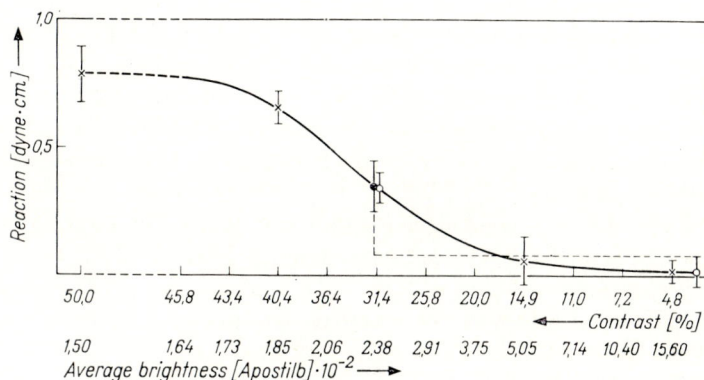

FIG. 12

Test of one- or multi-quantum reaction in three-cylinder arrangement. A, *Crosses (solid curve)*: optomotor reaction versus average brightness of inner stationary ground-glass cylinder. Illumination with fluorescent lamps and with light program type 1 (constant intensity in time) provided by oscilloscope tube. The intensity of the fluorescent lamps was dimmed by neutral filters so that a brightness density of $1 \cdot 5 \times 10^{-2}$ Apostilb was measured at the inner surface of the inner ground-glass cylinder. At this brightness level the pattern contrast measured from the fly's position amounted to $m = 50\%$. The light flux provided by the oscilloscope tube raises the average brightness at the surface of the inner ground-glass cylinder and in turn diminishes the pattern contrast as indicated. Spatial wavelength of sinusoidal pattern $\lambda = 45°$; patterned cylinder speed $w = 49 \cdot 25°$/sec. The crosses (reaction curve) represent averages, each average taken from seven measurements obtained from an individual fly. The standard error $\pm \sigma$ of each average is indicated by a vertical line. B, *Full circle* and *open circle:* the full circle represents a reaction average obtained from the same fly with light program type 1. The standard error $\pm \sigma$ of this average, indicated by a vertical line, is calculated from five measurements. The open circle represents a reaction average obtained from the same fly under light program type 2. The standard error $\pm \sigma$ of this average is calculated from five measurements. Light program type 2 consisted of pulsed light with the same average quantum flux as in program of type 1. Pulse frequency 1 c/s; pulse length 5×10^{-2} sec; ratio of peak intensity of pulse to average intensity $I_2/I_1 = 20$. Open circle above abscissa value $15 \cdot 6 \times 10^{-2}$ Apostilb demonstrates optomotor reaction to be expected under light program type 2 for a two-quantum receptor if condition $\tau \leqq 5 \times 10^{-2}$ sec is fulfilled. The abscissa value of this open circle is derived from the abscissa value of the open circle actually measured and multiplied by the factor $I_2/I_1 = 20$. This factor determines the increase in effectiveness of the oscilloscope light during program type 2, since the effective molecular cross-section of the two-quantum receptor changes by this factor. The horizontal dashed line indicates the shift of the open circle, whereas the vertical dashed line gives a significant limit for one- versus two-quantum receptors. Spatial wavelength of pattern and patterned cylinder speed as indicated under A.

time τ were of the same order of magnitude as, or smaller than, the length of the individual pulses ($\tau \leq 5 \times 10^{-2}$ sec). In this case the effective molecular cross-section of the photopigment system would have been increased by the factor $I_2/I_1 = T/\Delta t = 20$. Consequently the expected reaction can be predicted by shifting the open circle representing the actually measured average reaction to light program of type 2 along the abscissa by the factor 20 and raising it to the reaction value on the solid line corresponding to the reaction at that average brightness and contrast under constant illumination (program type 1). The shifts are indicated by the horizontal and vertical dashed lines. The vertical dashed line then represents the difference in reaction strength between the one- and the two-quantum receptor case.

The typical result presented in Fig. 12 tells us that the receptors of the fly *Musca* behave like one-quantum receptors. They could be of the two-quantum type only if the coincidence time τ were equal to or greater than 1 sec, the time interval between successive light pulses in program type 2.

F. *Upper Estimate of Light Flux Incident on Single Receptor*

We have not yet calculated an upper estimate of the average number of quanta incident on a photoreceptor of a *Musca* ommatidium during light programs type 1 and 2 under the experimental conditions of the two- and three-cylinder arrangements (for details see Fermi and Reichardt, 1963). For this calculation the sensitivity of an individual rhabdomere in all directions is required, in units of quanta absorbed per unit time, brightness, and solid angle. The angular sensitivity of a retinula cell has been measured by Kirschfeld (1965b) and found to be approximately Gaussian in form with an angular width of $s = 7 \cdot 7°$ at half-height of the distribution. Let θ be the angle between the axis of a horizontally oriented ommatidium and an arbitrary vertical plane through the ommatidium, φ an angle of elevation in that plane, I the average brightness of the stimulus pattern cylinder at the point on its surface defined by φ and θ and $d\omega$ an element of solid angle about the (φ, θ) direction. The Gaussian angular sensitivity distribution for an individual retinula cell then states that light incident on the surface of an ommatidium from within the elementary solid angle $d\omega$ contributes an amount dr to the rate of absorption of quanta by the photopigment of the rhabdomere that is given by the equation

$$dr = b \cdot Ie^{-\dfrac{4\ln 2}{s^2}\left[(\varphi-\varphi_o)^2+(\theta-\theta_o)^2\right]} d\omega, \qquad (1)$$

where s is the angular width at half-height of the sensitivity distribution, b the absolute sensitivity to light parallel to the optical axis of the ommatidium and φ_o, θ_o the angular coordinates determining the direction of the optical axis of an individual retinula cell. A maximum estimate of the value of b can be calculated as follows. The element of luminous flux $d\Phi$ (in lumens), through the surface of the aperture of an ommatidium A (in meter²), that is due to light from within an elementary solid angle $d\omega$ about the ommatidial axis, is given by

$$d\Phi = (^1/\pi)\ AI\ d\omega. \qquad (2)$$

Since the complex eye of *Musca* is of the apposition type, the corresponding flux through the surface of one receptor element within an ommatidium cannot exceed $d\Phi$. Hence, if c is the rate of absorption of quanta by a photoreceptor per lumen flux incident on its surface, then an upper limit for b is

$$b = \frac{c}{I}\ \frac{d\Phi}{d\omega} = \frac{1}{\pi}\ Ac. \qquad (3)$$

An upper limit to the value of c can be estimated by supposing that for light of wavelength 555 mμ all quanta incident on a surface of a photoreceptor are absorbed. For 555 mμ light, 1 lumen $= 1\cdot61 \times 10^{-3}$ watt and 1 quantum of energy $= 3\cdot54 \times 10^{-19}$ joule; an upper limit for c is thus $c = (1\cdot61 \times 10^{-3})/(3\cdot54 \times 10^{-19}) = 4\cdot5 \times 10^{+15}$ quanta/sec^{-1} lumen^{-1}. Since the radius of an ommatidium in the *Musca* eye is about $8 \times 10^{-6}\ m$, the surface area of its aperture is approximately $A = 2 \times 10^{-10}\ m^2$. Thus an upper limit for the sensitivity of an ommatidium to light parallel to its optical axis is

$$b = \frac{1}{\pi}\ Ac = 2\cdot9 \times 10^{+5}\left(quanta\ sec^{-1}\ Apostilb^{-1}\ steradian^{-1}\right). \qquad (4)$$

An upper estimate for the rate r of absorption of quanta by a photoreceptor of an ommatidium can now be calculated if in eqn. (1) we replace $d\omega$ by $\cos\varphi \cdot d\varphi \cdot d\theta$, and integrate over a hemisphere. Although the limits of integration for φ and θ should thus be $\pm\pi/2$, these limits may be replaced by $\pm\infty$ if the value of s is not too large. An error of less than 1 % occurs if $s < \pi/4$. When this approximation is made, the following expression is obtained as an upper limit for the rate of absorbtion of quanta:

$$r = b \cdot I \int_{-\infty}^{+\infty} \int_{-\infty}^{+\infty} e^{-\frac{4\ln 2}{s^2}\left[(\varphi - \varphi)^2 + (\theta - \theta_o)^2\right]} \cos\varphi\ d\varphi\ d\theta \qquad (5A)$$
$$= B \cdot I,$$

where

$$B = \frac{\pi}{4\ln 2} \cdot bs^2 e^{\frac{-s^2}{16\ln 2}} = (3\cdot3 \times 10^{+5})s^2 \cdot e^{\frac{-s^2}{11\cdot1}}$$
$$(quanta\ sec^{-1}\ Apostilb^{-1}). \qquad (5B)$$

If we substitute in eqn. (5B) the value $s = 7.7° = 0.134$ radians of arc, one arrives at

$$B \approx 6 \times 10^{+3} \; (quanta \; sec^{-1} \; Apostilb^{-1}). \tag{5C}$$

In the experiments reported here the light programs type 1 and type 2 were applied at an average brightness level of about 10^{-2} Apostilb, which leads in connection with eqn. (5C) to an upper estimate of 60 quanta per second incident, on the average, on a photoreceptor of the *Musca* eye. This low rate of quantum absorption makes it very improbable that the kinetics of the photochemical reaction are not determined primarily by the quanta, but by other processes.

CONCLUSION

The results of the experiments described lead to the conclusion that coincidences of two or more quanta are not registered by the fly's eye—at least not for coincidence time intervals as long as 1 sec. The observations suggest that absorption of a single quantum with a finite probability elicits a primary physiological event, which in turn triggers a sequence of secondary events. Considering the low rate at which quanta impinge on the photoreceptors, the statement implies that in the optomotor reaction system of the fly *Musca* there are no temporal and/or spatial coincidences *before* perception of motion is carried out by the central nervous system.

ACKNOWLEDGEMENTS

This research was done in collaboration with Dr. Gisela Weidel and Dr. Valentin Braitenberg. I extend here my sincerest thanks for their help and patience. In addition, I would like to thank Dr. Karl Georg Götz for valuable discussions.

REFERENCES

FERMI, G. and REICHARDT, W. 1963. Optomotorische Reaktionen der Fliege *Musca domestica*. *Kybernetik* 1, 15–28.

FUORTES, M. G. F. and YEANDLE, S. 1964. Probability of occurrence of discrete potential waves in the eye of *Limulus*. *J. Gen. Physiol.* 47, 443–63.

GÖTZ, K. G. 1964. Optomotorische Untersuchung des visuellen Systems einiger Augenmutanen der Fruchtfliege *Drosophila*. *Kybernetik* 2, 77–92.

HASSENSTEIN, B. 1951. Ommatidienraster und afferente Bewegungsintegration. *Z. vergl. Physiol.* 33, 301–26.

HASSENSTEIN, B. 1958. Über die Wahrnehmung von Figuren und unregelmässigen Helligkeitsmuster *Z. vergl. Physiol.* 40, 556–92.

HECHT, S., SHLAER, S. and PIRENNE, M. H. 1942. Energy, quanta and vision. *J. Gen. Physiol.* 25, 819–40.

KIRSCHFELD, K. 1965a. Discrete and graded receptor potentials in the compound eye of the fly (*Musca*). This volume.

KIRSCHFELD, K. 1965b. Das anatomische und das physiologische Sehfeld der Ommatidien im Komplexauge von *Musca*. *Kybernetik* 2. In press.

MacNichol, E. F. 1958. Subthreshold excitatory processes in the eye of *Limulus*. *Exp. Cell Res.* **5**, 411–25.

Reichardt, W. 1957. Autokorrelations-Auswertung als Funktionsprinzip des Zentralnervensystems. *Z. f. Naturforsch.* **12b**, 448–57.

Reichardt, W. 1961. Autocorrelation, a principle for the evaluation of sensory information by the central nervous system, pp. 303–17. In W. A. Rosenblith (Ed.) *Sensory Communication*. MIT Press, Cambridge, Mass.

Reichardt, W. 1962. Nervous integration in the facet eye. *Biophysics J.* **2**, 121–43.

Reichardt, W. and Varjú, D. 1959. Übertragungseigenschaften im Auswertesystem für das Bewegungssehen. *Z. f. Naturforsch.* **14b**, 674–89.

Scholes, J. H. 1964. Discrete subthreshold potentials from the dimly lit insect eye. *Nature* **202**, 572–3.

Varjú, D. 1959. Optomotorische Reaktionen auf die Bewegung periodischer Helligkeitsmuster. *Z. f. Naturforsch.* **14b**, 724–35.

Yeandle, S. 1957. Ph.D. Thesis, The Johns Hopkins University.

Yeandle, S. 1958. Electrophysiology of the visual sytem—Discussion. *Amer. J. Ophthalmol.* **46**, 82–7.

DISCRETE AND GRADED RECEPTOR POTENTIALS IN THE COMPOUND EYE OF THE FLY (*MUSCA*)*

K. KIRSCHFELD

Max-Planck-Institut für Biologie, Abteilung Reichardt, Tübingen, Germany

ANALYSES of intracellularly recorded light receptor responses have shown that a considerable number of light quanta incident on the surface of the eye are necessary to evoke a just detectable response, which is a discrete miniature transmembrane potential ("bump") (Fuortes and Yeandle, 1964, *Limulus*: 3×10^3 quanta per flash and ommatidium; Scholes, 1965, *Locusta*: 10^3 quanta per flash and ommatidium; Walther, 1964, *Hirudo*: 10^3 quanta per flash and sense cell). On the other hand, statistical analyses dealing with the occurrence of the individual "bumps" (*Limulus*: Fuortes and Yeandle, 1964; *Locusta*: Scholes, 1964) has not contradicted the idea that one quantum is enough to elicit just one "bump"-response with finite probability. If this is the case we might conclude that a large fraction of incident quanta are lost on their path along the optic media and/or that only a small percentage of the quanta absorbed in the photopigments elicit "bump" potentials at the site of the sense cells.

Optomotor response studies with flies recently have shown (Fermi und Reichardt, 1963) that *Musca* is able to react to a moving drum even if the average pattern luminance is set as low as $2 \cdot 2 \times 10^{-3}$ Apostilb (1 Apostilb $= 10^{-4}$ Lambert). (Similar results are reported by McCann and MacGinitie, 1965.) In *Musca* the mean sensitivity distribution of the individual retinula cell in the dark-adapted state as measured by the receptor potential was found to have a mean half-value of $7 \cdot 7°$ in the horizontal plane (Kirschfeld, 1965; similar result: Vowles, 1965). If this distribution is effective for vision we can calculate that at the threshold of the optomotor reaction only some 30 visible quanta per second hit the cornea of one ommatidium ($\lambda = 555$ mμ, corneal surface $6 \cdot 0 \times 10^{-10}$ m^2; compare Fermi and Reichardt, 1963). We might therefore expect that in the *Musca* ommatidia no important percentage of quanta are lost on their path through the optic media. It is for this reason that *Musca* eyes have been used to investigate responses to low-intensity light stimuli by means of electrophysiological techniques in order to determine the absolute sensitivity of this compound eye.

* This work was supported in part by the Stiftung Volkswagenwerk.

METHODS

Heads of dark adapted (for at least 3 hr) females of *Musca* (age: 3–15 days) were fixed under dim red illumination on a ball-pivot by means of bees-wax which had been blackened with a suspension of lampblack. A small window (0·5 mm²) was opened in the back of the head. A microelectrode (3M KCl, resistance 20–100 MΩ measured in Ringer's solution) was inserted into the layer of the sense cells (Fig. 1). This arrangement avoids stray light originating from the electrode entering the sense cells. The blackened indifferent electrode was placed on the cornea of the same eye.

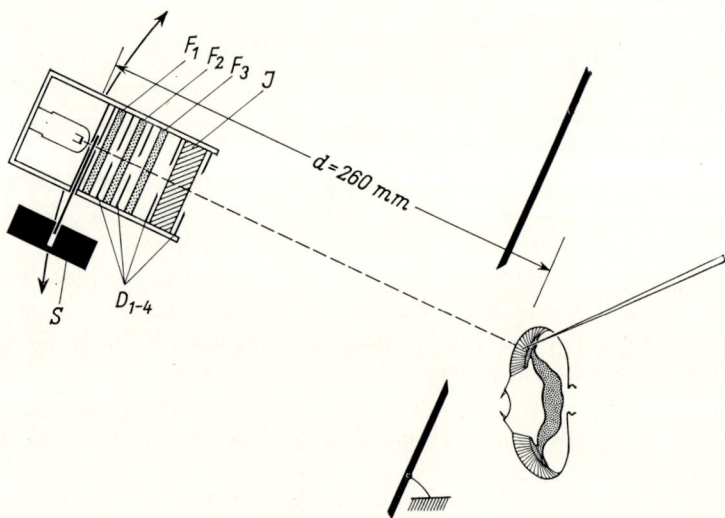

FIG. 1

Schematic diagram of apparatus used for stimulating and recording from the fly's retina. *S*, electromechanical shutter. F_1–F_3, neutral filters. *I*, interference filter (λ = 478 mμ). D_1–D_4, diaphragms to eliminate stray light.

The tungsten filament of a d.c.-operated lamp provided the stimulating light source. It was mounted at a distance of 260 mm from the preparation and subtended at the preparation an angle of 25 min of arc. An electro-mechanical shutter (built from a loudspeaker) controlled light stimuli of 5 msec duration (or longer) with an accuracy of $\pm$ 2 %. An interference filter which transmitted light of a centre wavelength of 478 mμ (half-width 16·5 mμ) was used throughout the experiments. Side bands of the interference filter in the red and ultraviolet regions of the spectrum were suppressed to values smaller than 1 % by means of added filters. Most fly visual cells give maximal response to this color (Burkhardt, 1962). Light intensities of the stimuli were adjusted by neutral filters. Their transmission for λ = 478 mμ was directly determined in the experimental arrangement by means of a 1P28 photo-multiplier; the linearity of the photomultiplier response to light intensities was checked and found to be better than $\pm 1\cdot5\%$ over the range employed in the experiments (compare Engström, 1947). Whenever combinations of various light filters were used, their overall transmission was determined directly and was not calculated from the individual transmission values. Various sets of diaphragms were used to eliminate stray light.

The entire stimulus apparatus was designed in such a way that it could be fixed in different angular positions relative to the preparation without changing the distance between source and eye. In most experiments it was fixed in a position which gave maximal responses. Most responses were recorded on film and analog tape to allow data processing with a CAT computer. Room temperature was kept between 20 and 24°C.

EXPERIMENTAL RESULTS

I. "Discrete" and "Graded" Responses

Penetration of cells in the receptor layer of the compound eye of *Musca* by micropipettes enables one to record light-induced potentials which are interpreted as generator potentials of single retinula cells (Burkhardt and Autrum, 1960; Naka, 1961; Naka and Eguchi, 1962; Autrum and von Zwehl, 1962, 1964). With maintained step stimuli they show the typical characteristics of responses of receptors of the "phasic-tonic" type. In the experiments reported here short flash stimuli of 6–8 msec duration have been used. These are short compared with the response durations, at least at low stimulus energies.

Responses to short flashes of different stimulus energies m_i as they are measured in most cases are shown in Fig. 2. (The unit of m_i is given in incident quanta per flash per ommatidium. Absolute calibration is discussed later.) After a latency between 4 and 25 msec (depending upon stimulus energy) a depolarization which lasts for some 100 msec can be seen. The amplitudes ΔU of the responses decrease with decreasing light energy and are finally masked by the noise. This type of response will be called a "graded" response.

In other, more rare, cases we get at the lower energy range clearly distinguishable, discrete responses, which either occur or do not occur (Fig. 3, I). They are qualitatively similar to those described for the *Limulus* and locust eyes. These responses will be called "discrete" responses.

Responses to maintained step light stimuli are different for the two types of responses with respect to the fact that the relative noise in discrete responses is higher (Fig. 4). The rising phase of the graded response (Fig. 4, I) becomes faster and the potential more "phasic" with stimulus intensities k higher than 8×10^4 (not shown in the figure).

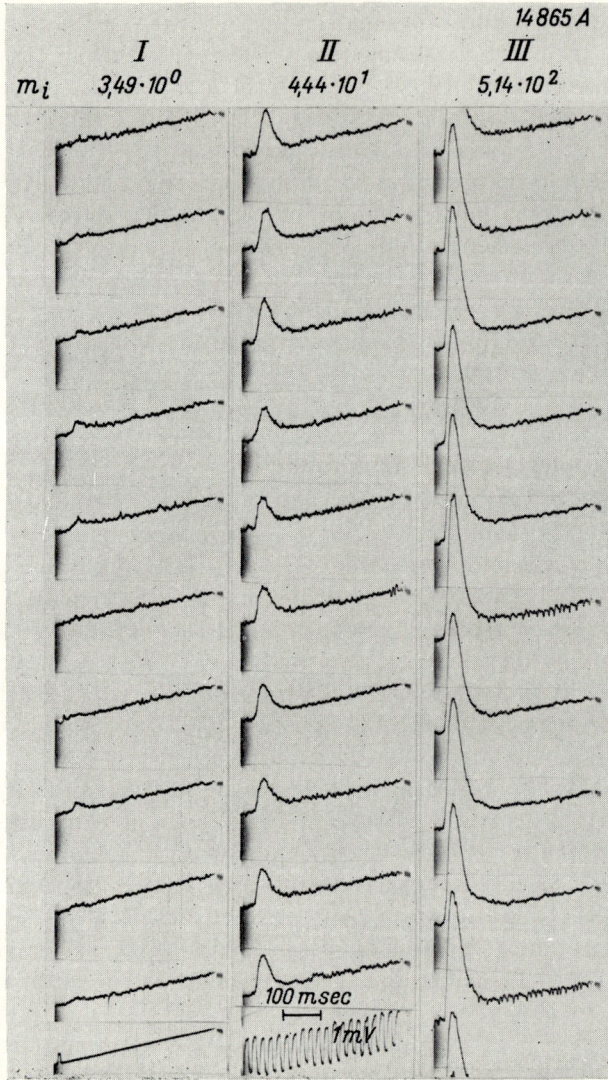

FIG. 2

"Graded" type of response to short (6 msec duration) stimuli. Stimulus shown in the last record of column I. m_i, stimulus energy in mean number of incident quanta ($\lambda = 478$ mμ) per flash per ommatidium. Upward deflection indicates depolarization of the membrane. Number at the top of the figure is the data-file of the impaled cell.

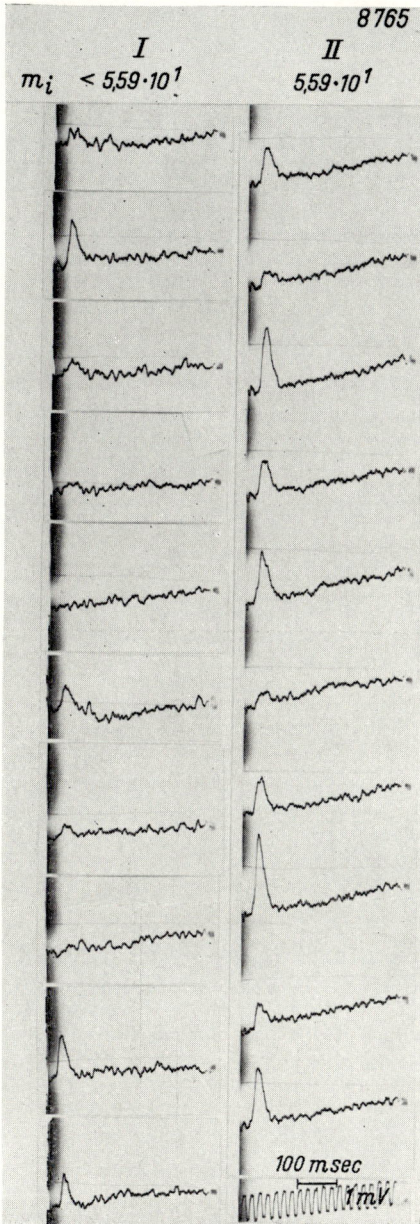

FIG. 3

"Discrete" type of response to short (7 msec duration) stimuli. m_i as in Fig. 2.

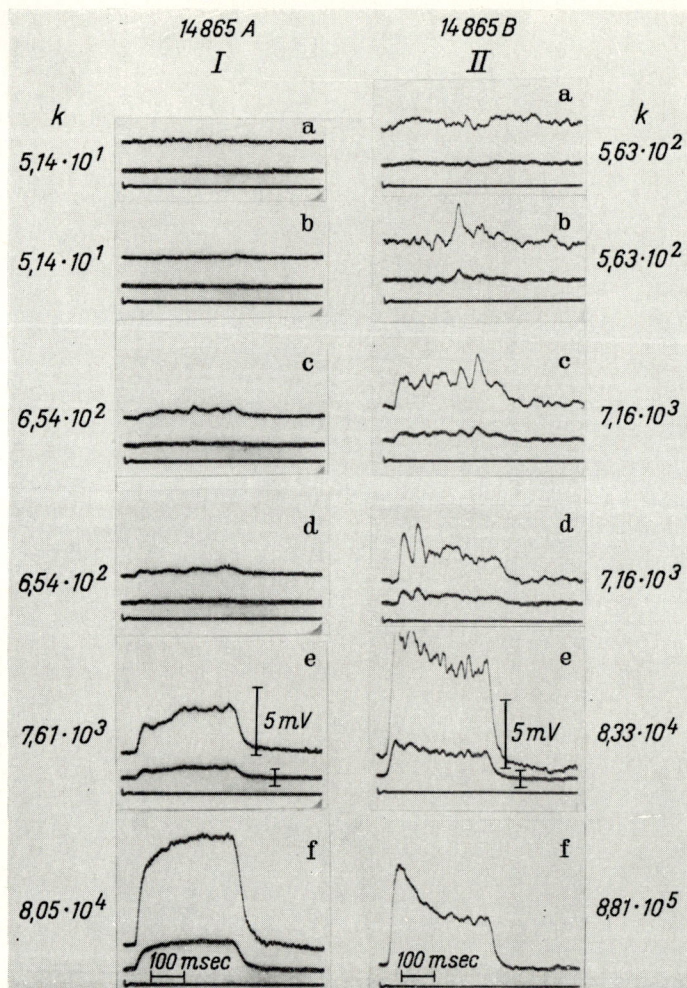

FIG. 4

"Graded" and "discrete" responses to maintained step stimuli. Upper and middle track potentials recorded with different sensitivity. Lower track: trigger impulse (II. f, only middle and lower track on the record). k, stimulus intensity in quanta per second per ommatidium. Notice that stimulus intensities in corresponding figures at left and at right are different.

The occurrence of the "peaks" in the responses (Fig. 4, II, c, d) are statistically distributed in time. Averaging over several responses leads to response curves with strongly reduced noise (Fig. 5).

No difference in angular sensitivity distribution between the two types of responses was found, the half-value θ of the angular sensitivity distribution lying between 5° and 10° for both types (cf. Kirschfeld, 1965). Amplitudes of responses to high intensity stimuli were between 40 and 60 mV for both types (cf. Fig. 10).

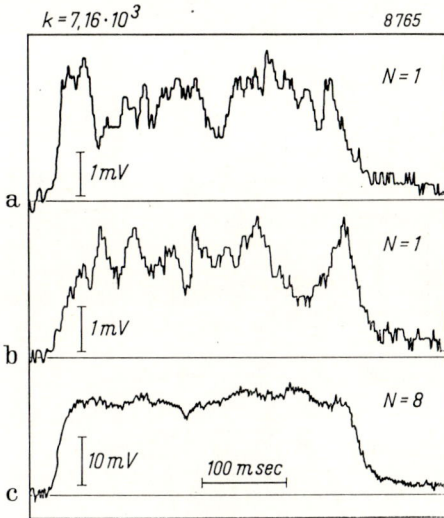

FIG. 5

Potentials of a cell with discrete responses to maintained step stimuli: *a*, *b*, individual receptor potentials. *c*, $N = 8$ responses averaged by means of CAT-computer. The step-like time course in *a* and *b* is an artifact associated with the CAT-computer.

The time courses of discrete and graded responses to short light flashes are very similar. Figure 6 shows records of three cells which gave graded responses and three cells which gave discrete responses; 20 to 50 individual responses have been superimposed for each cell by means of a CAT averager. Discrete potentials seem to be somewhat faster in time course.

II. Discrete Potentials from Poor Preparations

The potentials recorded from insect retinae become increasingly slower in time course as the cells die (Naka, 1961). We may ask whether the time course of the bump potentials changes in a similar way as the cells die.

The head preparation of a fly was left in the dark for 1 hr before the experiment began. Light flashes of energy $m_i = 5 \cdot 71 \times 10^3$ led in this case to responses of some 5 mV amplitude (Fig. 7, I). Responses to maintained step stimuli showed the typical noise behaviour of the discrete responses (not shown in the figure). Lowering the intensity (5 min later) led to all-or-none responses (Fig. 7, II). Ten minutes later, responses to flashes of $m_i = 6 \cdot 28 \times 10^3$ (Fig. 7, III) showed responses composed of discrete bumps. The time course

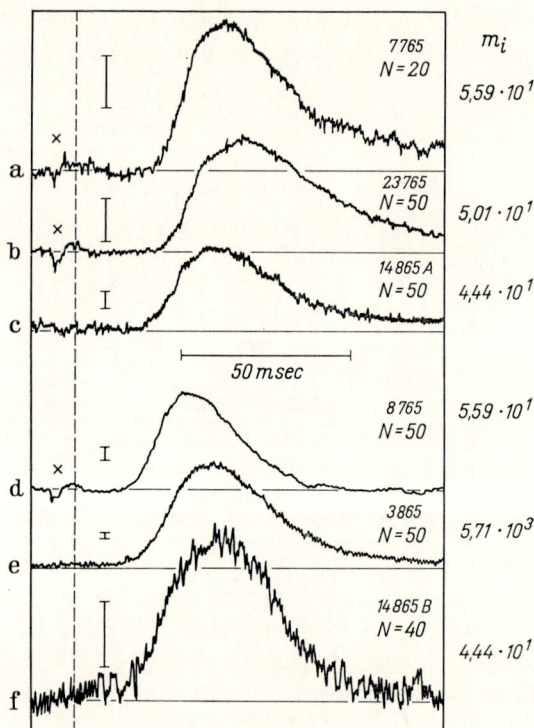

FIG. 6

"Graded" (*a–c*) and "discrete" (*d–f*) responses to short stimuli in 6 different cells. *N* responses have been superimposed for each record by means of the CAT-averager. The vertical broken line marks the centre of the 6–8 msec long stimulus. *x*, artifact from the magnetic field of the light-shutter coil. Vertical calibration, 10 mV. The mean amplitude of the single response is obtained if one divides the amplitudes seen in the figures by *N*. m_i, stimulus energy in incident quanta per flash per ommatidium ($\lambda = 478$ mμ).

of the individual bumps was similar to that in fresh preparations (cf. Fig. 3), but the latencies were much more scattered. More and more bump potentials could be seen without illumination, which was not the case with fresh *Musca* preparations. Responses in Fig. 7, I also show some scattering of the latencies of the bump potentials, indicating that deterioration of the cell had already begun. At the end of the experiment, flashes of higher stimulus energy (Fig. 7, IV) showed responses of a time course which was clearly slower than that of comparable responses of fresh preparations (maximal depolarization after 60 msec, which is twice as long as with good preparations). Therefore deterioration seems not to affect the mechanism that generates the bump potentials, but it influences the mechanism which determines the latency of the bumps after stimulation.

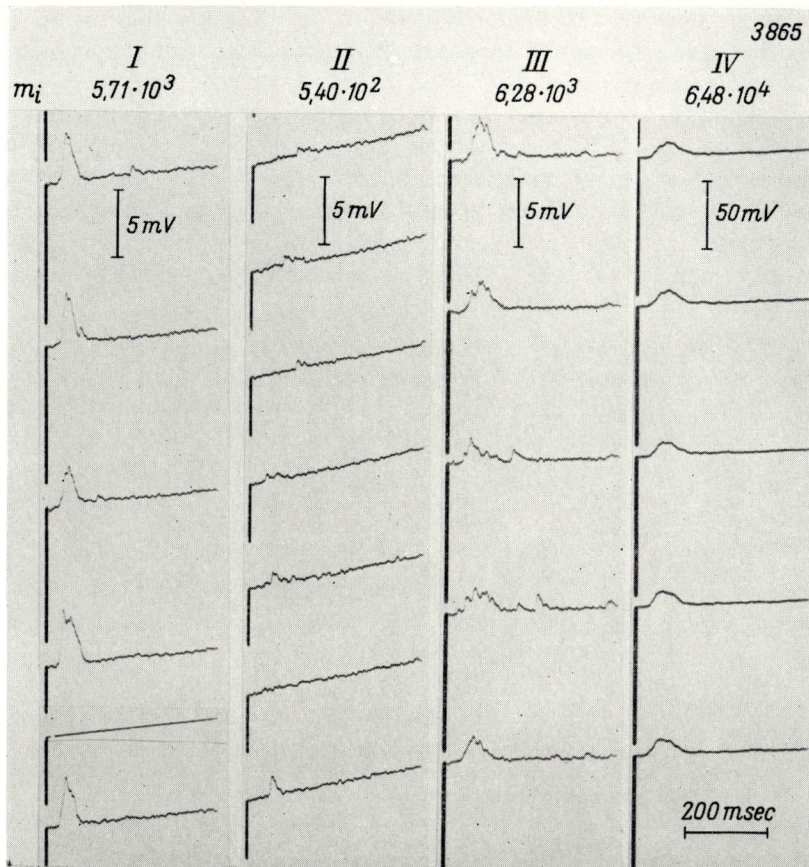

FIG. 7

Potentials of a cell giving discrete responses during deterioration of the cell. Stimulus duration 7 msec (stimulus in column I, 5th record). I. At the beginning of the experiment. II. After 5 min, stimulus energy reduced. III. After 15 min, response composed of individual bumps with different latencies. IV. After 17 min, response to stronger stimulus slowed down in time course (factor 2) compared with normally responding cell. Units of m_i as in Fig. 2.

III. *Amplitude Distributions of Graded and Discrete Responses*

The results described in Section I lead to the hypothesis that in the discrete response records the electrode was located in a favourable position in the cell and the responses therefore are recorded with higher amplitude; thus the improved signal-to-noise ratio would enable one to detect discrete bumps which in the graded records are lost in the noise. To test this hypothesis the relative sensitivities of both types of responses were determined. The histograms in Fig. 8 show the distributions of amplitudes ΔU; r is the number of occurrences of responses of amplitude ΔU in response to N short light flashes of stimulus energy m_i. Cell no. 7765 in Fig. 8a, which gave graded responses, clearly shows less scattering of the amplitudes than cell no. 8765, a "bumping" cell. This is the case irrespective of the fact that the mean amplitude $\overline{\Delta U}$ of cell no. 8765 was higher than that of cell no. 7765. It means that the single response to a flash of the cell with a graded response is a more accurate measure of the stimulus energy m_i. Amplitudes $\overline{\Delta U}$ of other cells which gave graded responses to flashes of energy $m_i \approx 50$ have been measured between

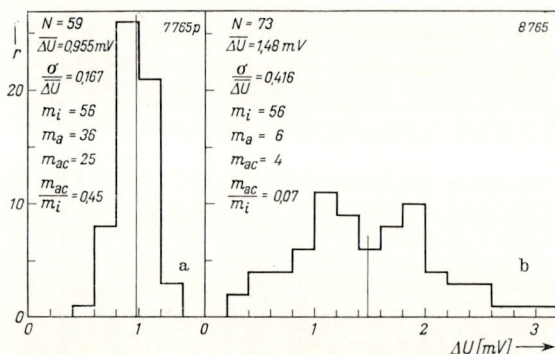

FIG. 8

Amplitude histograms for responses from a "graded" (a) and a "discrete" (b) cell. r, number of occurrences of responses of amplitude ΔU. $\overline{\Delta U}$ mean amplitude. N, number of responses counted. $\sigma/\overline{\Delta U}$, relative standard deviation of the amplitude distribution (in diagram a calculated with class unit $0 \cdot 1$ mV). m_i, m_a, m_{ac} and m_{ac}/m_i, see Fig. 9.

$0 \cdot 5$ and $1 \cdot 0$ mV and are reproducible in this range. Bump responses, which have been recorded for sufficiently long periods in only five cases showed more scatter in the mean bump height. Element no. 8765 (Fig. 8b) was the cell with the highest amplitudes for light flashes of energy $m_i \approx 50$.

The above results indicate that the graded responses cannot be explained simply as bump responses recorded with a less sensitive electrode position. If this were the case, the relative scattering of the graded response amplitudes should be equal to or greater than that of bump responses, as long as stimulus energies are equal in both cases. In the *Musca* ommatidium we have one (or two) eccentric cells (Dietrich, 1909), and we therefore cannot exclude the possibility that the two types of responses may be recorded from the two different types of cells. On the other hand, cell no. 7, the eccentric cell, is similar to the other cells with respect to the volume of cell body, and it has a well developed rhabdomere. Therefore the two types of responses are not easily explained by the two types of cells. One other hypothesis proposed here is that the graded response indicates the activity of an entire cell whereas the discrete response reflects activities of restricted areas of, for instance, the cell membrane, a small part of the rhabdomere, or perhaps the proximal portion of the cell near the optical cartridges (Trujillo-Cenóz and Melamed, 1963), where synaptic vesicles are located. On the basis of this hypothesis one would be able to explain the higher variation of the response amplitudes irrespective of the higher mean amplitude. Further experiments are needed to test this hypothesis.

IV. *Absolute Sensitivity*

Flash energies m_i and light intensities k are given in absolute units in order to arrive at an estimate of the absolute sensitivity of the measured responses. The necessary calibrations were carried out as described below.

PHOTOMETRY

The absolute intensity of the light stimuli applied was determined by a thermopile (Kipp and Zonen, Holland); the thermopile was calibrated by means of a standard lamp (SL, Osram Wi 40) in combination with an infrared filter. The light power calibration of the standard lamp (with IR-filter) was checked by the Physikalisch Technische Bundesanstalt, Berlin. The maximal error for the stimulus energies (in absolute units) at the surface of the fly's eye was estimated as $\pm 28\%$, the probable error as $\pm 10\%$.

This error is composed of errors due to uncertainty of SL-calibration ($\pm 5\%$), of SL current ($\pm 2\%$), of distance of SL from thermopile ($\pm 3\%$), or error due to aging effects of SL ($\pm 1\cdot5\%$), error due to inhomogenity in space of the illuminated area in the plane of the preparation ($\pm 3\%$), error due to uncertainty of distance of preparation from radiation source ($\pm 4\%$), inaccuracy of absorption coefficients of neutral filters ($\pm 1\cdot5\%$), inaccurate measurement of stimulus duration ($\pm 3\%$). The reproducibility of the measurement of absolute intensity at different times during the time course of the experiments was $\pm 5\%$.

Beyond these physical errors there exists variation among the diameters of the cornea of the ommatidia. The surface projection of single facets in the investigated region of the eye in females of *Musca* was determined from 25 ommatidia as 594 $\mu^2 \pm 15\%$. The facets were drawn from microscopic projection and the areas measured with a planimeter.

The individual errors reported here add up to a total error of about 20–30%, which has to be kept in mind if one calculates the number of quanta that fall upon an individual cornea.

The absolute numbers of quanta (for light of wavelength $\lambda = 478$ mμ) that hit a cornea of 594 μ^2 surface were calculated and are given in mean number of incident quanta per flash per ommatidium (m_i) and in mean number of incident quanta per second per ommatidium (k). The figures (2, 4, I, 8a, 9, 10) indicate that the sensitivities of the graded receptor responses are very high: thresholds for flashes are reached at $m_i = 5$ to 20 quanta per flash per ommatidium, thresholds for maintained step stimuli at $k = 50$ to 500 quanta per second per ommatidium. These thresholds are close to the thresholds determined from optomotor experiments (Fermi and Reichardt, 1963). If the potentials measured are recorded from the photoreceptors, as is generally assumed, we have to conclude that the small depolarizations which are on the order of fractions of a millivolt are above the biological threshold.

DISCUSSION

Accepting that the graded response reflects the electrical activity of single receptor cells in response to quanta received by an individual facet, we are able to derive a lower estimate of the average number of quanta from a light flash which are absorbed by one of the rhabdomeres and are effective for the electrical response.

To begin with, let us assume that the variation of the amplitudes ΔU in response to light flashes is due only to the statistical fluctuation in the number of absorbed and effective quanta and that one quantum has a finite probability of eliciting one individual response (cf. Yeandle, 1958; Fuortes and Yeandle, 1964; Scholes, 1964; Reichardt, 1965). Under this assumption one can approximate the measured amplitude distributions by the Poisson equation

$$P(n) = \frac{e^{-m_a} m_a^n}{n!}, \tag{1}$$

where P is the probability of occurrence of n absorbed and effective quanta from an individual flash, and m_a is the mean number of absorbed and effective quanta per flash. An estimate of m_a is derived from the relative standard deviation of the measured distribution of amplitudes ΔU by the equation

$$\frac{\sigma}{\overline{\Delta U}} = \frac{1}{\sqrt{m_a}} \tag{2}$$

In Fig. 9 a histogram of ΔU values taken from one experiment is presented. This distribution is approximated by a Poisson distribution with the same relative standard deviation as given by the experimental data. The parameter m_a for the fitted Poisson distribution has the value 42·5. Flash energy in this experiment was set at $m_i = 44$ ($\pm$ 20–30 %).

If our starting assumptions are correct, that is, if the variation of the amplitudes ΔU is due only to the mean number of absorbed and effective quanta per flash per rhabdomere, and if we deal with a one quantum process, then the parameter m_a of the Poisson distribution indicates the mean number of absorbed and effective quanta per flash per rhabdomere.

If other factors influence the standard deviation of the measured amplitudes, m_a is changed by these factors too and therefore is no measure of the mean number of absorbed and effective quanta per flash.

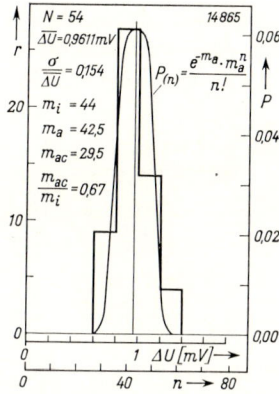

FIG. 9

Amplitude histogram (━) of a cell giving graded responses. Stimulus duration 7 msec. r, N, $\overline{\Delta U}$,$\sigma/\overline{\Delta U}$ as in Fig. 8. mi, mean number of incident quanta per flash per ommatidium ($\lambda = 478$ mμ); m_a, parameter of the Poisson distribution $P(n)$; m_{ac}, parameter of the Poisson distribution corrected for the nonlinear stimulus-response characteristic (see text). m_{ac} is a lower estimate of the number of absorbed quanta per flash. m_{ac}/m_i, quantal efficiency of the receptor. ——, Poisson distribution with $m_a = 42\cdot5$. P, probability of occurrence of n absorbed quanta per flash.

It is clear that in a biological system we have to account for the possibility that the sensitivity of the system varies from moment to moment. For instance, the electrical event at the membrane triggered by one effective light quantum may vary in amplitude and/or the percentages of light quanta that become effective at the membrane may vary with time. These effects would lead to an increase in the measured standard deviation. This means that with respect to these unknown factors the mean number of absorbed and effective quanta per flash could only be larger, but not less than, m_a; m_a therefore represents a lower estimate for the mean number of absorbed and effective quanta per flash and ommatidium.

On the other hand, we may ask whether there may exist mechanisms which could change the relative standard deviation to smaller values, so that the determined value of m_a is higher than the actual mean number of absorbed and effective quanta per flash. One conceivable mechanism that could decrease the relative standard deviation is an interaction between successive responses tending to stabilize the response amplitude. However, serial correlation of the amplitudes ΔU of successive responses showed that such a correlation does not exist (this holds for both graded and discrete responses). Therefore the temporal separation between successive stimuli ($m_i \approx 50$; time interval between successive flashes: 1–3 sec) is long enough to avoid adaptation effects and no correction for the value of m_a is necessary. But we still have to consider another mechanism which influences the relative standard deviation of the measured amplitudes. If we increase the stimulus energy m_i of short flashes, the mean response amplitude $\overline{\Delta U}$ increases linearly only for very small values of m_i (Fig. 10; the dashed line indicates

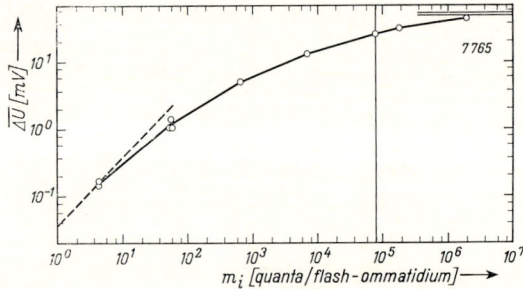

FIG. 10

Mean amplitude $\overline{\Delta U}$ as function of the mean number of incident quanta per flash per ommatidium m_i. Stimulus duration 7 msec. The values of $\overline{\Delta U}$ in response to the three lowest-intensity stimuli have been determined by CAT-averaging over 100–20–4 single responses. Time between successive stimuli varies between 1 sec and 5 min (at the lowest and highest stimulus intensities, respectively). Amplitudes of responses to stimuli $m_i = 10^6$ were determined with white light (after withdrawal of interference filter). The quantal effectiveness of the white light relative to monochromatic light ($\lambda = 478$ mμ) was independently determined by stimuli with white light in the lower intensity range. Horizontal lines: responses to very strong stimuli (photo flash) with unknown energy, demonstrating the saturation amplitude of 50–60 mV. Light in this case was not parallel. One point at $m_i = 5 \cdot 4 \times 10^1$ measured as the first, one other as the last of the series.

proportionality). Each deviation from proportionality changes the signal-to-noise ratio of the output relative to that of the input. The measured relative standard deviation of the amplitudes therefore have to be corrected for this effect. The deviation from proportionality for $m_i = 56$ which is seen in Fig. 10 leads to a decrease of $\sigma/\overline{\Delta U}$ by a factor of $0 \cdot 834$.

If one calculates the mean number of absorbed and effective quanta per flash, the measured values of $\sigma/\overline{\Delta U}$ have to be multiplied by a factor of $1 \cdot 2$. This correction leads to the values of m_{ac} shown in Figs. 8 and 9. At the moment we are not aware of any other mechanism which could possibly decrease the relative error of the measured amplitudes. The values of m_{ac} are therefore taken as a lower limit of the mean number of absorbed and effective quanta per flash.

The lower limit of the quantal efficiency of the receptor elements is given by dividing the mean number of absorbed and effective quanta per flash per ommatidium m_{ac} by the mean number of incident quanta per flash m_i. Values from three cells with graded responses have been determined as 67 % (Fig. 9), 45 % (Fig. 8a) and 76 % (without fig.) with a mean of 62·7 %. (For cells that give discrete responses m_{ac}/m_i is much smaller: 7 % in Fig. 8b, in other cases below 2 %.) The 62·7 % value for the graded responses is unexpectedly high as we know that in the human eye less than 10 % of the incident blue–green quanta will be absorbed by the dark adapted rods (Hecht, Shlaer and Pirenne, 1942). If we take into account that higher responses have been reported with polarized light (Naka and Kuwabara, 1959; Burkhardt and Wendler, 1960; Autrum and von Zwehl, 1962), which has not been used in the present experiments, the value of $m_{ac}/m_i = 62·7$ % for graded response cells would be increased to some 80 %. Finally, we cannot be sure that the wavelength of 478 mμ for the three arbitrarily chosen cells has been in each case exactly at the maximum of the spectral sensitivity curve. However, this source of uncertainty would only cause the estimated 62·7 % for the quantal efficiency to be too small, and would not produce an overestimate.

Ommatidia of flies, with rhabdomeres that are unfused, seem to be especially adapted for high light-gathering power when compared with the fused-rhabdomere ommatidia of other insects. This can easily be shown for parallel light. It falls upon only one of the seven rhabdomeres in the *Musca* eye where it is restricted by a light guide effect (Kuiper, 1962; Autrum and Wiedemann, 1962). On the other hand, in ommatidia with fused rhabdomeres the light quanta are divided between the rhabdomeres of all retinula cells, at least if the fused rhabdomeres act together as one integrating light guide.

In the human eye one-half of the quanta are lost in the dioptric media, which have a length of some 25 mm. If we use the mean absorption coefficient of the human eye for the dioptric media of 50 μ length in the *Musca* ommatidium, then one arrives at a quantal loss of less than 1 %. In the human eye 20 % of the quanta that fall upon the outer segments of the rods, which are some 28 μ long (Wolken, 1963), are absorbed in the sense cells. Again, if we use the absorption coefficient of the human cone outer segment, it is found that some 55 % of the incident quanta are absorbed in the 100 μ long *Musca* rhabdom. From this point of view the high quantal efficiency determined in these experiments does not seem inconceivable.

The fly's ommatidia, with a light-gathering power which—due to the small diameter of the cornea—is 10^4 to 10^5 times smaller than that of the human eye, may regain one order of magnitude by means of the small length of the crystal cone and the extended length of the photosensitive rhabdomere.

C.E.—X

SUMMARY

Slow potentials were recorded intracellularly from the receptor layer of the compound eye of *Musca*. Short flashes of low intensities normally give depolarizations with low scatter in amplitudes. With very low intensities these responses ("graded" responses) are masked by the noise of the record. In other, more rare cases, responses with much more scatter in amplitude are recorded. These elements give with very low stimulus intensities either no responses or clearly visible discrete responses of the "bump" type as described for other photoreceptors. Elements giving graded responses and elements giving discrete responses show the same angular sensitivity distribution (half-width θ: 5–10°) and the same maximal depolarization (40–60 mV) for strong stimuli. Latency and time course of both types of responses to short stimuli are very similar. Absolute sensitivity is higher for the graded type of response. Thresholds for short light flashes lie at 5 to 10 quanta per flash per ommatidium and for longer lasting stimuli at 50 to 200 quanta per second per ommatidium ($\lambda = 478$ mμ). With the assumption that the graded potentials are responses from single retinula cells a quantal efficiency of more than 60 % is derived. This high quantal efficiency is discussed on the basis of the "unfused" rhabdomeric structure of the dipteran ommatidium.

ACKNOWLEDGEMENTS

I wish to express my appreciation to Professor Dr. W. Reichardt and to Dr. J. Thorson for their criticism and assistance in preparing the manuscript, to Dipl. Phys. H. Wenking and Dr. K. G. Götz for discussing the absolute calibration of the light source and to Dr. D. Varjú for checking some numerical calculations. The figures have been drawn by E. Freiberg.

REFERENCES

AUTRUM, H. and VON ZWEHL, V. 1962a. Die Schzellen der Insekten als Analysatoren für polarisiertes Licht. *Z. vergl. Physiol.* **46**, 1–7.

AUTRUM, H. and VON ZWEHL, V. 1962b. Zur spektralen Empfindlichkeit einzelner Sehzellen der Drohne (Apis melliffica ♂) *Z. vergl. Physiol.* **46**, 8–12.

AUTRUM, H. and VON ZWEHL, V. 1964. Die spektrale Empfindlichkeit einzelner Sehzellen des Bienenauges. *Z. vergl. Physiol.* **48**, 357–84.

AUTRUM, H. and WIEDEMANN, J. 1962. Versuche über den Strahlengang im Insektenauge (Appositionsauge). *Z. Naturforsch.* **17b**, 480–2.

BURKHARDT, D. 1962. Spectral sensitivity and other response characteristics of single visual cells in the arthropod eye. *Symp. Soc. Exp. Biol.* XVI, 86–109.

BURKHARDT, D. and AUTRUM, H. 1960. Die Belichtungspotentiale einzelner Sehzellen von Calliphora erythrocephala Meig. *Z. Naturforsch.* **15b**, 612–6.

BURKHARDT, D. and WENDLER, L. 1960. Ein direkter Beweis für die Fähigkeit einzelner Sehzellen des Insektenauges, die Schwingungsrichtung polarisierten Lichtes zu analysieren. *Z. vergl. Physiol.* **43**, 687–92.

DIETRICH, W. 1909. Die Facettenaugen der Dipteren. *Z. wiss. Zool.* **92**, 465–539.

ENGSTRÖM, R. W. 1947. Multiplier photo-tube characteristics: Application to low light levels. *J. Opt. Soc. Amer.* **37**, 420–31.

FERMI, G. and REICHARDT, W. 1963. Optomotorische Reaktionen der Fliege *Musca domestica*. *Kybernetik* **2**, 15–28.

FUORTES, M. G. F. and YEANDLE, S. 1964. Probability of occurrence of discrete potential waves in the eye of *Limulus*. *J. Gen. Physiol.* **47**, 443–63.

HECHT, S., SHLAER, S. and PIRENNE, M. H. 1942. Energy, quanta and vision. *J. Gen. Physiol.* **25**, 819–40.

KIRSCHFELD, K. 1965. Das anatomische und das physiologische Sehfeld der Ommatidien im Komplexauge von *Musca*. *Kybernetik* **2**, 249–57.

KUIPER, J. W. 1962. The optics of the compound eye. *Symp. Soc. Exp. Biol.* **16**, 58.

MCCANN, G. D. and MACGINITIE, G. F. 1965. Optomotor response studies of insect vision. *Proc. Roy. Soc. (Lond.) B*. In print.

NAKA, K. and KUWABARA, M. 1959. Response of a single retinula cell to polarized light. *Nature (Lond.)* **184**, 755–6.

NAKA, K. J. 1961. Recording of retinal action potentials from single cells in the insect compound eye. *J. Gen. Physiol.* **44**, 571–84.

NAKA, K. J. and EGUCHI, E. 1962. Spike potentials recorded from the insect photoreceptor. *J. Gen. Physiol.* **45**, 663–80.

REICHARDT, W. 1965. Quantum sensitivity of light receptors in the compound eye of the fly *Musca*. *Cold Spring Harbor Symp. of Quantitative Biology*.

SCHOLES, J. H. 1964. Discrete subthreshold potentials from the dimly lit insect eye. *Nature* **202**, 572–3.

SCHOLES, J. H. 1965. The electrical responses of insect visual cells. Abstracts of papers presented at the Cold Spring Harbor Symposium on Quantitative Biology. June 4th to June 11th, XXX. Sensory Receptors.

TRUJILLO-CENÓZ, O. and MELAMED, J. 1963. On the fine structure of the photoreceptor second optical neuron synapse in the insect retina. *Z. Zellforschg.* **59**, 71–7.

VOWLES, D. M. 1965. The receptive fields of cells in the retina of the housefly (*Musca domestica*). *Proc. Roy. Soc. (Lond.) B*. In print.

WALTHER, J. B. 1964. Unregelmässigkeiten im Generatorpotential der Sehzellen von *Hirudo medicinalis* nahe der Reizschwelle. *Pflüg. Arch. ges. Physiol.* **279**.

WOLKEN, J. J. 1963. Structure and molecular organization of retinal photoreceptors. *J. Opt. Soc. Amer.* **53**, 1–19.

YEANDLE, S. 1958. Electrophysiology of the visual system—Discussion. *Am. J. Ophth.* **46**, 82–7.

A NON-LINEAR MODEL OF SENSORY ADAPTATION IN THE EYE OF THE WOLF SPIDER*

R. DeVoe

Department of Physiology, The Johns Hopkins University School of Medicine, Baltimore, Maryland, U.S.A.

THE response of a visual receptor to an abrupt but maintained change in illumination is itself but rarely maintained; rather, after a period of time, the receptor adapts to the new stimulus. Adaptation may take many forms. In particular, during the first second or so following the stimulus change, the response to this change may greatly exceed or overshoot the final level to which it subsides. This type of adaptation has long been known as *sensory adaptation*.

Sensory adaptation is of great use to an animal, for it provides information about the rate of change of a stimulus. Thus, for example, the overshoot in the electrical responses from the eye of the fly *Calliphora* to a maintained flash decreased as the rate of rise of the flash decreased, but the steady-state responses were in all cases the same (Washizu, 1964). Also, sensory adaptation serves in a way as a first line of defense against saturation of the visual system by an exceedingly strong stimulus; after the sensory adaptation has reduced the initial response to this stimulus, the slower process of light adaptation makes the strong stimulus still less effective.

The origin of sensory adaptation is quite another matter, however. It is clear that sensory adaptation is not a form of photochemical adaptation, for not only may photochemical adaptation be far too slow (Dowling, 1963), it may also be of entirely the wrong order of magnitude (Rushton, 1965). Some workers have proposed that sensory adaptation may be due to "masking" (Boynton, 1958) or to "rapid desensitization" (Fuortes and Hodgkin, 1964). For example, there has been proposed an RC feedback model in which reduction in the sensitivity of initially dark adapted *Limulus* ommatidia is used to explain the overshoot of the receptor potentials elicited from these ommatidia by long, bright flashes (Fuortes and Hodgkin, 1964; Marimont, 1965). This RC feedback model also predicts that there will be sensory adaptation in incrementally stimulated light-adapted eyes (Pinter, 1966), as is found in *Limulus* (Hartline, Wagner and MacNichol, 1952), and in the wolf spider (DeVoe, 1963).

* This investigation was supported by U.S. Public Health Service Research Grant NB-03750 from the National Institute of Neurological Diseases and Blindness.

Now the wolf spider is an excellent arthropod in which to further study sensory adaptation in light-adapted eyes. For one thing, there appear to be only primary visual receptor cells within the eye (Baccetti and Bedini, 1964), and so gross, massed, electrical responses to light (retinal action potentials) recorded at the corneas of intact animals are good representations of what occur in single receptor cells. Thus, intact animals may be used, precluding the visual fatigue which may occur upon light-adapting excised eyes. Finally incremental responses of light-adapted spider eyes may be linear, and hence sensory adaptation in these eyes may be readily quantitated (DeVoe, 1963).

Thus in going on to find a description of non-linear responses it was first of use to see if the quantitative descriptions of linear responses from light-adapted wolf spider eyes may be accounted for by a "light-adapted", linearized, RC feedback model. What was found, however, was that although the RC feedback model would predict the presence of sensory adaptation in light-adapted eyes, in the case of linear responses from wolf spider eyes it was unsatisfactory. The model did not predict any phase lead whatsoever in the responses to sinusoidal modulations of the adapting light, whereas considerable phase lead of the responses compared to the stimuli occurs at low frequencies in wolf spider eyes (DeVoe, 1964). Indeed, there are serious difficulties in adapting the RC feedback model to responses of the same *Limulus* ommatidium in both its light- and dark-adapted states (Pinter, 1966).

It is for reasons such as these that a different sort of model for sensory adaptation in light-adapted wolf spider eyes is sought. Like the RC feedback model, this one too must be purely formal, which is to say that with our present ignorance about the causes of sensory adaptation, the most that can be hoped for is a neat, quantitative package summarizing what is known about its manifestations. The approach to be taken is to find a model which describes the linear responses of the spider eye to transient and sinusoidal stimulation but which also appears to be a linearized form of an intrinsically non-linear mechanism. Therefore, although non-linear responses from light-adapted wolf spider eyes must of course be examined to see what sorts of non-linear mechanisms might be suitable, this presentation will begin with the description of the linear responses from these eyes.

MATERIALS AND METHODS

All experiments were performed upon intact light-adapted, adult spiders of the genus *Lycosa*. These were restrained as described previously (DeVoe 1963), and salt bridges leading to silver–silver chloride electrodes were placed upon the illuminated eye and upon an indifferent location, usually the posterior carapace, where no electrical artifacts from the eyes can be recorded (Magni, Papi, Savely and Tongiorgi, 1965). The light which illuminated the eye was obtained from a Sylvania R1131C glow modulator tube driven a a mean current of 25 mA by a novel circuit (MacDonald, 1960); this light source and associated circuitry provided both positive and negative flashes and steps as well as sinusoidal modulations of the background illumination.

Retinal action potentials recorded from the eye with DC amplification were stored on analogue tape and averaged off-line by the LINC computer. From 32 to 256 responses to each stimulus were averaged; these averages consisted of about 200 points each. Amplitudes and phases of averaged responses to sinusoidal stimuli were measured using the LINC computer, but for all subsequent calculations recourse was had to the IBM 7094 computer.

RESULTS

A. *The Linear Responses of the Spider Eye*

It is, in general, a dubious proposition to study the properties of a non-linear system in terms of its small-signal, linear behaviour, inasmuch as the linear behaviour is more apt to be a special case of the non-linear behaviour than vice-versa. But the eye, fortunately, responds to light in a way that makes knowledge of its linear, incremental responses quite useful for the further understanding of its non-linear input–output characteristics. For one thing, it responds quite linearly to bright but short incremental flashes which, were they sufficiently prolonged, would elicit quite non-linear response amplitudes (Kirschfeld, 1961; DeVoe, 1963). What is the same thing, the initial portions of a non-linear response to a bright and prolonged flash may well be proportional to the intensity of the flash even though the later portions of the response most definitely are not (Fuortes and Hodgkin, 1964). Further, it is by output controlled variations in the parameters of a model describing the linear behaviour of single visual cells that this sort of linear–non-linear behaviour may be accounted for in dark-adapted *Limulus* eyes (Fuortes and Hodgkin, 1964; Marimont, 1965). The non-linear analysis of spider eye retinal action potentials will therefore begin by an examination of how they behave under linear response conditions.

That the spider eye may respond linearly seems amply established (DeVoe, 1963). The next step is to find quantitative input–output relations (differential equations, transfer functions, analogues, etc.) for these linear responses; the question is, how may they be best obtained? In principle, the same quantitative information about a linear system is present in both its responses to transients (flashes, step changes in light, etc.) and its responses to sinusoidal stimulation, for example. Thus, Fuortes and Hodgkin (1964) described the linear responses of *Limulus* ommatidia by differential equations fitted to the transient responses, which lacked sensory adaptation. The linear transient responses of light-adapted wolf spider eyes possess sensory adaptation, however; the response to a 15 % incremental step is shown in Fig. 1 as the solid line. After a delay, or latent period, the response rises above or over-

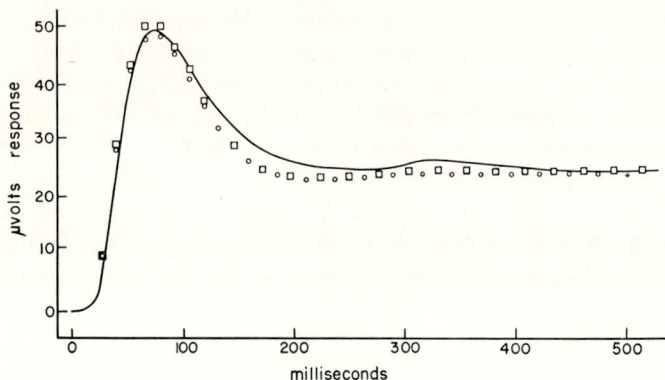

FIG. 1

The step response of the wolf spider eye. The solid line represents the average of 128 responses recorded from a light-adapted wolf spider eye when presented with incremental steps whose amplitudes were 15% of the background. The open circles represent responses to this 15% step calculated from the transfer function in Fig. 2, while the open squares represent responses calculated from the set of non-linear equations described in the text. Negativity of the cornea of the illuminated eye with respect to the indifferent electrode is upwards.

shoots the final DC level to which it slowly subsides. Now differential equations which describe sensory adaptation of this sort are going to be more complicated than those describing linear transient responses, such as those from *Limulus*, which lack sensory adaptation. Therefore the quantitative input–output relations for light-adapted spider eyes were determined, in the form of a transfer function (a transformed differential equation), from the amplitudes and phases of response to sinusoidal modulations of the background illumination.

Results of one experiment in which this was done are given in Fig. 2. In common with engineering usage, the amplitude data are plotted on a decibel (logarithmic) scale, and in this case represent 20 times the logarithm of the ratio of the stimulus amplitude required at a given frequency to elicit 10 μV peak-to-peak response to the amplitude of the DC (zero frequency) stimulus necessary to produce 5 μV of response. The course of the attenuation in the light-adapted eye as a function of frequency seems clear; the eye gives a smaller response to a DC (step) stimulus than to one of 4–6 c/s and the response in turn becomes progressively less as the frequency is raised above 6 c/s. This sort of low frequency peaking and high frequency cut-off has much in common with the frequency response of light-adapted human (deLange, 1961; Kelly, 1961) and *Limulus* (Pinter, 1966) eyes, and has been termed low-pass filter action by deLange (1966).

To account for the latent period in the linear response of dark-adapted *Limulus* eyes, Fuortes and Hodgkin (1964) proposed an RC analogue having

7 to 10 stages of exponential delay. The same sort of analogue does quite well for explaining the high frequency responses of the light-adapted spider eye (DeVoe, 1964). The transfer function given in the inset may be represented by the electrical analogue in Fig. 3, where it can be seen that the right-hand portion of the analogue is composed of n exponential delay stages. The amplitudes and phases of sinusoidal responses which are predicted by the transfer function, and hence would result from the analogue were it sinusoidally driven, are shown in Fig. 2 as the full lines. The fit to the measured high frequency amplitudes and phases appear quite satisfactory using $n = 7$ and $\tau = 1/\omega_n = 3.35$ msec.

Quite a different sort of analogue or transfer function is needed to fit the

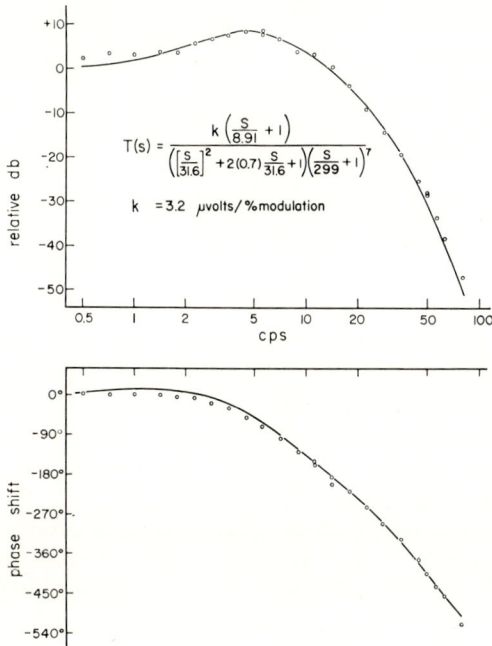

$$T(s) = \frac{k\left(\frac{s}{8.91} + 1\right)}{\left(\left[\frac{s}{31.6}\right]^2 + 2(0.7)\frac{s}{31.6} + 1\right)\left(\frac{s}{299} + 1\right)^7}$$

$k = 3.2$ μvolts/%modulation

FIG. 2

The responses of the light-adapted wolf spider eye to sinusoidal modulations of the background. Top: on the abscissa, the frequency on a logarithmic scale is plotted versus the relative amplitudes of response (open circles) on the ordinate, also on a logarithmic or decibel scale. Decibels are here defined as 20 times the logarithm of the ratio of the amplitude of the sinusoidal stimulus required to elicit 10 μV peak-to-peak response to the step stimulus amplitude required to elicit 5 μV DC response. Bottom: phases of responses relative to phases of stimuli, shown as open circles, are plotted on the ordinate on a linear scale versus frequency on the abscissa on a logarithmic scale. Inset: this transfer function was fitted to the measured amplitudes and phases of responses as shown by the solid lines. Percent modulation is defined as 100 times the ratio of 1/2 the peak-to-peak amplitude of the sinusoidal stimulus to the background intensity.

low-frequency, peaked responses portrayed in Fig. 2. The time response equivalent to peaking in the frequency domain is overshoot or sensory adaptation in the response to a step, and this is what was observed in the step response of the light-adapted spider eye (Fig. 1). Now overshoot implies differentiation of the input waveform, so that some form of electrical analogue that acts as a differentiator is needed to complete the analogue of the spider eye's frequency response.

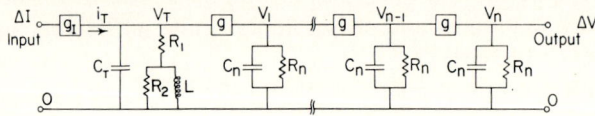

$$T_{(S)} = k \frac{(\frac{S}{Z} + 1)}{\left(\left[\frac{S}{\omega_T}\right]^2 + 2\zeta\frac{S}{\omega_T} + 1\right)\left(\frac{S}{\omega_n} + 1\right)^n}$$

$$\frac{1}{\omega_n} = \Upsilon = R_n C_n$$

$$\frac{1}{Z} = \frac{L}{\left(\frac{R_1 R_2}{R_1 + R_2}\right)}$$

$$\frac{1}{\omega_T} = \sqrt{L C_T \frac{R_1 + R_2}{R_2}}$$

$$\frac{2\zeta}{\omega_T} = \frac{L}{R_2} + R_1 C_T$$

FIG. 3

An electrical analogue of the frequency responses of the light-adapted wolf spider eye shown in Fig. 2. The generic transfer function for this analogue is shown below, and the equations illustrate the relations of the physical elements in the analogue to the parameters in the transfer function. $\triangle I$ is the stimulus intensity, while the output $\triangle V$ represents the recorded response. The conductances g_1 and g have the dimensions of amps/intensity and amps/volt, respectively, while n is the number of the exponential delay elements.

In the past, a number of transfer functions, whose low-frequency behaviour could be matched by analogues containing only capacitance and resistance, were proposed for the spider eye (DeVoe, 1963, 1964). However, more recent experiments have given peaked amplitude frequency response curves too narrow to be fit by such analogues; their deficiency was too great an amount of damping. Consequently, it appeared worthwhile to investigate LRC networks in an analogue, such as is shown on the top left of Fig. 3. This particular one was arrived at, first, because a simpler analogue comprised of a capacitor in parallel with a series resistance and inductance (Cole, 1941), was inconsistent with the best fit transfer function; and secondly, because a four-element LRC network was quite sufficient, and therefore a more complicated network was uncalled for. Of course, the location in the analogue network of the fourth element (R_2) is open to some manipulation, but the network illustrated does have the virtue of representing known, linearized behaviour of, for example, the potassium conductance of the squid membrane (Hodgkin and Huxley, 1952) as well as a variety of model membranes and thermonegative physical elements (Mauro, 1961). Capital shall be made of this virtue when the non-linear responses of the spider eye are considered.

The electrical analogue for the low-frequency behaviour of the light-adapted spider eye does satisfactorily describe the measured amplitudes and phases of response; the solid lines in Fig. 2 are calculated from the transfer function given in the inset, and this form of transfer function has identical behaviour to the analogue, as has been explained. The constants chosen for the transfer function predict more phase lead at the lowest frequencies than was found, but in other experiments, considerably greater phase lead at low frequencies was measured than here (DeVoe, 1964).

What is perhaps more important, the low-frequency lead network in the analogue, in series of course with the exponential delay units, suffices very nicely to predict the transient responses of the light-adapted spider eye. The sensory adaptation in Fig. 1 is well predicted by the analogue, the open circles being calculated from the transfer function in Fig. 2. The calculated response does oscillate a bit more than the recorded response; on the basis of other experiments it would appear that the damping in the calculated response was a bit too low. However, the better match between recorded and calculated step responses perhaps to be afforded by manipulation of the damping was not felt worth the effort.

It may thus be said that the form of the analogue chosen to represent the linear behaviour of the light-adapted spider eye mimics well both the transient and frequency responses to incremental stimuli. The linear analogue postulated by Fuortes and Hodgkin (1964) for the *Limulus* receptor potential will not do for the light-adapted retinal action potentials from the spider; indeed it will not even do for the receptor potentials elicited from constantly illuminated *Limulus* visual cells (Pinter, 1966). But their concept of a chain of exponential delay stages does quite nicely for explaining the latent periods of response as well as the high frequency amplitudes and phases of response of the spider eye and so has been incorporated into the present linear model.

B. *Non-linear Responses to Short Step Changes in Background*

The incremental analysis of the light-adapted eye just described was dictated by the desire to perturb the visual system just sufficiently so that responses might be recorded, but not so much that the state of adaptation of the eye would alter and render these responses non-linear. The presence of background illumination seemed an excellent method of maintaining a constant state of adaptation, particularly as there had to be some mean amount of illumination present anyway in order to elicit flicker responses. This same cautious approach of perturbing activity already present shall be used in this study of non-linear responses; specifically, the non-linear responses to be examined shall be those elicited from the already light-adapted eye by large positive as well as negative step changes in the background illumination already present. Thereby it is hoped to make the transition from the linear to the non-linear model as smooth as possible, so that the utmost transfer of detail may be carried from the one model to the other.

The basic features of the responses to step changes in illumination which go all the way from nearly doubling the background to removing it entirely are shown in Fig. 4; unfortunately, it was not possible to further increase the background with the light source available. During the one-half second

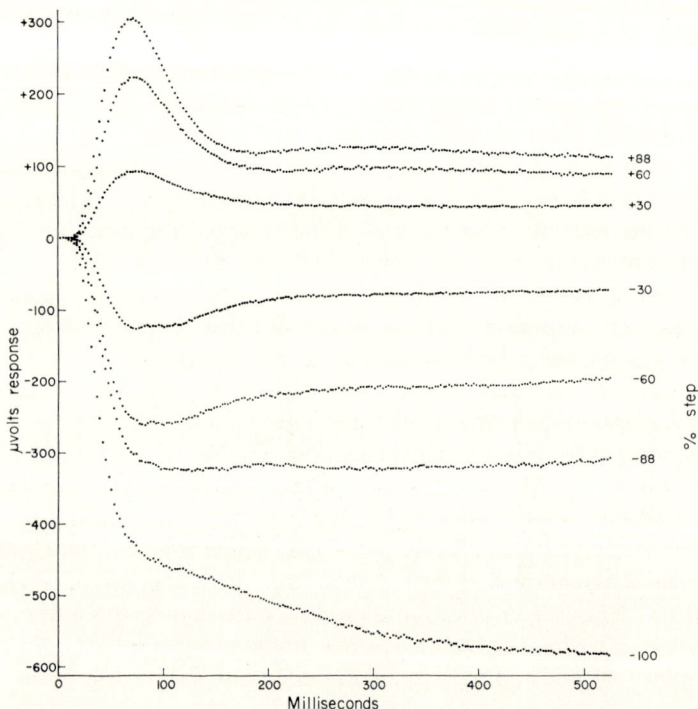

FIG. 4

Averaged responses of the light-adapted spider eye to large step changes in the background illumination. The points making up each response are the averages of 32 recorded responses to ±30% steps, and of 16 recorded responses to the other steps. Sampling time in all cases was 2·624 msec. Negativity of the cornea of the illuminated eye with respect to the indifferent electrode is upwards. Same experiment as in Fig. 1 and Fig. 2.

or so illustrated by these time courses, a new DC response level was achieved, although just barely so when the background was altogether terminated (-100% step). The magnitude of these DC responses is, however, definitely not proportional to the amount by which the background was changed; on the contrary, decreases in the background (negative steps) elicited rather larger potential excursions from the initial baseline than did equal increases (positive steps) in background illumination. This is all reminiscent of some sort of rectification, and since the early parts of these responses may be linear (DeVoe, 1963; Fuortes and Hodgkin, 1964), of delayed rectification at that. The rectification may be better evidenced in a plot of DC response versus step amplitude, as in Fig. 5, where the circles are data points from the experiment of Fig. 4. The same data are also plotted with background intensity on a logarithmic scale (Fig. 5, inset), from which it can be seen that the rectification is simply the old, familiar, logarithmic stimulus–response relation. In these two graphs, the solid lines are theoretical curves whose derivation will be described later.

Rectification quite similar to this has been previously described in the retinal action potentials of light-adapted beetle eyes to positive and negative steps of light (Kirschfeld, 1961), and Washizu (1964) has obtained rectification in the peak intracellular responses to light- or dark-adapted retinula cells of the fly, *Calliphora*, while passing positive and negative current through the cell membrane. It is tempting to suppose that these two sorts of rectification might somehow be related, but the equivalence of light- and current-induced membrane potential changes remains to be proven.

Another way in which the responses to increases and to decreases in the amount of background illumination in Fig. 4 differ from one another is in the extent to which the DC response is different from the maximum or peak transient response, that is, in the amount of sensory adaptation. For example, as the amount of increase in background is made greater, the greater is the peak response relative to the DC response. For increasingly negative changes in background, the converse is true; the undershoot becomes less. Moreover, these peaks are achieved in the shortest time when the increase in background is greatest, and they become progressively delayed in time as the amount of background increase is made smaller or is made negative. Thus the time to peak for the response to the $+88\%$ step was 68 msec, while the response to the -88% step took 130 msec to reach its minimum value. At complete removal of the background light there was no peak at all, and the response declined monotonically to its final DC level.

C. *Non-linear Responses to Long Step Changes in Background*

An altogether different picture of the responses of the light-adapted spider eye to large step changes in background emerges if responses to maintained steps are followed for periods longer than one-half second, which was the duration of the responses in Fig. 4. Then, a distinct, long-term adaptation process appears to occur which brings the DC responses back towards (but not necessarily to) the original baseline. This return towards baseline is illustrated in Fig. 6, where there are drawn averaged responses to 5 sec long, positive and negative 90% step changes in the background. The return towards baseline is especially evident in the response to the -90% step, where, after all, the illumination upon the eye had been reduced to one-tenth of its starting value. It is to be expected that, with a reduction in illumination,

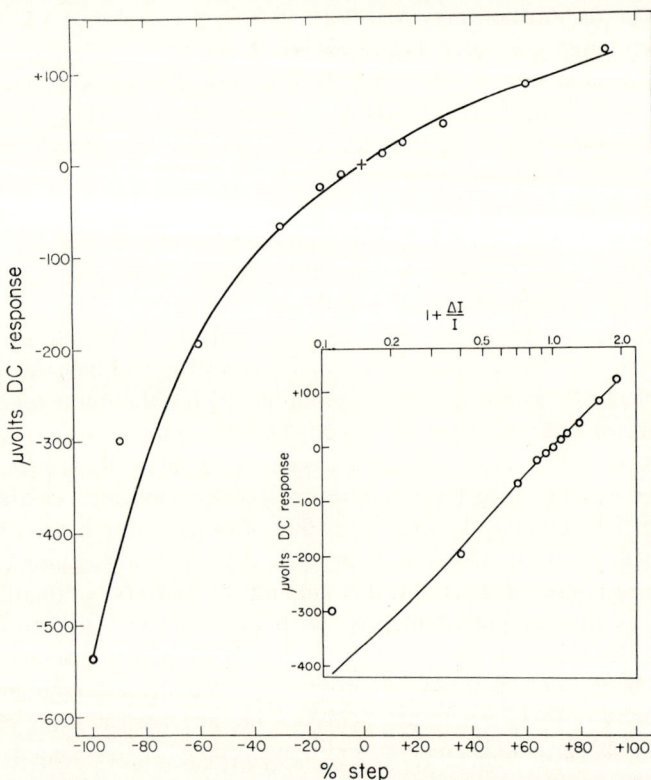

FIG. 5

Steady-state or DC responses of the light-adapted wolf spider eye achieved one-half second or so following the abrupt, maintained percent change in background shown on the abscissa. The open circles are microvolts of DC response relative to the baseline due to the original background illumination, and are taken from the experiment illustrated in Fig. 4. Positive DC responses correspond to upward deflections in Fig. 4. Inset: these same responses are plotted as open circles versus $1 + \Delta I/I$ on a logarithmic scale, where $\Delta I/I$ is the fractional change in background due to a step stimulus. The solid lines are theoretical curves fitted to the points in the manner explained in the text. The DC response to the -88% step is smaller than predicted due to technical difficulties.

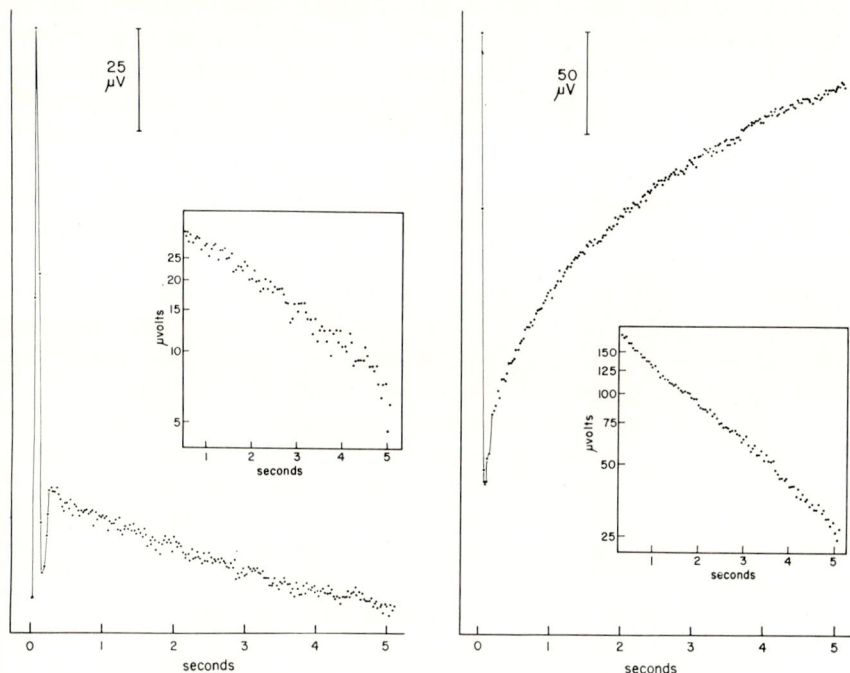

FIG. 6

Averaged responses of the light-adapted wolf spider eye to 5 sec long positive (left) and negative (right) 90% changes in background illumination. Each response depicted by the points is the average of 4 recorded responses; the sampling rate was one point every 24·8 msec. Solid lines drawn by eye connect the first 9 or 10 points in each response to make evident the initial portions of these responses. These initial portions thus occupy about one-half the duration of the responses to positive and negative steps illustrated in Fig. 4, which were from a different experiment. Insets: the roughly exponential decays during the last 4·5 sec of these responses towards some new response level are here illustrated by plotting, on a logarithmic scale, the differences between these new response levels and the responses existent at the times shown on the abscissa. For the left-hand response this new level was taken to be the bottom of the graph; for the right-hand response, the new level was taken to be the vertical position of the initial point in the response. The time constants of decay are, in the left-hand inset, about 3 sec, and on the right, about 2·5 sec.

the eye should show a long-term gain in sensitivity corresponding, perhaps, to the fall in threshold which occurs in the human eye when a bright adapting light is replaced by a weaker one (Rushton, 1965). In the spider eye, perhaps the DC response to a negative step should not be measured from the baseline potential established by the original background illumination, but rather from the baseline established in darkness. One way to establish the baseline in darkness is to turn off the background light completely, as was done in Fig. 4 by the − 100 % step, and see to what new level the potential from the eye falls. It was found then that the potential achieved at the end of one-half second was maintained essentially constant for the next 5 sec, so this potential has been taken as that in the dark for the purposes of this paper. Thus, for responses less than one-half second, the DC response to a − 88 % step would be the difference between the DC responses to − 88 % and − 100 % steps in Fig. 4; this difference is a positive number. Then, any slow return of the DC potential towards baseline, as in Fig. 6, may be interpreted not as a decrease in response amplitude, but, on the contrary, an increase in response amplitude to the 10 % illumination remaining after the 90 % decrease in the original background illumination. This increase would then reflect an increasing sensitivity of the eye.

Conversely, the slow decline in the DC response to the +90 % step reflects a true decrease in response amplitude relative to that in the dark, a decrease which may presumably be related to further light adaptation. The same sorts of slow potential decrease following the achievement of a steady-state in the responses of dark-adapted *Limulus* ommatidia have been reported by Marimont (1965).

The time courses of return towards the original baseline, shown in Fig. 6, are approximately exponential. This may be seen in the insets of Fig. 6, where the responses are plotted on logarithmic ordinates. The final levels which these responses would achieve in time were estimated to be the bottom of the graph for the response to the +90 % step, and the first point in the response to the −90 % step. However, it is not known where the original baselines for these figures was, as the rate at which the computer sampled these responses was so slow (every 25 msec) that the first points are not necessarily the baselines. The time constants of return towards baseline are quite similar, being about 3 sec for the +90 % step, and about 2·5 sec for the −90 % step, as estimated by eye. These figures may be compared with a time constant of 6 sec found by Pinter (1966) for the slow neural adaptation in light-adapted *Limulus* eyes, and are compatible with the rates of light adaptation in rats (Dowling, 1963).

D. *A Two-stage Model for the Light-Adapted Spider Eye*

It is not unreasonable to assume that two processes underlie the rapid and slow portions of the non-linear responses illustrated in Figs. 4 and 6. It is inviting to assign these two processes to the two stages of the model whose linear analogue is illustrated in Fig. 3. The question must be, which stage is to be assigned to which of the two phases of the non-linear responses?

There is precedent for supposing that the LRC lead stage in Fig. 3 might be a suitable explanation of the slow adaptation pictured in Fig. 6 (Pinter, 1966) and the exponential delay stages a suitable explanation, via the RC feedback model (Fuortes and Hodgkin, 1964; Marimont, 1965) of the rapid, non-linear responses in Fig. 4. However, the time constant of the LRC lead stage of Fig. 3 (31·6 msec) is two orders of magnitude too small to account for this slow adaption, while the time constants of the exponential delay stages (3·35 msec) are probably too small to account for the variations in amount of sensory adaptation in the rapid non-linear responses, although calculations using the RC feedback model have not been made.

On the other hand, it is known that in both the spider eye and in the eye of *Limulus*, large changes in sensitivity may occur, but with small changes in the time scale of response (Fuortes and Hodgkin, 1964). These parallel changes in time scale and sensitivity may, in *Limulus* at least, be explained by variations in the shunt resistances in exponential delays in analogues such as that in Fig. 3 (Fuortes and Hodgkin, 1964). It is not too unreasonable to suppose that the slow adaptation changes pictured in Fig. 6 reflect such changes in sensitivity and that these sensitivity changes are thus explained by variations in the resistances R_n (or what is the same if the C_n's are constant, the time constants τ). It is quite another matter, of course, to explain how changes in these resistances come about. It cannot be by way of the RC feedback model in its present form, because the measured time constants of the exponential delay stages are most certainly too small, as mentioned above. The point of emphasis is not how these shunt resistances are changed, however; it is rather that the short-term non-linear responses of Fig. 4 are not to be parceled out to the exponential delay stages of the model. On the contrary, the time constants of these stages shall be assumed to change not at all during the first half-second of the non-linear responses to large step changes in illumination. This assumption is necessary if tractable expressions are to be found for these short-term non-linear responses; it means that to all inputs lasting less than one-half second, the exponential delay stages of the analogue will behave linearly.

There remains to be found some sort of physical element which, when placed in an analogue in series with the above stages of exponential delay, will behave under incremental stimulation like the LRC lead network in the linear analogue in Fig. 3 and will display instantaneous linearity but delayed rectification. Nerve membranes may behave in this manner (Hodgkin and Huxley, 1952); so too may a variety of physical devices (Mauro, 1961). One such particularly convenient physical device to place in an analogue is a thermistor, since its behaviour in electrical networks is well known (Ekelöf and Kihlberg, 1954). The analogue for short-term non-linear responses then looks like that in Fig. 7, where R_T represents the thermistor resistance. It can be shown (Ekelöf and Kihlberg, 1954) that this analogue will become the analogue in Fig. 3 when incrementally driven; the question to be answered is, however, whether the analogue of Fig. 3 may become the analogue of Fig. 7 when the responses of the eye to large stimuli are to be mimicked.

C.E.—Y

E. *The Steady-state Properties of the Non-linear Model*

The linear analogue in Fig. 3 does not represent the only order in which the stages may be placed, but in a linear system, by virtue of superposition, the order does not matter. In a non-linear system the order of the stages may matter very much, as in general they are not commutable. Quite a number of different orderings of the stages in Fig. 7 are possible, but only two have been

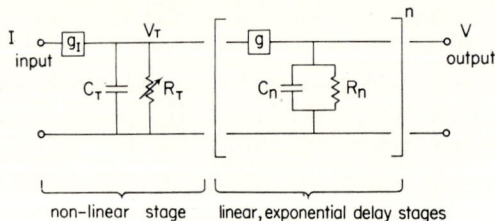

FIG. 7

The non-linear analogue of the light-adapted wolf spider eye. In the left-hand portion of this analogue the resistance R_T represents the resistance of a thermistor and is variable. On the right the exponential delay stages are shown in brackets, and there are n of them, where n for the experiment illustrated in Fig. 2 is 7. The conductances g_1 and g have the dimensions of amps/intensity and amps/volt, respectively. I is the stimulus intensity and V is the potential measured from the baseline in the dark.

considered, namely, the one shown and one in which all the exponential delay stages precede the non-linear, thermistor-containing stage. The differential equations describing the non-linear stage in these two arrangements are practically identical, the major difference being that, in Fig. 7, the input to this stage is the light itself, while, in the other arrangement, the output of the exponential delay stages serves as input to this stage. However, because the time constants in the exponential delay stages are so small and the resultant transients in the response from these stages are so short, either arrangement of linear and non-linear stages gives the same output from about the time of the peaks in the response on. The particular ordering given in Fig. 7 was chosen simply because it gave a slightly better fit to the initial portions of the responses in Fig. 4, but either set of calculated responses would have done. The equations for the non-linear, thermistor-containing stage will, however, only be developed for the analogue in Fig. 7.

To quantitatively specify the steady-state properties of the thermistor in the analogue, there must be known the voltage V_T across it and its resistance R_T. However, these are but conceptual entities and they must be derived from the inputs and outputs, which alone are observable quantities. Following the procedure of Fuortes and Hodgkin (1964), it can be shown that, at steady rate,

$$\tau = R_n C_n,$$

$$V = I A \tau^n R_T C_T, \qquad A = \frac{g_1 g^n}{C_T C_n{}^n}. \qquad (1)$$

Here, V is the potential referred to the baseline in the dark, which is found, for example, by the DC response to a -100% step. From (1) there may be defined quantities proportional to V_T and R_T, assuming C_T and C_n to be constant,

$$V_T' = \frac{V}{A \tau^n}. \qquad (2)$$

$$R_T C_T = \frac{V}{I A \tau^n}. \qquad (3)$$

From (3) it can be seen that changes in the absolute sensitivity V/I, which result in the rectification in Fig. 5, are represented in the analogue by changes in R_T.

The constant $A \tau^n$ may be found from the linear, incremental DC response ΔV to an incremental step ΔI by the analogue in Fig. 2:

$$\Delta V = \Delta I A \tau^n R_1 C_T, \qquad (4)$$

$$R_1 C_T = \frac{Z}{\omega_T{}^2}. \qquad (5)$$

To be able to find the time constant $R_T C_T$ as a function of the intensity I alone, a second relation between I, $R_T C_T$ and V_T is necessary. According to Becker, Green and Pearson (1946), the resistance R_T of a thermistor is the following function of its temperature θ:

$$R_T = R\infty \exp[B/\theta], \qquad (6)$$

where $R\infty$ and B are constants. Ekelöf and Kihlberg (1954) pointed out that the dissipated power P of a thermistor is directly proportional to its temperature, assuming no heat loss by radiation:

$$P = k(\theta - \theta_o); \quad k = \text{incremental dissipation constant},$$
$$\theta_o = \text{ambient temperature.} \qquad (7)$$

On combining (6) and (7), and introducing the time constant instead of the resistance, there results:

$$R_T C_T = C_1 \exp\left[\frac{C_2}{P/C_3 + 1}\right]; \quad \begin{aligned} C_1 &= R\infty C_T, \\ C_2 &= B/\theta_o, \\ C_3 &= k\theta_o. \end{aligned} \qquad (8)$$

From (1) and (2), there may be defined a dissipated power P':

$$P' = \frac{VI}{A\tau^n}. \tag{9}$$

These relations, (3), (8) and (9), now allow the constants C_1, C_2 and C_3 to be determined; for the spider eye these constants were obtained from a least squares fit to the measured steady-state response V using a non-linear parameter iteration method (Marquardt, 1963). A satisfactory fit was obtained with $C_1 = 5.78$, $C_2 = 2.36$ and $C_3 = 69.6$, as shown by the solid lines in Fig. 5. Thus, the thermistor analogue gives a good account of rectification by the eye.

F. *The Dynamic Behaviour of the Model*

The rate at which the dissipated power, and hence the resistance, of a thermistor may change is determined by the thermal time constant T and the applied power. Using the "thermistor equation" of Ekelöf and Kihlberg (1954), and deriving the applied power from the analogue and (2), (3), and (9), there results:

$$\frac{T dP}{dt} + P' = \frac{V'^2_T}{R_T C_T}. \tag{10}$$

The value of T may be determined from the linear analogue in Fig. 2 by means of the electrical time constant Te, which is equal to L/R_2:

$$Te = \frac{2\xi}{\omega_T} - \frac{Z}{\omega_T^2}. \tag{11}$$

The thermal time constant is then given (Ekelöf and Kihlberg, 1954) by:

$$T = Te \frac{\dfrac{2V_o}{I_o}}{\dfrac{V_o}{I_o} \Delta \dfrac{\Delta V}{\Delta I}}, \tag{12}$$

where V_o is the baseline potential due to the background I_o. For the experiment in Fig. 2, $T = 53.8$ msec.

Finally, from the non-linear analogue there may be derived:

$$C_T \frac{dV_T}{dt} + \frac{V_T}{R_T} = g_I I.$$

Upon rearranging this equation, and substituting V'_T for V_T, there results:

$$\frac{dV'_T}{dt} + \frac{V'_T}{R_T C_T} = I. \tag{13}$$

The portion of the non-linear analogue containing the thermistor may thus be described completely by eqns. (8), (10) and (13). The output V of the entire analogue may then be obtained by convoluting the output V_T' of the thermistor stage of the analogue with the impulse response En of the exponential delay stages, assuming as was stated above that they remain linear during the first one-half second or so of the non-linear response:

$$V(t) = \int_0^t V_T'(X)En(t-X)dX, \tag{14}$$

$$En(t) = \left(\frac{A\tau^n}{}\right)\frac{1}{\tau}\left(\frac{t}{\tau}\right)^{n-1}\frac{e^{-t/\tau}}{(n-1)\,!}. \tag{15}$$

The responses of the analogue have been calculated by solving the above equations for various stimuli $I_o + \Delta I$ using the IBM 7094 computer. It was first desirable to see that these equations and the constants determined would indeed predict the linear behaviour of the eye, as the analogue itself can be shown to do. Consequently, the response to a $+15\%$ step was calculated, and is shown in Fig. 1 as the open squares. It may be compared with the response,

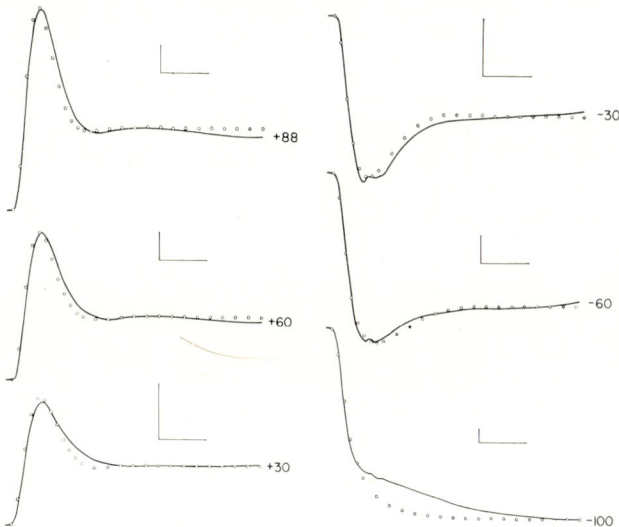

FIG. 8

Comparison of the recorded and predicted responses to large positive and negative step changes in background illumination upon the light-adapted wolf spider eye. The solid lines are the averages of responses to the percent of positive and negative steps shown and are redrawn from Fig. 4. The open circles are the responses predicted by means of the equations derived in the text. The vertical calibration markers represent 40 μV; the horizontal calibration markers represent 100 msec. Upward deflection indicates that the cornea of the illuminated eye has become negative to the indifferent electrode.

shown by open circles, to this same step calculated using the transfer function in Fig. 2. The two calculated responses are virtually the same, and both agree well with the average of the measured responses, which, of course, is the main point.

What is more, the responses to large step changes in background which were calculated from the above equations also fit the recorded responses to these steps quite well. This is illustrated in Fig. 8, in which the full lines are averages of recorded responses and the open circles are the calculated responses. Only between the calculated and measured responses to -100% steps (light off) is there a serious discrepancy, and this has been true in all experiments performed. The predicted response dies away too rapidly. Fuortes and Hodgkin (1964) experienced similar difficulties in getting their RC feedback model to account for the off response in *Limulus* generator potentials.

For the rest, however, the agreement between recorded and measured responses is as good for these non-linear responses as it was for the linear responses described earlier. This is an encouraging validification of the assumptions which were used to make these calculations.

CONCLUSIONS

The formal mathematical model used in this paper to describe the non-linear responses of the light-adapted wolf spider eye, although derived from and explained in terms of the electrical analogue, nonetheless may be presented in a qualitative fashion in terms more usual in visual physiology. As was mentioned above, the resistance R_T of the analogue is simply proportional to the absolute sensitivity V/I of the eye. Now the basic thing which occurs in the analogue when stimulated is that this resistance changes, although it does not change at once. Consequently, the sensitivity of the eye changes when it is stimulated, although, again, it does not change at once. There results from this delayed change in sensitivity the phenomenon of sensory adaptation. It may be added that, even for linear responses, the model would assign to sensitivity changes the observed sensory adaptation, although in practice these sensitivity changes are too small to measure by such methods as superposition of responses (DeVoe, 1962).

Both the present model and the RC feedback model (Fuortes and Hodgkin, 1964) give an explanation of sensory adaptation in terms of changes in visual sensitivity. All this merely shifts the emphasis to origins of sensitivity changes. But sensitivity and its changes are defined operationally in terms of inputs and outputs just as are the features of the model here developed. Only the sensitivity changes caused by variations in photopigment concentration have any known molecular basis (Dowling, 1963), and these sorts of sensitivity changes most likely do not underlie sensory adaptation, for reasons given earlier. So it would seem that there is little to be gained by attempting to "explain" sensory adaptation solely in terms of the eye's sensitivity. Rather, it would appear more profitable in the future to explore the similarities between the dynamics of the eye, as expressed in the model, and the similar dynamics of structures such as membranes (Mauro, 1961) whose molecular basis is better, if still incompletely, understood.

ACKNOWLEDGEMENTS

The computations with IBM equipment were done in the Computing Center of the Johns Hopkins Medical Institutions, which is supported by Research Grant FR-00004 from the National Institutes of Health and by educational contributions from the International Business Machine Company. The LINC computer was available under the evaluation program of the National Institutes of Health (Research Grant MH-08352-01).

REFERENCES

BACCETTI, B. and BEDINI, C. 1964. Research on the structure and physiology of the eyes of a Lycosid spider. I.—Microscopic and Ultramicroscopic structure. *Arch. ital. Biol.* **102**, 97–122.

BECKER, J. A., GREEN, C. B. and PEARSON, G. L. 1946. Properties and uses of thermistors—thermally sensitive resistors. *Trans. Amer. Inst. Electr. Engrs.* **65**, 711–25.

BOYNTON, R. M. 1958. On-responses in the human visual system as inferred from psychophysical studies of rapid adaptation. *A.M.A. Arch. Ophthal.* **60II**, 800–10.

COLE, K. S. 1941. Rectification and inductance in the squid giant axon. *J. Gen. Physiol.* **25**, 29–51.

DeLANGE, H., DZN. 1961. Eye's response at flicker fusion to square-wave modulation of a test field surrounded by a large steady field of equal mean luminance. *J. Opt. Soc. Amer.* **51**, 485–21.

DEVOE, R. D. 1962. Linear superposition of retinal action potentials to predict electrical flicker responses from the eye of the wolf spider, *Lycosa baltimoriana* (Keyserling). *J. Gen. Physiol.* **46**, 75–96.

DEVOE, R. D. 1963. Linear relations between stimulus amplitudes and amplitudes of retinal action potentials from the eye of the wolf spider. *J. Gen. Physiol.* **47**, 13–32.

DEVOE, R. D. 1964. Linear electrical flicker responses from the eye of the wolf spider. *Docum. Ophthal.* **18**, 128–36.

DOWLING, J. E. 1963. Neural and photochemical mechanisms of visual adaptation in the rat. *J. Gen. Physiol.* **46**, 1287–301.

EKELÖF, S. and KIHLBERG, G. 1954. *Theory of the Thermistor as an Electric Circuit Element.* Gothenburg, Sweden, Trans. Chalmers Univ. Tech. No. 142.

FUORTES, M. G. H. and HODGKIN, A. L. 1964. Changes in time scale and sensitivity in the ommatidia of *Limulus*. *J. Physiol.* **172**, 239–63.

HARTLINE, H. K., WAGNER, H. G. and MACNICHOL, E. F., Jr. 1952. The peripheral origin of nervous activity in the visual system. *Cold Spring Harbor Symp. Quant. Biol.* **17**, 125–41.

HODGKIN, A. L. and HUXLEY, A. F. 1952. A quantitative description of membrane current and its application to conduction and excitation in nerve. *J. Physiol.* **117**, 500–44.

KELLY, D. H. 1961. Visual responses to time-dependent stimuli. I. Amplitude sensitivity measurements. *J. Opt. Soc. Am.* **51**, 422–9.

KIRSCHFELD, K. 1961. Quantitative Beziehungen zwischen Lichtreiz und monophasischem Electroretinogramm bei Rüsselkäfern. *Z. vergl. Physiol.* **44**, 371–413.

MacDonald, H. S. 1960. Note on the use of glow modulator lamps for studies of vision. *J. Opt. Soc. Am.* **50**, 1138.

Magni, F., Papi, F., Savely, H. E. and Tongiorgi, P. 1965. Research on the structure and physiology of the eyes of a Lycosid spider. III.—Electroretinographic responses to polarized light. *Arch. ital. Biol.* **103**, 146–58.

Marimont, R. B. 1965. Numerical studies of the Fuortes-Hodgkin *Limulus* model. *J. Physiol.* **179**, 489–97.

Marquardt, D. W. 1963. An algorithm for least-squares estimation of non-linear parameters. *J. Soc. Indust. Appl. Math.* **11**, 431–41.

Mauro, A. 1961. Anomalous impedance, a phenomenological property of time-variant resistance. An analytic review. *Biophys. J.* **1**, 353–72.

Pinter, R. B. 1966. Sinusoidal and delta function responses of visual cells of the *Limulus* eye. *J. Gen. Physiol.* **49**, 565–93.

Rushton, W. A. H. 1965. Visual adaptation. *Proc. Roy. Soc.* **B162**, 20–46.

Washizu, Y. 1964. Electrical activity of single retinula cells in the compound eye of the blow fly *Calliphora erythrocephala* Meig. *Comp. Biochem. Physiol.* **12**, 369–87.

SINGLE CELL RESPONSES FROM THE PRIMITIVE EYES OF AN ANNELID

J. B. WALTHER

I. Zoologisches Institut der Universität Göttingen, Germany

THE substrate for the primary photochemical event of visual excitation is localized in certain regions of the receptor cells. This general idea is supported by comparative gross (Hesse, 1896, etc.) and fine (cf. Eakin, 1965) morphology of eyes and their receptor cells, and by experimental evidence, e.g. from extraction of visual pigments (cf. Wald, 1959), from studies with local light stimulation (Hagins *et al.*, 1962), and from absorption measurements (Brown, 1961; Liebmann, 1962; Marks *et al.*, 1964) of isolated parts of such cells.

These regions, as seen in the electron microscope, are characterized by complex membrane structures, each made up of large numbers of disc-shaped or tubular subunits, closely packed, usually in a very regular arrangement (cf. Eakin, 1965). The visual membrane complexes are reported to be continuous with the cell membrane, or to originate from the cell membrane and remain in very close proximity to it.

On the basis of the above, it is often implied that structural continuity or proximity are essential prerequisites for the transduction of light stimuli into corresponding receptor potentials. There is, however, no experimental evidence supporting this view. The following comments, based on recent findings about the fine structure (Hansen, 1962; Jung, 1963; Röhlich and Török, 1964), and on our own studies of the visual responses (Walther, 1963, 1964, 1965) of single cells in the eyes of the medicinal leech, *Hirudo medicinalis* L, bear on this point.

The numerous cells inside of the heavily pigmented wall of the ten cup-shaped eyes of *Hirudo* contain a peculiar structure, known from light microscopy as the central body, Binnenkörper, Phaosom, or Vakuole (cf. Hansen, 1962). Recent electron micrographs (Hansen, 1962; Jung, 1963; Röhlich and Török, 1964) show the phaosome as a spheroid or gastruloid body, and its surface as composed of densely packed, tubular microvilli. The long axes of the microvilli are arranged more or less radially, their inner ends closed, and their outer ends open to the cytoplasm. The phaosome may thus be regarded as the structural and presumably functional analogue to the rhabdomeres in

* This work was supported by grants from the Deutsche Forschungsgemeinschaft.

compound eyes and to the distal segments in vertebrate visual cells. In *Hirudo*, however, the cytoplasm completely surrounds the phaosome, and membranes or other continuous structures connecting the microvilli with the cell membrane cannot be detected. Röhlich and Török (1964), being aware of the physiological implications of this repeated finding, specify the thickness of the layer of cytoplasm around the phaosome to be "at least 3μ". They also measured the average length, diameter, and wall thickness of the microvilli as $2\cdot3$ μ, 1150 Å, and 70 Å, respectively. The maximal diameter of the spherical or club-shaped cells is about 40 μ. Each cell sends an axon to one of the head ganglia. The axons are embedded in sheath cells, which also partly surround the individual receptor cells.

When receptor cells in *Hirudo* eyes are impaled with conventional micropipette electrodes (3 mol. KCl; $\geq$ 30 MΩ), resting potentials of up to -75 mV, although most frequently around -45 mV, and resting resistances of 20 . . . 100 MΩ are observed. With the prussian blue technique (Purple, 1964) marks were deposited in over thirty experiments, and they verify that the tip of the electrode was indeed located inside of the membrane of a receptor cell when the electrical measurements indicated it. The marks do not allow one to discriminate whether the electrode was lodged in the phaosome or the cytoplasm.

When the eye is illuminated, the resting potential depolarizes, and the cell resistance decreases. The response amplitudes are proportional, within a certain range, to the intensity and duration of the stimuli. This range usually extends over 2–4 log units of intensity (Fig. 1). With brighter stimuli, the response amplitude reaches a saturation value which, however, never depolarizes the cell to less than about -10 mV. With stimuli on the lower end of this intensity range, the scattering of response amplitudes and latencies increases. There is no definite threshold, but rather a range of intensities (about 1 log unit) where single short stimuli may elicit a response or not, presumably in a random manner. With the most sensitive preparations, each stimulus on the lower end of this range delivered at the surface of the eye an average of approximately 1000 but not less than about 300 quanta to the area of a medium-sized cell.

The latency of the responses is inversely proportional to the stimulus intensity. This holds for the total intensity range used (more than 6 log units in some experiments). Its values fall between about 30 and 300 msec at 20°C.

On inspection of the records it is evident that the graded depolarizations to even the highest stimuli are made up of small, discrete ($0\cdot5$–2 mV), perhaps unitary depolarizations. Resistance measurements at rest and during excitation indicate that these are correlated to brief, small, perhaps unitary conductance increases ($0\cdot2$–1 $\times$ 10^{-9} Ω^{-1}), which sum algebraically (except at very high stimulus intensities) when they are synchronous (Fig. 2).

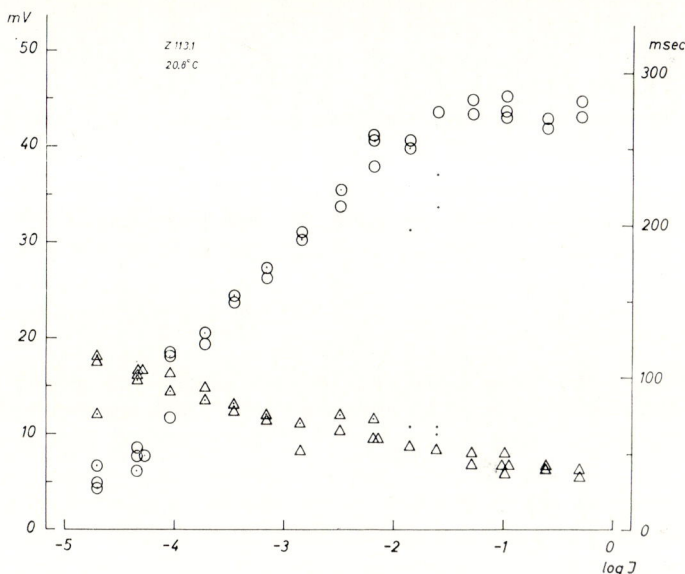

FIG. 1

Amplitude ($\bigcirc$, left ordinate) and latency ($\triangle$, right ordinate) of the generator potential of a visual cell of *Hirudo* plotted against the logarithm of the relative light intensity (abscissa) of 3·4 msec stimuli presented at 10 sec intervals. One run each with decreasing (open) and increasing (dotted symbols) intensities is shown to demonstrate typical scatter. Cell deteriorates towards end of second run, and the three last measurements (note difference between amplitude and latency) are shown by dots only.

In order to obtain clues as to which mechanisms are underlying and in particular preceding the conductance and potential changes, a number of experimental conditions have been varied systematically. Three examples are given.

Positive or negative currents delivered through the recording microelectrode depolarize or hyperpolarize the membrane of the impaled cell, and decrease or increase the amplitude of the generator potentials, respectively. With depolarizations or weak hyperpolarizations, the observed amplitude changes correspond to the voltage drop developed by the imposed current across the cell membrane resistance. With stronger negative currents (about $> 2 \times 10^{-9}$ A), the receptor potential amplitudes increase beyond the values expected on this basis. In contrast, even under the strongest de- or hyperpolarizations used, the time course of the electrical responses, at least of their rising phases, remains unchanged (Fig. 3).

By changing the normal bathing solution of the preparation to solutions containing various concentrations of ethanol, one can produce an initial, temporary (1–2 min) decrease of the resting potential. The amplitudes of the

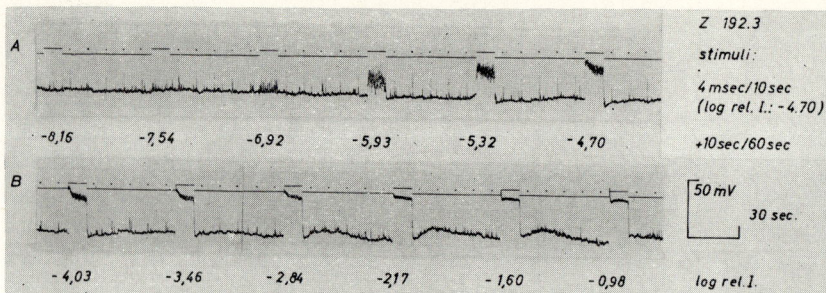

FIG. 2

Generator potentials of a visual cell of *Hirudo* elicited by 10 sec stimuli of
increasing light intensity (log relative I below each record) presented at 60 sec
intervals, and by 3·4 msec test stimuli of constant intensity (log rel. I = − 4·7)
at 10 sec intervals. B is a continuation of A. Upper trace carries stimulus pattern.
Its baseline indicates − 20 mV reference level (approximately) for intracellular
potential on lower trace. Note "spontaneous" small depolarizations between light-
induced responses.

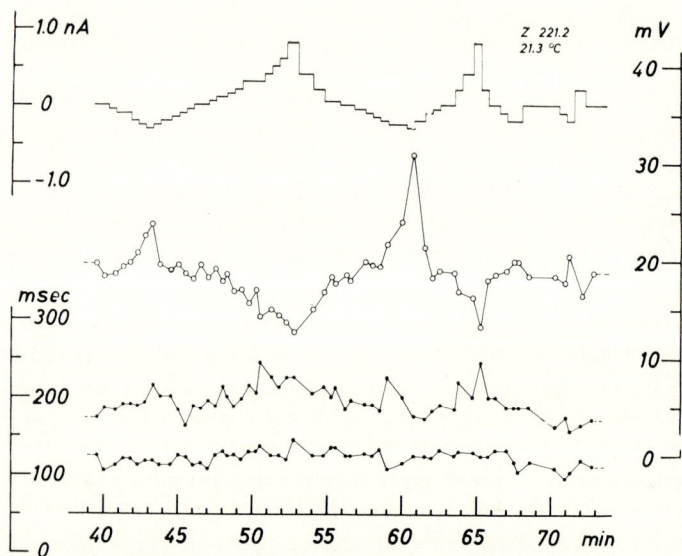

FIG. 3

Amplitude (○, right ordinate), latency and peak time (●, left lower ordinate) of the
generator potential of a visual cell of *Hirudo* which is polarized by various
currents (top curve, left upper ordinate), plotted against the time after impalement of the cell (abscissa).

responses to appropriate, constant test flashes are depressed immediately when the ethanol solution is applied, and remain so until it is washed out again by normal solution. The latency of the generator potentials, on the other hand, shows almost no change under the same conditions. Progressively later phases of the response (e.g. peak time, return-to-half time), though, are increasingly delayed by ethanol (Fig. 4).

Rapid changes in the temperature of the eyes, in steps of a few centigrades in the range between 10 and 30°C, have only a small effect on the amplitude

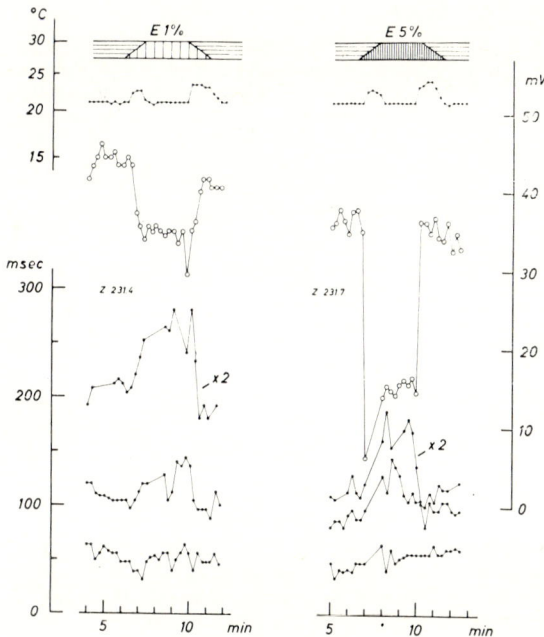

Fig. 4

Amplitude (○, right ordinate), latency, peak time, and return-to-half time (●, left lower ordinate) of the generator potentials of two visual cells of *Hirudo* under the influence of two different concentrations of ethanol in the surrounding solution, plotted against the time after impalement of the cells. The approximate time course of the exchange of the solutions is indicated on top of the diagram. Temperature of the solution around the eye is also shown (●, top curve, upper left ordinate), since it could not be kept constant while the solutions are changed (see Fig. 5). Curve for return-to-half time is scaled down to half its real value to fit the diagram.

of generator potentials elicited by constant test flashes. The latency (and also the peak time, etc.) of these responses, however, shows a significant, immediate and reversible decrease when the temperature is raised, and vice versa (Fig. 5). The Q_{10} values of the two criteria were determined to be slightly larger than 1, and between about 2 and 3, respectively.

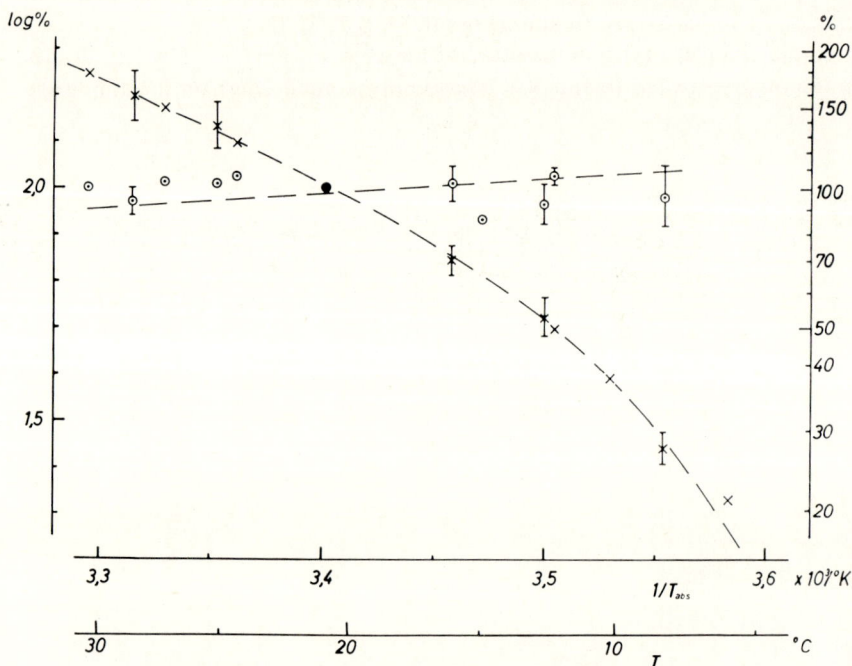

FIG. 5

Relative mean amplitudes ($\bigcirc$), and relative mean latencies ($\times$) of generator potentials of visual cells of *Hirudo* (right ordinate), plotted against absolute temperature (abscissa). The mean values at 21°C serve as reference (100%, $\bullet$). Vertical bars show standard errors. Regression line is shown for amplitude; curve for latency is drawn by inspection. Absolute temperature is plotted as its reciprocal, and percentages are plotted against logarithmic ordinate at left, in order to facilitate determination of Arrhenius energies. Latency is plotted as its reciprocal on the consideration that, rather than the time measured, the velocities of the underlying reaction(s) are relevant in this connection.

The visual cells of the *Hirudo* eye thus furnish an example that the presumed light-sensitive membrane structures may be separated from the cell membrane by a considerable distance, while their sensitivity and general performance as light receptors, judged from their electrical responses, are comparable in many respects to those of other visual cells. Unless the analogy of the phaosomes to rhabdomeres, or their presumed function as the site of the primary visual event, or the role of the cell membrane as the structure where the observed electrical changes originate, are challenged, one is led to conclude that continuity or close proximity of these two membrane structures are not essential for effective transduction of visual information.

The spatial separation of the two sites in *Hirudo* visual cells, more clearly than the evidence obtained from light-sensitive cells in other eyes, thus calls for an intermediate, additional mechanism to link the unknown primary receptor event in the phaosome to the electrical responses observed at the distant cell membrane. With respect to the electrical events at the membrane, the results of the temperature, polarization, and drug experiments, and of the conductance measurements, would support the assumption that the early phases of the generator potential, as measured by the amplitude criterion, are an expression of a diffusion process, which is initiated by an increase of membrane permeability.

The different behaviour of the latency criterion under the same experimental conditions suggests that it is determined by a process or a sequence of processes of quite a different nature. These precede, and should eventually cause, the permeability changes of the cell membrane, and would correspond to the hypothetical intermediate mechanism postulated above, on the basis of the morphological separation of phaosome and membrane.

Among the physiological findings the temperature characteristic of the latency, in particular, supports some limiting and minimal, general predictions about this mechanism. The process, or at least one process if there is a sequence, should involve a chemical reaction. Also, if the characteristic is indeed nonlinear as shown, more than one pace-setting reactions are required to account for the finding; these need not be sequential. Finally, diffusion is not a factor which predominantly determines the temperature dependence of the latency. This would exclude diffusion of very large molecules (or other entities) and very long diffusion distances from the overall process.

The morphological and physiological data available for *Hirudo* seem to lend no support to an hypothesis which invokes bioelectrical events of the conventional type, i.e. on membranes, as the required intermediate mechanism.

The results rather suggest the possibility that a chemical transmitter mediates between the primary and electrical events of visual excitation. Chemical transmission is a mechanism well established elsewhere (cf. Katz, 1962; Eccles, 1963). There are important differences, however, between the situation in these cases and that considered here. The distance between the phaosome and the cell membrane is about four orders of magnitude larger than that across endplate or synaptic clefts, or (if applicable) between retinulae and eccentric cells in the *Limulus* compound eye (Fuortes, 1959; Adolph, 1964). Also, in *Hirudo*, information has to be transmitted within a cell, not across an extracellular space.

Intracellular information flow through movement of substance is found in other systems (e.g. along neurosecretory neurons; cf. Scharrer and Scharrer,

1963). Thus, the proposed intermediate mechanism which should link the photochemical event(s) in the phaosome to the generator potential would not necessarily require the assumption of an entirely novel mechanism.

ACKNOWLEDGEMENTS

The complete results and the methods used have been published in manuscript form previously (Walther, 1965). They are being prepared for publication in a more readily accessible form. The investigations have been supported by grants from the Deutsche Forschungsgemeinschaft.

REFERENCES

ADOLPH, A. R. 1964. Spontaneous slow potential fluctuations in the *Limulus* photoreceptor. *J. Gen. Physiol.* **48**, 297–322.

BROWN, P. K. 1961. Spectral absorption of single retinal rods. *J. Opt. Soc. Am.* **51**, 1000.

EAKIN, R. M. 1965. Evolution of photoreceptors. *XXX Cold Spring Harbor Symposion on Quantitative Biology* (In press).

ECCLES, J. C. 1963. *The Physiology of Synapses.* Springer, Berlin.

FUORTES, M. G. F. 1959. Initiation of impulses in visual cells of *Limulus. J. Physiol.* **148**, 14–28.

HAGINS, W. A., ZONANA, H. V. and ADAMS, R. G. 1962. Local membrane current in the outer segments of squid photoreceptors. *Nature* **194**, 844–7.

HANSEN, K. 1962. Elektronenmikroskopische Untersuchung der Hirudineen-Augen. *Zool. Beiträge* NF7, 83–128.

HESSE, R. 1896. Untersuchungen über die Organe der Lichtempfindung bei niederen Tieren. III. Die Sehorgane der Hirudineen. *Z. wiss. Zool.* **62**, 671–707.

JUNG, D. 1963. Bau und Feinstruktur der Augen auf dem vorderen und hinteren Saugnapf des Fischegels *Piscicola geometra* L. *Zool. Beiträge* NF9, 121–172.

KATZ, B. 1962. The transmission of impulses from nerve to muscle and the subcellular unit of synaptic action. *Proc. Roy. Soc. London.* B, **155**, 455.

LIEBMANN, P. A. 1962. Microspectrophotometry of retinal rods. *Biophys. J.* **2**, 161.

MARKS, W. B., DOBELLE, W. H. and MACNICHOL, E. F. 1964. Visual pigments of single visual cones. *Science* **143**, 1181–3.

PURPLE, R. L. 1964. The integration of excitatory and inhibitory influences in the eccentric cell in the eye of *Limulus.* Rockefeller Institute Doctoral Thesis, New York.

RÖHLICH, P. and TÖRÖK, L. J. 1964. Elektronenmikroskopische Beobachtungen an den Sehzellen des Blutegels, *Hirudo medicinalis* L. *Z. Zellforsch.* **63**, 618–35.

SCHARRER, E. and SCHARRER, B. 1963. *Neuroendocrinology.* New York, Columbia University Press.

WALD, G. 1959. The photoreceptor process in vision. *Handbook of Physiology*, Neurophysiology I, Washington D.C.

WALTHER, J. B. 1963. Intracellular potentials from single sense cells in the eyes of the leech, *Hirudo medicinalis. Proc. XVI Internatl. Congr. Zool.*, Washington, D.C.

WALTHER, J. B. 1964. Untersuchungen zur Temperaturabhängigkeit des Generatorpotentials einzelner Sehzellen in Augen von *Hirudo medicinalis.* Verhandlg. Dt. Zool. Ges. Kiel, 1964.

WALTHER, J. B. 1965. Untersuchungen über die Erregungsvorgänge einzelner Lichtsinneszellen in den Augen des Blutegels, *Hirudo medicinalis.* Habilitationsschrift, Math.-Naturw. Fakultät, Universität Göttingen.

PART IV

Integration of visual input

ELECTRON MICROSCOPE OBSERVATIONS ON THE PERIPHERAL AND INTERMEDIATE RETINAS OF DIPTERANS*

O. Trujillo-Cenóz and J. Melamed

Instituto de Investigación de Ciencias Biológicas, Departamento de Ultraestructura
Celular, Montevideo, Uruguay

INTRODUCTION

THE compound eye of insects consists of myriads of cylindrical units or ommatidia each of which has its own set of photoreceptor cells and its own dioptric system. In spite of their peripheral independence there is opportunity for functional interaction between axons of different ommatidia at the level of the intermediate retina (Cajal and Sánchez, 1915). This is a complex neuropilic layer at the level of which the photoreceptor axons establish synaptic connections with the second order neurons of the visual pathway.

The purpose of this paper is twofold: firstly, to add new details about the structural organization of the ommatidia in Dipterans and, secondly, to report some results concerning the projection of these ommatidia upon the intermediate retina or lamina (Horridge, 1965). All these observations are based on the systematic study of long series of sections obtained from precisely oriented pieces of compound eyes.

MATERIAL AND METHODS

The observations reported in this paper were made on the central portion of the compound eyes of flies of genus *Sarcophaga* and *Lucilia*. The animals were anesthetized with CO_2 and dissected under a binocular microscope. After removing the chitinous capsule of the head, the brain and visual centers were bathed in cold fixative solution (10% paraformaldehyde or 5% glutaraldehyde in phosphate buffer). The head was then separated from the thorax and transferred to a Petri dish containing the same fixative. After 15–30 min the head was transected along its medial plane in such a way that each compound eye could be removed together with its visual centers. The pieces were briefly washed in the buffer solution and immersed for 1 hr in 1% OsO_4 in phosphate buffer. Dehydration was carried out as usual in a graded

* Research sponsored by the Air Force Office of Scientific Research, Office of Aerospace Research, United States Air Force, under AFOSR Grant No. 618–64.

series of alcohol or acetone. In some cases the whole eye was embedded; in other cases the corneal lens layer was removed during dehydration. Araldite or Vestopal were used as embedding agents. The eyes were re-embedded in order to secure the correct orientation of the nerve elements in regard to the desired plane of sectioning. Serial sections were cut with an LKB Ultrotome using glass knives. Usually the sections were double stained with uranyl acetate and lead citrate; in other cases they were stained only with uranyl acetate (2% uranyl acetate in water, 2 hr at 60°C). All the electron micrographs were taken with a Siemens electron microscope (Elmiskop 1) at 80 kV.

OBSERVATIONS

a. *General Description of the Peripheral and Intermediate Retina*

A cross-section passing through the medial portion of the compound eye illustrates the anatomical arrangement of the different components of the fly visual system (Fig. 1). The peripheral retina appears as a thick (300 μ)

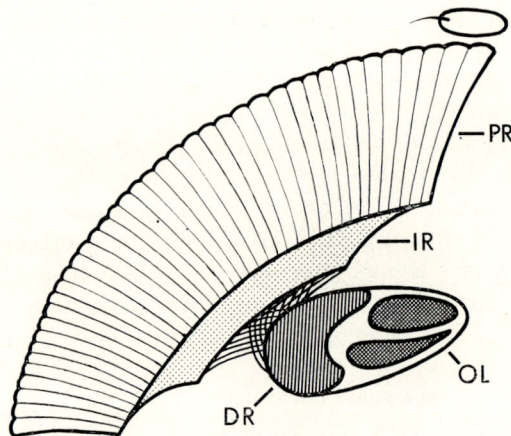

Fig. 1

This drawing shows the different components of the fly visual system. *PR*, peripheral retina; *IR*, intermediate retina or lamina; *DR*, deep retina or medulla; *OL*, optic lobe or lobula. The external chiasm or optic nerve connects the intermediate and the deep retinas.

striated layer consisting of thousands of ommatidia separated from one another by cells containing granules of pigment. Its external convex surface is covered by numerous corneal lenses while the inner concave surface lies in contact with the intermediate retina. Interposed between these two layers there is a discontinuous basement membrane corresponding to the "membrane limitante postérieure" of Ciaccio (1876). In addition to the corneal pigment cells surrounding the dioptric apparatus there are two other types of cells containing granules of pigment. These are: (1) the outer pigment cells, and (2) the inner pigment cells (Hickson, 1885).

The intermediate retina (lamina) is a heterogeneous layer approximately 80 μ thick lying between the peripheral retina and the external chiasm of Cajal and Sánchez (1915) (optic nerve of other authors). When stained with common histological dyes it shows at least two different zones: (a) an external zone containing neuron somata together with glial cells (usually only their nuclei are visible), and (b) an inner zone consisting of a palisade of cylindrical units—the "optical cartridges" (Cajal and Sánchez, 1915). The optical cartridges correspond to the "elements of the periopticon" of Hickson (1885) and to the "neurommatidies" of Viallanes (1892). Each optical cartridge is a polysynaptic unit by means of which six photoreceptor axons establish synaptic contacts with two second order nerve fibers (Trujillo-Cenóz and Melamed, 1963; Trujillo-Cenóz, 1965).

b. *The Structural Organization of the Ommatidium*

An ommatidium consists essentially of an image-forming system and a group of photoreceptor cells. For the sake of clearness a separate description of these two ommatidial components will be made.

1. *The dioptric apparatus.* In the fly the dioptric apparatus is formed by the following elements: (a) a corneal lens developed as a specialization of the chitinous sheath, (b) a pseudocone cavity containing, *in vivo*, a semi-fluid substance, and (c) four Semper cells forming the floor of the pseudocone cavity.

Observations on the fine structure of the cornea of *Musca* have been reported recently by Bernhard, Miller and Møller (1965). In the course of this investigation we have routinely trimmed away the corneal lens layer in order to facilitate cutting long series of sections. Consequently all our observations concern regions located below the corneal lens layer.

Just below the cornea there is a cavity having, in longitudinal section, the shape of a truncated cone. This cavity usually contains irregular strands of fine granular material. According to Grenacher's classification (Grenacher, 1879) most flies possess a "pseudocone type" of eye. This means that a solid crystalline cone is lacking; in its place there is a liquid or gelatinous substance. It is probable that the strands of granular material found in fixed tissues represent part of the semi-fluid "pseudocone" described by Grenacher.

The wall of the pseudocone cavity is formed, usually, by the apposition of two pigment cells (corneal pigment cells) (Figs. 2 and 3). Short microvilli (1500 Å long and 500 Å wide) arise from the pigment cell surface and project into the pseudocone cavity. Transverse as well as longitudinal sections of the apical portion of the ommatidium show the presence of four Semper cells (Fig. 4). These are wedge-shaped elements closing from below the pseudocone cavity. When seen in transverse section each cell has a triangular outline with the nucleus located near the base of the triangle.

The portion of the cell containing the nucleus lies outside the path of the light rays and is partially covered by cytoplasm of the corneal pigment cells (Figs. 2 and 3). Small dense granules with the aspect of glycogen can be seen concentrated in the perinuclear region; the remainder of the cytoplasm is practically filled with small tubules 200 Å in diameter and of undefined length. The superior surface of the Semper cells has small irregularities;

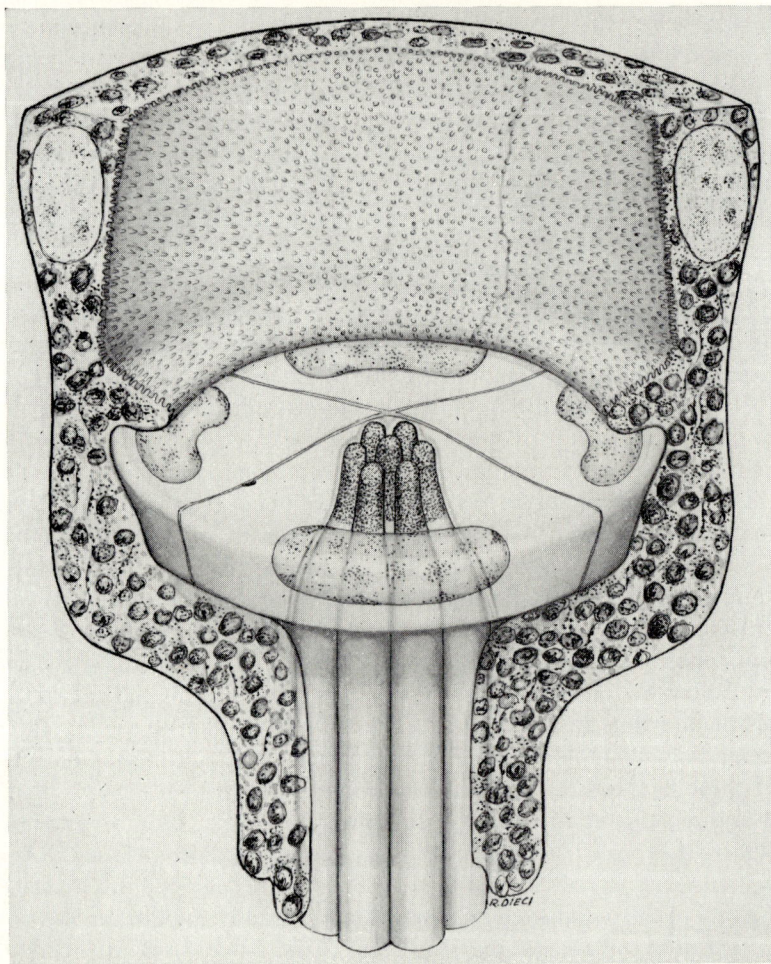

FIG. 2

This drawing is a three-dimensional representation of the apical portion of one ommatidium. The wall of the pseudocone cavity consists of two pigment cells (corneal pigment cells). The floor of the cavity is formed by four Semper cells which are represented as transparent elements. Note the presence of seven rods which prolongate the apical segment of the photoreceptors. These rods lie partially recessed in the inferior surface of the Semper cells.

medially, the inferior one shows deep indentations (Figs. 2 and 5). These indentations are occupied by a dense osmiophilic substance which prolongs the apical portion of the seven rhabdomeres (Fig. 5).

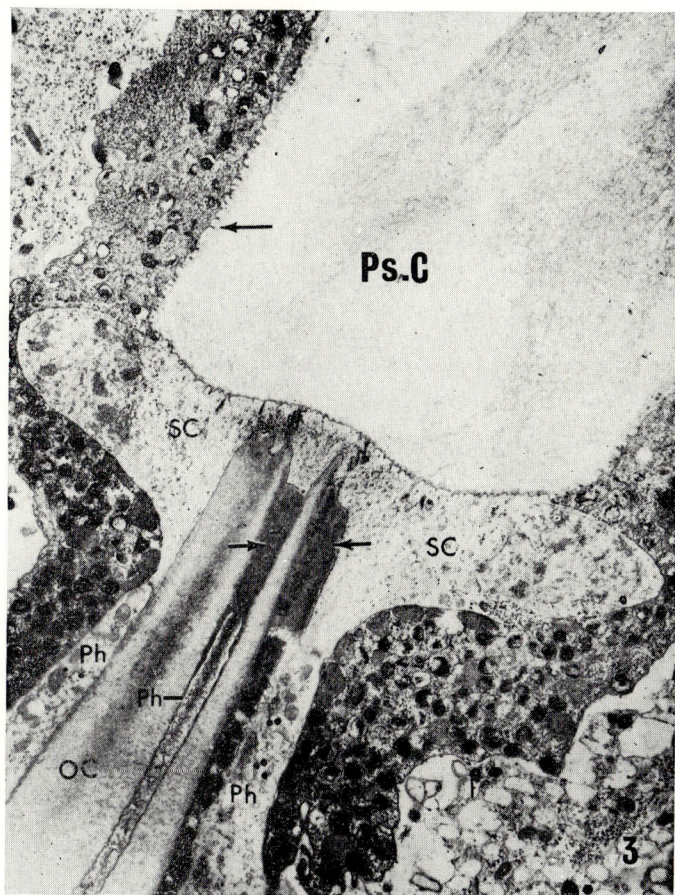

FIG. 3

Longitudinal section through the apical portion of one ommatidium. The pseudo-cone cavity (*PsC*) contains a fine granular material which represents the liquid or gelatinous substance forming *in vivo* the "pseudocone" of Grenacher. The wall of the pseudocone cavity is formed by the cytoplasm of the corneal pigment cells. Prolongations of these cells surround the apical segments of the photoreceptors. Note the presence of short microvilli arising from the surface of the corneal pigment cells and projecting into the pseudocone cavity (arrow). The Semper cells (*SC*) form the floor of the pseudocone cavity. The superior surface of the Semper cells shows small numerous irregularities; the inferior surface has deep indentations occupied by cylindrical rods consisting of a dense homogeneous substance (arrows). Three photoreceptor cells (*Ph*) can be seen in the lower left corner of the plate (two of them show their rhabdomeres). *OC*, ommatidial cavity. × **4700.**

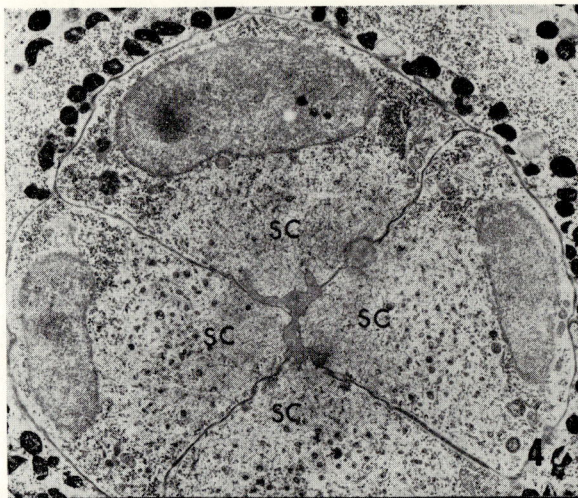

FIG. 4

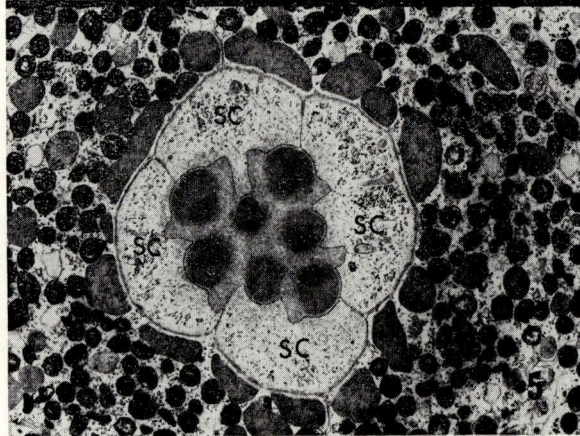

FIG. 5

FIG. 4

This electron micrograph shows, in a cross-section, the four Semper cells (*SC*) which form the floor of the pseudocone cavity. Each cell has a triangular outline and the nucleus lies near the base of the triangle. Note the presence of small dense granules concentrated in the perinuclear cytoplasm. × 6000.

FIG. 5

A cross-section passing just below the level of the Semper cell nuclei shows the seven osmiophilic masses which cover the distal portion of the rhabdomeres. These masses lie partially recessed within deep indentations of the Semper cells surface. The ommatidial cavity appears filled by a fine granular dense substance. A crown of large mitochondria can be seen surrounding the four Semper cells. These mitochondria belong to the corneal pigment cells. *SC*, Semper cells. × 6000.

2. *The photoreceptor cells.* Following a structural plan commonly found in the invertebrate phyla, the arthropod photoreceptor cells have a distal photo-receptive segment bearing specialized structures and a basal segment from which the axon arises. In the fly retinular cells the receptive segment is very long (250 μ) while the basal segment is short. The basic morphology of these cells is well known as result of the work of Goldsmith and Philpott (1957) and Fernández-Morán (1958). The most peculiar structure found in the arthropod photoreceptor cell is the rhabdomere. It appears with the light microscope as a highly refractive rod running along the inner surface of the cell. The electron microscope shows that the rhabdomere actually consists of closely packed microvilli perpendicularly oriented to the main axis (Miller, 1957). Each microvillus is about 0·5 μ long and 500 Å wide. It is connected to the photoreceptor cell surface by an exceedingly short, slender neck about 200 Å wide (Figs. 10–13). The existence of this neck explains the double line appearing at the base of the rhabdomere in thin sections observed at relatively low magnification. One of these lines represents the cell plasma membrane, the other scalloped line is the result of the close contiguous apposition of the proximal portion of the microvilli (an artificial limit determined by the plane of section). The space between the two lines corresponds to the "neck" lying out of the plane of section. Profiles of vesicles and tubules can be seen in connection with the base of some microvilli. The other cell components usually found in the photoreceptor cells are mitochondria, multivesicular bodies, and short profiles of cisternae of the ER system. Small granules of pigment have constantly been found in the photoreceptor cell cytoplasm.

Desmosomes, identical to the ones observed by Goldsmith (1962) in *Apis* and by Waddington and Perry (1960) in *Drosophila*, have been consistently found at the sites of contact between adjacent photoreceptors. These structures are present only along the inner borders of the cells forming a seal around the ommatidial cavity.

Round profiles corresponding to slender fibers running parallel to the photoreceptor main axis can be seen in the upper half of each ommatidium. These fibers lie close to the desmosomes in the extracellular space limited by two neighbouring photoreceptor cells. Goldsmith (1962) found similar structures between the photoreceptor cells of *Apis*.

In order to obtain precise information about the spatial arrangement of the photoreceptor cells it is necessary to explore the ommatidium by means of series of cross-sections taken at predetermined critical levels. Three different levels were systematically studied in the course of this investigation. These are: (a) an apical level passing just below the Semper cells, (b) a medial level passing through the middle of the ommatidium (approx. 150 μ from the basement membrane), and (c) a basal level passing just above the basement membrane. A cross-section passing just below the Semper cells shows seven photoreceptor cells distributed around a central cavity—the ommatidial

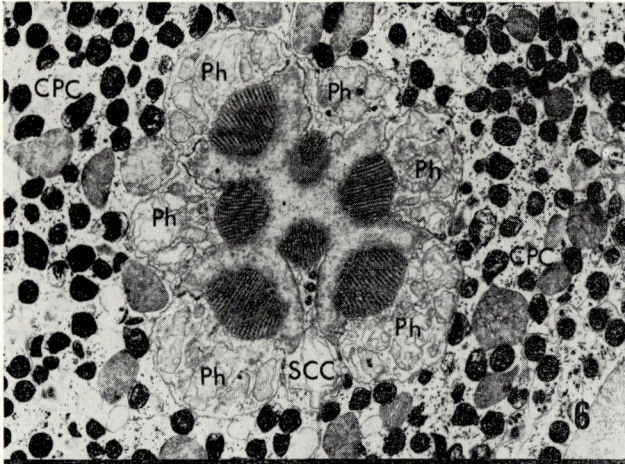

FIG. 6

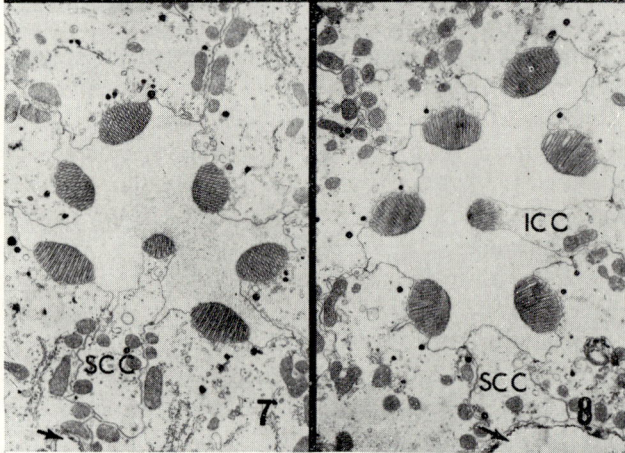

FIG. 7   FIG. 8

FIG. 6

This electron micrograph shows a cross-section through the apical segment of the photoreceptor cells. At this level there are seven photoreceptors (*Ph*), each of which bears a rhabdomere. Note that the rhabdomere of one of these photoreceptor cells occupies a more central position. It corresponds to the superior central cell (*SCC*). Mitochondria are particularly abundant at this level. *CPC*, corneal pigment cell. × 9000.

FIG. 7

Medial segment of an ommatidium showing the superior central cell (*SCC*). Note that a fine trachea (arrow) lies near the superior central cell. × 6000.

FIG. 8

Medial segment of an ommatidium showing both central cells. The superior central cell (*SCC*) has lost its rhabdomere and its place is occupied by the rhabdomere of the inferior central cell (*ICC*). The arrow indicates the cross-section of a trachea lying close to the superior central cell. × 6000.

cavity (Fig. 6). In this apical portion of the ommatidium the seven rhabdomeres are covered by a dense osmiophilic substance. This substance covers like a cap the apical segment of each rhabdomere and extends into the indentations existing at the base of the four Semper cells.

As shown in Fig. 6 the rhabdomere of one of the seven photoreceptors occupies the center of the ommatidial cavity. This photoreceptor will be referred to in this paper as the *superior central cell*. The superior central cell always lies in proximity to one of the numerous trachea running between the ommatidia. This relationship is lost only within the apical portion of the ommatidium just below the level of the Semper cells.

The most distal segments of the photoreceptor cells are particularly rich in mitochondria, which occur in densely packed groups which fill the cytoplasm (Fig. 6). Scattered between the mitochondria are small granules of pigment. As reported by Fernández-Morán (1958), homologous rhabdomeres of cells in adjacent ommatidia have the same orientation. This fact is particularly evident when observing, in cross-sections, the position of the superior central cell. The ommatidium is surrounded at this level by the proximal prolongations of the corneal pigment cells. The presence of seven photoreceptors is maintained to the medial portion of the ommatidium (Fig. 7). Below this level the superior central cell loses its rhabdomere and is reduced in size (Fig. 9). Concomitantly, a new central cell appears at right angle to the superior central cell; this is the *inferior central cell* (Figs. 8–17). Therefore, profiles corresponding to eight retinular cells are now seen in cross-sections (Fig. 8). This number is in accordance with the number of photoreceptor cells reported by Waddington and Perry (1960) in *Drosophila*.

A complicated system of invaginated membranes has been consistently found in the cytoplasm of the superior central cell at the level where the rhabdomere is lost (Figs. 10–13).

Just above the basement membrane separating the peripheral from the intermediate retina the ommatidium has the appearance shown in Fig. 18. All the photoreceptor cells have lost their rhabdomeres and the ommatidial cavity is occupied by pigment cell cytoplasm (inner pigment cells). It is still possible to distinguish the two central cells because they are thinner than the other six ordinary photoreceptors.

In summary, our observations confirm previous light microscope studies (Dietrich, 1909) reporting the existence of eight retinular cells. However, none of these cells can be considered an aberrant or rudimentary element (Goldsmith, 1964).

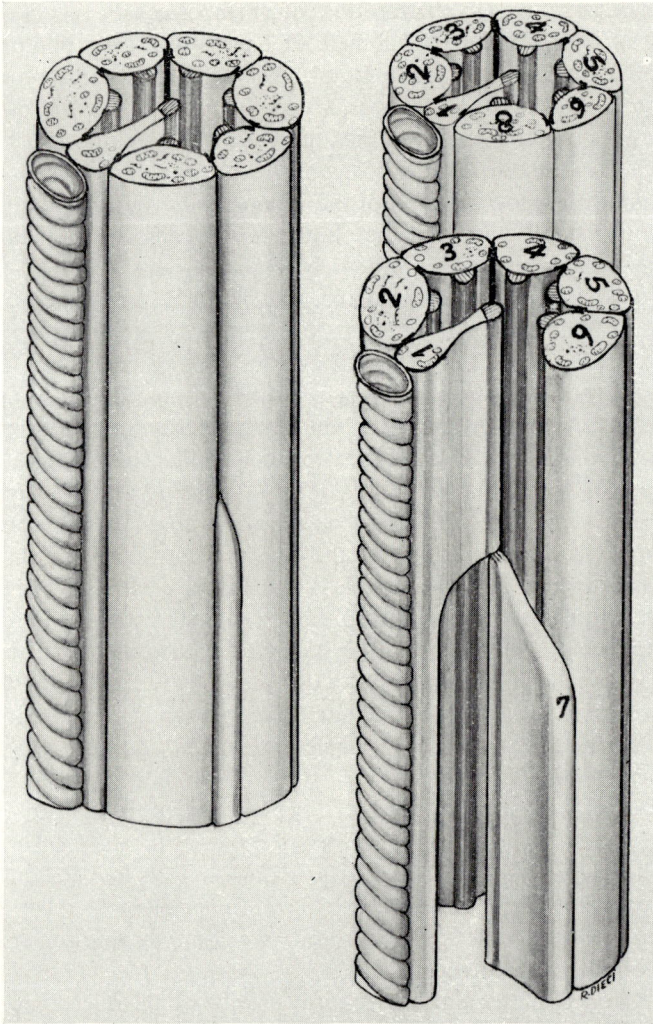

Fig. 9

This drawing illustrates the spatial arrangement of the two central cells. At the level at which the superior central cell (1) loses its rhabdomere a new central cell appears. This is the inferior central cell (7). Note that the central cells lie in perpendicular planes. 2, 3, 4, 5, 6, 8, common photoreceptor cells. (Not at scale.)

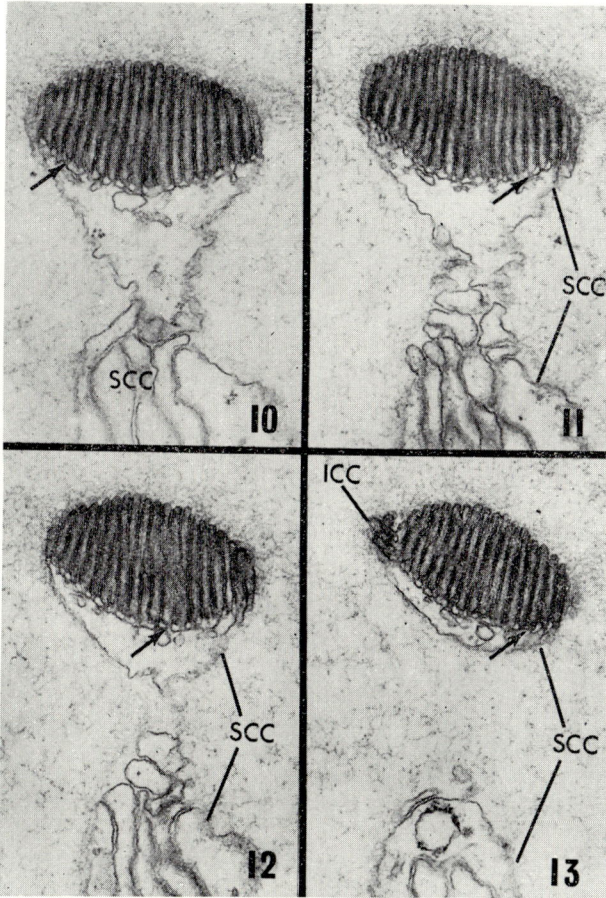

Figs. 10–13

This sequence of electron micrographs (Figs. 10–17) show, serially, the transition from the superior to the inferior central cell. It is possible to observe that the superior central cell (*SCC*) gradually loses its rhabdomere and that the rhabdomere of the inferior central cell (*ICC*) occupies its place. Both rhabdomeres lie in perpendicular planes. Note that the microvilli forming the rhabdomere are connected to the cell surface by a short, slender neck (arrows). A complicated system of invaginated membranes can be observed within the superior central cell cytoplasm at the levels where the rhabdomere is gradually lost. Complementary information about the spatial arrangement of these cells can be obtained from Fig. 9. Figs. 14–15, × 40,000; Figs. 10–13, × 30,600; Figs. 16–17, × 36,000.

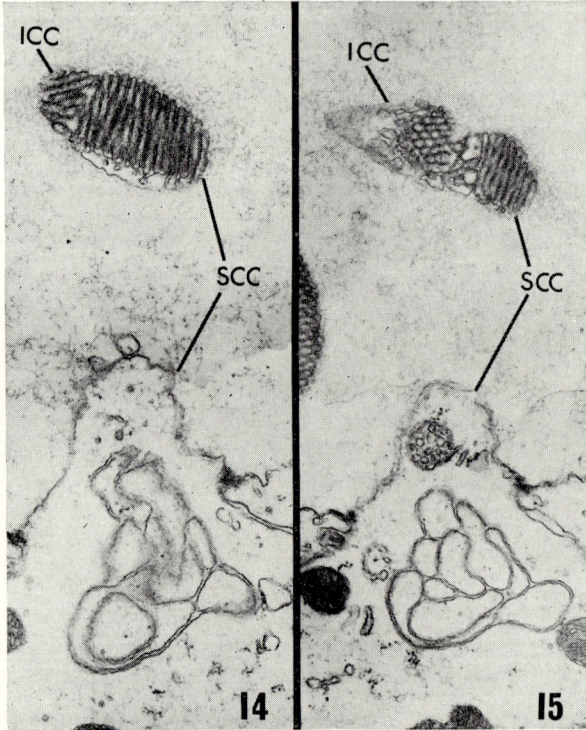

FIGS. 14–15

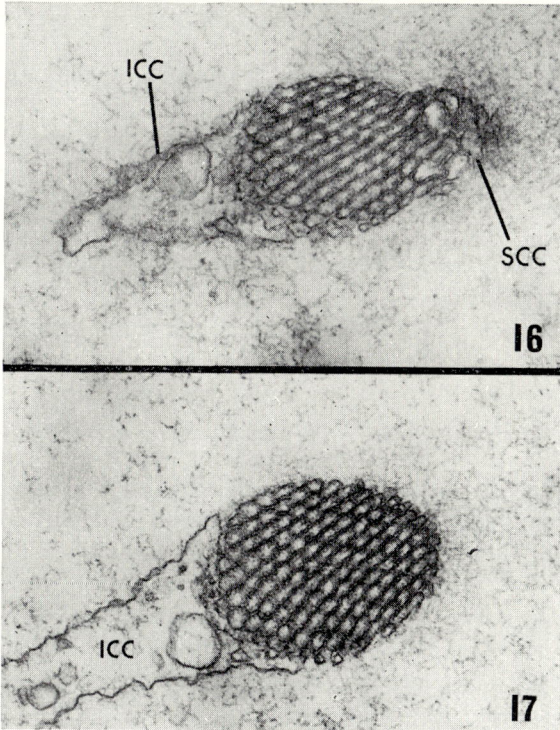

Figs. 16–17

c. *The Projection of the Ommatidia upon the Intermediate Retina*

Eight axons originate from each ommatidium and, after crossing the basement membrane, enter the intermediate retina. As pointed out before, the intermediate retina is a heterogeneous layer which was divided by Cajal and Sánchez (1915) into the following sub-layers: (a) the fenestrated zone, characterized by the presence of a great number of trachea, (b) the zone of the neuron somata (the second order neurons of the visual pathway), and (c) the external plexiform zone, characterized by the presence of the optical cartridges. Cajal and Sánchez (1915) also described the external chiasm (optic nerve) as belonging to the intermediate retina. In this paper, however, the external chiasm is considered as an anatomical region independent of the intermediate retina.

Immediately after crossing the basement membrane, photoreceptor axons belonging to different but neighbouring ommatidia join to form thick bundles. Two different non-nervous cell types are found at this level. Close to the basement membrane there are small, dense cells sending out irregularly shaped prolongations. These prolongations form a loose sheath around the group of axons originating from each ommatidium.

In deeper regions the small, dense type of cell gradually disappears, and its place is occupied by large, clear cells. This second type of non-nervous element is characterized by the presence of numerous small tubules running within the cytoplasm. Long, thick cytoplasmic processes originate from these cells and separate the photoreceptor axons, grouping them in large fascicles (Fig. 19). Apparently, at this level the ommatidia lose their anatomical individuality and their identification is possible only in a sequence of serial sections. However, in deeper regions it is again possible to recognize discrete groups of fibers corresponding to the eight photoreceptor axons originating from individual ommatidia. Each of these groups or units consists of a ring of six photoreceptor axons surrounding the two axons of the superior and inferior central cells (Fig. 20). Considering that this geometrical configuration is similar to the one exhibited by the optical cartridges in the external plexiform layer, the name "pseudo-cartridge" is proposed to identify each of these units.

The topographical distribution of the pseudo-cartridges within the intermediate retina is exactly the same as that of the ommatidia within the peripheral retina. This fact facilitates the study of the inter-ommatidial relationships, reducing by one-third the number of serial sections needed to follow the ommatidial units to their projections in the synaptic units (optical cartridges).

In the sub-layer occupied by the neuron somata, new fibers begin to appear within the pseudo-cartridges. These are the main prolongations of the second order neurons. Usually one or two of these fibers can be found together with the axons of the central cells. Near the outer limit of the external plexiform

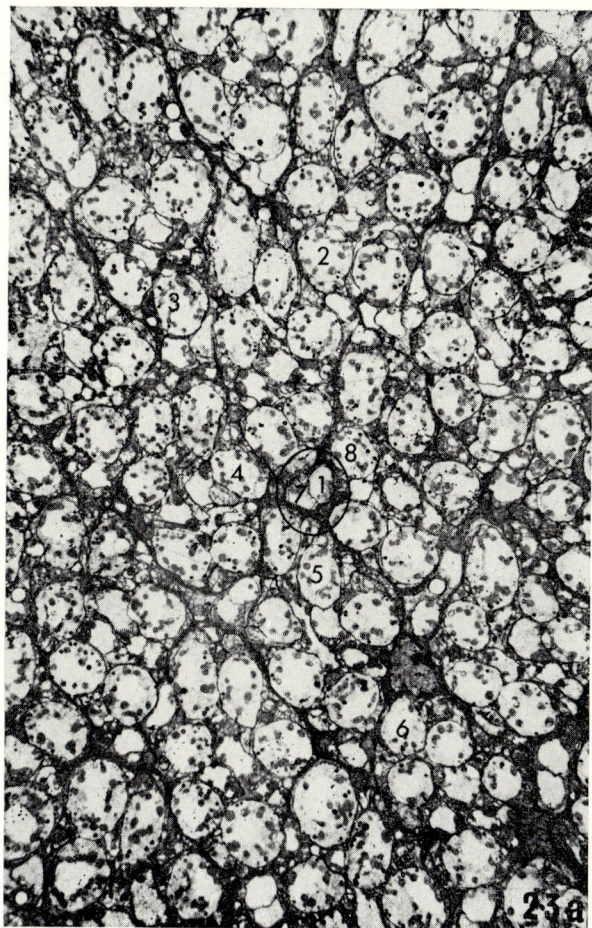

FIG. 23a

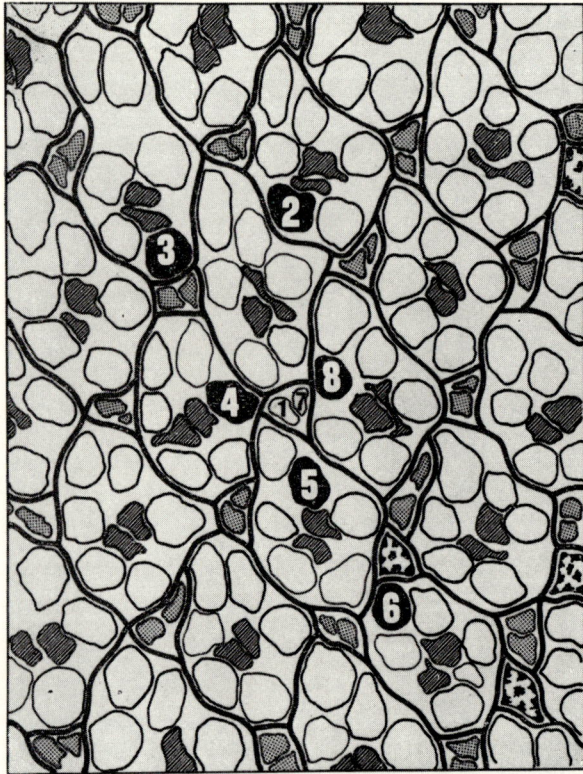

Fig. 23b

layer the pseudo-cartridges "explode" and the photoreceptor axons of different ommatidia run in all directions (Fig. 21). In spite of this redistribution of fibers the axons of the two central cells remain in approximately the same topographical position.

More or less concomitantly with the ommatidial dispersion the photoreceptor axons undergo structural modifications. There is a sudden increase in the number of mitochondria which is accompanied by densification of the peripheral axoplasm (Fig. 22). Perhaps the most striking feature shown by the photoreceptor axons at their entrance into the external plexiform layer is the presence of numerous small invaginations of the plasma membrane. Each of these invaginations is occupied by a small bulbous glial process termed the "capitate projection" (Trujillo-Cenóz, 1965) (Fig. 24). The diameter of the widest part of the capitate projection is approximately 1000 Å. The high magnification electron micrographs show a dense osmiophilic substance associated with the outer layer of the capitate projection composite membrane. This substance appears in low power electron micrographs as a "third" interposed membrane. Between the glial membrane and the invaginated photoreceptor membrane there is a cleft 250 Å wide. As previously described, the capitate projections originate from tall columnar neuroglial cells which are regularly distributed between the optical cartridges (Fig. 23).

The presence of capitate projections is a sign indicating the beginning of the optical cartridges.

It is important to recall that the structure of the axons of the superior and inferior central cells remains unchanged. We have confirmed that they correspond to the so-called "long visual fibers" of Cajal and Sánchez (1915), which by-pass the first synaptic relay and terminate within the deep retina or medulla. However, neither Cajal (1909) nor Cajal and Sánchez (1915) recognized the presence of two long visual fibers arising from each ommatidium. It is possible that following silver impregnation these two closely apposed, thin axons appeared as a single thick fiber.

It is well known since the work of Cajal and Sánchez (1915) that each optical cartridge consists of six axons arising from more than one ommatidium. The Spanish authors wrote: "We have determined with certitude, in a single section, the penetration of the elements of one ommatidium into three to four adjoining cartridges." Our findings confirm and complete Cajal's observations. As shown in the sequence of electron micrographs (Figs. 18, 23) each of the six photoreceptor axons of one ommatidium forms part of six different optical cartridges following a constant and asymmetrical pattern. As stated in a preceding paragraph, the axons of the two central cells correspond to the long visual fibers of Cajal (1909) running outside the cartridges.

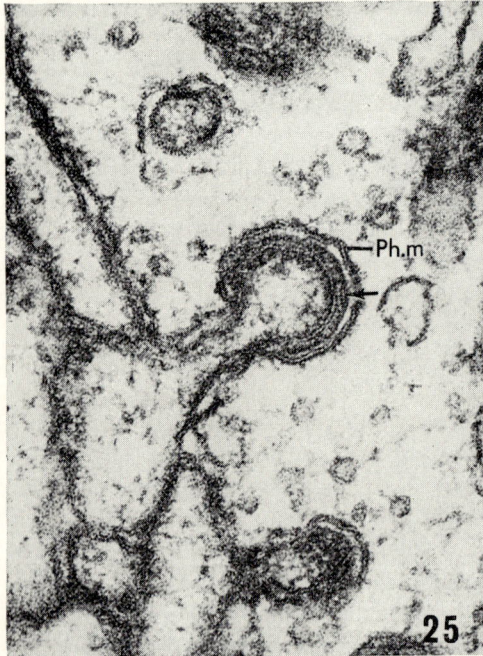

FIG. 24

High magnification electron micrograph showing one capitate projection. Note the dense osmiophilic substance associated with the external layer of the glial composite membrane (arrow). *Phm*, photoreceptor membrane. × 112,500.

DISCUSSION

Two different lines of investigation have been developed to study the mechanisms involved in nervous integration within the arthropod visual system. One is based on electrophysiological techniques by means of which units or complex neuronal responses can be recorded and analyzed (Autrum, 1958; Naka, 1961, 1962; Burkhardt, 1962). The other is based on the study of measurable motor responses to a measurable optical stimulus. This input–output relation is analyzed in terms of engineering control systems and expressed in the form of a minimum mathematical model (Reichardt, 1961, 1962; Thorson, 1964).

If we expect, however, to discover some of the basic principles of visual physiology it is necessary to integrate these findings in a framework of solid anatomical knowledge.

When dealing with compound eyes, the basic point is to have a clear picture of the ommatidia and the way in which they can be functionally interconnected. In the fly each ommatidium contains eight photoreceptor cells. Six of them are long cells (approx. 300 μ) whose rhabdomeres are located in the periphery of the ommatidial cavity. The other two cells have their rhabdomeres occupying the center of the ommatidial cavity; they are here referred to as the superior and inferior central cells. The superior central cell, like the other six common photoreceptors, is a long element which runs along the whole length of the ommatidium. Its rhabdomere, however, is limited to the superior half of the ommatidium. The inferior central cell, on the contrary, is short (approx. 150 μ) and occupies only the lower portion of the ommatidium. The most striking characteristic of these cells is that their rhabdomeres lie in perpendicular planes.

This peculiar anatomical arrangement suggests that they may play an important role in the detection of polarized light. Whatever their function may be, it is evident that their axons convey information towards a visual center (medulla) different from the one in which the other six common photoreceptor axons synapse.

It was reported in a previous paper (Trujillo-Cenóz, 1965) that each of the two second order fibers lying in the center of the optical cartridges establish numerous synaptic connections with each of the six peripheral photoreceptor axons. These synaptic contacts occur at different levels of the cartridge, either on the surface of the main second order prolongations, or on the surface of their collateral branches. This synaptic configuration suggests that spatial summation may be a relevant factor in the functional activity of the second order fibers. Considering that each cartridge receives only one fiber from each of six ommatidia, and assuming that activity in a minimum of two fibers is needed to stimulate the second order neurons, it can be concluded that a minimum of two ommatidia must be activated to provoke a response at the first synaptic relay. However, it is important to remember that the long visual fibers provide a direct individual line toward higher centers.

Reichardt's experiments on the beetle *Chlorophanus* (1961–2) demonstrate that at least two ommatidia, separated by no more than one, have to be stimulated in order to elicit the optomotor reflex. In order to test in the fly the anatomical possibilities of Reichardt's observations it is necessary to study the geometrical distribution of the six ommatidia represented in each cartridge. This investigation is now under way and the results will soon be reported in a separate publication.

SUMMARY

The compound eyes of dipterans consist of myriads of ommatidia, each of which has its own dioptric system and its own set of photoreceptor cells. In the fly the dioptric system consists of a chitinous cornea, a pseudocone cavity filled with a liquid substance and four Semper cells. The wall of the pseudocone cavity is formed by the cytoplasm of the corneal pigment cells. The four Semper cells close the pseudocone cavity from below. Medially, the inferior surface of the Semper cells have deep indentations which are occupied by a dense osmiophilic substance. This substance extends distally the apical segments of seven photoreceptor cells.

Each ommatidium has eight photoreceptor or retinular cells. Six are long elements occupying the whole extent of the ommatidium and have their rhabdomeres located in the periphery of the ommatidial cavity. One of the other two cells, the superior central cell, is also a long element which occupies the whole length of the ommatidium. Its rhabdomere, however, lies near the center of the ommatidial cavity and is present only in the superior half of the ommatidium. A new short cell appears in the inferior half of the ommatidium; its rhabdomere, like that of the superior central cell, is centrally located. This is the inferior central cell. The superior and the inferior central cells lie in perpendicular planes.

Eight photoreceptor axons originate at the base of each ommatidium. After crossing the basement membrane they enter the intermediate retina and some of them synapse with the second order neurons of the visual pathway. Synaptic contacts occur at the level of discrete cylindrical units known as the optical cartridges.

When these eight axons are followed in a long series of sections it is possible to demonstrate that six of them integrate six different optical cartridges, while the two arising from the superior and inferior central cells remain outside of the cartridges. These are the so-called long visual fibers.

REFERENCES

AUTRUM, H. 1958. Electrophysiological analysis of the visual systems in insects. *Exptl. Cell Res.* Suppl. **5**, 426–39.

BERNHARD, C. G., MILLER, W. H. and MØLLER, A. R. 1965. The insect corneal nipple array. *Acta Physiol. Scand.* **63**, Suppl. 243, 9–74.

BURKHARDT, D. 1962. Spectral sensitivity and other response characteristics of single visual cells in the arthropod eye. *Symp. Soc. Exptl. Biol.* **16**, 86–109.

CAJAL, S. R. 1909. Nota sobre la estructura de la Retina de la Mosca (*M. vomitoria* L.). *Trab. del Lab. de Invest. Biol. Madrid* **7**, 217–57.

CAJAL, S. R. and SÁNCHEZ, D. 1915. Contribución al conocimiento de los centros nerviosos de los insectos. *Trab. del Lab. de Invest. Biol. Madrid* **13**, 1–164.

CIACCIO, M. G. 1876. De l'oeil des Diptères. *J. de Zool.* **5**, 313–19.

DIETRICH, W. 1909. Die Facetten-Augen der Dipteren. *Z. wiss Zool.* **92**, 465–539.

FERNÁNDEZ-MORÁN, H. 1958. Fine structure of the light receptors in the compound eye of insects. *Exptl. Cell Res.* Suppl. **5**, 586–644.

GOLDSMITH, T. H. 1962. Fine structure of the retinulae in the compound eye of the honey-bee. *J. Cell Biol.* **14**, 489–94.

GOLDSMITH, T. H. 1964. The visual system of insects. In *The Physiology of Insecta* (M. Rockstein, ed.). Academic Press, New York and London.

GOLDSMITH, T. H. and PHILPOTT, D. E. 1957. The microstructure of the compound eyes of insects. *J. Biophys. Biochem. Cytol.* **3**, 429–40.

GRENACHER, H. 1879. *Untersuchungen über das Sehorgan der Arthropoden.* Vandenhoeck and Ruprecht, Göttingen.

HICKSON, S. J. 1885. The eye and optic tract of insects. *Quart. J. Microsc. Sci.* **25**, 215–51.

HORRIDGE, G. A. 1965. Arthropoda. Receptors for light, and optic lobe. In *Structure and Function in the Nervous Systems of Invertebrates.* T. H. Bullock and G. A. Horridge. Freeman and Company, San Francisco.

MILLER, W. H. 1957. Morphology of the compound eye of *Limulus. J. Biophys. Biochem. Cytol.* **3**, 421–28.

NAKA, K. I. 1961. Recording of retinal action potentials from single cells in the insect compound eye. *J. Gen. Physiol.* **44**, 571–84.

NAKA, K. I. 1962. Effect of background illumination on the retinal action potential. *Science* **136**, 877–9.

REICHARDT, W. 1961. Autocorrelation, a principle for the evaluation of sensory information by the central nervous system. In *Sensory Communication* (W. Rosemblith, ed.).

REICHARDT, W. 1962. Nervous integration in the facet eye. *Biophys. J.* **2**, 121–43.

THORSON, J. 1964. Dynamics of motion perception in the desert locust. *Science* **145**, 69–71.

TRUJILLO-CENÓZ, O. 1965. Some aspects of the structural organization of the intermediate retina of Dipterans. *J. Ultrastruct. Res.* **13**, 1–33.

TRUJILLO-CENÓZ, O. and MELAMED, J. 1963. On the fine structure of the photoreceptor-second optical neuron synapse in the insect retina. *Z. Zellforsch. Mikroskop. Anat.* **59**, 71–7.

VIALLANES, H. 1892. Contribution à l'histologie du système nerveux des invertébrés. La lame ganglionnaire de la langouste. *Ann. des Sc. Nat.* 7ᵉ Serie **13**, 385–98.

WADDINGTON, C. H. and PERRY, M. M. 1960. The ultrastructure of the developing eye of *Drosophila. Proc. Roy. Soc. London,* B **153**, 155–78.

THE FINE STRUCTURE OF OPTIC TRACTS
OF DECAPODA*

R. F. NUNNEMACHER

Clark University, Worcester, Massachusetts, U.S.A.

WITH the clearer understanding of the functional mechanisms of the ommatidia of the compound eyes of Arthropods there is an increased interest in the correlative function between the two distally located light receptor organs, optic ganglia and the protocerebrum. Such recent studies on the impulse traffic in the optic tract of *Podophthalmus* (Bush, Wiersma and Waterman, 1964) call for an investigation of its fiber composition and uniformity in various Arthropods. This paper surveys the fine structure of the optic tract of seven decapod Crustacea; the numbers, sizes and arrangements of fibers and their relation to the numbers of facets of the eye. These findings, together with the only similar, previous preliminary report on *Orconectes* (Nunnemacher, Camougis and McAlear, 1962), present the general composition of the tract and some of the variations to be found.

The optic tract of most decapods extends as a compact bundle of very many and various sized fibers from the antero-dorso-lateral portion of the protocerebrum to the medulla terminalis, the most proximal of the four optic ganglia usually located in the distal portion of the prominent eyestalk. The tract is quite uniform along its length, without branches, and is surrounded by a distinct perineural sheath and is associated with a large artery. Surrounding the tract lie the muscles of the eyestalk and laterally the oculomotor nerve which is frequently closely attached to it at the proximal end.

The animals studied are in the Order Decapoda, Section Macrura: *Homarus americanus, Orconectes virilis;* Section Anomura: *Pagurus longicarpus, Upogebia affinis, Emerita talpoida*; and in the Section Brachyura: *Cancer borealis* and *Uca pugilator.*

MATERIALS AND METHODS

The crabs were collected along the Massachusetts shore, and kept for brief periods in a salt-water aquarium in the laboratory. The crayfish were obtained in local ponds. Corneas of many additional Reptantia were obtained at the Bermuda Biological Station. The smallest, mature animals were

* Supported by US-PHS-NIH grants NB 02664 and NB 03989.

363

selected because the difficulty of sectioning and photographing optic tracts increased disproportionately with larger animals. The brain and optic tracts were rapidly dissected out of the animals and most frequently fixed in cold veronal buffered (pH 7·4) 2 % osmic acid, dehydrated in acetone and imbedded in methacrylate or araldite. The sections were mounted on 75 mesh, 0·5 % Formvar coated grids and photographed at low magnifications of 1000–9000 ×. The composite photograph of the optic tract of *Cancer* and *Orconectes* was made with an RCA EM U3 (courtesy of Professor J. Walter Wilson, Brown University), all others were made with a Siemens Elmiskop I. The largest montages required the assembly of 140 individual pictures. Final magnifications of montages were between 5000 and 20,000 ×. The nerve fibers within the optic tracts were individually counted and graded according to arbitrary sizes. The counts were verified by having two people make separate tallies. After removal and fixation of the optic tracts the corneas were cut from the chitin of the optic stalk, cut radially, and mounted under a coverglass. The facets of both eyes were usually counted by use of phase contrast and camera lucida projection.

RESULTS

Homarus americanus

This lobster measured 140 mm from rostrum to tail. The nearly round optic tract had a diameter of 0·5 mm but because of the large size a complete section has not been obtained. Estimates were made of the numbers of small fibers and the numbers of fibers in two missing areas (which comprised only 5·5% of the total cross-sectional area). Distribution of counted and estimated fibers was:

Diameter in μ	0·15–1	1–1·5	1·5–3	3–6	6–9	*Total*	*Facets*
Counted		3116	1550	530	43		11,487 L 12,495 R
Estimated	65,000	150	75	25	5		
Total (est.)	65,000	3266	1625	555	48	70,494	

From two corneal counts (11,487 and 12,495), or an average of 12,000 facets and 7 sensory cells for each ommatidium, one can assume about 84,000 primary fibers passing into the lamina.

Conspicuous in the tract is a very large, homogeneous fine fiber bundle comprising 23 % of the cross-sectional area but encompassing an estimated 85 % of the nerve fibers in the tract. The bundle showed fibers arranged in irregular lamina; the fibers were almost all between 0·15 and 0·6 μ in diameter.

There were only very few aggregations of similar fine fibers outside of the large fine fiber bundle. The largest fibers, those 48 with a diameter between 6 and 9 μ, were randomly scattered throughout the tract. Intermediate and small fibers of similar sizes are aggregated into groups or bundles.

Orconectes virilis

Two optic tract maps were obtained from the right and left eyestalks of a crayfish 3 cm long and a third map, the best, was made from an animal 3·4 cm from rostrum to telson. All three showed the same general pattern of fiber distribution, but most of the detailed information will be taken from the latter preparation because it was the most complete.

Three corneas taken from slightly larger animals showed counts of 2954, 3250, and 3440 facets. It is assumed that 3250 approximates the number of facets in the eyes studied and one might therefore conclude 22,750 primary nerve fibers pass from the retina into the distal lamina ganglionaris.

The montage, an oval 61 by 88 cm, yielding the primary source of data on the crayfish was composed of 29 micrographs at a final magnification of 5000 × (Plate 1; "Tract B" in table below). The fine fiber bundle, because it

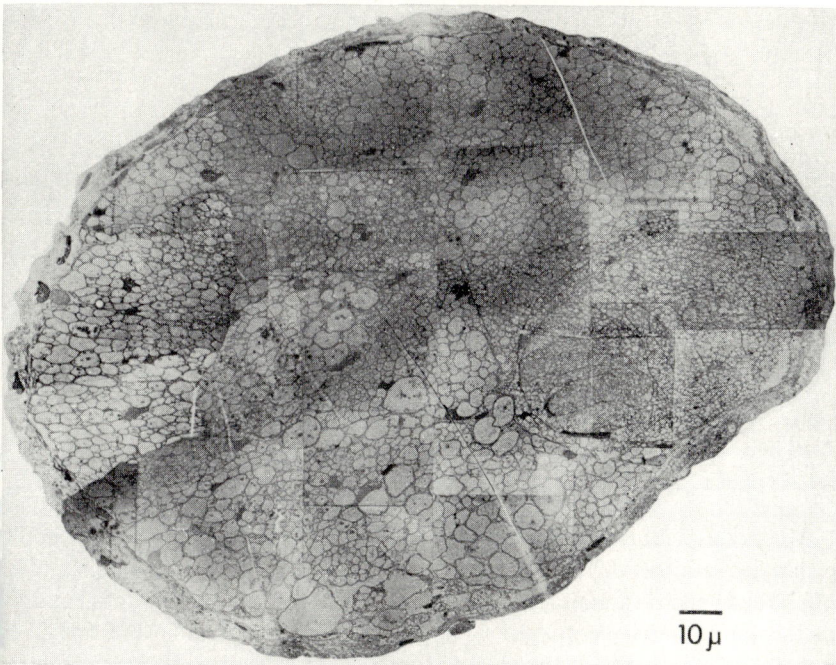

PLATE 1

The optic tract of *Orconectes virilis* (original × 5000).

contained so many closely packed fibers, was rephotographed at a final magnification of 15,000 × and was assembled from 15 micrographs (see Plate 2; "Tract B" in table below). The distribution of nerve fibers by size groups follows.

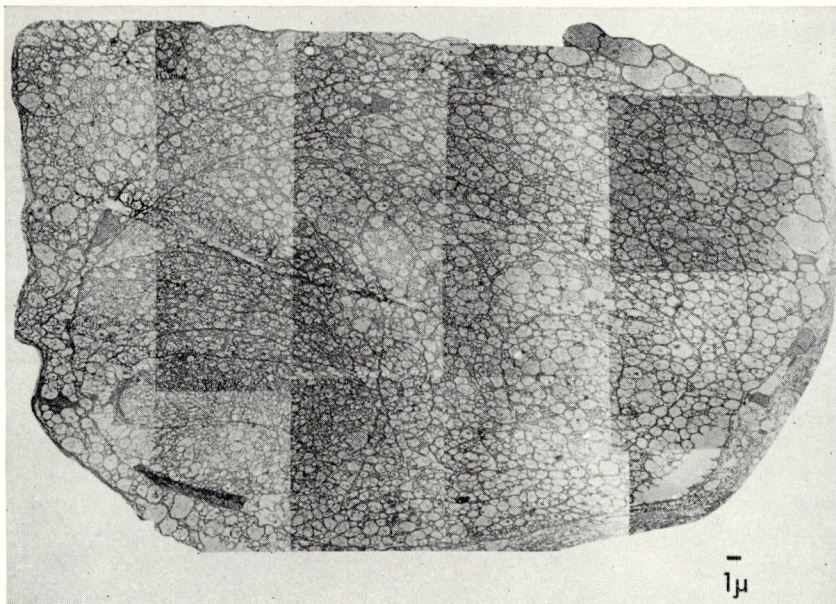

The optic tract of *Orconectes virilis*. Enlargement of the fine fiber bundle (original × 15,000).

Diameter in μ	0·14–0·3	0·3–1	1–2	2–3	3–5	5–7	7–10	10–12	Total	Facets
Tract A	10,319	4558	1406	293	—	141	—		16,717	2954
Tract B:										3250
(Plate 1)										3440
fine fiber bundle only (Plate 2)	8390	2248	882						11,700	
Total in B	12,000	3968	1650	710	120	16	3	1	18,468	

Most conspicuous and remarkably uniform was the large fine fiber bundle occupying almost 20% of the cross-sectional area but encompassing 65% of all the fibers. It extends from the median, ventral surface towards the middle of the tract, and is composed of about 11,700 fibers. Unlike the fine fiber bundles of *Cancer* and *Pagurus*, in *Orconectes* there are eight concentric layers, each composed of 1000 to 2000 fibers separated from each other by a distinct connective tissue septum.

Pagurus longicarpus

The proximal end of the optic tract was very flattened with a long and short diameter of 265 and 115 μ respectively. The final picture was enlarged 10,000 times. One complete cornea had 4658 facets while the two eyes of another similar sized crab showed 4685 and 4650 facets to show a startling uniformity. One might assume 32,800 primary afferent fibers passing from the retina into the lamina.

Two independent counts revealed 42,671 and 42,685 fibers in the optic tract. They were distributed as follows.

Diameter in μ	0·18–0·5	0·5–2	2–5	5–10	10–20	*Total*	*Facets*
Fibers	36,058	5684	912	27	4	42,685	4658 4685 4650

The conspicuous bundle of fine fibers is composed primarily of fibers of 0·2 and 0·3 μ and includes some as small as 0·18 μ. The estimated cross-sectional area occupied by large fibers is only 6% of the total area, whereas medium-sized fibers comprise 77% of the cross-sectional area of the tract. The fine fiber bundle with 84% of all the fibers takes up only 17% of the cross-sectional area.

While most of the smallest fibers are in the large compact fine fiber bundle there are small bundles of fine fibers in other areas. The large fibers are distributed in five aggregations along the periphery of the tract.

Upogebia affinis

The eyes of the mud shrimp (75 mm long) are much reduced. The facets could not be accurately counted, but it is estimated from three corneas that the eye contains 500 facets. It is believed that the optic ganglia are included in the head and not in the distal eyestalk, therefore the fibers passing from the retinular cells to the protocerebrum constitute the true optic nerve unlike the condition in all other forms studied. It consists of only 2707 fibers which fall into two sizes: 389 of 1 μ, 2318 of 2 μ. The fibers are unusually uniform and all closely packed together. There is no subdivision into bundles, even the perineural sheath is very thin. What appear to be muscle cells closely surround the nerve.

Emerita talpoida

This 32 mm long sand crab has small eyes composed of about 870 ommatidia as indicated by two corneal counts of 895 and 839 for left and right eyes. Assuming an average of 7 sensory cells per ommatidium then approximately 6100 primary afferent fibers pass into the lamina.

A montage of 20,000 magnification allowed making an accurate count of the left optic tract. Counts of the right tract were not considered as accurate because the final magnification of the montage was at 12,000. Fibers were distributed as follows.

Diameter in μ	0·10–0·15	0·15–0·6	0·6–1	1–1·5	1·5–3	3–6	Total	Facets
Left tract	575	4241	384	35	17	18	5270	839
Right tract	243	4328	90	28	16	13	4718	895

Unusual are the small number of fibers (about 5000), in comparison with other decapods, and the absence of any fibers larger than 6 μ and the absence of a fine fiber bundle. The larger fibers (1·5–6 μ) comprise 17% of the cross-sectional area while the smaller fibers (less than 1·5 μ) which constitute 99·3% of all the fibers occupy 83% of the cross-sectional area. The very smallest fibers, which number almost 5000, are quite evenly distributed throughout the tract. The larger fibers extend in a band from the ventro-lateral to the medio-dorsal edge, at which latter point there is an aggregation of fibers of intermediate size (about 0·8 μ).

Sections of both left and right tracts were cut at three levels: where the tract emerged from the brain, and at two more distal levels 0·6 and 1·5 mm from the first, but prior to the point where the tract enters the slender optic stalk. Over this distance there was no evidence of fibers branching, but while the fibers retained their same general pattern of distribution, there was a change in the relative position of the larger fibers to one another.

Cancer borealis

The carapace of this animal was 80 mm wide and 53 mm long. The optic tract had an average diameter of 196 μ. There were 5995 and 6166 facets in the eyes. Assuming an average of 6000 ommatidia each with 7 sensory cells there should be approximately 42,000 sensory fibers passing through the basement membrane into the most distal lamina ganglionaris.

Two independent counts of fibers in the tract yielded totals of 29,550 and 28,952, a deviation of about 1% from the mean. Two small peripheral segments were missing in the photograph and represented about 1·6% of the total area and were estimated to include about 630 fine fibers and 50 medium sized fibers. The fibers were distributed as follows.

The pattern of distribution of fibers is not symmetrical. The tract is roughly composed of three sections, one containing the greatest concentration of the finest fibers all having a diameter of less than 1 μ and comprising about 18% of the cross-sectional area of the tract but including over 70% of all the fibers. A second sector composed of small and medium-sized fibers comprised roughly 42% of the area, while the remaining sector of 40% area was composed of medium and large-sized fibers. The latter were aggregated in two groups, one at the periphery of the tract and next to the extensive fine fiber bundle, the second located more deeply within the tract. The 21 largest fibers account for 8% of the cross-sectional area.

Diameter in μ	0·12–0·8	0·8–1·6	1·6–2·4	2·4–4·8	4·8–9·6	9·6–20	28	Total	Facets
									5995
Fibers	23,513	4637	435	314	36	16	1	28,952	6166

Uca pugilator

The fiddler crab measured 19 mm across the carapace and had a slightly oval optic nerve 0·23 mm across (Plate 3). Left and right tracts photographed

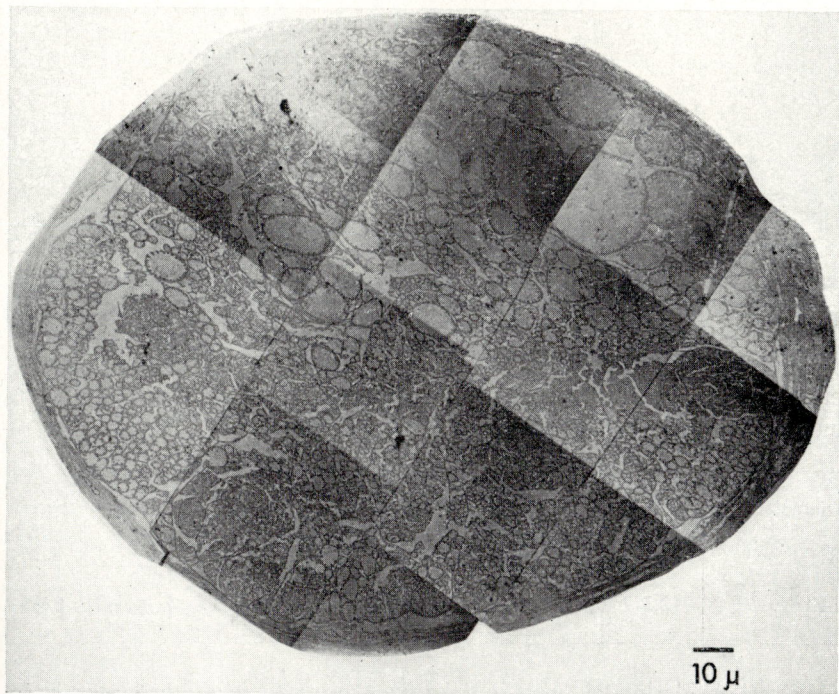

10 μ

PLATE 3
The optic tract of *Uca pugilator* (original × 3600).

at a magnification of 3600 showed a similar pattern of fiber arrangement. There was one group of 6 large fibers (8 μ average) along one edge and a second group of 7 slightly smaller fibers (6 μ) which were located more medially. A densely packed bundle of very fine fibers (average 0·15 μ) which was subdivided into 7 roughly laminated areas lay along the medial surface near to the large fiber group (Plate 4). Most of the tract was composed of

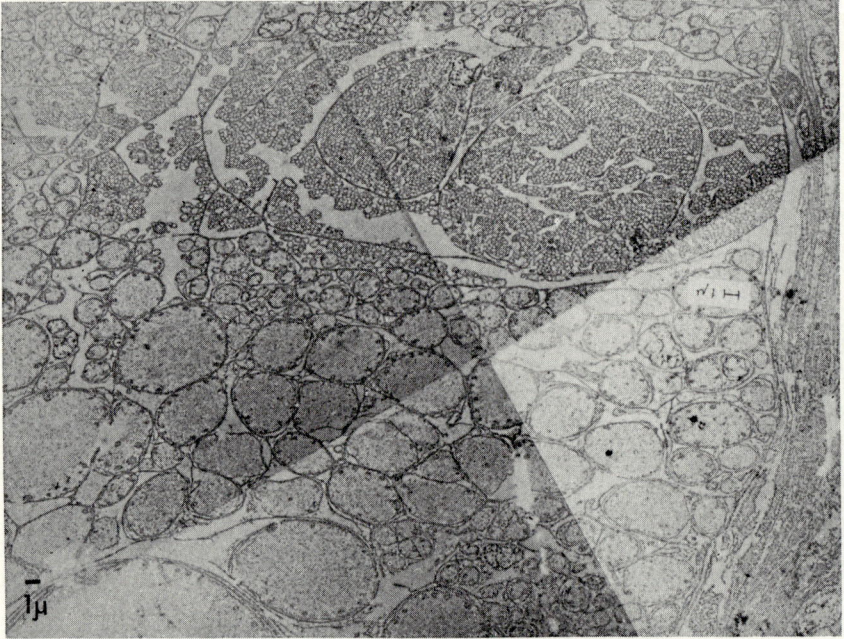

PLATE 4

The optic tract of *Uca pugilator*. Enlargement of the fine fiber bundle (original $\times$ 3600)

medium and fine fibers randomly distributed. Distribution by size groups is indicated below.

Diameter in μ	0·15–0·6	0·6–1	1–1·5	1·5–3	3–6	6–9	9–12	12–24	Total fibers	Facets
Right eye	16,803	1581	665	521	105	18	4	4	19,701	9096
Left eye	12,317	1544	991	798	147	21	6	8	16,742	9286

When considering the fibers in three size groups, there are the largest fibers (6–24 μ) which represent 0·1 % of all the fibers but constitute 15 % of the cross-sectional area. Medium sized fibers (1–6 μ) make up 6·5 % of the total but occupy 74·6% of the area. The finest fibers (0·15–1 μ) comprise the distinct fine fiber bundle and two other areas in combination with slightly larger fibers. These three constitute 93·3% of all the fibers in the tract but occupy only 10·21% of the cross-sectional area. It is interesting to note a difference in numbers of fibers of about 15% between left and right optic tracts. Could this be associated with the enormous development of one of the claws?

Each eye contains about 9200 facets and presumably there are 73,000 primary fibers passing from the retinular area into the lamina of the optic ganglia.

DISCUSSION

The optic tracts of the Decapoda examined show a basic uniformity of structure with the exception of *Upogebia* and *Emerita* which will be discussed later. The tracts (Graph 1) have a very large number (16,000 to 65,000) of fibers under 1 μ in diameter which comprise in each case nearly 91% of all fibers (Table 1). By comparison the circumoesophageal nerve of the crayfish

TABLE 1

SUMMARY OF OPTIC TRACT FIBERS AND FACETS

	Fibers 1 μ (approx.)	% Fine fibers	Total no. of fibers	Facets	Fiber facet ratio
Homarus	65,000	92	70,494	12,000	5·8/1
Orconectes	16,000	86	18,468	3250	5·7/1
Pagurus	39,000	92	42,685	4658	9·1/1
Upogebia	389	14	2707	500	5·4/1
Emerita	5200	98	5270	895	5·9/1
Cancer	26,000	90	29,952	6166	4·7/1
Uca	18,000	92	19,701	9096	2·1/1

has only 25% of its fibers smaller than 1 μ. 75–80% of the fine fibers of the tract had diameters less than 0·5 μ with the smallest 0·15 μ, except again in *Emerita* where 575 were between 0·12 and 0·15 μ.

Large fibers over 10 μ are few in number ranging from *Homarus*, none, to *Cancer* where there are 17 and only one in the latter was as large as 28 μ. In this respect the optic tract differs markedly from the central nerve cord. In the crayfish the circumoesophageal nerve has 92 fibers over 10 μ, two of which were 50 μ and 180 μ (Nunnemacher *et al.*, 1962). The ventral nerve cord of the same animal has about 80 fibers over 10 μ including two of 78 and two of 48 μ. The large fibers in the first and second thoracic nerves are comparable to those in the optic tract but the latter has many more small fibers.

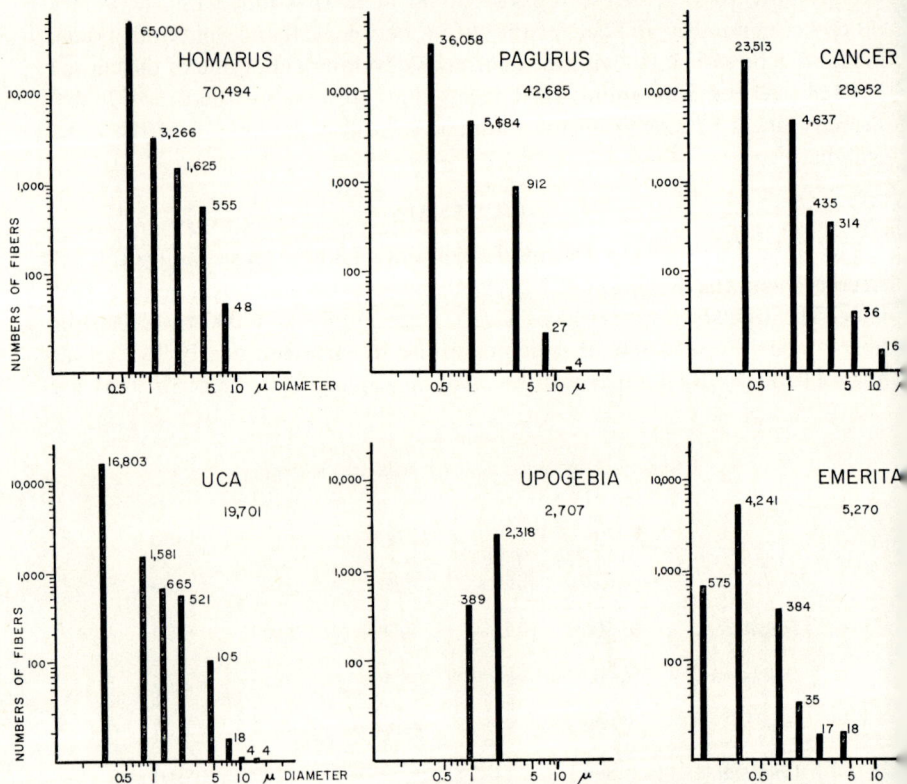

GRAPH 1

Numbers of nerve fibers by size groups in the optic tracts of six reptantian Decapoda.

The arrangement of the fibers in the tract shows considerable variation (Plate 1). The large fibers are most often dorsal and peripheral, mixed medium-sized fibers comprise most of the cross-sectional area (about 75 %), and a prominent bundle of fine fibers is generally located along the medial surface and encompasses 16 % of the cross-sectional area. The individual fibers within all tracts show neurofibrillae and small mitochondria. In the smaller fibers the latter always appear in the central position, but in the larger fibers the mitochondria are either central or more frequently peripheral. They have not been noticed in the finest fibers. Only occasionally will some of the medium-sized fibers show whole clusters of mitochondria (*Orconectes*). Large fibers may be surrounded by one or more sheath cells, the largest ones having several layers of cells, but never in the pattern of coiled circum ferential lamellae of myelin as in the vertebrates. Several or many small fibers appear "imbedded" in the sheath cell cytoplasm, but so closely packed together that the nerve fibers appear to lie in direct contact. Sheath cell nuclei appear infrequently in any one section.

The fine fiber bundle which extends from the proximal optic ganglia into the protocerebrum is a distinctive feature of all the optic tracts of the Reptantia examined except *Upogebia* and *Emerita*. In *Pagurus* it is composed of uniformly very small fibers $0.2–0.3$ μ in diameter, while in *Orconectes* it consists of small fibers of mixed sizes from $0.14–1.3$ μ. In no case were there any large fibers associated with the bundle. Separating the bundle from the rest of the tract is a connective tissue sheath, but in *Homarus* and *Orconectes* the fine fiber bundle is further subdivided into 10 to many well-defined lamina each containing 1000 to 2000 fibers. In *Cancer*, *Pagurus* and *Uca* the bundle also shows some subdivisions but not in the concentric layers of the Macrura. While the fine fiber bundle is most prominent, as it averages 16% of the cross-section, all forms showed other, much smaller aggregations of similar fine fibres. Of particular interest is that the fine fiber bundle accounts for an average of 80% of all of the fibers in the tract (*Homarus* 85%, *Orconectes* 65%, *Pagurus* 84%, *Cancer* 70%, *Uca* about 90%). Not only is the function unknown, but it is not even certain whether it is composed of afferent, efferent or mixed fibers with respect to the protocerebrum, nor indeed whether the fibers conduct individually, collectively or not at all. It should be possible to insert a microelectrode into the middle of the fine fiber bundle as it is 125 μ in diameter in *Homarus*. Even though the tip of the electrode might not be within or even directly in contact with one minute fiber, the relative isolation from large fibers ought to permit recording, without interference, from the fine fibers.

In Anomura with reduced eyes as in *Porcellana, Petrolisthes, Callianassa*, as well as a few other forms, the optic ganglia are absorbed into the head and the optic nerve consists of the axons of retinular cells (Bullock and Horridge, 1965). In *Upogebia affinis*, which is closely related to *Callianassa*, we assume this same condition because the optic nerve consists of only 2707 fibers and these of very uniform size. There is no fine fiber bundle, there are no large fibers, and all are between 1 and 2 μ in diameter. It appears certain that these must be the axons of the retinular cells. The irregularity of the facets made it difficult to determine the true number of facets, but three corneal estimates of 441, 506, and 550 implied an average of 500 ommatidia which in turn implies an average of 5.4 axons associated with each ommatidium. It may very well be, however, that the peripherally located ommatidia, while showing facets at the surface, have a very reduced retinular organization and that only the central ommatidia have the typical 7+1 pattern of most Decapoda.

In *Emerita talpoida* there is a condition intermediate between that of *Upogebia, Callianassa*, etc., and the majority of decapods in that the proximal optic ganglia, possibly all but the lamina, are incorporated into the head. The optic tract therefore lies between proximal and distal optic ganglia. This very unusual condition permits the analysis of intraganglionic fibers which is otherwise not possible because of the curvature and narrowness of the more typical intraganglionic space. This tract distinguishes itself from the others in that there is no distinct fine fiber bundle although there are many evenly distributed fine fibers, which include many of the smallest fibers seen, 0·10 μ. There are no large fibers at all. The largest ones, some 30 to 35, have diameters between 1·5 and 6 μ. The relatively small number of fibers, about 5000 in *Emerita* in comparison with 18,000 to 70,000 of other Reptantia, may be explained either by the intraganglionic position of the tract or by the small number of ommatidia. Favoring the latter interpretation would be the fact that the ratio between tract fibers and facets is equivalent to the situation in *Orconectes* and *Cancer*. The absence of large fibers and the high proportion of very small fibers in *Emerita* may be attributed either to the intraganglionic position of the tract or to the relative insignificance of the eyes as indicated by the reduction in the number of ommatidia. As this is the only instance in which we have an analysis of fibers between proximal and distal optic ganglia no conclusions can be drawn for the Reptantia; there is only the suggestion that the numbers of fibers on either side of the proximal ganglia with respect to the number of ommatidia are similar. A study of other modified optic tracts as found in *Porcellana*, *Petrolisthes*, etc., is desirable.

The ratio of primary axons to facets is 7:1 for Decapoda (Waterman, 1961). The ratio of optic tract fibers to facets gives some indication of the extent of integrative function of the optic ganglia not only for the primary afferent fibers but also for the efferent fibers from the protocerebrum and contralateral eye. Waterman, Wiersma, and Bush (1964, and in their subsequent papers) have shown that the afferent as well as efferent impulses can be considerable in *Podophthalmus*.

Corneal facets were counted in 22 Reptantians and vary in number from 2900 in *Microphrys bicornutus* to 17,900 in *Grapsus grapsus* if one excludes consideration of the reduced eyes of *Upogebia* (500) and *Emerita* (895). The number of facets is generally larger in land forms such as *Ocypode arenarius* (16,500), *Uca pugilator* (9300) and *G. grapsus* (17,900) and in the highly predacious marine Reptantians such as *Penaeus duorarum* (17,400) and *Callinectes ornatus* (8200). There are, however, unaccountable exceptions as in *Eriphia gonagra*, a slow, heavy chelated form which has 15,600 facets, and *Homarus* with 12,500 facets. More typically, however, most Reptantians have about 5400 facets as represented in this survey by *Pagurus longicarpus* (4650) and *Cancer borealis* (6200).

Despite the wide variation in the number of facets and the number of optic tract fibers, there is a fairly uniform fiber-facet ratio in several of the Reptantia studied and two interesting variants (Table 1). Similar are: *Homarus* 5·8:1,

Orconectes 5·7:1, *Cancer* 4·7:1, and similar also in *Emerita* (intraganglionic fiber–facet) 5·9:1. The two exceptions are the hermit crab *Pagurus* 9·1:1, and the fiddler crab *U. pugilator* 2·1:1. The low ratio in the latter implies a high degree of integration in the optic ganglia both of afferent and efferent impulses. Could this be associated with its land habitat and active scanning habits? Do forms of similar habits like *U. pugnax* and *O. arenaria* show a similar condition?

In *P. longicarpus* there are about 4650 facets and presumably 32,550 primary fibers entering the lamina. Unlike all other forms there are more fibers (42,680) in the optic tract than the presumed number of primary axons. Why this form should have a higher fiber–facet ratio than all others is unclear but might be associated with its habit of withdrawing rapidly into its acquired shell when threatened with danger. The condition in other hermit crabs must be investigated.

SUMMARY

1. The numbers and sizes of fibers within the optic tracts of 9 reptantian Decapoda (*Homarus americanus, Orconectes virilis, Pagurus longicarpus, Upogebia affinis, Emerita talpoida, Cancer borealis, Uca pugilator*) were determined from composite electron micrographs. Fiber counts ranged from 19,000 to 70,000.
2. The diameter of 80 % of all fibers was less than 1 μ, very few were larger than 10 μ.
3. Most of the fine fibers (0·12–1 μ) were aggregated in a compact bundle situated along the medial surface of the tract.
4. The intraganglionic tract of *E. talpoida* and the optic nerve of *U. affinis* were exceptions.
5. The average ratio of optic tract fibers to facets (ommatidia) was 5·4:1. A ratio of 9·1:1 was found in *P. longicarpus* and 2·1:1 in *U. pugilator*.

REFERENCES

BULLOCK, T. H. and HORRIDGE, G. A. 1965. *Structure and Function in the Nervous Systems of Invertebrates.* W. H. Freeman, San Francisco.
BUSH, B. M. H., WIERSMA, C. A. G. and WATERMAN, T. H. 1964. Efferent mechanoreceptive responses in the optic nerve of the crab *Podophthalmus. J. Cell. Comp. Physiol.* **64**, 3, 327–46.
NUNNEMACHER, R. F., CAMOUGIS, G. and MCALEAR, J. M. 1962. The fine structure of the crayfish nervous system. In *Fifth Internatl. Cong. Electron Micros.*, Vol. 2, No. 11 (S. S. Breese, Jr.) Academic Press, New York.
WATERMAN, T. H. 1961. *The Physiology of Crustacea.* Vol. II. Academic Press, New York.
WATERMAN, T. H., WIERSMA, C. A. G. and Bush, B. M. H. 1964. Afferent visual responses in the optic nerve of the crab *Podophthalmus. J. Cell. Comp. Physiol.* **63**, 2, 135–56.

THE RELATIONSHIP OF THE OPTIC FIBERS TO THE COMPOUND EYE AND CENTERS OF INTEGRATION IN THE BLOWFLY *PHORMIA REGINA**

J. R. LARSEN

Department of Entomology, University of Illinois, U.S.A.

THERE has been a considerable amount of work done on the behavior of the blowfly, *Phormia regina*, and to some extent on the mechanisms which mediate or are responsible for some of the behavioral patterns. Dethier and his colleagues have been looking at the morphological and physiological processes of chemoreception, mechanoreception and olfaction in *Phormia* for a number of years (Dethier, 1952, 1953, 1955; Dethier *et al.*, 1963; Larsen, 1962). No one as yet has considered to any great extent the phenomenon of vision in *Phormia*, either physiologically or morphologically, since the two-volume work of Lowne (1890). Both light and electron microscope studies of other species of Diptera (*Calliphora, Drosophila, Musca, Sarcophaga, Tabana,* etc.), some of which are closely related to *Phormia*, have been studied, however.

The material presented here is part of a larger project directed toward mapping the entire brain in *Phormia* at both the light and electron microscope levels. It is felt that such information will be of value in future studies of correlating the studies of neural and behavioral physiology. With the wealth of information available on the behavioral studies of *Phormia*, it will be just a matter of time until correlations are made between behavioral patterns and major centers of integration and their concommitant nerve cells in the insect brain similar to the study of Vowles (1954) for bees and ants. Also the establishment of the identity of the major fiber tracts, individual nerve cells, their synapses, and structure of the optical apparatus in *Phormia*, will be one more link in the overall understanding of the visual processes and their related morphology in insects.

MATERIALS AND METHODS

For light microscope studies the heads of the flies were removed just prior to emergence from the puparium. By removing the heads at this point, the cuticle had not yet undergone the tanning process, and was much easier to

* This work was supported in part by the Air Force Office of Scientific Research (Grant AFOSR 889–65) and National Science Foundation (Grant GB 2833).

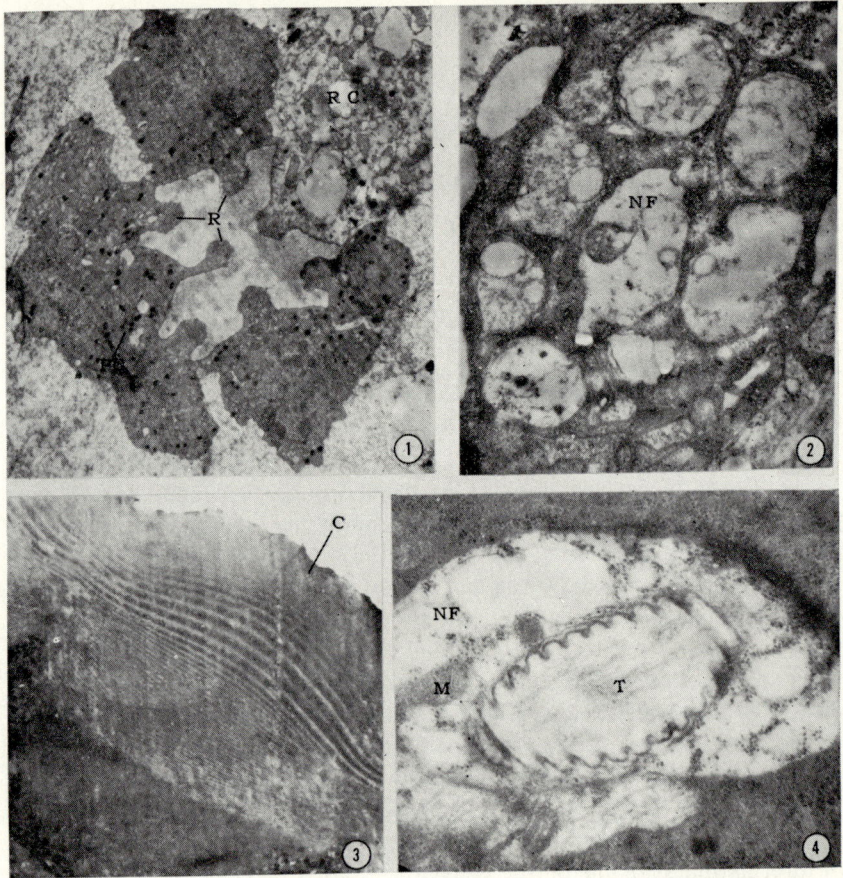

PLATE I

FIG. 1

Cross-section through the rhabdome showing the rhabdomeres (*R*) and a retinula cell (*RC*). Note the pigment granules (*PG*) in the rhabdome. × 14,000.

FIG. 2

Cross-section at the base of a rhabdome where the rhabdomeres are no longer seen. There are extending centripetally eight nerve fibers (*NF*) corresponding both in number and location to the rhabdomeres. × 31,000.

FIG. 3

Tangential section of the cornea (*C*). Note the lamellar structure and the indentations on both the convex and concave surface of the lens. × 4000.

FIG. 4

Cross-section through a nerve fiber (*NF*) showing trachea (*T*) and mitochondria (*M*) in the nerve. × 38,500.

section. The entire head was removed, fixed in alcoholic Bouin's, dehydrated in the usual manner, and embedded in Paraplast. Sections were cut at 5 and 7 μ and the tissue stained in a modification of Holmes' silver stain (Larsen, 1960). This stain proved most efficient in delineating nerve fiber tracts and nerve structures in general.

The material for electron microscopy was dissected in 6% glutaraldehyde buffered with veronyl acetate to a pH 7·4 and left for 30 min at 4°C. The tissue was then placed in 1% osmic acid and buffered to pH 7·4 with veronyl acetate at 4°C for 15 min. Dehydration was carried out in graded alcohols to a 50–50 mixture of propylene oxide and Epon. The material to be studied was embedded in Epon 812 and sections were cut with glass knives on a Porter-Blum MT2 ultramicrotome. Sections were stained for 2 hr at room temperature with saturated uranyl acetate (alcoholic) and subsequently with lead citrate for 7 min after the method of Reynolds (1963). Micrographs were taken with an RCA-EMU-3-H.

RESULTS

Ommatidia

The ommatidia in *Phormia* are of the apposition type, in that the rhabdome extends from the basement membrane all the way up to the cone (Fig. 29) and there is probably very little movement of pigment in the pigment cells under different conditions of illumination. The laminated nature of the external cornea can be observed in Fig. 3. The cornea can be seen to have an indentation on both external and internal edges. The Semper cells are seen projecting between the invaginations of the cornea, delineating the individual ommatidia (Figs. 3 and 6). Beneath the cornea can be seen the crystalline cone (Figs. 3 and 29). The Semper cells secrete the cornea and the crystalline cone. The four nuclei of the Semper cells can be observed in cross-section just under the cornea (Fig. 32). In Fig. 10 can be seen the numerous microvilli extending from the Semper cells that are responsible for the secretion of the cornea. Immediately under these cells are the pigment cells. The Semper cells are also highly pigmented and resemble closely the pigment cells. They are, however, of greater optical density. The retinular cells are arranged in a similar fashion to that observed by Fernández-Morán (1958) in the house fly, *Musca* (Fig. 17). In a cross-section of the rhabdome of *Phormia* there are 6 rhabdomeres symmetrically arranged around the smaller central 7th rhabdomere (Fig. 1). The rhabdomeres are easily grouped into 3 pairs of matching elements located on opposite sides of the central matrix with the asymmetrical rhabdomere arranged in the center. The transverse optically dense bands of the rhabdomere are oriented parallel to the radius of the ommatidium. The rhabdomeres are attached along a serrated medial edge of the retinula cell borders (Fig. 7). The transverse optically dense bands of the rhabdomere are

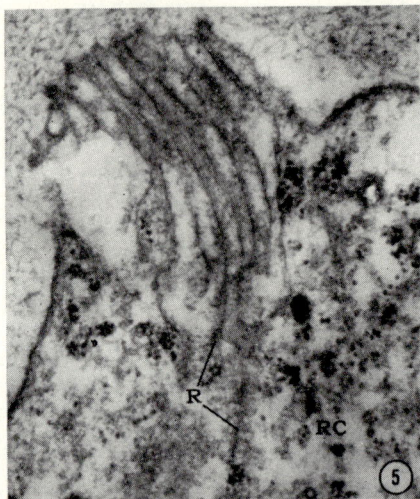

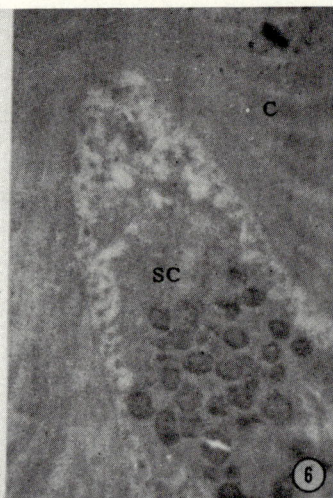

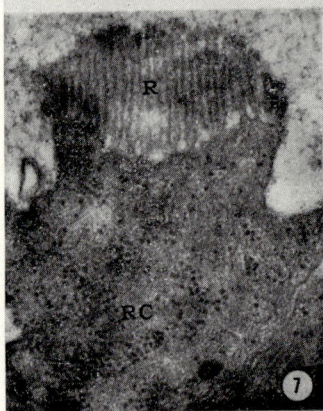

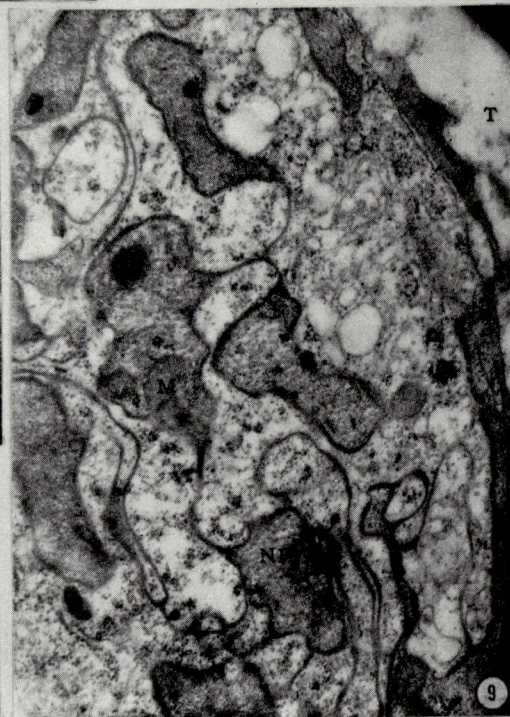

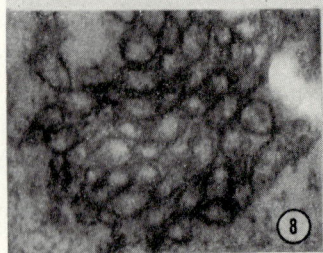

observed to penetrate into the cytoplasm of the retinula cell (Fig. 5). In cross-section the bands of the rhabdomere resemble the pattern observed by Wolken and Gupta (1961) for the cockroach being somewhat but not distinctly hexagonal. There are a number of pigment granules in all of the retinula cells (Fig. 16). There is a sheath of pigment cells surrounding each ommatidium (Fig. 29).

The ommatidia terminate at the acellular basement membrane which has neurons, trachea, and nerve fibers running through it (Fig. 19). Proximally the central matrix of the rhabdome does not show any distinct morphology, but appears as a somewhat loose precipitate as described by Goldsmith and Philpott (1957), suggesting that the central cavity is filled with a fluid. Centripetally, however, this is not the case. As the rhabdomeres proceed inward toward the basement membrane the typical rhabdomere structure is lost and nerve fibers appear in the center of the rhabdomal area. At the present stage of interpretation each rhabdomere appears to give way as it extends toward the brain to a distinct nerve fiber. The nerve fibers are seen in a cluster still surrounded by the retinula cells (Fig. 2). Also in this same area were observed inter-retinular fibers completely surrounded by the retinular cells (Fig. 16). This is a similar condition to that observed by Waddington and Perry (1963) in *Drosophila*. Similar to the work of Fernández-Morán (1958) on *Musca* and Goldsmith and Philpott (1957) on *Sarcophaga*, the rhabdomeres of *Phormia* appear in cross-section as oval to round bodies 1–3 μ in diameter, with a periodic lamellar structure of about 400–600 Å. The seventh or acentric rhabdomere is only 0·5–1 μ in diameter. There are approximately 30 parallel dense bands, about 130 Å in width, in each rhabdomere (Fig. 7). The notation of Fernández-Morán (1958) that the mosaic pattern of the

---

PLATE II (*opposite*)

FIG. 5
Tangential section through a rhabdomere (*R*) retinula cell (*RC*). × 54,250.

FIG. 6
Invagination of a Semper cell (*SC*) into the cornea (*C*). × 19,250.

FIG. 7
Tangential section of a rhabdomere (*R*) retinula cell (*RC*). × 54,250.

FIG. 8
Cross-section of a rhabdomere with a somewhat hexagonal pattern. × 112,000.

FIG. 9
Section through a series of nerve fibers (*NF*) at the base of the retinular cells near the lamina; mitochondria (*M*), trachea (*T*). × 31,000.

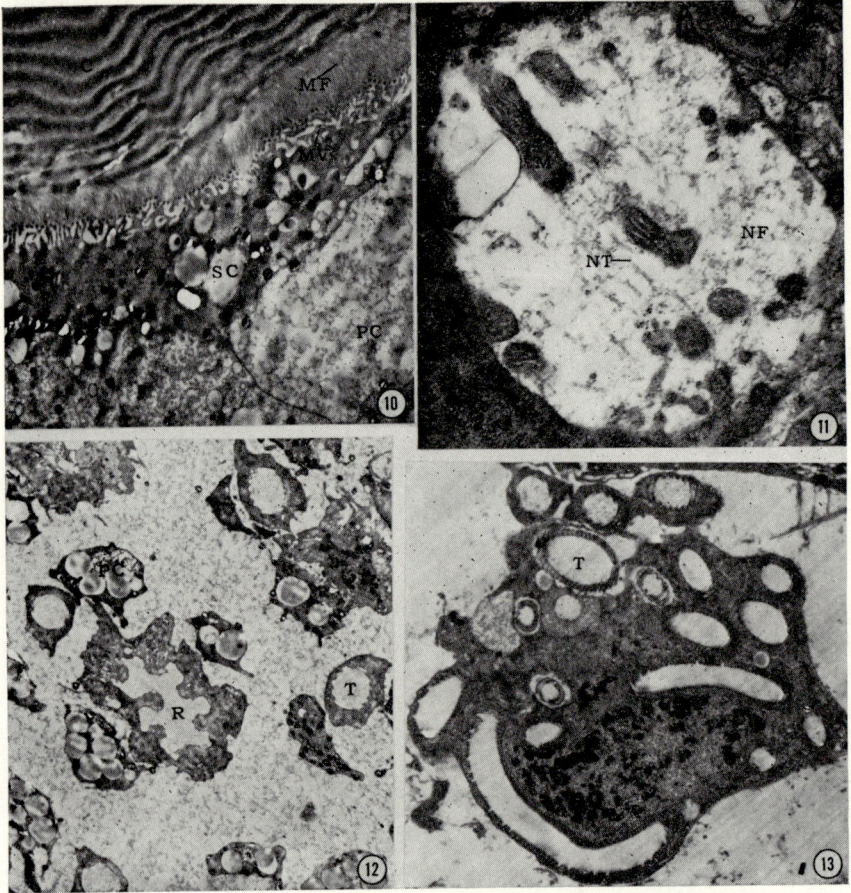

PLATE III

FIG. 10

Tangential section through the corneal area. Note the Semper cell (*SC*) and the microvilli (*MV*) which are responsible for the secretion of the cornea (*C*), pigment cell (*PC*), microfibrilae (*MF*). × 5250.

FIG. 11

Cross-section of a nerve fiber (*NF*) showing neurotubules (*NT*) and mitochondria (*M*). × 38,500.

FIG. 12

Section through a rhabdome (*R*). Note the symmetrical arrangement of the large tracheal trunks (*T*) around the rhabdome, pigment cell (*PC*). × 8000.

FIG. 13

Section through a series of large trachea (*T*) near the basement membrane. × 8000.

compound eye results not only from the orderly arrangement and inter-relationship of the ommatidia, but also from the fact that equivalent rhab-domeres of continuous ommatidia are oriented with their main axes in the same direction, has also been confirmed for *Phormia* (Fig. 14). Also, as previously noted by Goldsmith and Philpott (1957) and Fernández-Morán (1958), and also for *Phormia*, there are large numbers of mitochondria and tracheoles in the retinula cells, particularly along the edges of the cell membrane (Fig. 15). There is also a large accumulation of mitochondria and trachea in the area of the rhabdome (Fig. 17), and in the nerve fibers (Fig. 11). The nerve fibers which are seen in the area of the rhabdomeres are seen containing large tracheal trunks and mitochondria (Figs. 4 and 11). The extensive tracheation can be observed in Fig. 13 where numerous large tracheal trunks are seen coming into the area of the rhabdomes near the basement membrane. Also there appears to be a symmetrical arrangement of tracheal trunks (4–6 in number) extending up through the cytoplasm around each rhabdome proper (Fig. 12).

The cytoplasm of the pigment cells can be distinguished by the presence of large pigment granules, $0\cdot30$–$0\cdot35$ μ in diameter (Fig. 21).

The cytoplasm of the nerve cells, located in the centripetal area near the basement membrane, has large numbers of neurotubules. These neurotubules appear for the most part to be oriented parallel to one another and to the long axis of the nerve fiber (Fig. 20). The individual neurotubule is a long slender structure of uniform diameter (*ca.* 200 Å). In cross-section they appear with a dense margin surrounding a less dense center. They are similar to the neurotubules described by Porter (1965). There is no evidence that they are continuous with the slender elements of the endoplasmic reticulum also present in the same cell.

In the sheath of the pigment cells surrounding the ommatidium in *Phormia* are electron dense areas containing not only the pigment material but a random distribution of large numbers of amorphous vacuoles 3–9 μ and larger in diameter (Figs. 12 and 14).

Optic Neuropile

The optic lobes make up a large portion of the brain in *Phormia* as in other insects. These lobes have been designated by a variety of names (see Goldsmith in *Physiology of Insecta*, 1964). The terminology used here will be that recently proposed by Bullock and Horridge (1965) which is as follows.

The first or outermost optic neuropile is called the lamina, the second or medial optic neuropile the medulla, and the third or inner optic neuropile the lobula (Fig. 25). From the light microscope studies, there appear to be two types of axons from the retinular cells. There are short fibers which appear to terminate in the lamina (Fig. 23) and longer fibers which pass through the lamina into the medulla (Fig. 24). It is not at all clear, from the light microscope

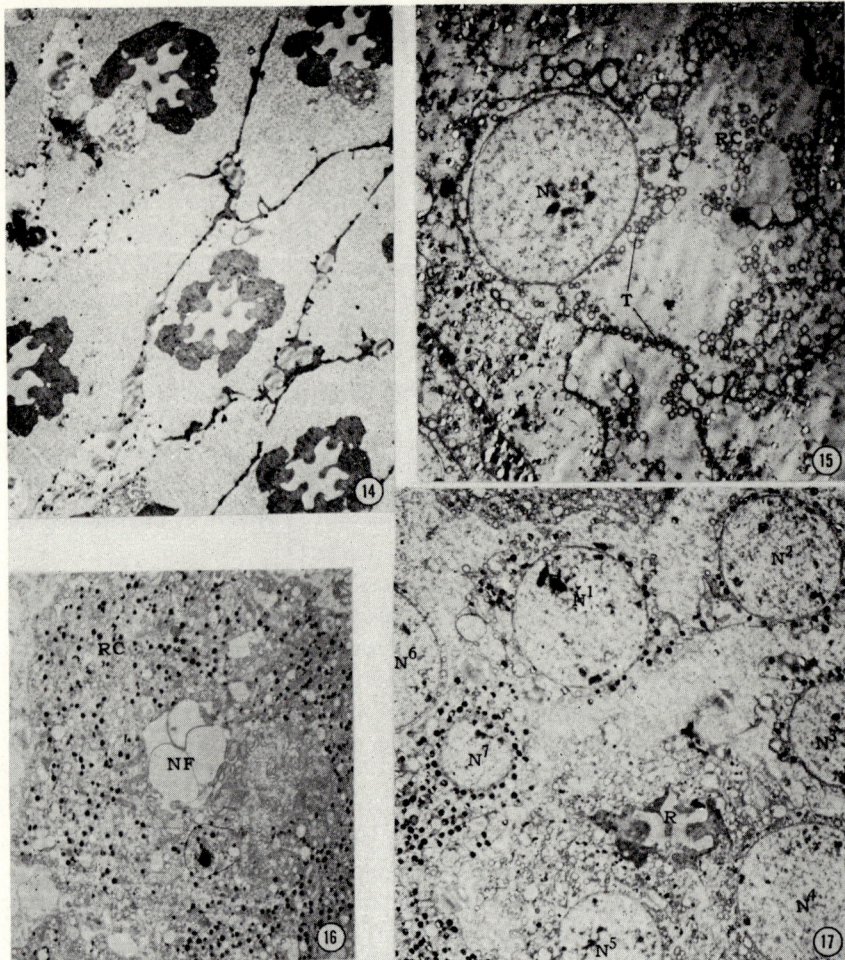

PLATE IV

Fig. 14

Section through a series of rhabdomes showing identical orientation of each rhabdome. × 3000.

Fig. 15

Section through retinular cells (*RC*). Note numerous trachea (*T*) particularly along the cell membranes and around the nucleus (*N*). × 8000.

Fig. 16

Cross-section through retinular cells (*RC*) showing inter-retinular cell nerve fibers (*NF*). × 5250.

Fig. 17

Cross-section through a rhabdome complex (*R*) at the level of the retinula cell nuclei (*N*). Note the nuclei of the seven retinular cells arranged symmetrically around the rhabdome. × 19,250.

studies, which fibers are the axons of the retinular cells. However, in the electron microscope studies it appears that the axons of the retinular cells replace the rhabdomeres and in turn leave the area of the ommatidia, passing through the basement membrane into the first lamina.

In the lamina, using the light microscope, one can see the large, monopolar neurons described by Cajal and Sánchez (1915) (Fig. 23). These cell bodies lie in a region between and centrifugal to the decussation of the short retinular fiber and the highly tracheated area on both sides of the basement membrane (Fig. 23). Also directly below and in between the decussation of the short retinular fibers in the lamina are located a uniform layer of large nerve cell bodies which are probably the "pavement cells" of Cajal and Sánchez (1915) (Fig. 26).

The numerous highly arborized dendritic branches as described by Cajal and Sánchez (1915) were observed in the region of the lamina in *Phormia* (Figs. 26 and 30). There are also numerous different types and sizes of ganglion cells in the lamina. In the lamina the short axons from the ommatidia decussate below the basement membrane and associate with several second order cells (Fig. 23). There are approximately 6–8 sensory axons grouped around each large ganglion cell to form the "neurommatidium" of Cajal and Sánchez (1915) (Fig. 26). The long axons of the retinular cells and the axons of the monopolar neurons pass from the lamina through a chiasma into the medulla (Fig. 24). There are also a large number of smaller multipolar neurons (Fig. 26) whose endings are difficult to trace because of a dense felt work of neural structure in the lamina. There are also present a number of small unipolar neurons whose dendrites spread sideways for a distance of several ommatidia. As was pointed out by Bullock and Horridge (1965) the functional significance of this spread is unknown. One can see many of these elements as described by Cajal and Sánchez (1915) and other more recent workers on other dipterous flies. There is a tremendous arborization of some of the centrifugal fibers in the neuropile of the lamina (Figs. 26 and 30). The most common are those whose cell bodies do not appear to lie in the lamina but probably are located in the medulla (Fig. 26). The lateral branching of these fibers is about the spread of one ommatidium (Fig. 26). There are also numerous cell bodies located between the axons in the region between the lamina and the medulla (Fig. 22). There are a number of large centripetal axons which branch just as they enter the medulla (Fig. 24). The real complexity of this area is only fully realized when one begins to study the interrelationship of these neural elements with the electron microscope. The study at the present time is just reaching the area of the lamina.

The medulla is made up of numerous layers of dendritic endings. The medulla appears to contain 9–11 separate parts or optically dense layers. This laminar appearance is brought about by the regularity of the arrangement of the neural elements such as those fibers which Cajal and Sánchez

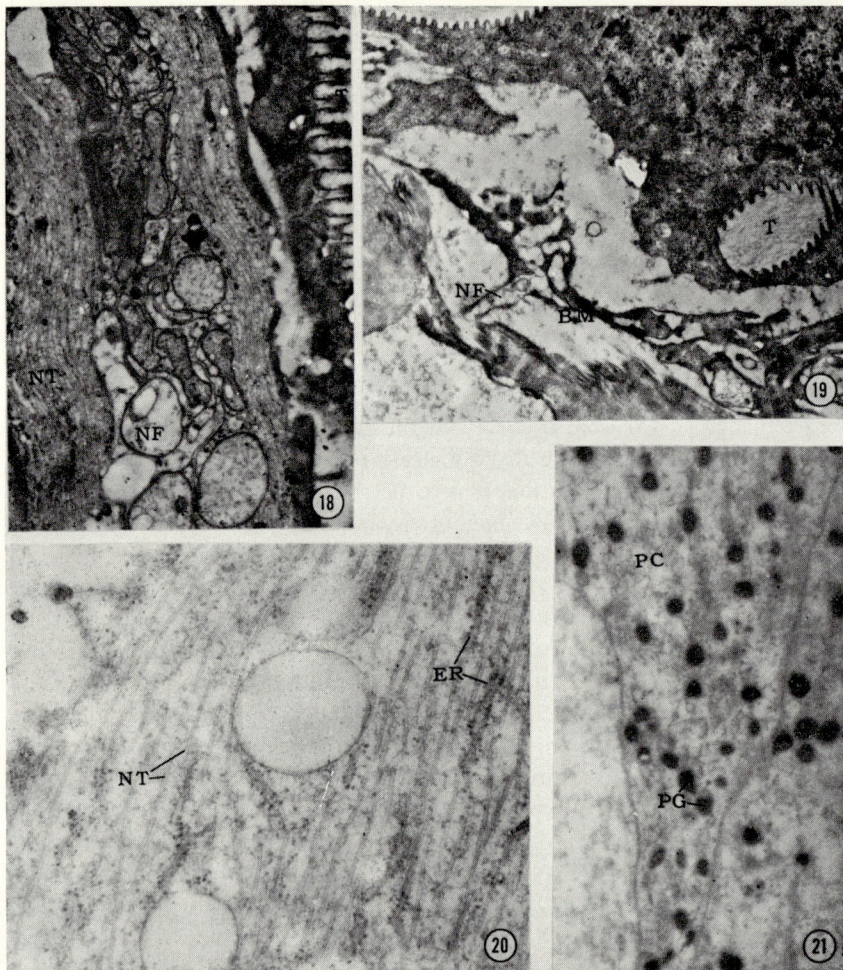

PLATE V

FIG. 18

Tangential section through nerve fibers (*NF*) showing neurotubules (*NT*) (see also Figs. 9 and 20), and trachea (*T*). × 16,000.

FIG. 19

Section through the basement membrane (*BM*) at the base of the ommatidia showing nerve fibers (*NF*) and trachea (*T*) passing through the membrane. × 11,000.

FIG. 20

Longitudinal section of neurotubules (*NT*) in the axoplasm. Also note the endoplasmic reticulum (*ER*). × 44,000.

FIG. 21

Tangential section through a pigment cell (*PC*) showing the pigment granules (*PG*). × 19,250.

(1915) refer to as "tangential meandering fibers". Space does not allow at this time the describing of all the cell types observed in *Phormia*. They are, however, very similar in form and arrangement to those described by Cajal and Sánchez (1915) for *Calliphora* and also similar to descriptions of other dipterous insects.

There is a single layer of evenly spaced dark nuclei lying within the medulla near its lateral convex border. This row of nuclei together with the transverse striped appearance caused by the axons which cross through the medulla, are the most characteristic visible traits of this body when seen with the lower powers of the light microscope. The major transverse axons which give the medulla its characteristic striped appearance are large axonal trunks probably containing many different types of neuronal elements (Fig. 31).

The medulla lies in the brain with its longer axis oriented dorsal ventrally and its convex side outermost. It is so situated that its lateral convex surface is approximately parallel with the curvature of the corneal facets (Fig. 25). The component fibers run in two directions. Those which come in from the external chiasma enter it and extend parallel with one another directly from the convex to the concave side. Because they are thus perpendicular to its surface, they are referred to as transverse fibers (Figs. 25 and 35). In addition to these fibers there are those which extend through the medulla in the plane at right-angles to the transverse fibers. That is, they are parallel to the concave and convex surfaces. The most conspicuous of these fibers is the serpentine layer which lies about one-third the thickness from the medial concave side (Fig. 25). It is made up of strong fibers which form the commissure which leaves the anterior medial edge of the medulla to pass posteriorly and connect with the opposite medulla (Fig. 38). This fiber tract will be described in more detail at a later point.

Some of the transverse fibers extend entirely through the medulla and leave it from the concave side to form part of the internal chiasma between the medulla and lobula (Fig. 25). Other fibers terminate within the medulla by arborization and make contact with the ends of peripherally extending centrifugal fibers.

The medulla contains two categories of transverse components—centrifugal and centripetal ones. Although a few longer centripetal fibers extend entirely through the medulla, this body is the most important zone of articulation or station of relay between centripetal and centrifugal fibers.

In *Phormia* all of the fibers from the lamina so far observed end in the medulla (Fig. 26). The long visual fibers from the acentric retinulae and the axons from the cells in the layer of monopolars extend no more deeply than the medulla (Fig. 26). The longitudinal fibers in the medulla are limited to the more or less well defined serpentine layer, which is parallel to the concave and convex surfaces (Fig. 25). But in addition to the serpentine layer, other

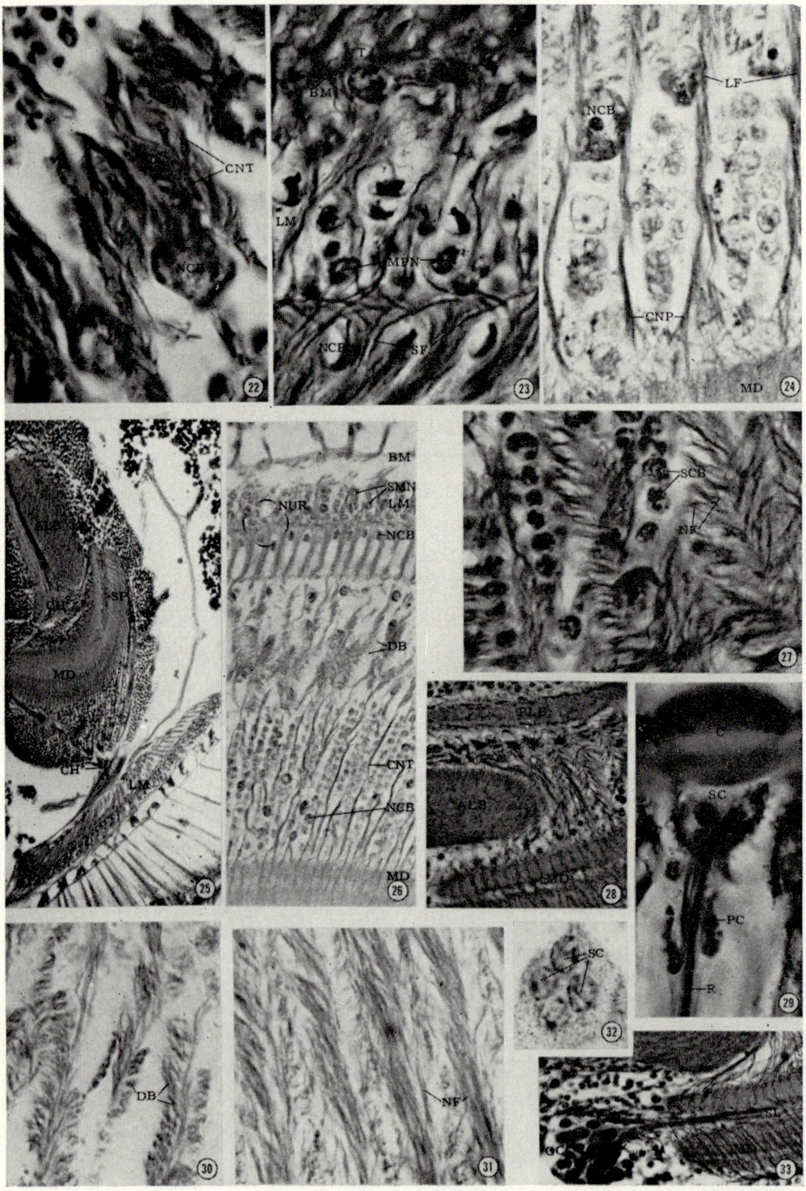
CNT
NCB
22
BM
LM
MPN
NCB
SF
23
LF
NCB
CNP
MD
24
SP
CH
MD
CH
LM
25
BM
SMN
NUR
LM
NCB
DB
CNT
NCB
MD
26
SCB
NF
27
PLB
ALB
MD
28
C
SC
PC
R
29
DB
30
NF
31
SC
32
SL
GC
33

PLATE VI (*opposite*)

FIG. 22

Tangential section through nerve cell bodies (*NCB*) and centrifugal (*CNT*) fibers in the lamina. × 5625.

FIG. 23

Section through the lamina (*LM*) showing basement membrane (*BM*) monopolar neurons (*MPN*) and the short fibers (*SF*) of the retinular cells at the point of decussation. Note the nerve cell bodies (*NCB*) centripetally to the decussation. × 7875.

FIG. 24

Section near the medulla (*MD*) showing the long fibers (*LF*) coming centripetally (*CNP*) from the lamina. Nerve cell body (*NCB*). × 5625.

FIG. 25

Section through the optic lobe showing the lamina (*LM*), first chiasma (*CH¹*), medulla (*MD*), second chiasma (*CH²*) and the anterior (*ALB*) and the posterior (*PLB*) lobula. × 200.

FIG. 26

Section through the lamina showing the regions from the basement membrane (*BM*) to the medulla (*MD*). Note the small multipolar neurons (*SMN*) and the large monopolar neurons (*LM*), also note the nerve cell bodies (*NCB*) centripetal to the decussation in the lamina. Dendritic branches (*DB*), centripetal fibers (*CNT*). × 1125.

FIG. 27

Section through the nerve fibers which run between the medulla and the posterior lobula. Cell bodies (*SCB*), nerve fibers (*NF*). × 6750.

FIG. 28

Section at a lower power showing the same region as Fig. 27. Medulla (*MD*), anterior lobula (*ALB*), posterior lobula (*PLB*). × 400.

FIG. 29

Tangential section through a single ommatidium. Note the cornea (*C*), Semper cells (*SC*), pigment cells (*PC*), and the rhabdome (*R*). × 6750.

FIG. 30

Section through the dendritic branches (*DB*) of a lamina. × 6750.

FIG. 31

Tangential section through the transverse nerve fibers (*NF*) of the medulla. × 4000.

FIG. 32

Cross-section through the Semper cells (*SC*) just under the cornea. × 1460.

FIG. 33

Section taken through the globuli cells (*GC*) as they enter the medulla (*MD*) in the region of the serpentine layer (*SL*). × 1460.

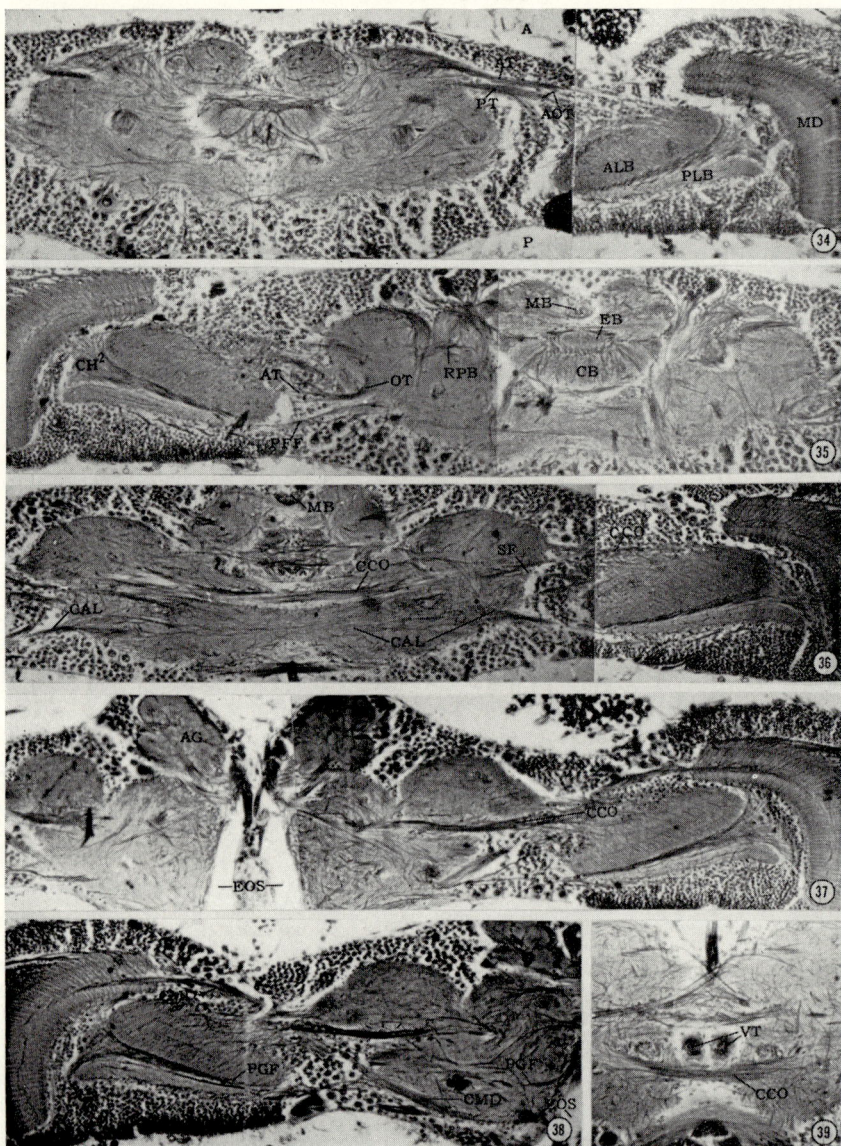

strata are present which together give the body an appearance of concentric stripes. These additional strata are formed by the lateral processes from the transverse fibers as previously stated.

The medulla is made up primarily of the following neural structures: first, the arborized ends of the visual axons coming in from the ommatidia; second, the terminal processes of the axons derived from the layer of mono-polar neurons of the lamina; and, third, fibers from the cells of the cortex which lie lateral to the medulla. In addition to the above three types there are also the serpentine fibers, and other centrifugal processes from certain neurons lying in the medial cortex such as the globuli cells (Fig. 33).

The External Chiasma

When fibers leave the lamina, they approach the focus of its arched shape and decussate to enter the opposite side of the medulla. The chiasma is only seen in sections which are cut in the frontal plane. For the decussation is from

---

PLATE VII (*opposite*)

Fig. 34

All of the sections of the brain on this plate are located in an anterior (*A*), posterior (*P*), orientation; anterior optical tract (*AOT*), anterior branch (*AT*), posterior branch (*PT*), anterior lobula (*ALB*), posterior lobula (*PLB*), medulla (*MD*). × 200.

Fig. 35

Section of the brain in a region ventral to section 34, second optical chiasma (*CH*²). The anterior branch of the anterior optical tract (*AT*), the optical tubercle (*OT*) and the root of the protocerebral bridge (*RPB*); posterior fine fiber tract (*PFF*), median bundle (*MB*), ellipsoid body (*EB*), central body (*CB*). × 200.

Fig. 36

Section of the brain taken at a level ventral to Fig. 35 through the area of the central commissures. Central commissures (optical branch) (*CCO*), commissure of the anterior lobula (*CAL*), small fibers (*SF*), possibly a fourth tract crossing the brain between the anterior lobular bodies, median bundle (*MB*). × 200.

Fig. 37

Section taken in the region of the oesophagus ventral to section 36. Antennal glomeruli (*AG*), oesophagus (*EOS*), central commissure (*CCO*), at the point where it connects with the antennal branch. × 200.

Fig. 38

Section of the brain taken ventrally to Fig. 37, however, still in the region of the oesophagus. Commissure of the medulla (*CMD*), oesophagus (*EOS*), posterior tract of giant fibers (*PGF*). × 200.

Fig. 39

Section through the region of the ventral tubercles (*VT*) showing the central commissure (*CCO*). × 400.

anterior to posterior and *vice versa*, and not from dorsal to ventral. The axis of the chiasma thus lies in a vertical plane (Fig. 25). The visual fibers arising from the ommatidia in the anterior regions of the eye cross to form part of the posterior portion of the medulla and those from the posterior region of the eye enter the anterior part of the medulla (Fig. 25). Those ommatidia in the center of the eye send fibers straight through the external lamina and into the central part of the medulla, without changing their course (Fig. 25). Those fibers which cross from the posterior side of the external lamina to the anterior part of the medulla are the longest, those which pass from anterior to posterior are shorter, and those which extend from the central region of the lamina to the central part of the medulla are the shortest (Fig. 25).

There is a large group of globuli cells located in the cortex in the region of the medulla which send their axons into the median anterior end of the medulla (Fig. 33). There are approximately 50 large monopolar globuli cells whose axons seem to terminate and make synapse with fibers coming from both the lamina and the lobula (Fig. 33). Fibers from these globuli cells enter the medulla at the point where it appears to separate at the level of the serpentine layer.

Cells with side branches of a very diffuse nature which Bullock and Horridge (1965) referred to as "collosal cells" with extensive arborization have been observed in the lobula but not in the medulla. Again one is referred to Cajal and Sánchez (1915) for a more complete description of the various neurons found in the medulla, using light microscopy.

The lobula of *Phormia* is divided into an anterior and posterior portion. The anterior is the lobula proper, and the posterior portion is a thin plate (Fig. 25). There are various fibers running across the internal or second large chiasma from the medulla to the lobula as well as from the two portions of the lobula itself. The internal, or second chiasma, is somewhat different from the external chiasma, and as Power (1943) pointed out in *Drosophila*, it is doubtful that this should be called a chiasma at all. Fibers which connect the medulla and the lobula do not decussate to the opposite side as they do in the external chiasma. Essentially, all of the fibers which connect the medulla and lobula do so through the triangular space which contains this chiasma (Fig. 25). As the fibers leave the medulla they converge through the triangle and enter the lobula largely through the sides which form the edges of the triangle (Figs. 25 and 35). Transverse sections show that a reasonable number of fibers enter the anterior, inner lobula in the transverse plane. A very large proportion of the fibers from the medulla enter the posterior and not the anterior lobula.

The anterior lobula is connected to the posterior lobula proper by fibers which pass across the triangle at approximately right-angles to the flow of fibers from the medulla (Figs. 27 and 28). In addition to these the anterior lobula contains terminal portions of the second largest fibers of the brain. These large fibers are found branching and extending lengthwise along both the anterior and posterior surfaces located in the center so that there are three layers in all. These very strong fibers extend into the central part of the brain in a manner which will be explained below.

In the region of the lobula and medulla there is a dense, extensive network of highly branched fibers running between the posterior plate of the lobula and the medulla (Fig. 27). Within this highly arborized mass are dendrites which appear to be closely related in morphology to the highly branched nerves seen in the lamina (Fig. 27). In addition to the extensively branched dendrites between the medulla and the posterior plate of the lobula there are a number of smaller cell bodies with very short axons running perpendicular to the highly arborized dendrites (Fig. 27).

Large fibers from the protocerebrum have extensive arborizations in both parts of the lobula and the medulla.

Following is a brief description of the major fiber tracts of the optic neuropiles where they enter into the protocerebrum. In describing various fiber tracts, the terms "enter", "leaves", "into", etc., have no physiological significance, but serve only to describe their morphological pathways.

The Commissure of the Medulla

This is the only bundle from this body. Although a few of its fibers are contributed by the external chiasma and by the anterior inner lobula, the majority are from the medulla and leave its anterior side at the level of the oesophageal canal (Fig. 38). The fibers turn posteriorly and medially to run in a frontal plane all the way across the brain between the anterior lobula and the central brain mass. The commissure of the medulla then passes along the posterior margin between the central fibrous mass and the cellular cortex behind the ocellar fibers, then turns anterio-laterad to enter the anterior margin of the medulla of the opposite side. This is a simple and symmetrical commissure which puts these two important optical relay stations in contact with each other. Presumably, as a result of this tract, a stimulus received by one eye can be immediately shared with the opposite side so that symmetrical impulses may be given to the brain nearly simultaneously.

The *posterior tract of giant fibers* (Fig. 38) is made up of very large, heavy fibers being associated with the posterior lobula. The tract is made of a small number of fibers which leave the median end of the posterior lobula at the level of the oesophageal canal and move toward the median line. The tract separates and one portion continues toward the median line where it becomes associated with the ocellar fibers, and then passes ventrally and posteriorly into the suboesophageal mass. It then moves out through the brain stem into the thoracic nerve center. The other portion of the bundle passes through the protocerebrum and ends in the central complex.

The *posterior tract of fine fibers* (Fig. 35) also leaves the posterior lobula at about the same place as the preceding tract so that its site of actual origin is difficult to determine. The tract arises in the region of the posterio-median vertex of the V-shaped internal chiasma and extends anterior medially into the central brain mass. It is difficult to follow beyond this point.

The *fibers of the commissure of the anterior lobula* (Fig. 36) leave the medial edge of this body at a level slightly dorsal to the oesophageal canal. The bundle turns briefly anteriorly, then back posteriorly going across the brain and entering at the same site on the opposite glomerulus.

The *optical component of the central commissure* (Fig. 36) leaves from the median surface of the anterior lobula bowing slightly medially and then back to join the anterior lobula of the opposite side.

The *anterior optic tract* (Fig. 34) is derived from the dorsal anterior side of the anterior lobula. Its point of origin is distinctly dorsal to any of those just described. Although the component fibers are of medium diameter, the tract itself is broad and definite. It extends forward and turns medially around the anterior surface of the fibrous part of the protocerebral lobe and splits into an anterior and posterior branch. The former branch proceeds anteriorly and breaks up into the optic tubercle making contact there with the roots of the protocerebral bridge (Fig. 35).

From the optic tubercle, fibers swing medial posteriorly. Some make contact with the central complex (central body, ellipsoidal body) (Fig. 35), the others are distributed in the protocerebrum. The second branch turns posterio-medially and ramifies in the protocerebral lobe.

One of the most important commissures of the protocerebrum is the central commissure. This lies in the brain at the level of the ventral tubercles (Figs. 36 and 39) of the central complex and posterior to them. The fibers of which it is made are derived from at least three different sources. The first of these has already been mentioned; that is, the optical component of the central commissure. The second source is the dorsal protocerebral lobes themselves, and the third class of constituents is from the antennal nerves. When the antennal nerves reach the protocerebrum they turn medially and join the central commissure to go to the opposite side of the brain (Fig. 37).

In addition, in the region of the central commissure are some *small fibers* which arise from the medial edge of the anterior lobula, and which pass across the brain tract of the central commissure anteriorly and enter the central complex and finally pass across the brain to the medial surface of the anterior lobula of the opposite side. This makes a fourth fiber tract going across the brain between the optic lobes.

These constitute the major tracts in the blowfly, *Phormia*, and are very similar to those observed by Power (1943) for *Drosophila*, and by Satija (1958) for *Calliphora erythrocephala*.

DISCUSSION

While this description of the optic components of the brain of the blowfly, *Phormia regina*, does not differ greatly from those of other Diptera, Cajal and Sánchez (1915), Power (1943), Satija (1958), Sato (1951, 1953), Fernández-Morán (1958), Goldsmith and Philpott (1957), and others, it is felt that the information presented here will be of some value in better understanding of the neural elements of the insect brain.

The preliminary electron micrograph studies at the present time are only into the layer of the first optic ganglion or lamina but give some indication of the complexity of the neuropile in the compound eye. It is quite obvious that it will take further study to work out completely at the ultrastructure level the relationship of the various neural elements.

At the ultrastructure level, the morphology of the ommatidia, of the rhabdome and rhabdomeres particularly, is very similar to that described by Fernández-Morán (1958), Wolken and Gupta (1961) and Goldsmith and Philpott (1957). The degree of tracheation in the region of the basement membrane is much greater than that previously described by light microscopy for Diptera. One can also see the acellular basement membrane with trachea and nerve fibers passing from the ommatidia to the lamina. There are large numbers of neurotubules in the nerve fibers in the region of the basement membrane. Thin sections of the axoplasm reveal a singular type of fine tubular structures which are found to be especially prominent within dendrites. The micrographs show the nerve fibers in the centripetal regions of the ommatidium to be greatly endowed with neurotubules. From the electron microscope studies it appears that as the rhabdomeres extend centripetally they are replaced in the same area by the nerve fibers of the individual retinula cells. As yet no union of these structures has been observed. However, the nerve fibers coming from the retinular cells are in the same location and relative position as the rhabdomeres. The nerve fibers and the retinula cells in the region of the basement membrane are both highly tracheated and contain large numbers of mitochondria.

The individual nerve cells as seen with the light microscope in *Phormia* are very much like those described by Cajal and Sánchez (1915) for *Calliphora*.

The pattern of the major nerve tracts from the optic neuropiles to the brain are not unlike those observed by Power (1943) for *Drosophila* and by Satija (1958) for *Calliphora*. Power (1943) and Satija (1958) both describe three major tracts running across the mid-brain in the region of the central complex. In *Phormia* there appears to be a fourth tract which goes across the brain. There are two groups of small fibers arising from the anterior lobula between the commissure of the anterior lobula and the central commissure which run anterio-medially through the central complex and back to the anterior lobula of the opposite side of the brain. There are then definitely three and probably four fiber tracts going across the brain between the optic neuropiles.

The structure of the second optical neuron synapse as observed in the house fly *Musca* by Trujillo-Cenóz and Melamed (1963) was not observed in *Phormia*. However, this may have been due to the fact that sections were not cut low enough in the lamina to see these structures.

Sections were cut near the base of the ommatidium in which inter-retinular fibers were observed as enclosed or surrounded by the retinular cells. This is an arrangement similar to that observed by Waddington and Perry (1963) in *Drosophila*.

SUMMARY

Other than the differences noted in the text the neuroanatomy (both at the light and electron microscope level) of the blowfly *Phormia* is similar to that of other Diptera previously studied.

The potential for studying the ultrastructure of nerve morphology is excellent in this kind of a system where you have the identifying structures of the rhabdome for landmarks and orientation.

ACKNOWLEDGEMENTS

Special appreciation is due Mr. Paul Killmer for electron microscope preparations and help in preparing the manuscript.

REFERENCES

BULLOCK, T. H. and HORRIDGE, G. A. 1965. *Structure and Function in the Nervous Systems of Invertebrates. II.* W. H. Freeman, London. 811 pp.

CAJAL, S. R. and SÁNCHEZ, D. 1915. Contribución al conocimiento de los centros nerviosos de los insectos. *Trab. Lab. Invest. Biol. Univ. Madr.* **13**, 1–164.

DETHIER, V. G. 1952. Adaptation to chemical stimulation of the tarsal receptors of the blowfly. *Biol. Bull., Woods Hole* **103**, 178–89.

DETHIER, V. G. 1953. Summation and inhibition following contralateral stimulation of the tarsal chemoreceptors of the blowfly. *Biol. Bull., Woods Hole* **105**, 257–68.

DETHIER, V. G. 1955. The physiology and histology of the contact chemoreceptors of the blowfly. *Quart. Rev. Biol.* **30**, 348–71.

DETHIER, V. G., LARSEN, J. R. and ADAMS, J. R. 1963. The fine structure of the olfactory receptors of the blowfly. pp. 105–14. In *Olfaction and Taste* (Y. Zotterman ed.). Macmillan, New York.

FERNÁNDEZ-MORÁN, H. 1958. Fine structure of the light receptors in the compound eyes of insects. *Exp. Cell Res. Suppl.* **5**, 586–644.

GOLDSMITH, T. H. 1964. The visual system of insects. In *The Physiology of Insecta* (M. Rockstein, ed.). Vol. 1, Academic Press, New York. 627 pp.

GOLDSMITH, T. H. and PHILPOTT, D. E. 1957. The microstructure of the compound eyes of insects. *J. Biophys. Biochem. Cytol.* **3**, 429–40.

LARSEN, J. R. 1960. The use of Holmes' silver stain in insect nervous tissue. *Stain Tech.* **35**, 223–4.

LARSEN, J. R. 1962. The fine structure of the labellar chemosensory hairs of the blowfly *Phormia regina*. *J. Insect Physiol.* **8**, 683–91.

LOWNE, B. T. 1890. *The Anatomy, Physiology, Morphology and Development of the Blowfly.* 2 vols. R. H. Porter, London. 776 pp.

PORTER, K. R. 1965. Illustrations of cell fine structure. In *Ideas in Modern Biology* (A. John, ed.). Moore Natural History Press, New York. 563 pp.

POWER, M. E. 1943. The brain of *Drosophila melanogaster*. *J. Morph.* **72**, 517–59.

REYNOLDS, E. S. 1963. The use of lead citrate at high pH as an electron-opaque stain in electron microscopy. *J. Cell Biol.* **17**, 208–12.

SATIJA, R. C. 1958. A histological study of the brain and thoracic nerve cord of *Calliphora erythrocephala* with special reference to the descending nervous pathways. *Res. Bull. Punjab Univ. (Zool.)* **142**, 81–96.

SATO, S. 1951. Development of the compound eye of *Culex pipiens* var. *pallens* Coquillett. (Morphological studies on the compound eye in the mosquito, No. II). *Sci. Rep. Tohoku Univ.* (4) **19**, 23–32.

SATO, S. 1953a. Structure and development of the compound eye of *Aedes* (*finlaya*) *japonicus* Theobald. (Morphological studies of the compound eye in the mosquito, No. III). *Sci. Rep. Tohoku Univ.* (4) **20**, 33–44.

SATO, S. 1953b. Structure and development of the compound eye of *Anopheles hyrcanus sinensis* Wiedemann. (Morphological studies on the compound eye of the mosquito, No. IV). *Sci. Rep. Tohoku Univ.* (4) **20**, 45–53.

TRUJILLO-CENÓZ, O. and MELAMED, J. 1963. On the fine structure of the photoreceptor. Second optical neuron synapse in the insect retina. *Z. Zellforsch.* **59**, 71–7.

VOWLES, D. M. 1954. The function of the corpora pedunculata in bees and ants. *Brit. J. Anim. Behav.* **2**, 116.

WADDINGTON, C. H. and PERRY, M. M. 1963. Inter-retinular fibers in the eyes of *Drosophila*. *J. Insect Physiol.* **9**, 475–8.

WOLKEN, J. J. and GUPTA, P. D. 1961. Photoreceptor structures. The retinula cells of the cockroach eye. *Periplaneta americana*. *J. Biophys. Biochem. Cytol.* **9**, 720–4.

THE DYNAMICS OF LATERAL INHIBITION IN THE COMPOUND EYE OF *LIMULUS*. I*

F. Ratliff, H. K. Hartline, and D. Lange

The Rockefeller University, New York, U.S.A.

Pronounced transient responses to changes in the spatial, temporal, and spectral distribution of illumination on the retina are characteristic features of the activity of the optic nerve in all well-developed visual systems, both vertebrate and invertebrate. These transient responses may result from the separate or combined effects of many and diverse processes, including the photochemical processes in the receptor itself, the electrochemical processes underlying the generation of nerve impulses, and the interplay of excitatory and inhibitory influences among neighboring elements in the retina.

The purpose of this paper is to examine a few major aspects of the dynamics of inhibition in the retina of the compound eye of *Limulus*. Our aim is to provide an empirical basis for the extension of our mathematical account of inhibitory interaction in the steady state to include the dynamic behavior of the lateral and self-inhibition in the neural network in this retina. This study is confined to the influences that are revealed by the discharge of impulses in the fibers of the optic nerve in response to various spatial and temporal patterns of illumination on the receptor mosaic. In a subsequent paper in this symposium we consider the dynamics of the inhibitory influences that result from various temporal patterns of antidromic impulses produced by electrical stimulation of the optic nerve, and develop a mathematical formulation of the dynamics. To provide a background for both studies let us first consider a few salient features of the anatomy and function of the compound eye of *Limulus* and briefly review our earlier quantitative account of the steady-state inhibitory interactions.

GROSS AND MICRO ANATOMY
OF THE COMPOUND EYE OF LIMULUS

The corneal surface of the compound eye of *Limulus* forms an ellipsoidal bulge on the carapace of the prosoma just below a spine-like projection of the ophthalmic ridge. In very young animals the projecting spine is quite

* This investigation was supported by a research grant (NB–00864) from the National Institute of Neurological Diseases and Blindness, U.S. Public Health Service, and by an Equipment Loan Contract Nonr. [1442(00)] with the U.S. Office of Naval Research.

prominent and the surface of the cornea is nearly spherical. The older the animal, the more oblate is the corneal bulge and the less prominent is the ophthalmic ridge and spine. When full maturity is reached (at about 10 years of age) the cornea is usually very much flattened and the protective spine on the ophthalmic ridge is almost completely absent.

Photographs of several aspects of the corneal surface of the right lateral eye of an adult male *Limulus* (width of carapace 22·5 cm) are shown in Fig. 1.

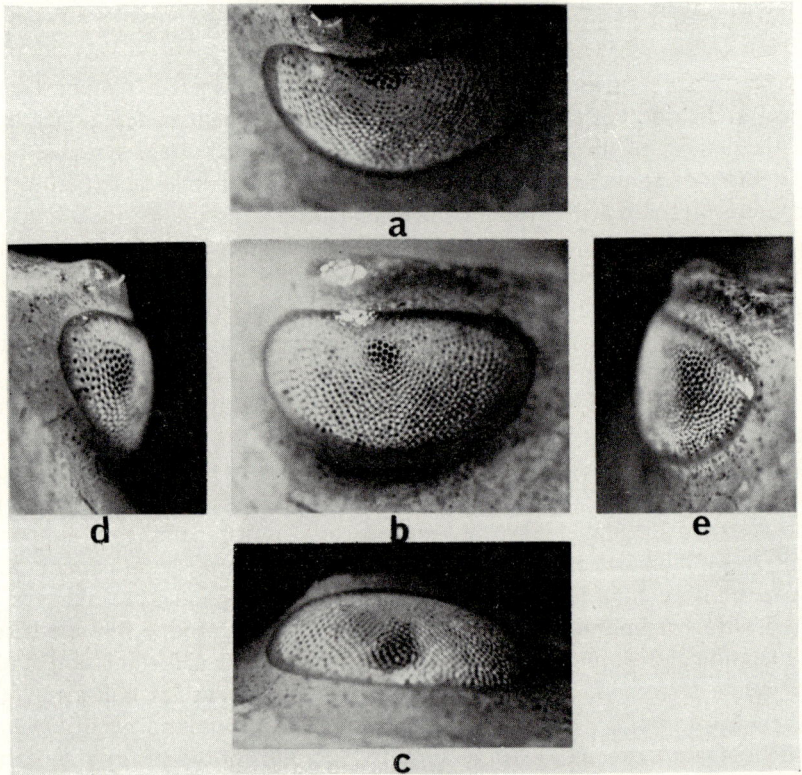

FIG. 1

Various aspects of the corneal surface of the compound eye of *Limulus*. a, dorsal; b, high lateral; c, low lateral; d, posterior; e, anterior. Length of eye: approximately 1·5 cm.

The optical axes of the approximately 1000 ommatidia diverge so that the visual field of the eye as a whole covers approximately a hemisphere. The divergence of the optical axes is greater than the divergence of the morphological axes because of the slant of the corneal surface, especially near the anterior and posterior margins of the eye. The acceptance angle of each ommatidium is quite large, the half-width being about 8° (Waterman, 1954; Kirschfeld and Reichardt, 1964), and the visual fields of closely neighboring ommatidia overlap one another to a considerable extent. The pseudopupil resulting from the low reflectance of the ommatidia oriented in the direction of the camera is not the same from all angles of view, for the divergence of the optical axes of neighboring ommatidia is not the same everywhere.

The optical axes of the ommatidia near the anterior portion of the eye, for example, are nearly all oriented in the anterior direction. Therefore, when viewed from the front, the pseudopupil appears very large—filling almost the entire anterior portion of the eye. Viewed from the side, the pseudopupil appears small and nearly circular. From the rear, it appears somewhat larger, but not as large as in the frontal view. Viewed from above, the pseudopupil generally appears somewhat elongated and flattened against the margin of the eye. From a low side view it appears large and circular. Occasionally, two distinct pseudopupils can be seen from some directions of view. In addition to these normal variations, deep scars on the cornea and malformations of the arrangement of the ommatidia resulting from injury or disease are common, particularly in the eyes of older animals obtained from the northern part of their range along the east coast of America (Nova Scotia to Yucatan). We mention these points because it is easy to fall into the error of thinking of the compound eye of *Limulus* as a more or less homogeneous structure. The normal variations in the size and shape of the pseudopupil, seen from different points of view, suggest that there may be some corresponding differences in the functional organization of the interconnections among the ommatidia in the retina or among the ganglion cells in the optic lobe. Excepting a few crude maps of iso-inhibitory contours (Hartline, Wagner, and Ratliff, 1956), however, these possibilities remain to be investigated.

A photomicrograph of a section of the compound eye of *Limulus* is shown in Fig. 2. It was cut more or less perpendicularly to the plane of Fig. 1b. At the top of the micrograph are the lower ends of the densely stained pigmented sheaths of the ommatidia, *O*. A portion of the photosensitive rhabdom, *Rh*, is visible in one ommatidium. (See Fig. 5 for a detailed drawing.) Axons, labeled *Rax* and *Eax*, arise from the several retinular cells and the one eccentric cell* in each ommatidium. These axons form small bundles which eventually come together to form the optic nerve, *ON*, a portion of which is shown at the bottom of the micrograph.

At various short distances below the layer of ommatidia, both the retinular cell axons and the eccentric cell axons give rise to numerous fine lateral

---

* Occasionally one finds an ommatidium with two eccentric cells, and—less frequently—one with no eccentric cell. The double eccentric cells probably generate the nearly synchronous double spikes sometimes observed in small strands of the optic nerve (see Tomita, 1957).

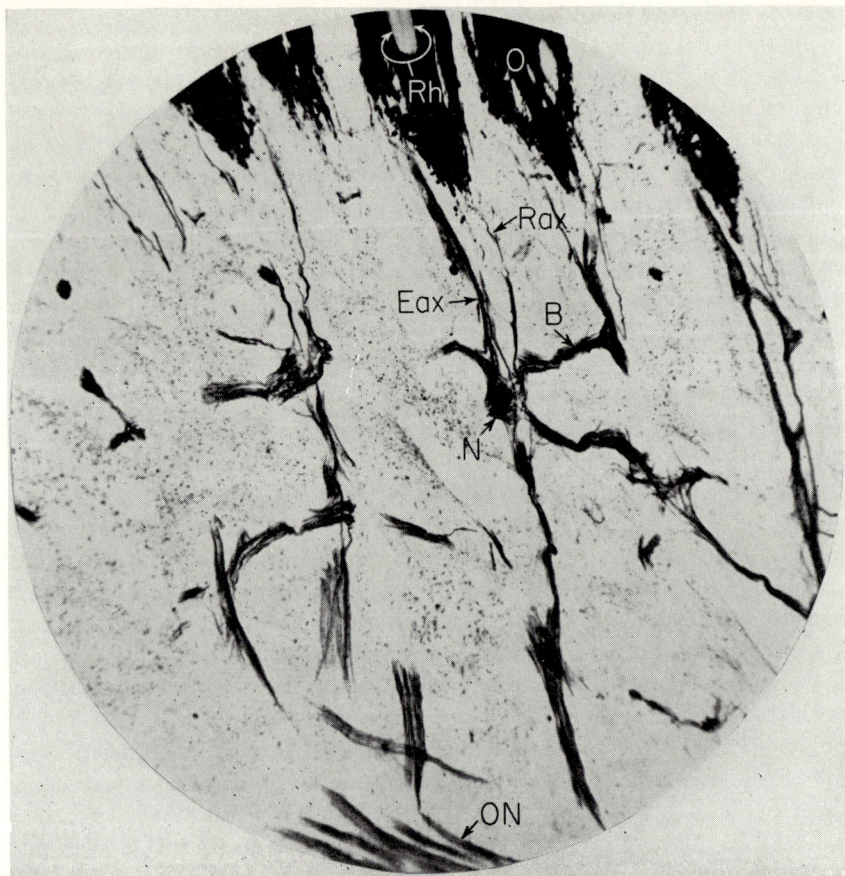

FIG. 2

Photomicrograph of a horizontal section through the compound eye of *Limulus* (cornea and crystalline cones removed). Samuel's silver stain. Micrograph prepared by W. H. Miller.

branches. Bundles of these branches, *B*, form a complex three-dimensional plexus of interconnections among the axons of the retinular and eccentric cells. The fibers in these bundles appear to terminate and form clumps of neuropile, *N*, mainly around the axons of the eccentric cells. The inhibitory interaction, discussed in this and in our succeeding paper, is mediated by this plexus of interconnections: cutting the lateral branches abolishes the inhibition (Hartline, Wagner, and Ratliff, 1956).

Sections through the plexus in planes perpendicular to the plane of Fig. 2 are shown in Figs. 3 and 4. The section in Fig. 3 gives a rough idea of the nature of the interconnections among the bundles of axons from about 30

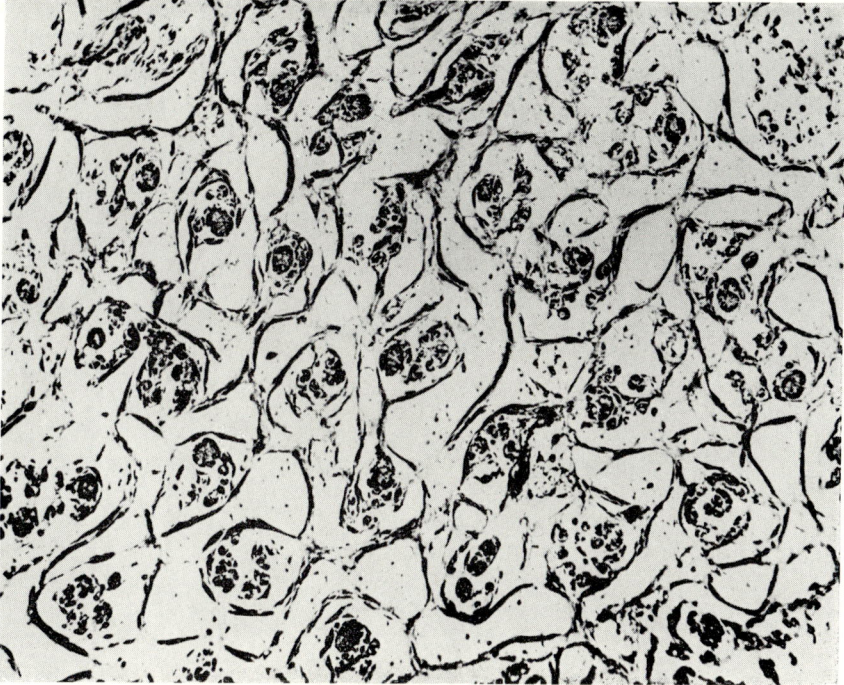

FIG. 3

Photomicrograph of section through the plexus, cut perpendicular to the bundles
of retinular cell and eccentric cell axons. Hematoxylin and eosin stain. Micrograph prepared by W. H. Miller.

ommatidia. The section was fixed in osmium and stained with hematoxylin
and eosin and, since this stain is not specific for neural tissue, shows many
non-neural structures in addition to the lateral plexus and the axons of the
retinular and eccentric cells.

Samuel's silver stain was used to prepare the section shown in Fig. 4 and
the dark linear structures in it are all branches of the plexus. Note that in some
cases (one of which is indicated by the arrow) the branches do not seem to go
directly from one bundle of axons to the next nearest bundle, but instead loop
around neighboring bundles and go to more distant ones. A section through
a higher or lower plane, however, may show direct connections between next
nearest neighbors where none exist in this section.

It has not yet been possible to determine the origin, course, and termination
of individual fibers in the plexus. This much is known, however: both the
retinular cell axons and the eccentric cell axons give rise to the small fibers
that form, and run laterally in, the bundles of the plexus. These fibers end in
clumps of neuropile which appear to be located mainly around the axons of

the eccentric cells. In addition to the relatively long lateral fibers, the eccentric cell axons give rise to short branches which extend some distance into the immediately surrounding neuropile where they appear to make intimate synaptic contact with the terminations of the plexus fibers. For a detailed study of the microanatomy of the plexus see Miller (1966).

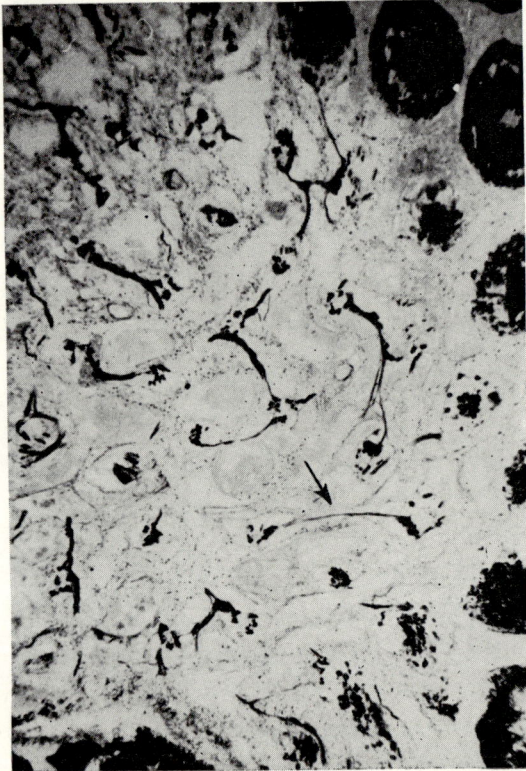

FIG. 4

Photomicrograph of section through the plexus at a somewhat higher magnification than Fig. 3. Samuel's silver stain. Micrograph prepared by W. H. Miller.

THE FUNCTIONAL PROPERTIES OF SINGLE OMMATIDIA

The photochemical and electrophysiological properties of an ommatidium in the compound eye of *Limulus* are summarized in a much oversimplified and highly schematic way in the drawing shown in Fig. 5.

Light enters the ommatidium through the cornea (not shown), passes through the crystalline cone, *CC*, and is at least partly absorbed by photopigment located in the rhabdomeres, *Rh*, of the retinular cells, *R*. The photo-pigment has been isolated and identified by Hubbard and Wald (1960): it is a retinene$_1$ rhodopsin, the absorption spectrum of which adequately accounts for the action spectrum of the ommatidium that was determined by measurements of the activity of single optic nerve fibers by Graham and Hartline

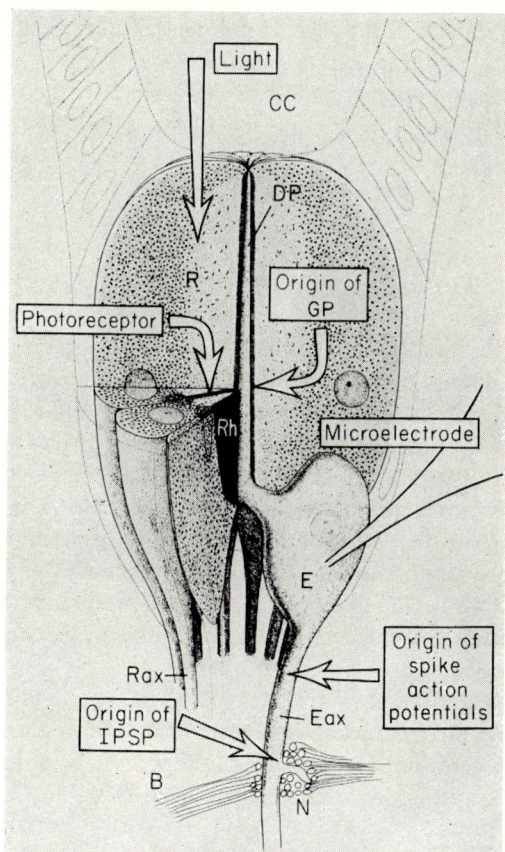

FIG. 5

Schema of structure and function of an ommatidium in the compound eye of *Limulus*.

(1935). The photochemical action leads to conductance changes and an accompanying depolarization of the eccentric cell, commonly referred to as the "generator potential", *GP*. For studies on these conductance changes see Tomita (1958), Fuortes (1959), Rushton (1959), and Purple (1964). The mechanism and exact locus of the conductance changes have not yet been determined; the label in Fig. 5, "Origin of *GP*", merely indicates a *possible* locus. For recent studies on the electrical connections between cells in the ommatidium see Tomita, Kikuchi, and Tanaka (1960); Purple (1964); Behrens and Wulff (1965); and Smith, Baumann, and Fuortes (1965).

The magnitude of the generator potential increases approximately linearly with the logarithm of the intensity of illumination (Hartline, Wagner, and MacNichol, 1952; MacNichol, 1956; Fuortes, 1959). (See Pinter, 1966, for a study on the dynamics of the generator potential.) Nerve impulses originate in the axon of the eccentric cell just below the cell body, and are conducted along the axon to the optic ganglion in the brain.* In the steady state, the frequency of discharge of nerve impulses is proportional to the amplitude of the generator potential.

Illumination of neighboring ommatidia—or antidromic electrical stimulation of the axons that arise from them—produces an inhibitory post-synaptic potential, *IPSP*, by way of influences transmitted across the lateral branches of the plexus to the neuropile (see Tomita, Kikuchi, and Tanaka, 1960; Hartline, Ratliff, and Miller, 1961; Ratliff, Hartline, and Miller, 1963; Purple, 1964). This inhibitory potential is in the hyperpolarizing direction and decreases the frequency of firing in the axon of the eccentric cell by an amount which, in the steady state, is proportional to the increase in frequency of discharge of impulses (or antidromic volleys) in the neighboring units. (The magnitude of the inhibitory post-synaptic potential also depends upon the number of neighboring elements activated and upon their distance from the ommatidium under observation.) In addition, each nerve impulse discharged by an eccentric cell is followed by an inhibitory potential in the discharging cell itself (see Stevens, 1964; Purple, 1964). Because of its similarity to the above-mentioned lateral inhibition, this phenomenon has been called "self-inhibition".

In brief, the photoexcitatory mechanism and the lateral and self-inhibitory mechanisms exert their opposing influences at or near a common point: the site of impulse generation. The net level of the membrane potential at this site determines the frequency of impulses (Tomita, 1958; Fuortes, 1960; Purple, 1964).

* Evidence has been obtained from time to time which suggests that the retinular cell axons may also conduct impulses. For example, some unpublished experiments by Gasser and Miller (personal communication, 1955) revealed two discrete components in the compound action potential elicited by electrical stimulation of the optic nerve. The latency of the large initial component indicated a conduction velocity (measured over 11·5 cm of nerve trunk) of 2·3 m/sec. The smaller later component indicated a conduction velocity of about 1·3 m/sec. Similar experiments by Stevens and Lange (personal communication, 1963) indicated conduction velocities of 1·9 m/sec for the large initial component and 0·7 m/sec for the small component (measured over 2·2 cm of nerve at 15°C). Presumably, the large component results from the activity of the eccentric cell axons and the small component from the activity of the retinular cell axons, but this is by no means firmly established. Furthermore, clear-cut evidence of unitary spike action potentials in the retinular cell axons, as obvious and unmistakable as in the eccentric cell, has not yet been obtained.

REVIEW OF THE QUANTITATIVE ACCOUNT
OF INHIBITORY INTERACTION

The interaction of two ommatidia may be expressed (to a first approximation) by a pair of simultaneous linear equations (Hartline and Ratliff, 1957):

$$r_1 = e_1 - K_{1,2}(r_2 - r_{1,2}^0),$$
$$r_2 = e_2 - K_{2,1}(r_1 - r_{2,1}^0). \tag{1}$$

The activity of each ommatidium is to be measured by the frequency of discharge of impulses in its eccentric cell axon. This response r is determined by the excitation e supplied by the external stimulus to the receptor, diminished by whatever inhibitory influence may be acting upon the receptor as a result of the activity of neighboring receptors. (The excitation of a particular receptor is to be measured by its response when it is illuminated by itself, thus lumping together in e the physical parameters of the stimulus and the characteristics of the photoexcitatory mechanism of the receptor.) The "threshold" frequency that must be exceeded before a receptor can exert any inhibition is represented by r^0. This and the inhibitory coefficient K are labelled in each equation to identify the direction of the action: $r_{1,2}^0$ is the frequency of receptor 2 at which it begins to inhibit receptor 1; $r_{2,1}^0$ is the reverse. In the same way $K_{1,2}$ is the coefficient of the inhibitory action of receptor 2 on receptor 1; $K_{2,1}$, the reverse.*

The inhibitory coefficients and thresholds must be labelled because they are not necessarily symmetrical. In one experiment on the eye of a large adult *Limulus*, for example, we found: $K_{1,2} = 0 \cdot 15$ and $K_{2,1} = 0 \cdot 06$; and $r_{1,2}^0 = 10 \cdot 9$ and $r_{2,1}^0 = 9 \cdot 9$. The two optic nerve fibers were not isolated by dissection; instead, rather large bundles containing several active fibers were placed on each of the two electrodes. An opaque wax (Cenco Tackiwax, loaded with lampblack) was melted and distributed evenly over the surface of the cornea. Small holes were then drilled through the wax so that illumination could reach just one ommatidium through each hole. The two ommatidia thus exposed were about 0·75 mm apart (center to center) and were separated by the width of at least one ommatidium. The fibers from the neighboring ommatidia on the electrodes served to monitor for possible scattered light. No impulses were recorded from them during the experiment and we were therefore fairly confident that there was little or no scatter to neighbors.

---

* Negative frequencies, of course, are not allowed; when the inhibitory term $K(r - r^0)$ is greater than the excitation e, the corresponding response r must be set equal to zero; when $(r - r^0)$ is negative, the inhibitory term must be dropped. Thus, the equations are not strictly linear; they are only piece-wise or segmentally linear. For discussions of the limitations of these linear approximations, see Hartline, Wagner, and Ratliff (1956), Purple (1964), and Lange (1965).

The inhibitory coefficient of 0·15, found in the above experiment, was unusually large and so was the degree of asymmetry. Although we cannot exclude with certainty the possibility that the much larger effect in one direction may have resulted from some light scattered to neighboring ommatidia that were not monitored, it seems likely—in view of the precautions taken—that the asymmetry was real. Indeed, only the degree of asymmetry was unusual—some asymmetry is the rule rather than the exception.

With more refined techniques of stimulation that make use of fiber optics (developed in our laboratory in collaboration with Robert B. Barlow, Jr.), we have frequently noticed that there are "holes" in the inhibitory field of a particular ommatidium. That is, an ommatidium may produce little or no effect on one of its near neighbors and yet a fairly strong effect on another neighbor at the same or even greater distance from it. When a compact group of several neighboring ommatidia are illuminated, however, the inhibitory effects that they produce do not seem to be so spotty. On the average, the effects of such a group clearly diminish with distance in a systematic way and seldom does one find, when using several ommatidia to produce the inhibition, that a nearby element is not affected by the group as a whole.*

When several ommatidia act simultaneously, the total inhibition they exert on a particular neighbor appears to be determined quantitatively by the separate inhibitory influences exerted by each, combined by simple addition. As a consequence, the responses of n ommatidia interacting with one another may be described (to a first approximation) by a set of n simultaneous equations, linear in the frequencies of the interacting units:

$$r_p = e_p - \sum_{j=1}^{n} K_{p,j}(r_j - r_{p,j}^0), \qquad (2)$$

where $p = 1, 2, \ldots, n$. (The restrictions on the equations mentioned above apply here also.) Self-inhibition is not considered here; that is, $j \neq p$.

---

* These kinds of effects may account, in part, for the quantitative discrepancies between the directly observed inhibitory coefficients reported by us and those calculated indirectly by Kirschfeld and Reichardt (1964), although their results and ours are qualitatively similar. In general, we select for our most extensive experiments those pairs that show a strong interaction and usually do not report results of numerous experiments in which little or no interaction is observed. The averages of our results, calculated by Kirschfeld and Reichardt, could not take this selection into account. Moreover, calculations of the inhibitory coefficients by Kirschfeld and Reichardt are based on the assumption that all of the ommatidia are interacting and that the influences are more or less homogeneous. If some ommatidia should fail to respond, or to inhibit near neighbors, this would tend to bias their estimates of the inhibitory coefficients in the opposite direction from the bias inherent in the averages of our selected results. In any event, the inhibitory coefficients between two ommatidia are small (we have never observed an inhibitory coefficient as large as 0·2; generally they are smaller than 0·1, even for near neighbors), and frequently no inhibition by one element on a near neighbor can be observed at all.

The strength of the inhibitory influence exerted by any one ommatidium on its neighbors diminishes markedly with distance; in terms of the above equations, the inhibitory coefficients $K_{p,j}$ decrease and the thresholds of inhibition $r^0_{p,j}$ increase. The distance effects are therefore implicit in the present form of the equations and no additional terms for distance appear to be required, at least not in the steady state.

Some preliminary experiments on the transient, dynamic phases of the inhibitory interaction have been described elsewhere (Hartline, Ratliff, and Miller, 1961; Ratliff, Hartline, and Miller, 1963; Ratliff, Hartline, and Lange, 1964). On the basis of these experiments, one of which is illustrated in Fig. 6, the steady-state equations (2) above were modified to include the temporal properties of the system as follows:

$$r_p(t) = e_p(t) - \sum_{j=1}^{n} K_{p,j} \left[r_j(t - T_{p,j}) - r^0_{p,j} \right]. \tag{3}$$

In these equations the response r_p of a particular ommatidium at any time t is determined by the level of excitation e_p of the ommatidium at that same time, diminished by the summated inhibitory influences exerted on it by the other ommatidia j. These influences are the ones initiated by the elements j at some earlier time $t - T_{p,j}$, where $T_{p,j}$ is the time lag of the action of any ommatidium j on the ommatidium p. This simple modification gives qualitatively correct results in most cases but is obviously only a rough first approximation.

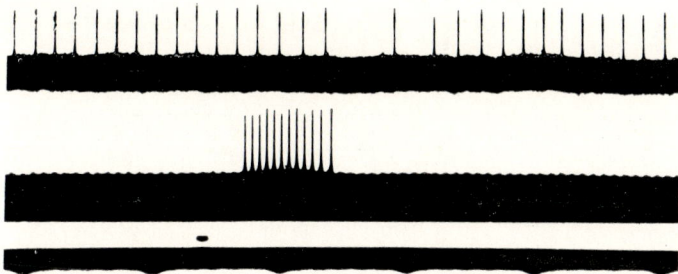

FIG. 6

Transient inhibition of the discharge from a steadily illuminated ommatidium (upper trace) by a burst of impulses discharged from a neighboring ommatidium (bottom trace) in response to a 0·01 sec flash of light (signaled by the black dot in the white band above the 1/5 sec time marks). From Hartline, Ratliff, and Miller, 1961.

AN ILLUSTRATIVE EXPERIMENT ON THE DYNAMICS OF EXCITATION AND INHIBITION

In the experiment summarized in Fig. 7, records of responses to step increments and decrements in illumination were obtained from two optic nerve fibers. These fibers arose from two ommatidia which were separated by the width of just one ommatidium. The test ommatidium, which we will call B, was illuminated by a very small spot (about 0·075 mm in diameter) confined to the facet of that ommatidium. The other ommatidium, which we will call A, was illuminated—along with at least two of its neighbors—by a larger spot of light, approximately 0·25 mm in diameter. The eye was partially covered with opaque wax and a razor blade was inserted a fraction of a millimeter into the cornea between the small group of ommatidia including A and the test ommatidium B so that light from one beam could not scatter into the region that was supposed to be illuminated by the other.

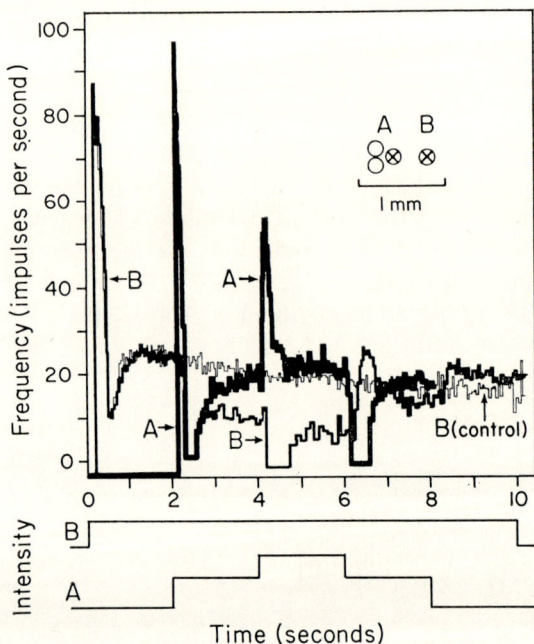

Fig. 7

Concurrent excitatory and inhibitory transients in the responses of neighboring ommatidia. Note that the intensity scale for B is displaced upward (both A and B begin and end at zero intensity).

The test ommatidium B was illuminated for 10 sec. Its response to this illumination alone is shown by the light line marked "B (control)" in Fig. 7. The one response of A shown in the figure resulted from illumination of it (and two of its adjacent neighbors) beginning 2 sec after the onset of another 10 sec period of illumination of B. The intensity of illumination on A remained at a steady level until the fourth second, at which time it was abruptly increased. The intensity then remained at this higher level until the sixth second, at which time it stepped down to the original level. The intensity of illumination then continued at this level until the eighth second, when the light was turned off.

Several expected excitatory transients appear in the record of the response of the fiber A, which served as the monitor of the response of the whole group of three adjacent ommatidia. First, there is an initial high frequency transient appearing about 75 msec after the onset of illumination. A pronounced silent period then follows, after which the frequency of response gradually climbs up and nearly reaches a steady level by the fourth second. The increment in illumination added at the fourth second yields a second excitatory transient (much smaller than the first, even though the intensity of illumination is greater), following which the response subsides to a steady frequency just slightly greater than that prior to the increment.

The response continues at this higher steady level until the intensity of the illumination is decreased to the original level at the sixth second. Following this decrease there is an abrupt and marked undershoot in the frequency of the response of A after which it returns to approximately the same steady level that it had during the initial period of illumination of the same intensity. When the illumination is turned off at the eighth second the discharge of impulses stops abruptly.

The frequency of response of the steadily illuminated test ommatidium B undergoes multiple changes concomitant with the changes observed in the activity of the small neighboring group monitored by A. First, corresponding to the initial transient in A following the onset of illumination on it and two of its adjacent neighbors at $t = 2 \cdot 0$ sec, there is a marked decrease in frequency of the response of the test ommatidium B. (Compare with "B control".) Following this large transient inhibitory effect, the frequency of B increases somewhat but still remains substantially below the corresponding control frequency.

With the second transient in A, produced by the increment in illumination at $t = 4 \cdot 0$ sec, there is an even larger transient inhibitory effect on the test ommatidium B. But it has a much shorter latency than the initial inhibitory transient, even though the excitatory transient is less pronounced than the first one. Following this second large inhibitory transient, the frequency of discharge of B increases as before, but still remains not only below the control level but also below its frequency during the first period of more or less steady inhibition because of the now higher frequency of response of A.

Following the sixth second, when the intensity of illumination on A and its two adjacent neighbors is abruptly decreased, producing a marked undershoot in the frequency of response of A, there is a marked increase in the frequency of discharge of the test ommatidium B, and it overshoots the control frequency by a substantial amount. As the frequency of A increases, returning to a high steady level, the frequency of B once again falls to a steady level considerably below the control frequency. Finally, when the light on *A* and its two adjacent neighbors is turned off, the frequency of *B* once again overshoots the control frequency and remains substantially above it until near the end of the tenth second, at which time the two no longer differ significantly.

The above experiment illustrates most of the major features of the dynamics of the inhibitory interaction. But the experiment is much too complex, and the effects of too many variables confounded, to permit the precise analyses required for a further more exact development of our quantitative formulation. Nevertheless, one can see in this illustrative experiment the direction that a more analytic approach must take and the nature of the modifications of the theory that will be required.

In general, the inhibitory effects are a slightly delayed and much reduced "mirror image" of the excitatory effects that produce them—as predicted by the simple modification of our steady-state equations (to include a constant time delay) that is represented in equations (3) above. In detail, however, these equations are not in accord with the observed phenomena.

First of all, the time delays are not constant. Indeed, the inhibitory effect produced by the large initial excitatory transient (at $t = 2 \cdot 0$) takes longer to develop than does the effect produced by the smaller excitatory transient resulting from the increment in illumination (at $t = 4 \cdot 0$). Second, the inhibitory transients are not simple mirror images of the excitatory transients. There is a marked overshoot, well above the control frequency, in the responses of the test ommatidium—not only following a similar undershoot in the response of the neighboring ommatidia exerting the inhibition (at $t = 6 \cdot 0$), but also following cessation of their response (at $t = 8 \cdot 0$). In addition, the magnitude of the inhibitory effect produced by the second smaller transient (at $t = 4 \cdot 0$) is larger than that produced by the initial large transient (at $t = 2 \cdot 0$). Let us now consider these problems in some detail.

FACILITATION OF THE INHIBITION

We have shown, in experiments not to be reported in detail here, that the time at which a single transient inhibitory influence is exerted on a test ommatidium—once the response of that ommatidium has reached a steady state—has no significant effect on the latency and magnitude of the inhibition.* For example, a burst of impulses discharged by neighboring ommatidia two sec after the beginning of the discharge of impulses from the test ommatidium

---

* This differs from the recurrent inhibition of motoneurones in the spinal cord of the cat. Granit and Rutledge (1960) found that the effects of antidromic volleys of constant frequency and duration are stronger the later they occur with respect to the maintained stretch reflex discharge.

produces essentially the same inhibitory effect on the test ommatidium as does an identical burst at the fourth second (each effect measured independently during a different period of illumination). Therefore, the difference between the latent periods and between the magnitudes of the transient inhibitory effects produced by the excitatory transients at $t = 2\cdot0$ and $t = 4\cdot0$ in the experiment illustrated in Fig. 7 cannot be attributed to the times at which the transients occur with respect to the onset of illumination on, or discharge of impulses from, the test ommatidium. Instead, such differences appear to result from *facilitation* of the second inhibitory transient—either by the concurrent steady suprathreshold inhibition produced by the ongoing steady discharge on which the second excitatory transient is superimposed, or by concurrent subthreshold inhibitory influences that are produced by, and persist for a time after, the initial excitatory transient, or both.

The difference between the inhibitory transients in the experiment illustrated in Fig. 7 can be seen more clearly in the actual film records of the oscilloscope traces obtained in a later part of this same experiment (Fig. 8). The numbers on the records are the times of occurrence of the impulses, to the nearest millisecond, which were flashed on the film by an automatic counting and gating device as the record was taken. (For details of the method of recording see Eisenberg and Ratliff, 1960.) The upper record shows the inhibitory effects produced by the initial excitatory transient at $t = 2\cdot0$. The lower record shows the inhibitory effects produced by the excitatory transient at $t = 4\cdot0$. (The numbers printed on the records show only fractions of seconds; the millisecond counters were reset to zero at the end of each second.)

Note that the first inhibitory transient (upper trace in upper record), when there was no ongoing inhibition, took longer to appear than did the second inhibitory transient (upper trace in lower record), when the test ommatidium was already subjected to some inhibition. Also, the first inhibitory transient appears to be smaller than the second. The experiment is not definitive, however: the two excitatory transients that produce the two different inhibitory transients are themselves dissimilar, and the steady frequencies of discharge from the test ommatidium preceding the two transients are not comparable.

The following experiment, some results of which are illustrated in Fig. 9, was designed to remedy these defects. The inhibitory transient was produced by a single compact burst of impulses from a group of about 6 neighboring ommatidia located approximately $0\cdot75$ mm from the test ommatidium. (The discharge of only one ommatidium in the center of the group was recorded.) First, the transient inhibitory effect exerted on the steady discharge of the test ommatidium by this burst of activity alone was determined (left half of the figure). The plot of the burst and the plot of the concomitant transient inhibitory effect are each the average of 5 experimental runs. The nearly straight line across the graph is a smoothed average of 11 control runs (no inhibition). For details of our method of computation of average frequencies see Schoenfeld (1964). Except during the inhibitory transient and the short post-inhibitory rebound, the control and experimental frequencies of the test ommatidium coincide. The lower graph shows the accumulating deficit of

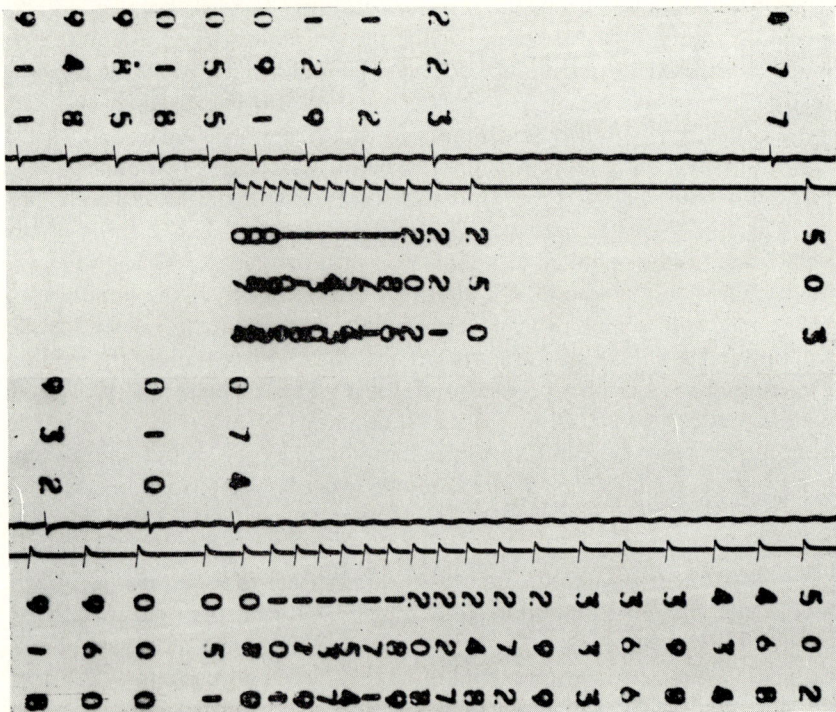

FIG. 8

Initial inhibitory transients (upper record) and subsequent inhibitory transient superimposed on steady inhibition (lower record). Millisecond counters reset to zero at $t = 2 \cdot 0$ sec in upper record and at $t = 4 \cdot 0$ sec in lower record. Compare with Fig. 7.

impulses over the same period of time, in the discharge of the test ommatidium, relative to the discharge immediately preceding the inhibition.

In the second part of the experiment (right half of the figure) the conditions were the same except that a low level of ongoing "background" inhibition was provided by steady low intensity illumination of another nearby group of about a half-dozen ommatidia. This group was also located about 0·75 mm from the test ommatidium, but on the side opposite the group that exerted the transient inhibition and therefore about 1·5 mm from it.

The steady inhibition was weak; the average frequency of the 5 experimental runs prior to and following the inhibitory transient and post-inhibitory rebound was only slightly less than the smoothed average of the 11 control runs. Nevertheless, this low level of background inhibition significantly increased the inhibitory transient and post-inhibitory rebound resulting from the short high frequency burst of impulses. The increase in magnitude of the effect is shown more clearly in the lower right hand graph where the deficit in number of impulses discharged in the test ommatidium (relative to the discharge just prior to the onset of inhibition) is plotted. Note, however, that the greater post-inhibitory rebound almost exactly compensates for the greater inhibitory effect, and thus there is no significant difference in the total deficit of impulses under the two different conditions from about $t = 6·8$ sec onwards. Differences in latency—if any—are slight. Unfortunately, such differences have to be rather large in order not to be obscured by "noise" on the baseline. Also, the accuracy of detection of the time of changes in average frequency is limited by the size of the intervals between impulses—about 40 msec at the critical point in this experiment.

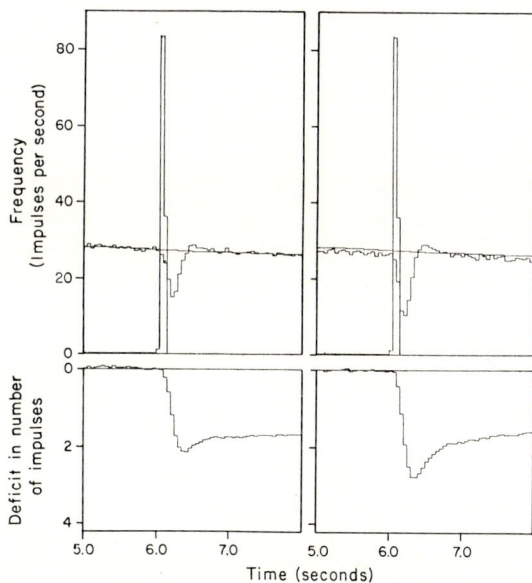

FIG. 9

Comparison of the transient inhibitory influences produced by a compact burst of impulses acting alone (left half of figure) and superimposed on a steady background of weak inhibition (right half of figure).

Facilitation of inhibition resulting from previous inhibition is illustrated in Figs. 10 and 11. The test ommatidium was illuminated, throughout the period shown, with a small spot of light of constant intensity confined to the facet of that ommatidium. To produce the inhibitory effects a neighboring ommatidium, at a distance of about 0·5 mm from the test ommatidium, was illuminated with short flashes of light. Presumably only one neighbor was

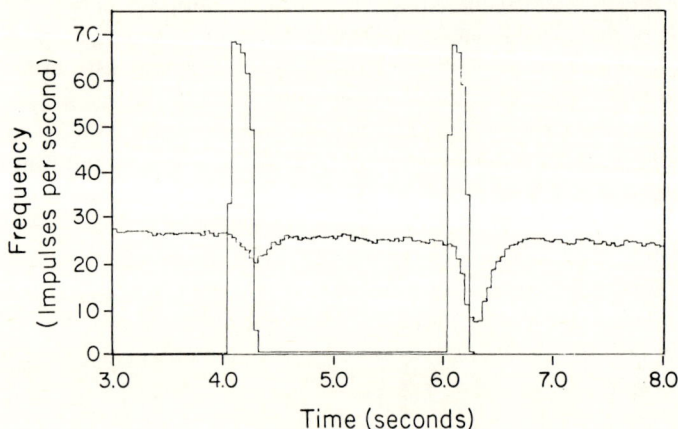

FIG. 10

Facilitation of inhibition.

illuminated, but no special precautions (such as masking with opaque wax) were taken to ensure that there was no light scatter from the focused spot. Prior to each experimental run this ommatidium was partially light-adapted so that the short flashes would generate short compact bursts of impulses with little or no after discharge. The intensities of the two flashes were the same. In order to generate nearly equal bursts of impulses it was therefore necessary to make the second flash longer than the first. In the experiment illustrated, the duration of the first flash was 0·01 sec, the duration of the second flash was 0·1 sec. (The curves plotted are the averages of 5 experimental runs.)

When the second burst of impulses followed soon after the first, the inhibitory effect that it produced was very much enhanced. The effect was greater the closer the second burst was to the first. With separations of about 4 or 5 sec between the two bursts (not illustrated here), there was no facilitation of the second inhibitory effect by the first. Evidently, some residual subthreshold inhibitory influence follows the first burst, takes several seconds to decay, and—while it still persists—adds to the inhibitory influence generated by the second burst. Even though these residual influences alone produce no observable effect on the discharge of impulses from the test ommatidium, they are, nevertheless, still present as is evidenced by the facilitation of the inhibition produced by the second burst.

It might be objected that the greater effect of the second burst is simply the result of the greater amount of light in the longer second flash that is required to produce a discharge approximately equal to that in the first burst.

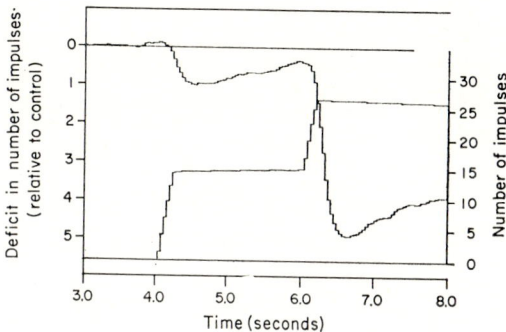

FIG. 11

Facilitation of inhibition. Same experiment as illustrated in Fig. 10. Deficit in number of impulses discharged from test ommatidium, relative to control, shown on left-hand ordinate. Number of impulses discharged from the neighboring ommatidium that produced the inhibitory effect is shown on the right-hand ordinate.

This is not the case, however. Indeed, we have observed that a weaker response, generated by the second of two flashes of *equal* duration and intensity, often produces an effect as great as or greater than that produced by the first flash. Furthermore, as we shall show in the subsequent paper, a similar facilitation of inhibition occurs when two identical bursts of antidromic activity are generated by electrical stimulation of the optic nerve.*

THE EFFECTS OF DISTANCE ON THE INHIBITORY TRANSIENT

The frequencies of impulses discharged from three widely separated ommatidia are illustrated in Fig. 12. The relative locations of the corneal facets of the three ommatidia, each indicated by a circle and cross, are shown at the right of the graph. The steady illumination on the two test ommatidia *B* and *C* was confined to their facets, and the intensities of the two spots were adjusted

* One preliminary experiment that we have carried out indicates that the facilitation of inhibition by residual subthreshold influences may not occur if the two inhibitory influences are produced by illuminating two separate groups of ommatidia. Further experiments are required, however, to elucidate this point.

C.E.—2E

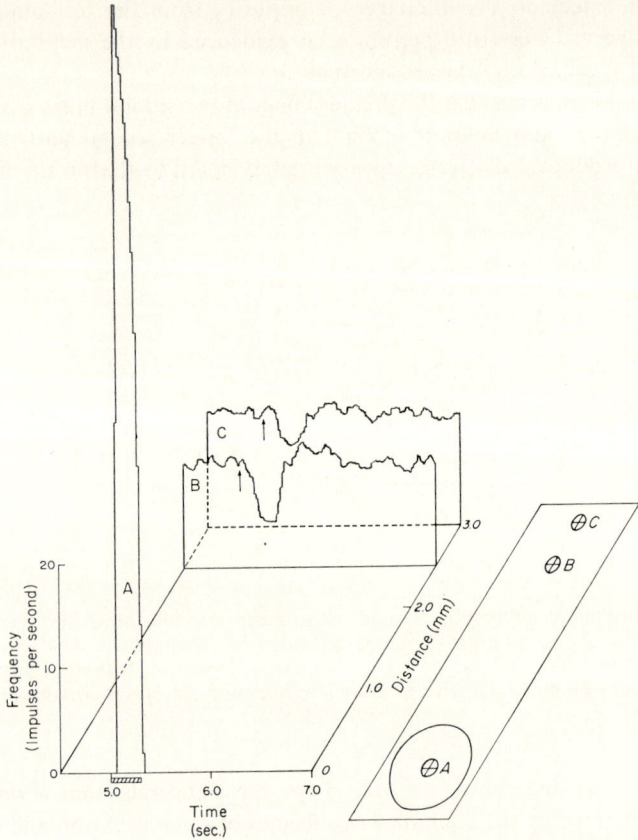

FIG. 12

The dependence of a transient inhibitory effect on distance.

so that the frequency of discharge of impulses from both was approximately the same. Ommatidium *A*, along with a group of its immediate neighbors, was illuminated by a short (0·3 sec) flash of light. The approximate dimensions of the spot of light are indicated by the large circle enclosing the ommatidium *A*.

To avoid possible complications due to interaction between *B* and *C*, the transient inhibitory effect of *A* on each was measured separately. The burst of impulses from *A* itself was so short that there was little or no possibility that the transients produced in the responses of *B* and *C* had any effect back on it.

The results of this experiment are more or less as would be expected from our previous experiments on the effects of distance on the steady-state inhibition. That is, the greater the distance the smaller are the inhibitory transient and the post-inhibitory rebound. Also, the greater the distance the longer the latency of the inhibitory transient. To make this latter point clearer in this three-dimensional figure, the time of occurrence of the first impulse in *A* is indicated by the small arrows in the planes of the graphs of the frequency of discharge of impulses from the test ommatidia *B* and *C*. The graphs shown are averages of 6 experimental runs.

Results of a similar experiment, on a different preparation, are illustrated

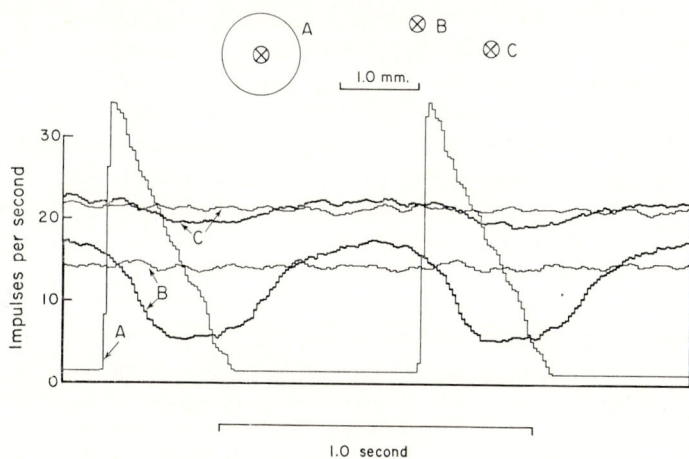

FIG. 13

The dependence of periodic transient inhibitory effects on distance.

in Fig. 13. In this experiment, however, the excitatory transients were produced by a succession of 0·2 sec flashes on *A*, repeated at 1·0 sec intervals within the 10 sec periods of steady illumination on *B* and *C*. The two full cycles shown are the average of 15 similar periods (the last six cycles in each of five experimental runs). The controls for *B* and *C* (no inhibition) are represented by the thin nearly straight lines across the graph. In general, the results are the same as those obtained in the single flash experiment illustrated in Fig. 12. The nearer the ommatidium inhibited, the greater is the amplitude of the effect and the shorter the latency. The results of this experiment appear simple, but in fact are difficult to interpret. The falling phase of the overshoot and the onset of the inhibition overlap in such a way that the inhibitory effect on *B* appears to begin before the occurrence of the impulses in *A* that cause it.

Ideally, if one could measure the spatial and temporal properties of the inhibitory effects produced by a single impulse and determine how these effects combine with those produced by a second impulse, then one could predict the effects produced by any temporal pattern of impulses. To achieve this ideal would require far more sensitive techniques than those we now have. The best we can do—at the moment—is to approximate this ideal by generating short compact bursts of impulses which produce easily measurable effects.

Using this technique we have performed a number of three-fiber experiments, similar to the one illustrated in Fig. 12, but as yet have insufficient data on which to base a general law relating the dynamics of the inhibition and distance on the retina. The amplitude and extent of the inhibitory influence varies somewhat from place to place in the same eye (see our remarks above on the pseudopupil) and from one preparation to another. For these reasons it is not permissible to combine the data obtained from these several experiments. Unfortunately, the technique outlined above does not permit one to map out the amplitude and extent of the inhibitory influence that a particular ommatidium exerts on all, or on a representative large sample, of its neighbors. The small sample that is obtained is selected more or less by chance in the process of dissection, and the necessary large number of control and experimental measurements do not allow sufficient time to vary the frequency of discharge of the ommatidia in question over a large range, or to dissect out additional fibers coming from other locations. The new technique using fiber optics, that we mentioned above, promises to solve some of these problems and to enable us to map more accurately and in more detail the inhibitory fields around single ommatidia.

VARIATIONS IN THE LATENT PERIOD OF THE INHIBITION

Early in the course of these three-fiber experiments we thought that it might be possible to measure the velocity of the conduction of the lateral inhibitory influences even though no propagated activity can be observed, as yet, in the fibers of the plexus. The plan was to measure the differences between the times of onset of inhibition exerted on two test ommatidia by a third ommatidium—or group of ommatidia. There was some hope that this adaptation of Helmholtz's classic technique for measuring the velocity of conduction in a nerve-muscle preparation might yield an estimate of the conduction time over the plexus between the two test ommatidia.

The hopes we had were slight, for the accuracy of pin-pointing changes in the frequency of discharge of discrete impulses is limited by the size of the intervals between impulses. Furthermore, the slight hopes we did have were short-lived. The *apparent* conduction times indicated by this method were of the order of a *millimeter* per second and seemed to depend more strongly on the frequency of discharge of impulses from the ommatidium (or group of ommatidia) exerting the inhibition than on the distance to, or between, the test receptors inhibited.

Details of one such experiment are illustrated in Fig. 14. The discharge of impulses was recorded from three ommatidia located on a nearly straight line, as indicated in the diagram inset in the figure. Ommatidia B and C—the test ommatidia—were steadily illuminated for 10 sec by small spots of light of constant intensity. Ommatidium A, along with a group of its neighbors, was illuminated by a large spot of light, centered on A, as indicated in the inset. This large spot of light was turned on for 0·05 sec at $t = 6·0$ (indicated by the small black rectangle on the abscissa) to produce a short compact burst of activity. As in the three-fiber experiment described above, the transient inhibitory effects on the two test ommatidia B and C were determined separately in order to avoid possible complications resulting from interaction between them.

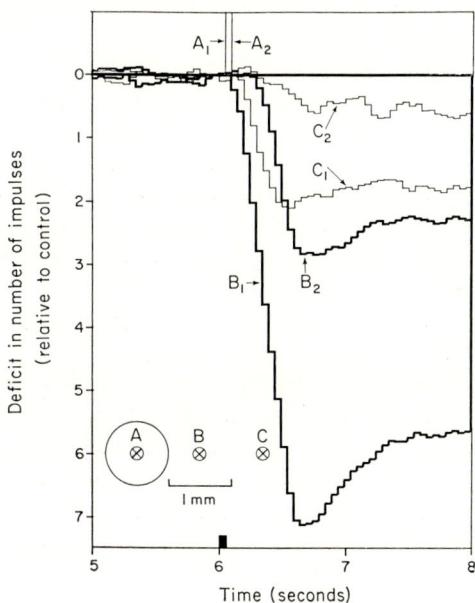

FIG. 14

Variations in the latent periods of transient inhibitory effects.

Each curve in the figure (an average of four comparable runs) is the integral of the difference between the frequencies of impulses in control and experimental runs following $t = 6·0$, the time at which A and its near neighbors were illuminated by a short flash of the large spot of light. The integral in each case is relative to the discharge of impulses in the one second period preceding the flash. Only small portions of the integrals of the bursts of impulses discharged from A—sufficient to indicate the time of the first impulse in the burst—are shown. (There was a low frequency after-discharge of impulses from A which began at about $t = 6\cdot7$ sec—too late to affect either the magnitude or latent period of the initial transient in the inhibitory effect.)

Consider first the curves A_1, B_1, and C_1. They were obtained when the intensity of illumination of the flash was high, producing a burst of impulses in A with a short latency and high frequency. The expected inhibitory effects on B and C were observed: a large effect with a short latent period on B (curve B_1) and a much smaller effect with a longer latent period on the more distant ommatidium C (curve C_1).

On the basis of these observations alone one might be tempted to attribute the time delay between the appearance of the first impulse in A and the onset of the inhibitory effect on B (and the difference between this latent period and the latent period of the effect on C) to the distance that the inhibitory influence has to traverse in the lateral plexus. Undoubtedly, a finite amount of time *is* required for the inhibitory influence to be conducted from one ommatidium to another, but it should be very small and nearly constant, according to all generally accepted notions about nervous conduction. The second half of this experiment shows that this apparent conduction time is *not* constant, but instead varies with the frequency of discharge of impulses from the group A that is exerting the inhibition on B and C.

Consider now the curves A_2, B_2, and C_2. These data were obtained in the same way as in the first half of the experiment. The only change was that the intensity of the flash on A was reduced. The result of this lower intensity was to produce a burst of impulses in A with a longer latency and a lower frequency than before.

As expected, the less vigorous discharge from A yielded a smaller inhibitory effect on the test ommatidia B and C. Also, because of the longer latent period in the response of A, one would expect to find all three curves A_2, B_2, and C_2 shifted to the right—which they are. But the shift of B_2 and C_2 is much greater than can be accounted for on the basis of the increased latency of response of A. Indeed, the difference between the times of the onset of inhibition on ommatidium B (curves B_1 and B_2) is about three times larger than the difference between the times of appearance of the first impulse in A (curves A_1 and A_2). Unfortunately, the weaker effect on C is so small (curve C_2) that no definite conclusions can be drawn from it. The increased delay, however, does appear to be much larger than could be accounted for on the basis of the longer latent period in the response of A.

The increases in the apparent conduction time of the inhibitory effect from A to B and C are not merely the result of the smaller inhibitory effect produced by the less vigorous burst of activity from A. In fact, there is a shorter delay to the weak effect on C (curves A_1 and C_1) than to the slightly stronger effect on B (curves A_2 and B_2). Judging by these latter two cases alone, it would appear that the longer the distance the shorter is the time delay. Evidently such anomalous results cannot be explained in terms of a constant velocity of conduction over the distance traversed by the inhibitory influence. Instead, the apparent transmission time *seems* to depend as much or more on the activity of the ommatidia exerting the inhibition. Further experiments with more flexible and more precise control over the excitatory transients than that afforded by short flashes of light are required, however, to determine whether this tentative interpretation is correct.

SUMMARY

Some of the gross features of the dynamics of the inhibitory interaction in the compound eye of *Limulus* are implicit in our earlier analysis of the steady-state interaction: the inhibitory effects are "mirror images"—more or less—of the excitatory effects that produce them and they diminish with distance. Furthermore, as expected, some time elapses between any excitatory transient and the inhibitory transients that result from it; in general, the greater the distance between the interacting ommatidia, the greater are the time delays.

Three major phenomena that appear in the dynamics of the inhibitory interaction, however, are not adequately accounted for by the mere addition of simple constant time delays to the steady-state equations. These include: (1) the facilitation of the inhibition by ongoing inhibition or by recent prior inhibition; (2) the overshoot or post-inhibitory rebound following a reduction in or cessation of inhibition; and (3) the apparent greater dependence of the latent period of the inhibition on the frequency of discharge of the ommatidia exerting the inhibition than upon the distance traversed by the inhibitory influence.

The problem we now face is to develop a comprehensive quantitative description of the inhibitory interaction which will not only account fully for these and other features of the dynamics but which will also reduce to the steady-state equations. In our subsequent paper we attempt such a formulation and subject it to a variety of tests.

REFERENCES

BEHRENS, M. E. and WULFF, V. J. 1965. Light-initiated responses of retinula and eccentric cells in the *Limulus* lateral eye. *J. Gen. Physiol.* **48**, 1081–93.

EISENBERG, L. and RATLIFF, F. 1960. Gating system for photographic printout of counts in neurophysiological research. *Review of Scientific Instruments*, **31**, 630–3.

FUORTES, M. G. F. 1959. Initiation of impulses in visual cells of *Limulus*. *J. Physiol.* **148**, 14–28.

FUORTES, M. G. F. 1960. Inhibition in *Limulus* eye, in *Inhibition of the Nervous System and γ-Aminobutyric Acid*. Pergamon Press, New York, 418–23.

GRAHAM, C. H. and HARTLINE, H. K. 1935. The response of single visual sense cells to lights of different wave length. *J. Gen. Physiol.* **18**, 917–31.

424   F. RATLIFF, H. K. HARTLINE, AND D. LANGE

GRANIT, R. and RUTLEDGE, L. T. 1960. Surplus excitation in reflex action of motoneurones as measured by recurrent inhibition. *J. Physiol.* **154**, 288–307.

HARTLINE, H. K. and RATLIFF, F. 1957. Inhibitory interaction of receptor units in the eye of *Limulus. J. Gen. Physiol.* **40**, 357–76.

HARTLINE, H. K., RATLIFF, F. and MILLER, W. H. 1961. Inhibitory interaction in the retina and its significance in vision, in *Nervous Inhibition*, E. Florey, ed. Pergamon Press, New York, 241–84.

HARTLINE, H. K., WAGNER, H. G. and MACNICHOL, E. F., Jr. 1952. The peripheral origin of nervous activity in the visual system. *Cold Spring Harbor Symposia on Quantitative Biology*, **17**, 125–41.

HARTLINE, H. K., WAGNER, H. G. and RATLIFF, F. 1956. Inhibition in the eye of *Limulus. J. Gen. Physiol.* **39**, 651–73.

HUBBARD, R. and WALD, G. 1960. Visual pigment of the horseshoe crab, *Limulus polyphemus. Nature* **186**, 212–5.

KIRSCHFELD, K. and REICHARDT, W. 1964. *Die Verarbeitung stationärer optischer Nachrichten im Komplexauge von* Limulus **2**, 43–61.

LANGE, D. 1965. Dynamics of inhibitory interaction in the eye of *Limulus*. Experimental and theoretical studies, Thesis, Rockefeller Institute.

MACNICHOL, E. F., Jr. 1956. Visual receptors as biological transducers. *Molecular Structure and Functional Activity of Nerve Cells*, Publication No. 1 of American Institute of Biological Sciences, 34–53.

MILLER, W. H. 1966. The anatomy of the neuropile in the compound eye of *Limulus*, in *Proceedings of the Second International Symposium on the Structure of the Eye* (held in Wiesbaden, August 1965) Pergamon Press 1966—in press.

PINTER, R. B. 1966. Sinusoidal and delta function responses of visual cells of the *Limulus* eye. *J. Gen. Physiol.* **49**, 565–93.

PURPLE, R. L. 1964. The integration of excitatory and inhibitory influences in the eccentric cell in the eye of *Limulus*. Thesis, Rockefeller Institute.

RATLIFF, F., HARTLINE, H. K. and LANGE, D. 1964. Studies on the dynamics of inhibitory interaction in the retina, in *Physiological Basis for Form Discrimination*, Symposium, Brown University, Providence, R.I.

RATLIFF, F., HARTLINE, H. K. and MILLER, W. H. 1963. Spatial and temporal aspects of retinal inhibitory interaction. *J. Opt. Soc. Amer.* **53**, 110–20.

RUSHTON, W. A. H. 1959. A theoretical treatment of Fuortes' observations upon eccentric cell activity in *Limulus. J. Physiol.* **148**, 29–38.

SCHOENFELD, R. L. 1964. The role of a digital computer as a biological instrument. *Ann. N.Y. Acad. Sci.* **115**, 915–42.

SMITH, T. G., BAUMANN, F. and FUORTES, M. G. F. 1965. Electrical connections between visual cells in the ommatidium of *Limulus. Science* **147**, 1446–7.

STEVENS, C. F. 1964. A quantitative theory of neural interactions: theoretical and experimental investigations, Thesis, Rockefeller Institute.

TOMITA, T. 1957. Peripheral mechanisms of nervous activity in lateral eye of horseshoe crab. *J. Neurophysiol.* **20**, 245–54.

TOMITA, T. 1958. Mechanism of lateral inhibition in the eye of *Limulus. J. Neurophysiol.* **21**, 419–29.

TOMITA, T., KIKUCHI, R. and TANAKA, I. 1960. Excitation and inhibition in lateral eye of horseshoe crab. *Electrical Activity of Single Cells*, Igakushion, Hongo, Tokyo, 11–23.

WATERMAN, T. H. 1954. Directional sensitivity of single ommatidia in the compound eye of *Limulus. Proc. Nat. Acad. Sci.* **40**, 252–7.

THE DYNAMICS OF LATERAL INHIBITION
IN THE COMPOUND EYE OF *LIMULUS.* II*

D. Lange, H. K. Hartline and F. Ratliff

The Rockefeller University, New York

The inhibitory effects produced by illumination of the lateral eye of *Limulus* have a very complex form as a function of time. Part of this complexity is inherent in the inhibitory process, but much of it stems from the complex excitatory transients in the responses of the photoreceptors themselves—as was evidenced by the results of the several experiments reported by Ratliff, Hartline and Lange (1966). To achieve better control over the activity of the optic nerve and the resulting inhibitory effects we have resorted to an electrical technique for stimulating the optic nerve proximal to the eye to provide trains of antidromic volleys. In this paper we will discuss the results of some experiments in which this technique is utilized, and then propose a quantitative mathematical model that accounts for many features of the experimental results.

ANTIDROMIC INHIBITION

Tomita (1958) showed that inhibition in the *Limulus* eye can be produced by antidromic volleys in the optic nerve. In our experiments, as in his, a single eccentric cell fiber was isolated by dissection and stimulated by light confined to the facet of the ommatidium from which it arose (the test ommatidium or test unit). Inhibition was produced by stimulating the rest of the optic nerve with brief electric shocks to generate volleys of antidromic impulses (see Fig. 1). The advantage of the antidromic technique is that it allows very precise control of the excitation of the optic nerve and enables one to avoid effects of the complex excitatory transients associated with light stimulation of the receptors. This element of control provided by the antidromic stimulation is valuable for a quantitative study of input–output relations.

* Substantial portions of this paper are based on a dissertation submitted by D. Lange to the faculty of the Rockefeller University in partial fulfilment of the requirements for the degree of Doctor of Philosophy.

This investigation was supported by a research grant (NB–00864) from the National Institute of Neurological Diseases and Blindness, U.S. Public Health Service, and by an Equipment Loan Contract Nonr. [1442(00)] with the U.S. Office of Naval Research.

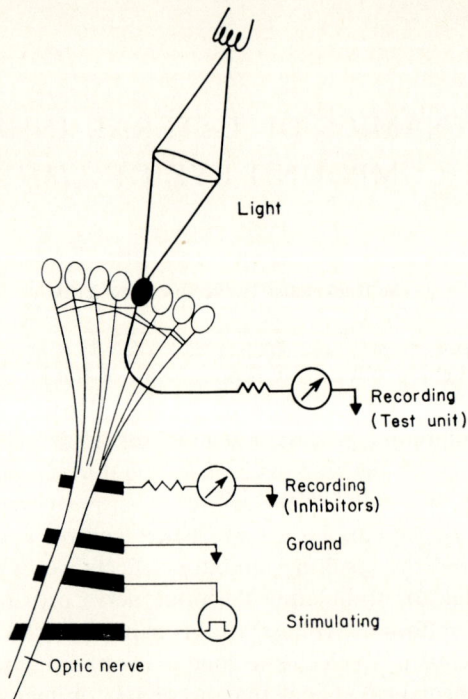

FIG. 1

Diagrammatic representation of the experimental set-up for producing antidromic inhibition. The eccentric cell fiber from the test unit (black) is isolated from the rest of the optic nerve. The remaining portion of the nerve is stimulated to produce the inhibition. Inhibition is measured by measuring changes in impulse frequency in the test fiber. (Figure modified from Purple, 1964.)

The inhibition produced by antidromic stimulation, although admittedly unphysiological, had many properties similar to that produced normally by light. Thus, steady-state inhibition increased with the pulse frequency of the antidromic stimulus, following a piecewise linear relationship as in light-induced inhibition. Antidromic inhibition also exhibited many of the same temporal properties as that produced by light: there was a substantial latent period before the inhibition appeared, an initial transient—or undershoot—preceding the steady state, and an overshoot above the control frequency, for a time, upon cessation of the antidromic impulses. It is important to note that some of these transients—so very prominent in the mirroring of excitatory transients—appear at the onset and cessation of *steady* antidromic stimulation. These transients (undershoots and overshoots) must therefore, in part at least, be ascribed to the inhibitory system itself.

The experimental methods employed in this work are similar to those used by Tomita (1958) and have been described fully elsewhere (Lange, 1965). The electronic equipment has also been described (Schoenfeld, 1964; Milkman and Schoenfeld, 1966) as has our use of computer techniques (Lange, Hartline and Ratliff, 1966).

In a typical experiment the light focused on the test ommatidium (test unit in Fig. 1) was allowed to shine steadily for 10–15 sec. Within 3 or 4 sec after the onset of this illumination the frequency of impulses generated by the receptor reached a more or less steady value. At this time stimulus pulses were delivered to a large bundle of optic nerve fibers that did not include the fiber from the test ommatidium. The changes in impulse frequency in the test unit fiber constituted the measure of inhibition. "Experimental" runs of this sort interspersed with "controls" (no antidromic stimulation) were repeated at intervals of 2–4 min.

There is some difficulty, of course, in assigning a significant pulse frequency to a non-uniform train of pulses. We have defined the "instantaneous frequency" at any time as the reciprocal of the interspike interval coincident with that time. We have used this measure of frequency throughout this paper.

STEADY-STATE EXPERIMENTS

Although the main reason for using antidromic inhibition was the ease of control of its temporal properties, it was necessary to collect some steady-state data as well. There were two reasons for this. First, we had to determine whether the steady-state equations were applicable in this artificial situation. Second, steady-state data were required to calculate the parameters of the mathematical model.

We have taken as our measure of activity the difference in instantaneous frequency between an experimental and a control run. Inhibition is thus indicated by a negative ordinate in plots of frequency difference versus time (see Fig. 2).

As seen in Fig. 3A the firing frequency of the test ommatidium tends to reach a steady inhibited level in the second or third second of the antidromic stimulus. Once this steady state has been reached it is appropriate to apply the same analysis as previously applied to the steady-state light-induced inhibition. Figure 4 is a typical plot of inhibition as a function of antidromic pulse frequency. The deviations from linearity are discussed later in the section entitled "Comparison of experimental results and model calculations". In the linear approximation drawn, the slope of the line gives the inhibitory constant, K. The inhibitory constants in antidromic inhibition are characteristically much larger than those published previously (0·5–1 as opposed to 0·1). This is reasonable, considering the probable linear summation of effects from all inputs to a cell.

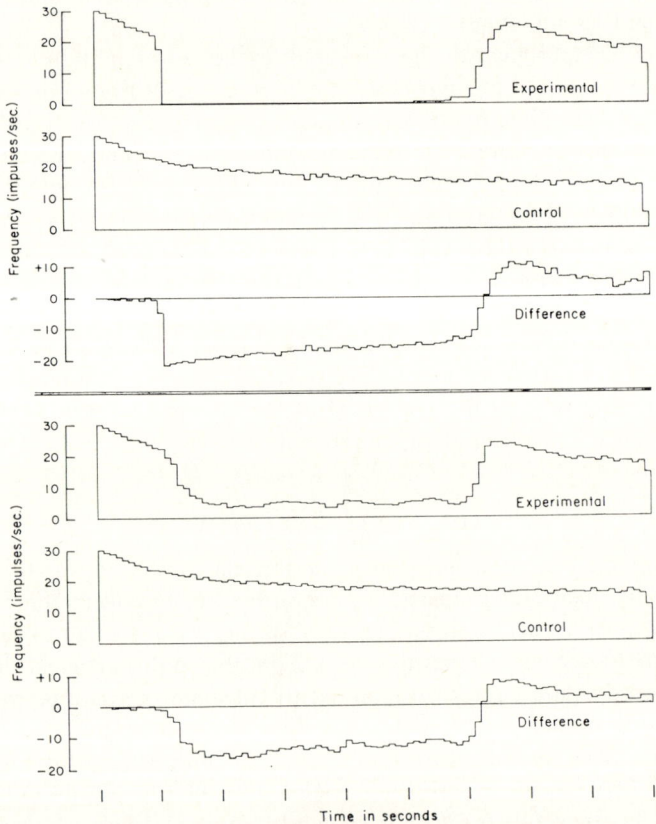

FIG. 2

Comparison of experimental runs with control runs by subtraction. The figure demonstrates the method by which the response curves of Fig. 3A were calculated. The first two experiments from that series are illustrated. The upper trace of each group is an average of four experimental runs. The middle trace is a similar average of four control runs in which no inhibitory stimuli were delivered. The lowest trace is the algebraic difference between the first and second traces. Notice that this procedure eliminates the downward drift of frequencies. In the upper experiment, however, where the experimental frequency reaches zero impulses per second, the drift cannot appear. The subtraction of the downward drifting control then leads to the misleading upward drift of the difference.

(Figure from Lange, Hartline and Ratliff, 1966.)

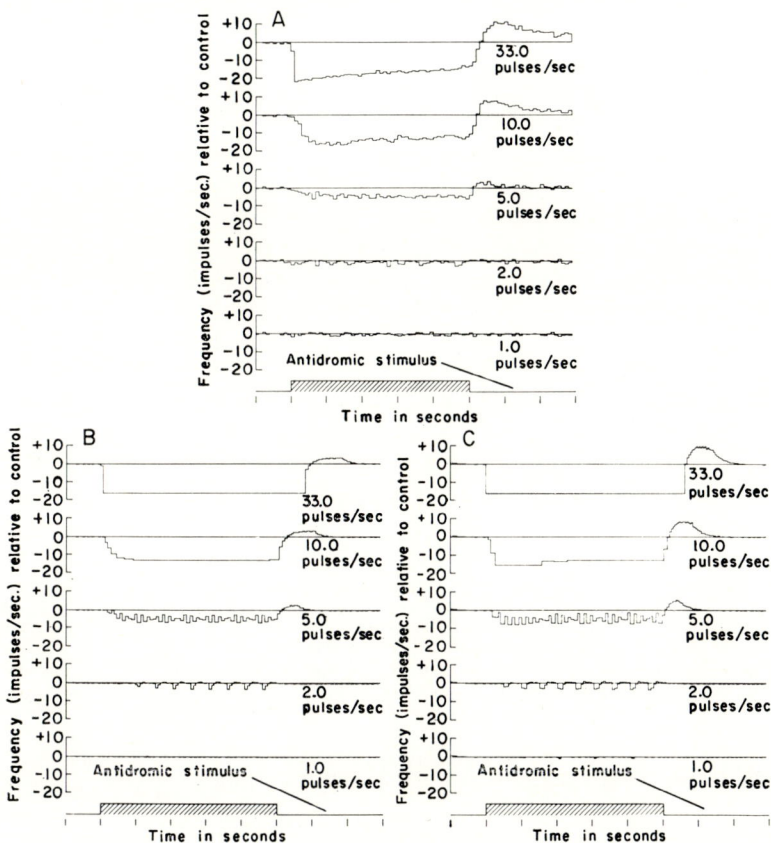

FIG. 3

Step function responses. Fig. 3A shows the response of an ommatidium in an actual experiment. The curves were obtained as described in the legend of Fig. 2. The numbers to the right of each trace are the pulse frequencies of the antidromic stimuli, the duration of which is designated by the hatched bar. The average control frequency was 18 impulses/sec. See text for detailed description of the dynamics. Figure 3B and C displays the results of calculations based on the theoretical "model" described later in the text. Figure 3B was produced by the model when a single time constant ($\tau_s = \tau_L = 0.67$) was used. Other constants were: $A_s = 4.125$; $A_L = 9.0$; and $C = 12$. Compare asymmetry of response, approach to steady state, apparent effects of single volleys at 2 impulses/sec and post-inhibitory rebound. Figure 3C was produced by the model when the time constants were allowed to differ ($\tau_s = 1.0$; $\tau_L = 0.5$). A_s and A_L were adjusted to keep steady-state inhibition constant ($A_s = 2.75$; $A_L = 12.0$). Notice better simulation of transients at onset of inhibition and during post-inhibitory rebound. (Figure modified from Lange, Hartline and Ratliff, 1966.)

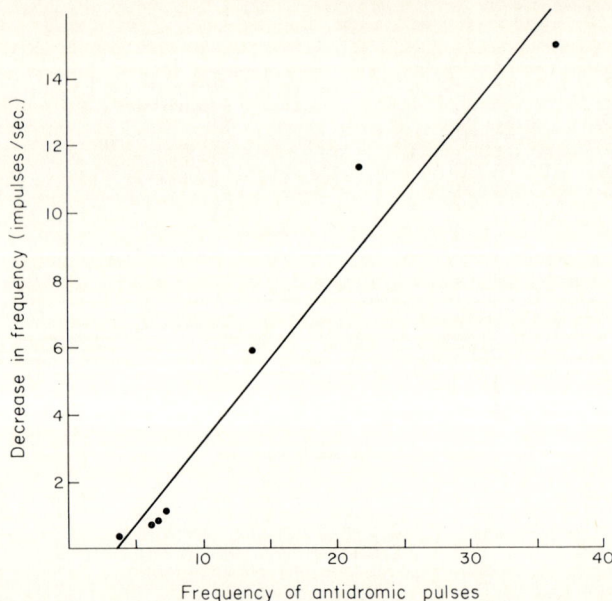

FIG. 4

Inhibition versus antidromic frequency. The ordinate values were calculated by subtracting the steady-state inhibited frequency from a control uninhibited frequency. The slope of the line (antidromic inhibitory constant) is 0·48 and was fit by a least squares method. The intercept (threshold frequency) is 3·5 impulses/sec.

The steady-state equations (see preceding paper) are:

$$r_p = e_p - \sum_j K_{p,j}(r_j - r_{p,j}^0). \tag{1}$$

As in our previous formulations, the response r_p of a particular ommatidium p is measured in terms of the frequency of discharge of impulses from that ommatidium. It is equal to the uninhibited response e_p of that same ommatidium, diminished by the summation of whatever inhibitory influences may be exerted on it by the other ommatidia j. Each of the separate inhibitory influences is the product of that part of the response r_j that exceeds the threshold of inhibitory action $r_{p,j}^0$, multiplied by the corresponding inhibitory coefficient $K_{p,j}$.

In the case where all pertinent thresholds have been exceeded the equations reduce to a special form in antidromic inhibition. Since an antidromic pulse frequency r_a is being imposed on the entire optic nerve (exclusive of the test bundle), eqn. (1) becomes:

$$r_p = e_p - r_a \sum_j K_{p,j} + \sum_j K_{p,j} r_{p,j}^0, \tag{2a}$$

$$r_p = e_p - \left(\sum_j K_{p,j} \right) \left(r_a - \frac{\sum_j K_{p,j} r_{p,j}^0}{\sum_j K_{p,j}} \right), \tag{2b}$$

or
$$I_p = e_p - r_p = \left(\sum_j K_{p,j} \right) \left(r_a - \frac{\sum_j K_{p,j} r_{p,j}^0}{\sum_j K_{p,j}} \right). \tag{2c}$$

The plot in Fig. 4 is of I_p (the total inhibition on the test unit p) versus r_a. The slope of the line is therefore the sum of the inhibitory constants

$$\left(\sum_j K_{p,j} \right)$$

and the intercept on the antidromic frequency axis is a mean of individual thresholds weighted according to their corresponding inhibitory constants. The line in the figure was plotted by the digital computer using a least squares fit.

DYNAMICS

The primary goal of this work is to describe in some detail, and perhaps to explain, the dynamical properties of the lateral inhibitory system. Since the steady-state equations are at least piecewise linear, some of the principles of linear systems analysis are applicable. Therefore, we have applied step function and delta function inputs to the lateral inhibitory system. As is well known, the responses of a linear system to such inputs are sufficient to characterize completely that system. In other words, if one knows the response of a linear system to either a step function or a delta function input, one can predict its response to all other inputs.

The definition of a step function or a delta function in a system where the input is a train of nerve spikes leads to some difficulty. Assuming that it is the spike frequency that is important, however, the step function input may be defined as an abrupt change from one pulse frequency to another.

Similarly, a delta function input may be most naturally defined as the input of one nerve impulse. This idealized definition can be achieved in the antidromic case to the extent that one impulse per optic nerve fiber (i.e. one volley) can be generated. (Such an experiment is discussed later in the paper, and the results are illustrated in Fig. 6.) In such experiments, however, the inhibition is often small. One may consider the inhibition from a short burst of volleys of inhibitory input as a delta function response in these cases. Such a generalization will hold as long as the burst is shorter than the important characteristic times of the system, and as long as the number of pulses in the burst is used to normalize the results. Of course, non-linearities in the system, which most assuredly exist, can completely invalidate the assertion that the response to n impulses is merely n times the response to one.

STEP FUNCTION RESPONSE

Figure 3A illustrates a typical set of step function responses. The number to the right of each plot represents the frequency of antidromic pulses occurring during the time represented by the hatched bar. Outside of this time there were no antidromic pulses.

At high input frequencies, production of impulses by the test unit stops; then, of course, no details of the inhibitory time course can be seen. (The technique of subtracting the control from the experimental frequency in this case leads to a misleading result, explained in the legend of Fig. 2.) On cessation of the antidromic input the unit began to respond at a low frequency, rapidly recovered to the control level (0·0) and finally transiently exceeded the control level and slowly reapproached it. In this plot the frequency never returned to the control frequency. This long-lasting post-inhibitory rebound at high input frequencies was observed in some but not all experiments. The shorter rebounds seen in the lower plots were always present and are seen with light-induced inhibition as well.

At lower input frequencies the activity of the test fiber is not completely suppressed but rather approaches a uniform inhibited level. As is seen in the second plot, the approach to this steady state is not necessarily monotonic; rather the frequency falls below the steady-state level and then returns. This behavior, which we will call the undershoot, was seen in some but not all the preparations. On cessation of inhibitory input the frequency quickly rises, overshoots and finally settles to the control level.

At still lower input frequencies (5 impulses/sec, here) the onset of inhibition seems decidedly sluggish with none of the undershoot seen above, while the release from inhibition is quick with a decided overshoot. This asymmetry between onset and release of inhibition will be of foremost importance in the discussions to follow.

At the lowest frequency showing inhibition (2 impulses/sec) we see what seem to be small inhibitory responses with a virtual return to the control level between them. These are very likely responses to individual inhibitory volleys which occur at each of the time marks and halfway between them. At these low frequencies it is perhaps unwise to continue to think in terms of a "step response" and of pulse frequency at all. The apparent response times of the system are such that responses to individual inputs are evident and hence the input is not seen as an integrated single step of frequency. These individual responses will be discussed further in the sections on delta function responses and in terms of the experimental model.

Returning to the description of Fig. 3A, it can be seen that at the very lowest input frequency (1 impulse/sec) there is no apparent inhibition. This is a manifestation of the inhibitory threshold in the steady-state analysis.

The theoretical model we will propose is based on the principles of linear analysis. It will therefore be useful to discuss the main features of the responses in terms of the expectations from a linear system.

First, were the system linear, we should expect the general shape of the responses to be unchanged as the magnitude of the input is changed. This is more or less the case for the release from inhibition but does not seem to hold well at the onset. Second, were the system linear, we should expect the onset of inhibition and the release from inhibition to be mirror images of one another. That this is not the case with very high inhibition is a trivial result of the fact that the fiber stops responding altogether and hence the frequency can have no undershoot. The response at 20 impulses/sec is most nearly symmetrical, having transient undershoots and overshoots at both onset and release. The responses at lower frequencies are again asymmetric with a sharper release than onset. At the frequencies where individual responses are seen the apparently non-linear effects are quite obviously due to the pulsatile character of the input.

In conclusion, then, it is apparent that although the steady-state levels of inhibition in the *Limulus* eye can be nicely predicted by a piecewise linear formulation, the time-dependent step responses show signs of asymmetries which are certainly the result of non-linear behavior. It will be seen, however, that the non-linearities necessary to explain the data again have the character of piecewise linearity.

TIME DELAYS

Delays in the onset of light-induced inhibition have been extensively discussed in the preceding paper. Delays also appear in the antidromic experiments. They can be as long as several hundred milliseconds. Figure 5 illustrates an experiment designed to study the properties of the time delay and, in particular, its dependence on the level of inhibition and past history of inhibition. The figure illustrates two experimental situations.

In the experimental run designated by the dashed arrow an antidromic frequency of 20 impulses/sec was begun at 1·0 sec and was then stepped to 33 impulses/sec at 3·0 sec (as indicated by the dashed lines). A delay of about 400 msec is observed before the first noticeable inhibition at the first step. The delay is very short at the second step.

In the run identified by a solid arrow a just suprathreshold antidromic frequency of 10 impulses/sec was begun 2 sec prior to the beginning of the record, and stepped to 33 impulses/sec at 3·0 sec (indicated by the solid lines). In this case the delay was greatly reduced (to about 100 msec), the same steady state was reached, and when the next step was imposed the response was

identical to that in the first experiment. We see, therefore, that the time delay
to the onset of inhibition is not constant but depends on the previous history
of inhibition. In another part of this experiment (not illustrated) the last step
was imposed without any previous inhibition. In this case, with this rather
high frequency, the delay was not much affected by the history. We see, therefore, that the time delay is shortened both by a previous background of

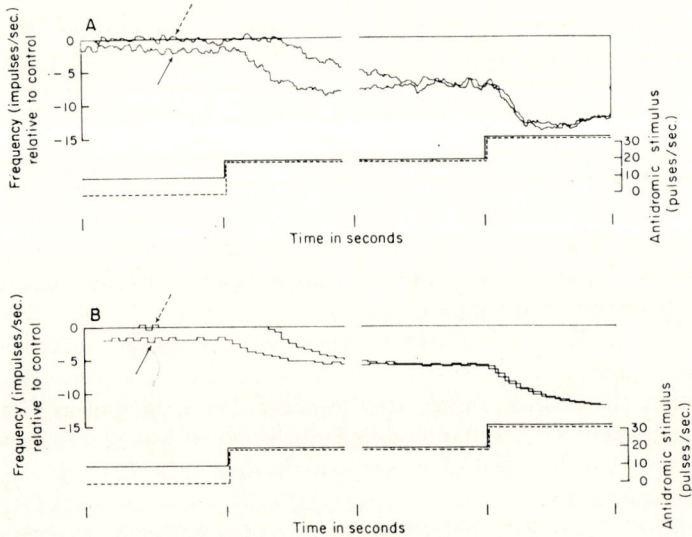

FIG. 5

Responses of an ommatidium (A) and of the model (B) to steps of antidromic
frequency, showing changes in delay. The average frequency of controls in this
experiment was 20 impulses/sec. See the text for further details. In Fig. 5B the
same inhibitory input was introduced into the model as described later in the
paper. The difference in the time delay due to previous inhibition is evident. The
constants used in the calculations were: $A_L = 1\cdot3$; $A_s = 2\cdot0$; $\tau_s = \tau_L = 1\cdot0$;
and $C = 7\cdot2$.

inhibition and by a large step in frequency. Similar results have been obtained
using the light-induced inhibition. We have previously proposed (Ratliff,
Hartline and Lange, 1964) that these delays may be partly explained in terms
of the times necessary to overcome the steady-state inhibitory threshold. In
this paper we hope to make this conjecture both plausible and quantitative.
A similar explanation in terms of hypothetical interneurons was proposed by
Stevens (1964) for both the threshold and the delays.

With antidromic stimulation of the whole nerve or a bundle of many fibers coming from different parts of the eye, we cannot say anything about the dependence of the time delays on distance. In fact these experiments are subject to a dispersion error to the extent that delays are distance-dependent. These distance effects are discussed in the preceding paper.

DELTA FUNCTION RESPONSES

As stated above, either single volleys of antidromic stimulation or short groups of volleys can be considered delta function inputs to the lateral inhibitory system.

Figure 6 illustrates the response to a single antidromic volley. This experiment was performed in a slightly different manner from those previously described. In this case the recording is from a bundle of fibers rather than a single test fiber. The upper trace in each photograph is the recording of the

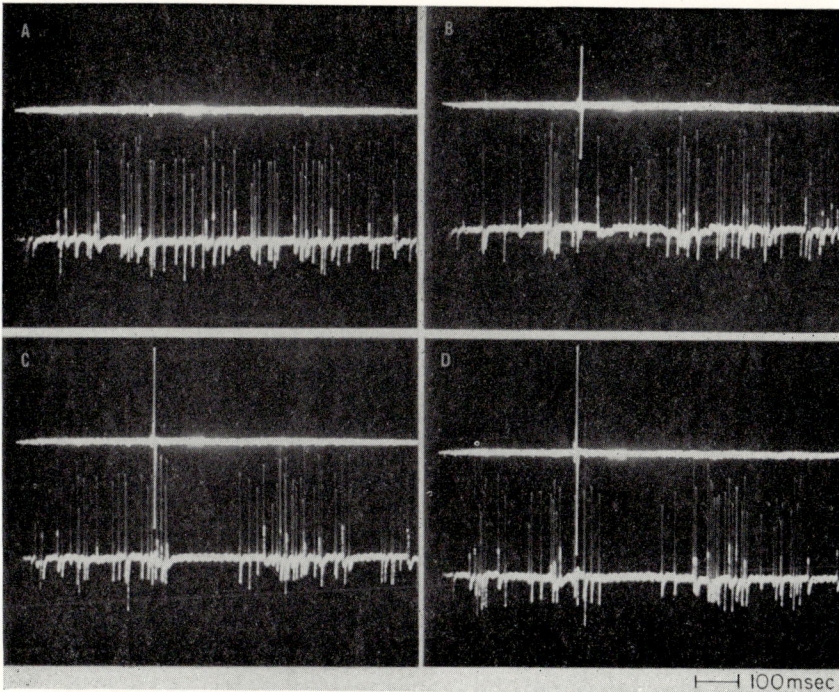

FIG. 6

Responses to single antidromic volleys. The upper trace in each oscillogram records the compound action potential from the electrically stimulated optic nerve. The lower traces are recordings from a bundle of fibers whose ommatidia were stimulated by light. The stimulus voltages are 2·5 (A), 2·8 (B), 5·0 (C) and 50·0 (D). See text for discussion.

compound action potential from the optic nerve, associated with the antidromic volleys. The lower trace of each photograph records the nerve action potentials from the test bundle.

In Fig. 6A the shock to the optic nerve was subthreshold (2·5 V) as is indicated by the lack of a compound action potential. There was no effect on the test bundle. In B there was submaximal stimulation (2·8 V) and a detectable deficit of impulses in the test bundle just after the antidromic volley. In C the stimulation (5·0 V) produced a maximal compound action potential and a larger inhibitory effect. In D the stimulation was increased 10 times over C (50 V). Both the compound action potential and the inhibitory effect remained sensibly the same in D as in C. This maneuver served as a control against the remote possibility that the electrical shock to the optic nerve was producing its inhibitory effect directly on the eye rather than through the response of the nerve fibers. Both this control and the sharp onset of inhibition closely following the compound action potential (compare A and B) argue against the possibility of a direct artifactual effect.

Although it is not possible to say much quantitatively about this composite response, it can be seen that the inhibition lasts for only about 200 msec and is followed by a post-inhibitory rebound of about the same duration.

GROUPS OF VOLLEYS

The use of short groups of antidromic volleys produces inhibitory inputs similar to those produced by short flashes of light to neighboring ommatidia that were described in the preceding paper. One of the most striking findings has been that if one separates two short flashes of light on a neighboring ommatidium by one to a few seconds there is an enhancement of the inhibition produced by the second burst which depends on the presence of the first burst. The enhancement is so strong that it often appears even when the second burst contains fewer impulses. The antidromic technique is an ideal one to use in studying this facilitation because it is possible to make the inhibitory inputs highly reproducible.

Figure 7A and C illustrates such an experiment. It is evident that the inhibitory response to the second burst is greater than that to the first. This is true even though there is no directly observable effect remaining from the first burst at the time the second occurs. Again, discussing these results in terms of a linear system we would expect the response to two bursts to be the sum of the responses to each burst taken separately. This is clearly not the case. This phenomenon can be explained using the same reasoning as that used to explain the variable time delay. That is, the presence of a threshold masks persisting subthreshold—and hence, by definition, nonobservable—events which contribute to the inhibition produced by the second burst of antidromic impulses.

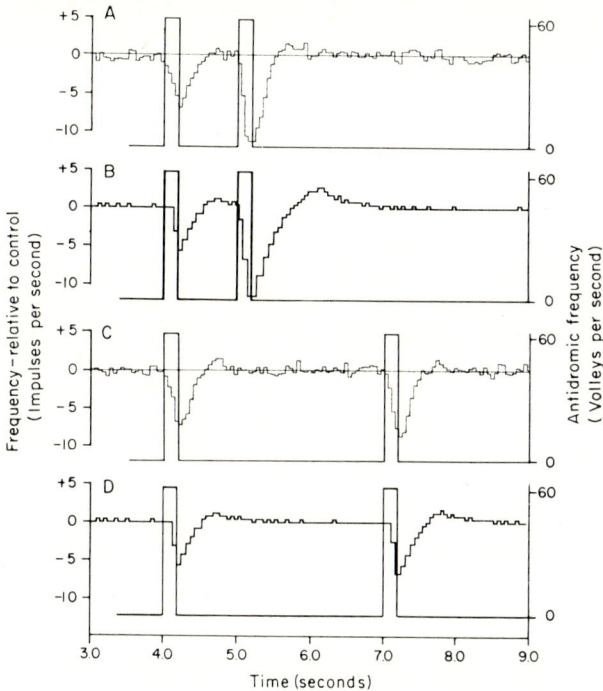

FIG. 7

Facilitation. Figure 7A and C illustrates the facilitation of inhibition when a burst of inhibitory pulses (at 4 sec) is followed by another (at 5 sec in A and 7 sec in C). It is evident that the facilitation decreases with increasing time between bursts. Figure 7B and D illustrates the model simulation of this experiment, as described later in the text.

This explanation of facilitation is strengthened by the following experiment. Bursts of antidromic volleys were produced at a constant pulse frequency but with different numbers of pulses in the burst. A plot was then made of the number of impulses lost by the test fiber in a given period versus the number of pulses in the inhibitory input (Fig. 8). Such a plot is analogous to the inhibitory plot in Fig. 4 except that Fig. 8 displays changes in number versus number rather than changes in frequency versus frequency. (Analogous results have been obtained using two flashes of light.)

As one might expect if the bursts of pulses in the inhibitory input are short enough to be essentially delta functions, these plots produce straight lines just as do the steady-state plots. The line through the open circles is for the first of two bursts while the line through the closed circles is for the second. Notice that the plots demonstrate an apparent threshold. That is, for this preparation no effect is seen when fewer than three volleys of antidromic pulses appear together. Once this threshold is exceeded the number of impulses lost is linearly related to the number of pulses in the burst. It can be seen that the slopes of the two lines are the same, but the threshold is lower in the case of the second burst. Evidently some subthreshold inhibitory influences persist for a time after the first burst and, in effect, lower the threshold for the inhibitory influences produced by the second burst.

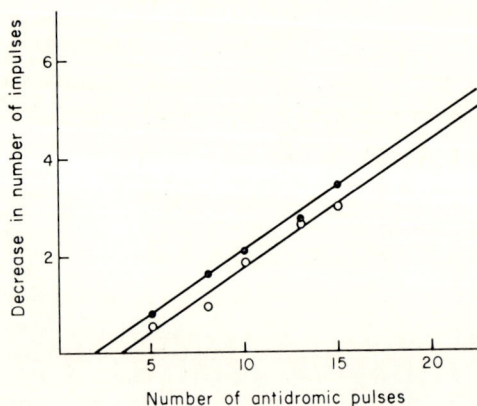

Fig. 8

Inhibition as a function of the number of antidromic volleys in a burst. The ordinates were calculated as the difference in the number of impulses from the test ommatidium in one second, in a control and in an experimental run. The abscissa is the number of pulses in the antidromic burst causing the inhibition. The open circles are for the first burst in a series similar to Fig. 7A, while the closed circles are for the second burst. The slopes of the lines (fit by least squares) are identical (0·25) but the intercept (threshold) has been decreased by the presence of a previous burst.

SUMMARY OF EXPERIMENTAL FINDINGS

We can now summarize the main features of the responses of the lateral inhibitory system in the *Limulus* eye. We may list these features in order of their appearance in the response:

(1) The onset of inhibition is delayed by an amount dependent on the previous inhibitory level and on the amplitude of the change in input.

(2) The onset of inhibition is sluggish at low levels of inhibitory input.

(3) The frequency undershoots at high levels of inhibitory input (not seen in all experiments).

(4) The level of inhibition in the steady state is linearly related to the inhibitory input.

(5) There is a steady-state threshold.

(6) There is a post-inhibitory rebound.

(7) Inhibitory deficits resulting from short bursts of antidromic volleys are linearly related to the number of volleys in the bursts; there is a threshold for the inhibitory responses.

(8) The inhibitory responses to short bursts of antidromic volleys are facilitated by previous inhibition.

Points 2 and 3 taken together with 6 are evidence of an asymmetry between the onset and release of inhibition.

Any theoretical treatment of this system should account for all of these phenomena if it is to be complete. It is clear, however, that a purely linear model will not account for the asymmetries, delays, or facilitations mentioned above. At this point we can anticipate, therefore, that any adequate model of the activity of this system will probably be non-linear.

THEORETICAL MODEL

We have developed a quantitative theoretical formulation which accounts for many of the features seen in the inhibitory response (cf. Lange, 1965). This formulation, or model, has been expressed in two ways. One, in the form of an integral equation, is a generalization of the steady-state formulation. This form will not be discussed in this paper. A complete treatment will be published in the future.

The second form of the model is expressed as a computer program. It is based on the impulse-by-impulse calculation of input and output and is equivalent to the integral form where individual nerve spikes are expressed as delta functions. It is this form of the model which is used to compute the responses of the system.

Both forms are based on the concept of nervous integration by summation. That is, it is asserted that the output of each cell of a nervous system is largely determined by, and is more or less proportional to, the sum of all excitatory and inhibitory influences on it. The extent to which this principle holds in various nervous systems varies widely. It is evident from the steady-state formulation, however, that the addition (or subtraction) principle holds well in the *Limulus* eye.

GENERAL PROGRAMMING CONSIDERATIONS

The model program was written in Control Data 160 Fortran A, a language nearly identical to the widely used forms of IBM Fortran. The calculations were performed on the Control Data Corporation 160-A computer in our laboratory.

A program is a set of rules for transforming one set of numbers into another. This transformation or mapping property of programs is really no different from the transformation or mapping property of mathematical operators and functions. The program can therefore perform the same function as that of a mathematical theory of a physical system. That is, it can predict the outcome of new experiments and thereby put the theory in a quantitatively testable form. In the present application, use of a digital computer program was particularly convenient because input data generated during experiments could be used directly as input data for the model.

The program was divided into three parts: input, model and output. There was provision for input of either real or idealized stimulus data and for input of the parameters of the model. Output consisted of typed and plotted displays of exactly the same form as that produced by the data processing program, thus facilitating the comparison of experimental and theoretical results.

The model itself was written in cyclic form. The basic cycle, called a clock cycle, represented one millisecond of time. The operations performed during each clock cycle will be described with the appropriate sections of the model.

SPIKE GENERATION

On the basis of empirical observations, a model for spike generation has been formulated over the past few years. This model asserts that the spike generating mechanism of the *Limulus* eccentric cell integrates the generator potential until a critical value of this integral is reached, at which time a spike is generated and the integration begins again. Stevens (1964) put this model into a formal statement in his discussion of slow potential theory as applied to the eccentric cell. The model is formally identical with one hypothesized by Hodgkin (1948) which was based on the classical notion of strength-duration reciprocity. At the time of production of each impulse the reciprocal of the interval since the last impulse is proportional to the average value of the generator potential during that interval. For constant generator potentials, such a model produces a frequency of impulses linearly related to the generator potential (cf. MacNichol, 1956).

In more symbolic terms we may say that a generator (g) was formed from the excitatory term (e) minus all inhibitory terms to be defined later. At each clock cycle of the program, the generator (g) was added to a running sum (s). When this sum reached a critical value a spike was recorded for the eccentric cell and the summation was begun again. The operation amounted to an integration of the generator and produced an impulse frequency proportional to it.

SELF-INHIBITION

In conformity with the work of Stevens (1964), Purple (1964) and Purple and Dodge (1966) the model was provided with self-inhibition in the following manner. A self-inhibitory pool (I_s) was set to zero at the beginning of the program. When the spike generator produced a spike, a quantity of inhibition (A_s) (in the same units as the generator) was added to this pool. At each cycle of the program a portion of this pool proportional to its current values and to the reciprocal of the self-inhibitory time constant (τ_s) was subtracted from it.

The total effect of the steps outlined above was to produce an exponentially decaying inhibitory potential following each impulse generated, leading to an exponential approach to the steady state of the spike frequency. This is consistent with Stevens' formulation and reproduces curves very similar to those calculated by a self-inhibitory simulation program written by F. A. Dodge (see Purple, 1964).

A neuron model of this type, with a summable inhibition following each impulse, should be carefully distinguished from models which set the membrane potential to a particular value following each impulse (Perkel et al., 1964). The latter type of model destroys all information concerning the size of the generator previous to the last spike produced. Transients in the firing rate of such models cannot be any longer than the time between impulses. This is clearly not the case in the *Limulus* eccentric cell where transients to a step change in generator potential can persist over many tens of interspike intervals.

So far we have discussed three variables in the model: the initial size of the generator (e), the time constant of decay of self-inhibition (τ_s) and the magnitude of the inhibitory quantum (A_s), added to the self-inhibitory pool following each spike.

LATERAL INHIBITION

The success of the self-inhibitory model in predicting the dynamical behavior of the eccentric cell naturally leads one to attempt to extend the same ideas to the case of lateral inhibition. This was done by Schoenfeld (1964) with some qualitative success.

The straightforward way to apply these concepts to antidromic inhibition in the model is as follows:

A list of times of occurrence of antidromic pulses is entered into the computer memory. At each cycle of the program (each millisecond) this list is consulted. If an antidromic pulse is encountered, a quantity of inhibition (A_L) is added to a lateral inhibitory pool (I_L). At each cycle the lateral inhibitory pool is diminished as in the self-inhibitory case, the decay being governed by the lateral inhibitory time constant (τ_L). Thus, two more parameters have been added to the model: the lateral inhibitory quantum of inhibition (A_L) and the lateral inhibitory time constant (τ_L).

THE LINEAR MODEL

At this point we can construct the total model in a linear form. In the case of the computer program this amounts to adding a step at each cycle which calculates the generator (g) by subtracting the two inhibitory terms from the excitatory term

$$g = e - I_s - I_L. \tag{3}$$

This generator (g) is the one we then apply to the sum (s) in the spike generating program.

The linear model has some of the necessary properties of lateral inhibition (see Fig. 9 and legend). It may be recalled, however, that many of the pro-

No Threshold

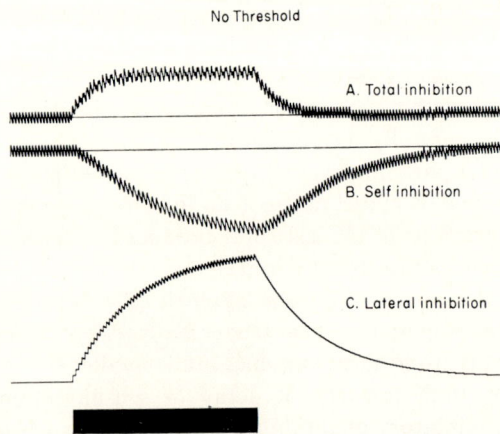

A. Total inhibition

B. Self inhibition

C. Lateral inhibition

FIG. 9

Model inhibitory pools with no threshold. Trace C shows the lateral inhibitory pool as it builds up during a train of inhibitory pulses designated by the black bar. The sawtooth build-up is essentially exponential. Trace B shows the self-inhibitory pool changing during the inhibition. The rate of increase and decrease of self-inhibition is such that it matches the lateral inhibition so that their sum (Trace A) has no overshoot. (Increase in total inhibition corresponds to decrease in the firing frequency of the test unit.)

perties of lateral inhibition discussed above were inconsistent with a linear model. Foremost among these were the lack of symmetry between onset and release of inhibition and the steady-state threshold. It should be noted that it is possible to produce inhibitory transients with an entirely linear model. If one makes the self-inhibitory time constant (τ_s) larger than the lateral inhibitory time constant (τ_L) an initial undershoot in the frequency and a post-inhibitory rebound will be present. The response will be symmetric, however.

INTRODUCTION OF A NON-LINEARITY

The responses displayed earlier were on the whole non-linear in their time-dependent properties. Recall that there were strong asymmetries in the step function response, there was facilitation and there were apparently non-linear time delays. We (Ratliff, Hartline and Lange, 1964) have previously suggested that there may be a connection between the delay phenomenon and the steady-state threshold. Ratliff (1965) has pointed out that there is an apparent relationship between threshold and inhibitory constant in a given eye. This relationship seems to be one of reciprocity, that is

$$r^0_{p,j} = \frac{C_p}{K_{p,j}} \tag{4}$$

where C_p is a constant depending on the test unit only. This relationship demands that all plots of the inhibition exerted on a unit p from its neighbors j will have a common intercept on the inhibition ordinate. This simplification substantially reduces the number of empirical constants required. With these approximate relations in mind, we have introduced a threshold into the model.

NON-LINEAR MODEL

The imposition of a critical level on the lateral inhibitory pool makes the model non-linear. As before, at the time corresponding to each inhibitory impulse a quantity (A_L) of inhibition was added to the pool (I_L). The full value of the pool was not used, however, in the calculation of the generator (g). Instead, a reduced inhibition (I) was used, calculated by subtracting a constant (C) from I_L (see Fig. 10C). If this subtraction produced a negative number, zero was substituted for I_r. Therefore, the expression for the generator becomes $g = e - I_s - I_r$.

A flow diagram of the complete model program has been published elsewhere (Lange, Hartline and Ratliff, 1966).

CONSISTENCY WITH THE STEADY-STATE EQUATIONS

The model is consistent with the steady-state equations. It provides an inhibition which is linear above threshold. In fact, one can calculate most of the parameters of the model from steady-state data. One can rigorously derive the steady-state equations from the integral equation formulation of the model. This has been done (see Lange, 1965), but its details are outside the scope of this paper.

When the integral equations are reduced to the steady state, relationships between the steady-state parameters and those of the dynamic model are established.

These are:
$$\frac{A_L\tau_L}{1+A_s\tau_s} = \sum_j K_{p,j} \qquad \frac{C}{A_L\tau_L} = \frac{\sum_j K_{p,j}r^0_{p,j}}{\sum_j K_{p,j}} \tag{5}$$

With Threshold

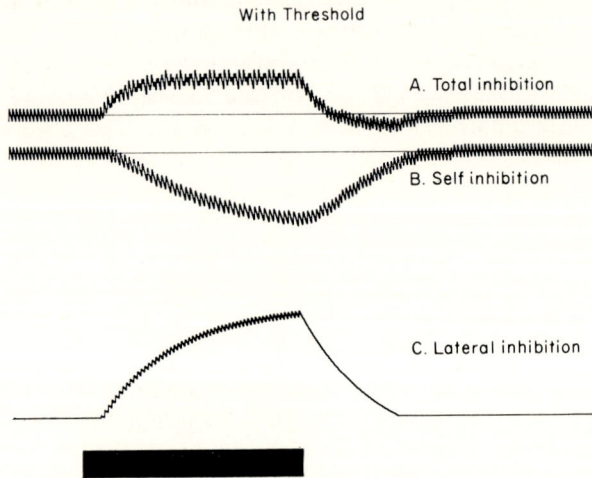

FIG. 10

Model inhibitory pools with a threshold. Trace C shows the lateral inhibitory pool. Notice the delay due to the time to achieve threshold; notice also the shortened decay. Because of this shortened decay the self-inhibition (Trace B) cannot compensate exactly for the lateral inhibition (Trace C), and therefore their sum (Trace A) exhibits an undershoot which leads to a post-inhibitory overshoot in the frequency of the test unit. The apparent noise in the total inhibition is a consequence of beats between the sawteeth of the lateral and self-inhibitory pools.

where the terms on the right of the identities are from eqn. (2c). If we plot inhibition as a function of antidromic frequency, as was done in Fig. 6, then

$\dfrac{A_L \tau_L}{1 + A_s \tau_s}$ is the slope of the line while $\dfrac{C}{A_L \tau_L}$ is the intercept on the abscissa

or the apparent threshold frequency. These quantities are therefore measurable. In order to evaluate the individual parameters we must make some assumptions. In the light-adapted state the initial transient to the onset of light in the test ommatidium follows a nearly exponential time course. In this case $(1 + A_s \tau_s)$ is the ratio of the initial frequency to the steady-state frequency. This allows $A_s \tau_s$ to be calculated from the experimental data. It only remains to estimate the time constants. This can be done by fitting the model to a typical inhibition curve or by assuming, as above, that the approach to steady state exhibited in the light-adapted state is primarily the result of self-inhibition. A third alternative is to choose an arbitrary time constant in the range found by Stevens.

PHYSIOLOGICAL SIGNIFICANCE OF PARAMETERS

The question now arises as to the physiological meaning of the parameters. The terms A_L and A_s can be conceptually associated with the release of unitary quantities of some inhibitory substance. Adolph has reported in this symposium that gamma amino butyric acid seems to mimic the effects of lateral inhibition when applied to the eye. Perhaps the assumption of a chemical transmitter substance is, therefore, not without some basis. If it is assumed that each synaptic ending produces some constant amount of inhibitory substance, then the magnitudes of A_L and A_s should be proportional to the number of active synaptic endings impinging on the test unit.

It would also be reasonable to assume that the dependence of the inhibitory constant on distance may be through a dependence of A_L on the distance to the inhibitors; perhaps widely separated receptors have fewer inhibitory endings on one another; perhaps conduction in the plexus is with decrement. Without specifying the actual mechanism, the assumption that A_L depends on distance will be made in future attempts to tie together spatial and temporal phenomena. Once we have made these assumptions concerning A_s and A_L, the time constants τ_s and τ_L might be associated with inactivation or diffusion of the transmitter substance.

The physiological interpretation of the thresholds is difficult. Their introduction into the model is most easily justified by pointing to the formal importance they have in properly predicting the data. There does, however, appear to be some real barrier in the lateral inhibitory system which affects the appearance of the hyperpolarizing inhibitory potential in intracellular recordings. Purple (1964) found that the inhibitory potential did not appear until the antidromic frequency had reached about 3 impulses/sec. The seat of the threshold must lie, then, either in the synaptic cleft or in the presynaptic ending. The dynamics, which require that the threshold be applied both as the inhibition is rising and as it is falling, would seem to place the barrier or inactivation in the synaptic cleft or at the site where the inhibitory substance first affects the post-synaptic membrane. At this time we can only make these speculations and hope that future experiments may shed more light on the mechanism.

COMPARISON OF EXPERIMENTAL RESULTS
AND MODEL CALCULATIONS

Having set numerical values of the constants needed in the model, we can calculate with the computer the time course of "responses" the model generates, and display outputs which are of the same form as those produced by the data processing of the actual experiment, Comparisons of experimental results with the "responses" generated by the model are shown in Figs. 3, 5 and 7. Referring to these figures, we will now discuss in detail the successes and failures of the model.

Figures 3B and C represent simulations of the experiment in Fig. 3A. In Fig. 3B the time constants of self- and lateral inhibition were equal, while in Fig. 3C they were allowed to differ. Both simulations reproduce the gross features of the response reasonably well. We expect the steady-state levels of inhibition to fit well because these were used to calculate the parameters of the model. We see, however, that the model has reproduced other features of the response as well, including asymmetries and post-inhibitory rebound.

The undershoot seen in the second run of Fig. 3A and the post-inhibitory overshoots are best fit by the second simulation (C). The sluggish onset of the inhibition in the third run is best fit by the first simulation (B). These discrepancies in detail suggest that the exponential time course for inhibitory events is probably too simple.

The recovery from inhibition in the first run of each simulation is too slow. This could result from either of two faults. Either the time constant for lateral inhibition is too long or the absence of a saturation of inhibition in the model is allowing it to be driven too far out of range. In the eye the level to which the generator can be driven in a hyperpolarizing direction is determined by the inhibitory equilibrium potential. The model has no such limit and hence at high frequency input the inhibition can continue to grow without bound, thus leading to an overly long recovery time.

Examination of Fig. 4 reveals a saturation phenomenon in the steady state. It can be seen that the experimental points are better fit by an S-shaped curve than by a straight line, and indeed this is a feature commonly observed. The upper curvature at high inhibitory levels is consistent with saturation. The curvature near threshold can be explained by assuming that there is a distribution of thresholds in the antidromic experiment due to the dependence of threshold on inhibitory constants and distance.

Some other successful results which were not, so to speak, built into the model are the individual inhibitory responses in the experimental curves corresponding to an antidromic frequency of 2 pulses/sec. These are represented in the model's response, and seem to be of about the right magnitude. This detail can only be reproduced by a model which calculates the response impulse-by-impulse.

Another phenomenon in the model's response which depends on the impulse-by-impulse calculations is the apparent "noise" during the inhibition in the curves corresponding to 5 pulses/sec in Fig. 3B and C. This phenomenon results from the beats generated between the antidromic input frequency and the average frequency of the simulated unit during inhibition (see also Fig. 10A). There is some indication of a similar phenomenon in the real experiment as well.

The time delays associated with the inhibitory interaction are the subject of the experiment illustrated in Fig. 5A. For the model, parameters were estimated from the steady-state results of the experiment and from the transients ascribed to self-inhibition. The reader will recall that in this experiment the difference between the two runs is the presence of a previous inhibitory input. As can be seen, the model accounts well for the *difference* between the two time delays (Fig. 5B). There is a residual delay in the real experiment which has no parallel in the model. The results do seem to confirm the earlier speculation that a substantial part of the delay is related to the threshold phenomenon. The delay in the model is clearly due to the time necessary for the inhibitory pool to exceed the threshold, the details of these events being illustrated in Fig. 10C, which shows the rise and fall of the inhibitory pools in the model.

Figure 7 compares the performance of the model with the experiments on facilitation of inhibition. Plots A and C show the experimental results while plots B and D show the results of the simulation. The simulation is good, except that the recovery from inhibition seems to be somewhat slower in the model than it is in the experiment on the eye. Facilitation is explained by a residuum of subthreshold inhibition from the first burst of antidromic volleys which is added to the effects of the second burst.

CONCLUSION

We have described some of the dynamic properties of the inhibitory interaction in the eye of *Limulus*, and proposed a theoretical model which describes quite well the results of a variety of experiments involving antidromic inhibition.

The parallels between the results of antidromic experiments and those with light-induced inhibition make it very likely that the model will also describe that body of data as well. The model is written in such a way that it is accessible to the use of data actually recorded from single fibers and, therefore, these data will be tried. The computed model has the advantage that it automatically considers the sampling problem and can reproduce the microstructure (that is, the detailed responses to each impulse) of the inhibitory response. Adding to these the simplicity of the theory and the fact that the parameters are few in number and have meaningful physiological interpretation leads us to hope that this may be a significant contribution.

The question arises as to the possible applications of a theory of this type to systems other than lateral inhibition in *Limulus*. One of the goals would seem to be to try to explain the behavior of more complex systems in terms of cells or subsystems having the same dynamical characteristics seen in this eye. It is quite clear that changes play a very important role in the vertebrate visual system. Hartline (1938) found that the large majority of optic nerve fibers in the frog retina showed little or no activity in response to steady illumination, and in recent years there has been a profusion of excellent studies of the visual systems of vertebrates, emphasizing the strongly phasic nature of much of the activity of retinal and central neurons. The importance of such responses in human vision is exemplified by the studies of Ditchburn and Ginsborg (1952) and by Riggs *et al.* (1953), who demonstrated the disappearance of objects whose image is stabilized on the retina. Therefore, it is quite clear that dynamical theories will be needed to explain the characteristics of these visual systems. Indeed, even in *Limulus*, where the optic nerve certainly does carry steady-state information, nervous activity in the optic lobes has elements of a phasic nature (Wilska and Hartline, 1941). Another type of study seeks to characterize the input to complex sensory motor systems by analyzing their transfer properties. With the *Limulus* photoreceptors this has recently been done by Pinter (1966) and by Purple and Dodge (1966). There have also been studies of the overall characteristics of arthropod sensory motor systems: the optomotor responses of the beetle (Reichardt, 1962), of the locust (Thorson, 1964, 1965), and of the fly (McCann and MacGinitie, 1965).

We believe that the area of application of our model probably lies between these extremes. Attempts have already been made to explain some aspects of motion perception in terms of lateral inhibition. Barlow and Levick (1965) have hypothesized lateral inhibition with time delays to explain the selective sensitivity of ganglion cells in the rabbit retina to direction of motion of the retinal image. In this case, the lateral inhibitory system is presumed to be at the bipolar cell or receptor level. Thorson (1965) has discussed the possibility that a non-linear lateral inhibitory system might provide the mechanism for motion perception necessary to explain the optomotor response in insects. Bicking (1965) has proposed an inhibitory model similar to ours, which seems to explain on and off responses in the goldfish retina. A model of the type discussed in the present paper can, hopefully, provide the necessary basis for putting some of these explanations in a quantitative and hence more precise and more testable form.

REFERENCES

ADOLPH, A. R. 1966. Excitation and inhibition of electrical activity in the *Limulus* eye by neuropharmacological agents. This volume.

BARLOW, H. B. and LEVICK, W. R. 1965. The mechanism of directionally selective units in the rabbit's retina, *J. Physiol.* **178**, 477–504.

BICKLING, L. A. 1965. Some quantitative studies on retinal ganglion cells, Thesis, the Johns Hopkins University.

DITCHBURN, R. W. and GINSBORG, B. L. 1952. Vision with a stabilized retinal image, *Nature* **170**, 36.

HARTLINE, H. K. 1938. The response of single optic nerve fibers of the vertebrate eye to illumination of the retina, *Amer. J. Physiol.* **121**, 400–15.

HODGKIN, A. L. 1948. The local electric changes associated with repetitive action in a non-medullated axon, *J. Physiol. (London)* **107**, 165–81.

LANGE, D. 1965. Dynamics of inhibitory interactions in the eye of *Limulus*: Experimental and theoretical studies, Thesis, the Rockefeller University.

LANGE, D., HARTLINE, H. K. and RATLIFF, F. 1966. Inhibitory interactions in the retina: techniques of experimental and theoretical analysis. *Ann. N.Y. Acad. Sci.* **128**, 955–71.

MACNICHOL, E. F., Jr. 1956. Visual receptors as biological transducers, in *Molecular Structure and Functional Activity of Nerve Cells*, Publ. No. 1, Am. Inst. Biol. Sci., 34–53.

MCCANN, G. and MACGINITIE, G. 1965. Optomotor response studies of insect vision, *Proc. Roy. Soc. B*, **163**, 369–401.

MILKMAN, N. and SCHOENFELD, R. L. 1966. A digital programmer for stimuli and computer control in neurophysiological experiments, *Ann. N.Y. Acad. Sci.* **128**, 861–75.

PERKEL, D. H., SCHULMAN, J. H., BULLOCK, T. H., MOORE, G. P. and SEGUNDO, J. P. 1964. Pacemaker neurons: effects of regularly spaced synaptic input, *Science* **145**, 61–3.

PINTER, R. B. 1966. Sinusoidal and delta function responses of visual cells of the *Limulus* eye, *J. Gen. Physiol.* **49**, 565–93.

PURPLE, R. L. 1964. The integration of excitatory and inhibitory influences in the eccentric cell in the eye of *Limulus*, Thesis, the Rockefeller Institute.

PURPLE, R. L. and DODGE, F. 1966. Self-inhibition in the eye of *Limulus*. This volume.

RATLIFF, F. 1965. *Mach Bands: Quantitative Studies on Neural Networks in the Retina*, Holden Day, San Francisco.

RATLIFF, F., HARTLINE, H. K. and LANGE, D. 1964. Studies on the dynamics of inhibitory interaction in the retina, in *Physiological Basis for Form Discrimination*, Symposium, Brown University, Providence, R. I.

RATLIFF, F., HARTLINE, H. K., and LANGE, D. 1966. The dynamics of lateral inhibition in the compound eye of *Limulus*. I. This volume.

REICHARDT, W. 1962. Nervous integration in the facet eye, *Biophys. J.* **2**, 121–44.

RIGGS, L. A., RATLIFF, F., CORNSWEET, J. C. and CORNSWEET, T. N. 1953. The disappearance of steadily fixated test objects, *J. Opt. Soc. Amer.* **43**, 495–501.

SCHOENFELD, R. L. 1964. The role of a digital computer as a biological instrument, *Ann. N.Y. Acad. Sci.* **115**, 915–42.

STEVENS, C. F. 1964. A quantitative theory of neural interactions: theoretical and experimental investigations, Thesis, the Rockefeller Institute.

THORSON, J. W. 1964. Dynamics of motion perception in the desert locust, *Science* **145**, 69–71.

THORSON, J. W. 1965. Small signal analysis of a visual reflex in the desert locust, Thesis, University of California, Los Angeles.

TOMITA, T. 1958. Mechanism of lateral inhibition in the eye of *Limulus*, *J. Neurophysiol.* **21**, 419–29.

WILSKA, A. and HARTLINE, H. K. 1941. The origin of "off-responses" in the optic pathway, *Amer. J. Physiol.* **133**, 491.

SELF-INHIBITION IN THE EYE OF *LIMULUS*

R. L. PURPLE

Department of Physiology, University of Minnesota Medical School,
Minneapolis, Minnesota, U.S.A.

and

F. A. DODGE

IBM Research, Yorktown Heights, New York, and The Rockefeller University,
New York, U.S.A.

INTRODUCTION

ONE achievement of modern neurophysiology has been the elucidation of the role of synapses in nervous tissue. The actual sites of synaptic connections, as well as their specific mechanisms, affect greatly the precision with which information in the nervous system is transferred. Precision in the sense of a direct transcription of the presynaptic event, as in the neuromuscular junction, is but one mode of action; more generally, synaptic action accentuates some particular feature of the presynaptic information. In this respect, it is not surprising that a variety of synapses have been described.

The purpose of this report is to discuss our experimental work on a recently postulated type of synaptic action in the *Limulus* eye which has been termed "self-inhibition". This form of synaptic action is produced by and acts on the same eccentric cell; self-inhibition is initiated by a propagated action potential and is presumably generated by the release of a chemical transmitter in the neuropile.

Hartline, Ratliff and Miller (1961) considered the possibility of self-inhibition in relation to one of the restrictions on the steady-state equations for lateral inhibition. While they drew no conclusions about it, the idea lingered on, to be taken up later by Stevens (1964) in his thesis study under Hartline. Stevens used the concept of self-inhibition to explain a phenomenon of eccentric cell activity which has been observed by several previous investigators (Hartline, Coulter and Wagner, 1952; MacNichol, 1956; Fuortes and Mantegazzini, 1962; and Fuortes and Poggio, 1963). The phenomenon is simply that the response of the eccentric cell to a constant step of depolarizing current is a train of spikes whose instantaneous frequency (one over the interval between spikes) declines exponentially from an initial high value to a steady-state that is one-third to one-half the initial frequency, the time constant of decline being approximately 300 msec.

451

In testing for possible explanations for the phenomenon, Stevens concluded that the decline in frequency was not consistent with an interpretation based on accommodation of the impulse-producing mechanism as it is presently understood through work on the squid axon (Hodgkin and Huxley, 1952). In the action potential, the time courses of the conductance changes which underlie accommodation are sensitive to membrane potential. Hyperpolarization of the membrane greatly speeds recovery from accommodation. Stevens tested this point in the experiment illustrated in Fig. 1. An eccentric

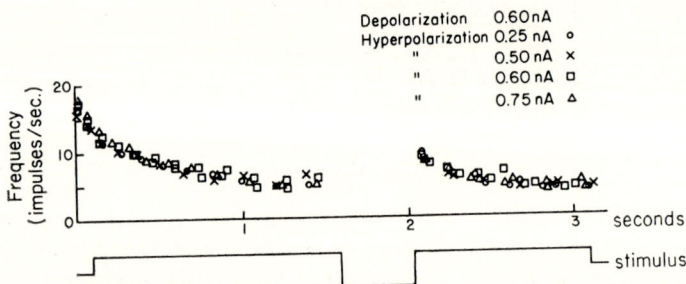

FIG. 1

Response of an eccentric cell to a step of constant depolarizing current interrupted by a short interval of hyperpolarization. (From Stevens, 1964.)

cell was depolarized by a step of constant current which was interrupted by a hyperpolarizing pulse after a steady-state was achieved. The figure illustrates the results of several such trials in which only the magnitude of the hyperpolarizing pulse was varied. It is obvious that the transient frequency change occurring after the interruption did not depend upon the magnitude of the hyperpolarizing current, since all the responses were virtually identical.

While inconsistent with an interpretation based on accommodation in peripheral nerve, the results in Fig. 1 are consistent with an interpretation based on synaptic mechanisms. Stevens therefore developed a formal model for self-inhibition which adequately explained the temporal changes in frequency observed when the eccentric cell was stimulated with various waveforms of current.

In the course of a series of studies designed to characterize electrically the responses of the eccentric cell under the influence of both excitation and inhibition (Purple, 1964; Purple and Dodge, 1965), we have measured simultaneous potential and conductance changes which follow each spike, which account for the temporal changes in frequency observed when the eccentric cell is stimulated with current, and which are compatible with Stevens's hypothesis of self-inhibition.

METHODS

To measure simultaneous changes in potential and conductance with a single intracellular pipette we used a bridge technique in which square pulses of current were applied. With pulses of sufficiently high frequency the impedance of the cell was negligible and we measured the resistance of the pipette. Pulses of sufficient duration to charge the membrane capacitance to a steady potential measured the sum of the resistive components of the pipette and cell. The resistance of the cell was then obtained by taking the difference in the two measurements. Using the lower frequency pulses during stimulated responses we could trace the simultaneous potential and conductance changes, as illustrated in Fig. 2. The upper recording in the figure is of a pure generator

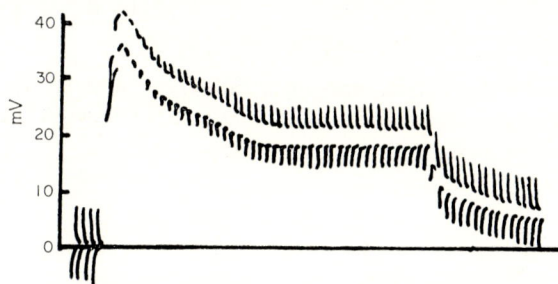

(a)

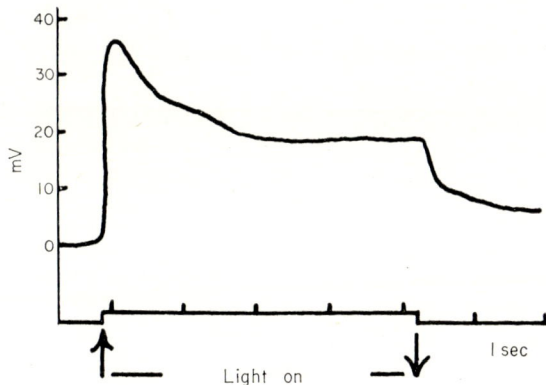

(b)

FIG. 2

(a) Response from a *Limulus* ommatidium when stimulated by light with current pulses stimulating the cell through the bridge circuit. The lower traces are the pulse-off condition, the upper traces the pulse-on condition. A smooth line drawn through the steady-state portions of the pulse-off traces gives the potential change during the response and is identical to the response shown in (b), which is from the same cell without the current pulses. Time and stimulus markers in (b) also apply to (a).

response in a *Limulus* ommatidium taken with the bridge technique. Initially the bridge was balanced at the resistance of the pipette plus cell. When the preparation was stimulated by light, the conductance increase during activity was given quantitatively by the separation of the pulse-on and pulse-off traces. The change in membrane potential was given by the steady-state portions of the lower (pulse-off condition) traces. When a smooth line is drawn through these, one obtains a response which is identical to the one reproduced in the lower record, which was the response of this unit to the same stimulus recorded without the bridge circuit and current pulses. We might add that occasional checks with the high frequency pulses allowed us to be sure that conductance changes of the cell were not perturbed by changes in pipette resistance.

RESULTS

One of the most striking features of eccentric cell activity monitored with the bridge technique was the transient conductance increase that followed each spike initiated by the cell. A record of this is shown in Fig. 3. In addition

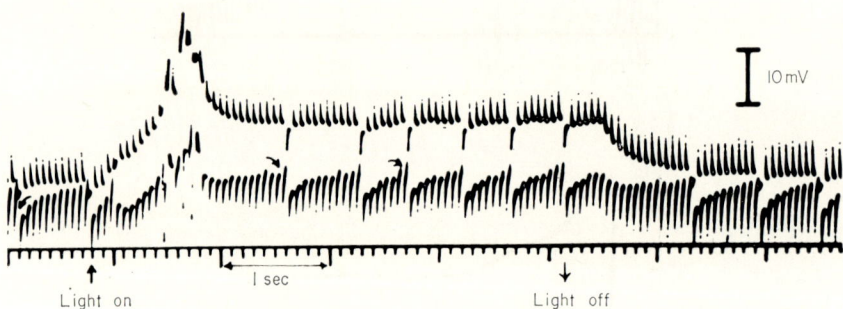

FIG. 3

Bridge records of the transient conductance increases following spikes. The small arrows illustrate the time of occurrence of three of the spikes on the record. The steady-state portions of the lower pulses trace the depolarizations induced by the stimulus, and the separation of the traces indicate the conductance increases. (From Purple and Dodge, 1965.)

to a general increase in conductance evoked by the light the transient conductance changes following each spike are quite evident. Two features should be noted about them: first, they had a duration of 400–500 msec, and second, the conductance increase was inhibitory in the sense that there was a hyperpolarization of the membrane, the net effect of which was to delay the onset of the next spike.

Another feature of these transient conductance changes is that they can sum. Figure 4 gives examples of this. Spikes were initiated from the resting level of an impaled cell with brief shocks of depolarizing current delivered at frequencies given to the left of each record. Again, in each record the steady-state portions of the lower traces give the change in potential which occurs concomitantly with the transient conductance increases.

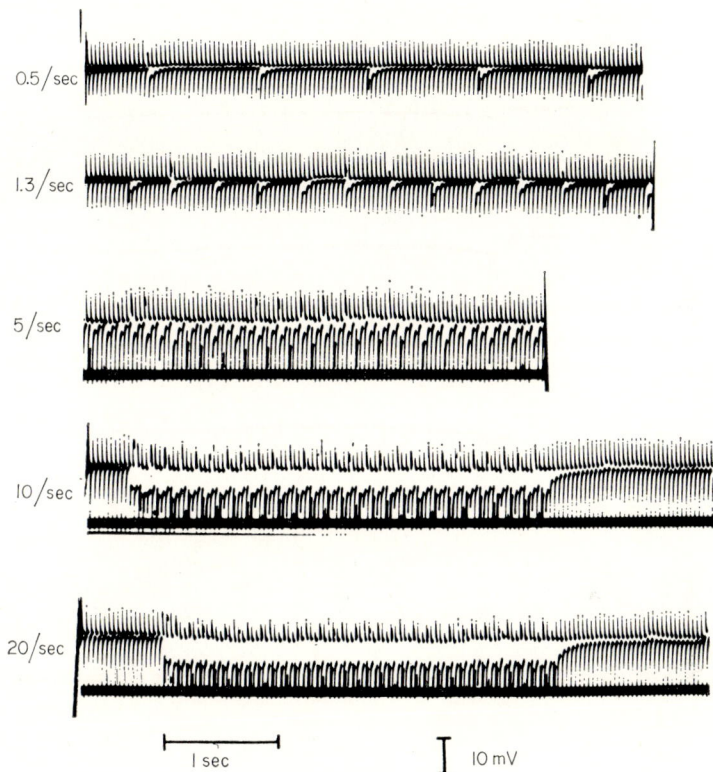

FIG. 4

Summation of transient potential and conductance changes following spikes. Time and voltage calibrations apply to all the responses illustrated. The frequency of the impulses is indicated beside each record. (From Purple and Dodge, 1965.)

An alternative experiment which illustrates much the same is shown in Fig. 5. Here bridge pulses were not used, and the cell was stimulated with brief shocks of current at a fixed frequency of 60 impulses per second with the number of spikes in the train increased from the top record downward. On all but the lowest record, only the after-potentials were photographically reproduced since the current shocks carried the spikes themselves off-scale. The membrane potential at which each successive shock in a train was applied is clearly seen to be moving in a hyperpolarizing direction. Moreover, the peak negativities of the initial portion of succeeding after-potentials move in a depolarizing direction, which indicates, as does the appearance of the last few spikes on the lowest record, that the truly regenerative portions of the response were being shunted increasingly by an accumulating increase in conductance.

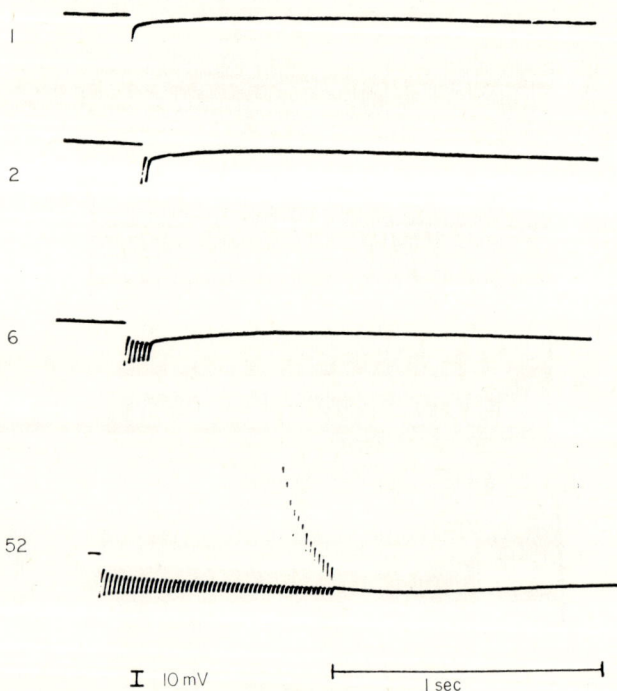

FIG. 5

Summation of hyperpolarization with increasing train lengths of spikes stimulated from the resting level at 60 per sec with 1 msec shocks of depolarizing current. The spikes themselves were not photographically reproduced since the current shocks carried them off-scale.

The relatively slow conductance and potential changes illustrated in both Figs. 4 and 5 have features which cannot be satisfactorily interpreted by conductance changes associated with accommodation in peripheral nerve. The conductance changes associated with accommodation do not sum since their time courses are effectively reset by each action potential.

The summation of the conductance increases can be satisfactorily interpreted on the basis of chemical synaptic action. Such an interpretation would, in fact, demand that the conductance changes be capable of just such a summation. Other points of compatibility are that the relation between the decrease in resistance and change in membrane potential occurring during the transients is a linear one, and that a determination of the equilibrium potential for the phenomenon yields a value that is essentially identical to the equilibrium potential for lateral inhibition, a phenomenon which is definitely mediated by a transmitter (Purple, 1964; Purple and Dodge, 1965).

On the basis of the above findings, one should expect to observe some form of potential change following the spike which exhibits the time course of an inhibitory postsynaptic potential, but this is generally not the case when spikes are recorded from an eccentric cell stimulated either by a pulse of current or by light. The reason for this appears to be that the initial phase of the IPSP occurs before the after-potential of the spike is over, and the time course of the IPSP is thus obscured. Occasionally, however, it was possible to obtain a preparation in which the impaling pipette tip was lodged not in the soma of the cell as was generally the case, but in the axon or axon hillock of the cell, positions which are nearer to the site of the actual generation of inhibitory potentials. When these preparations were chilled to about 10° Celsius, a slow component of the after-potential could be observed which resembled an IPSP in waveform, as shown in Fig. 6. The slow, IPSP-like

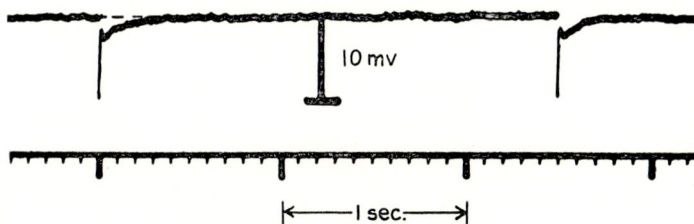

FIG. 6

Illustration of slow, "IPSP-like" component in the after-potential following a spike initiated from the resting level with a 1 msec shock of depolarizing current. The after-potentials of the spikes are shown, but the spikes themselves are not, since the depolarizing current carried them off-scale.

component could also be demonstrated in regular somal punctures at 20°C by hyperpolarizing the cell to the peak negativity of the after-potential and initiating spikes from this level with brief depolarizing shocks. An attenuated version of the slow component was then observable as illustrated in the lower record of Fig. 7.

In considering interpretations of the conductance and potential transients other than an accommodative or synaptic one, it is possible to show that none of the presently described mechanisms for producing after-potentials of a hyperpolarizing nature (Ritchie, 1961) are compatible with the experimental data. For example, the idea that the transient hyperpolarization could be due to a temporary depletion of extracellular potassium inside a thin sheath surrounding the nerve as a result of increased metabolic activity of a sodium–potassium coupled pump cannot account for the fact that the equilibrium potential of the conductance change remains essentially constant. As another example, an interpretation based on a non-coupled electrogenic pump of potassium or chloride cannot explain why the equilibrium potential of the transient can be reversed. Finally, other such possible interpretations have to be stretched to account for the time course of decay of the transient conductance increase, which is essentially the same as that of lateral inhibition.

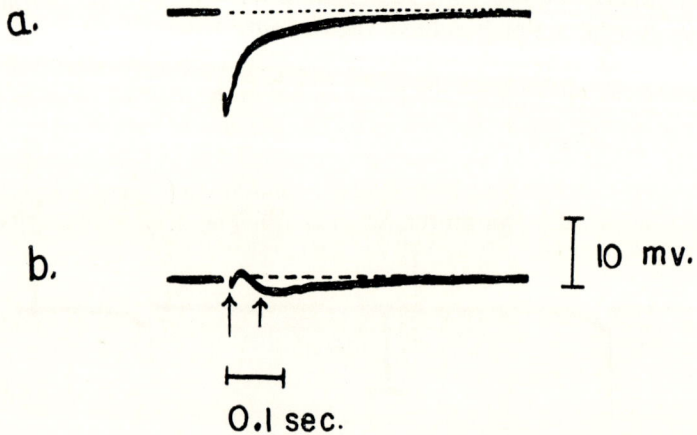

FIG. 7

(a) Normal after-potential of eccentric cell spike recorded from soma of cell when the cell is stimulated by a short depolarizing shock. (b) Slow component in the after-potential following an eccentric cell spike revealed by polarizing the membrane to the peak negativity of the after-potential before initiating a spike with a short shock of depolarizing current.

Thus it seems reasonable to conclude that self-inhibition in the eye of *Limulus* is a synaptic phenomenon that is probably mediated by a chemical transmitter.

In examining the influence of self-inhibition on the output of the eccentric cell, we first directed our attention to the response of the cell to a step of current to ascertain if the observed self-inhibitory conductance could indeed account for the exponential decline in the observed firing pattern. To do this we incorporated the unit of self-inhibition (which typically had a peak conductance of 5×10^{-9} mhos and an exponential decline with a time constant of 500 msec) into an electrical model of the eccentric cell which we formulated on the basis of our overall study of the cell (Purple and Dodge, 1965). When the model was programed for a step of constant depolarizing current at its soma, we obtained the results illustrated in Fig. 8. The left-hand columns give the depolarizations at the soma, and the vertical lines simply mark the time of occurrence of each spike. The right-hand columns plot the corresponding instantaneous frequencies. In agreement with experimental observations, the responses of the model declined exponentially to a steady state that was approximately one-third the initial frequency with a time constant of about 280 msec.

Assuming that the rest of the elements in our model were correct, we can conclude that the observed unit of self-inhibitory conductance does indeed

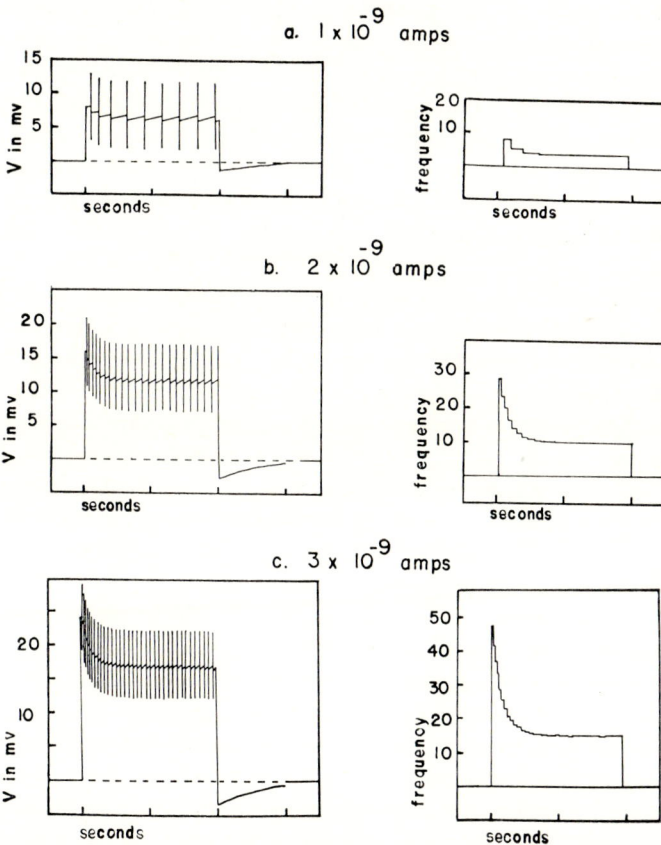

FIG. 8

Predictions of analogue model for responses induced by a depolarizing current injected at the soma when the self-inhibitory PSP is included in the model. (From Purple and Dodge, 1965.)

account adequately for the response of the eccentric cell to extrinsic depolarizing current. With the same assumption, it can also be shown that the unit of self-inhibitory action must be a necessary part of the model if the model is to predict correctly the transient responses of the eccentric cell to light (Purple and Dodge, 1965).

DISCUSSION

We shall now consider some questions about self-inhibition which are, at present, not completely answered. The first question concerns the pathway that leads to the generation of self-inhibition. Stevens (1964) has suggested two alternatives: (1) an axon collateral from an eccentric cell might make a synaptic connection with the axon proper of the cell or with another of its collaterals; and (2) self-inhibition might act by way of an interneuron, presumably a retinular cell in this case. Recent observations on the microscopic anatomy of the neuropile suggest a third alternative. Each neuropile, which is the presumed site for lateral inhibitory action, typically consists of a short, highly branched collateral of the eccentric cell axon interdigitating with branches from neighboring ommatidia. Virtually all branches, including those from the recipient axon, are densely packed with presumed synaptic vesicles. Thus it is possible that transmitter packets released from the axon collateral may diffuse to a receptor site on the same collateral not far from the point of release.

At present there is no direct physiological evidence which would allow us to differentiate between the alternatives, although an indirect line of evidence favors the third. According to this hypothesis, self-inhibition should be much more potent than lateral inhibition contributed by even a near neighbor, and, in fact, should be about as potent as the sum of all lateral inhibitory drives that could act on the cell. An estimate of the coefficients for self-inhibition derived from the Hartline–Ratliff equations do indeed show that the self-inhibitory coefficients are much greater than even the largest coefficients found for lateral inhibition. Coefficients for self-inhibition are generally around 2, while coefficients for lateral inhibition are usually less than 0·1. A corollary line of evidence for the potency of self-inhibition comes from experiments utilizing antidromic stimulation to produce lateral inhibition. In these experiments it was generally found that antidromic stimulation of the whole optic nerve at 30 per second or more was required to match an inhibitory conductance increase obtained by driving the cell with brief depolarizing shocks at only 15 per second.

The second question concerns the possible utility of self-inhibition in shaping the information that is relayed in the optic nerve. Self-inhibition obviously contributes a strong amount of negative feedback to the eccentric cell, and this could be of importance in assuring the stability of the tonic, or steady-state responses. Stevens (1964) has also pointed out that the transient changes in spike frequency (Fig. 1) resulting from the self-inhibitory feedback would have the effect of enhancing the high frequency response of the system. This feature takes on special significance when we consider the limited frequency response of the generator potential to a modulation of light intensity.

Assuming that the generator potential is the summation of small, exponentially decaying shots (Adolph, 1964) and that the mean amplitude of the shots would not change in response to small amplitude modulations of the light, then the frequency response of the generator could be described formally by the transfer function for a low-pass filter with a time constant equal to that for the decay of the shot (about 0·1 sec). Combining this with the transfer function for the self-inhibitory feedback (lower curve in Fig. 9) predicts

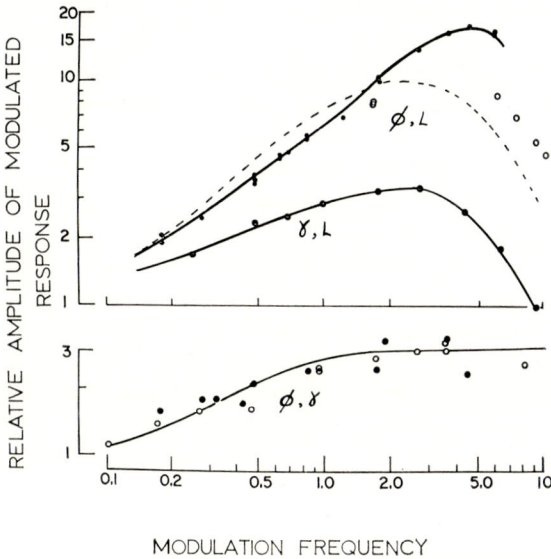

MODULATION FREQUENCY

FIG. 9

Transfer functions relating the modulation of spike frequency to modulation of light intensity (φ, L), generator potential to light (γ, L), and spike frequency to depolarizing current (φ,γ) measured in the eccentric cell as described in the text.

that the overall response should show a peak at about 1 c/s with a gain of about 2·5 times the zero frequency response. An experimental test of this prediction has recently been made by Dodge in collaboration with B. W. Knight at the Rockefeller University, and the results are summarized in Fig. 9.

In this experiment, a single ommatidium was stimulated by a step of light on which was superimposed a sinusoidal modulation with a peak-to-peak amplitude about 30% of the mean. Ommatidial responses were measured by a micropipette electrode impaling the eccentric cell. The data, either the instantaneous spike frequency or the amplitude of the generator potential, were processed for the period from 6 to 14 sec after the onset of the stimulus by a digital computer programed to do a least mean square fit of the data to a set of functions which determined the mean amplitude of the response, the linear drift, the amplitude and phase of the modulated component of the response, and the amplitude and phase of the first harmonic component. Over the period in which the data were processed, the drift was less than 2% of the mean, and the amplitude of the harmonic component was less than 5% of the amplitude of the fundamental. The temperature was not controlled, and drifted slowly from about 20°C to 24°C during the 3 hr duration of the experiment.

In Fig. 9 the amplitude of the fundamental sinusoidal response, measured relative to the difference between the steady-state response to the extrema of the modulation (i.e. the zero frequency response), is plotted against the frequency of the stimulus modulation. In the first series of tests, the modulation of the spike frequency (φ) was measured in response to a modulation of the light intensity, yielding the upper curve (φ, L). This transfer function shows a prominent peaking at about 3 c/s, but rather unexpectedly the peak "gain" was as large as 15. The observed peak-to-peak amplitudes of the modulated response were 2 impulses per second at zero frequency and 30 impulses per second at 3 c/s. For the second series of tests, the eccentric cell was hyperpolarized by a constant current applied through the micropipette of sufficient intensity that the membrane potential always remained below the threshold for spikes. Under this condition the modulation of the generator potential (γ) was measured in response to the same modulation of the light, yielding the second curve (γ, L). Obviously the generator potential did not follow the simplified hypothesis cited above but instead showed a prominent peaking at about 3 c/s with a gain somewhat greater than 3. In the third series of tests, the modulation of the spike frequency was measured in response to a step of depolarizing current on which was superimposed a sinusoidal modulation, in order to measure the transfer function for self-inhibition. The experimental points (lower figure) were fitted by the theoretical transfer function (φ) assuming a self-inhibitory coefficient of 2 and a time constant of 0·85 sec.

The transfer functions for the self-inhibitory feedback (φ, γ) and the empirical transfer function for the generator potential (γ, L) were then multiplied together to synthesize the transfer function for spikes to light (φ, L), yielding the dotted curve.

There is some considerable quantitative discrepancy between the synthesized and the empirical curve, presumably in consequence of the lack of temperature control and of deterioration of the preparation during the sequence of different types of measurements. This discrepancy notwithstanding, we believe that these results of Dodge and Knight establish that: (1) the self-inhibitory feedback plays a quantitatively significant role in enhancing the response of the eccentric cell to transient changes of illumination; and (2) the frequency response of the generator potential is an equally important determinant in the overall behavior of the eccentric cell to transients. At present, Dodge and Knight are attempting to formulate a quantitative description of the generator potential in terms of adaptation of the shot amplitudes along lines suggested by Adolph's (1964) investigations.

In conclusion, it appears that the phenomenon of self-inhibition in the *Limulus* eye is another form of synaptic action that may be added to the growing list of synapses which transfer and help to modify information in neural pathways. Whether self-inhibition is present in the *Limulus* eye as a unique mechanism or is in reality more widely distributed, is a question which can only be answered by further research.

ACKNOWLEDGEMENTS

This work was supported in part by PHS grant number NB 00864 and in part by PHS grant number NB 05756.

The authors wish to express their appreciation to Dr. H. K. Hartline, Mr. Bruce Knight, Dr. William H. Miller, and Dr. Floyd Ratliff for their generous help throughout the course of this work.

REFERENCES

ADOLPH, A. R. 1963. A stochastic model of neuron function, and its application to subthreshold processes in the *Limulus* photoreceptor and frog neuromuscular junction. Thesis. The Rockefeller University.

ADOLPH, A. R. 1964. Spontaneous slow potential fluctuations in the *Limulus* photoreceptor. *J. Gen. Physiol.* **48** (2), 297–322.

FUORTES, M. G. F. and MANTEGAZZINI, F. 1962. Interpretation of the repetitive firing of nerve cells. *J. Gen. Physiol.* **45**, 1163–1179.

FUORTES, M. G. F. and POGGIO, G. F. 1963. Transient responses to sudden illumination in cells of the eye in *Limulus*. *J. Gen. Physiol.* **46**, 435–52.

HARTLINE, H. K. and RATLIFF, F. 1957. Inhibitory interaction of receptor units in the eye of *Limulus*. *J. Gen. Physiol.* **40**, 357–76.

HARTLINE, H. K., WAGNER, H. G. and RATLIFF, F. 1956. Inhibition in the eye of *Limulus*. *J. Gen. Physiol.* **39**, 651–73.

HARTLINE, H. K., COULTER, N. A. Jr., and WAGNER, H. G. 1952. Effects of electric current on responses of single photoreceptor units in the eye of *Limulus*. *Fed. Proc.* **11**, 65–6.

HARTLINE, H. K., RATLIFF, F. and MILLER, W. H. 1961. Inhibitory interaction in the retina and its significance in vision. In *Nervous Inhibition* (E. Florey, ed.), pp. 241–84. New York, Pergamon Press.

HODGKIN, A. L. and HUXLEY, A. F. 1952. A quantitative description of membrane current and its application to conduction and excitation in nerve. *J. Physiol.* **117**, 500–44.

MACNICHOL, E. F., Jr. 1956. Visual receptors as biological transducers, In *Molecular Structure and Functional Activity of Nerve Cells* (R. G. Grenell, and L. J. Mullins, eds.), pp. 34–62. Washington D.C., American Institute of Biological Sciences.

PURPLE, R. L. 1964. The integration of excitatory and inhibitory influences in the eccentric cell in the eye of *Limulus*. Thesis. The Rockefeller University.

PURPLE, R. L. and DODGE, F. A. 1965. Interaction of excitation and inhibition in the eccentric cell in the eye of *Limulus*. *Cold Spring Harbor Symposium on Quantitative Biology*. (In press.)

RITCHIE, J. M. 1961. Possible mechanisms underlying production of afterpotential in nerve fibers. In *Biophysics of Physiological and Pharmacological Actions* (A. M. Shanes, ed.). Washington, D.C. Publication No. 69 of American Association for the Advancement of Science.

STEVENS, C. F. 1963. Input–output relation for *Limulus* receptor cells. In *Biophysical Society, Abstracts of 7th Annual Meeting*, New York City, Item WF6.

STEVENS, C. F. 1964. A quantitative theory of neural interactions: theoretical and experimental investigations. Thesis. The Rockfeller University.

results of preliminary experiments which show that a number of neuro-pharmacological agents, known to be active on other nervous system tissue, have strong excitatory action on the *Limulus* eye. Included among these agents are the monoamines glutamic acid, norepinephrin, epinephrin and serotonin.

The inhibitory activity which occurs in the *Limulus* eye is thought to be mediated by collateral nerve branches running between neighboring omma-tidia. Functional inhibition occurs in a given receptor element when its neigh-bors are selectively stimulated. The form of this inhibition is a reduction in firing frequency of the test ommatidium, which is occasionally accompanied by a hyperpolarization of the eccentric cell soma membrane potential (Hartline *et al.*, 1961). Massive, artificially induced inhibition results when impulses are fired antidromically up the optic nerve bundle. Such inhibition is often accompanied by substantial amounts of membrane hyperpolarization of the eccentric cell.

In addition to the physiological evidence of synaptically mediated inhibitory interaction between ommatidia, morphological studies show typical synaptic structures in abundance throughout the nerve plexus (Hartline *et al.*, 1961). The plexus is the region into and through which the collateral nerve branches course. The results of further preliminary experiments, which are reported in this paper, show that gamma-aminobutyric acid and related substances exert a potent inhibitory action on the eye. This action consists of suppression of impulse activity and hyperpolarization of the eccentric cell membrane potential. The inhibitory action of these substances on the peripheral and central nervous systems of other invertebrates and vertebrates is well known (Roberts, 1960; Florey, 1961).

EXCITATORY AGENTS

L-glutamic acid has been found to have an excitatory effect on neurons in the central nervous systems of numerous mammalian types and in at least one invertebrate, the snail (Salmoiraghi and Bloom, 1964). It also appears to excite the eccentric cells in the *Limulus* eye. Figure 2 illustrates the effect on frequency of spikes, recorded intracellularly by means of a micropipette electrode. In the experiment illustrated, the glutamic acid was in a sea water solution which was flowed onto the sectioned eye in a flow chamber. The concentration ultimately achieved in the chamber was probably of the order of 1 mM. The spike frequencies of three components of the response are given: the transient component, which is the frequency at the peak of the generator potential transient; the steady component, or frequency during the main-tained tonic phase of the generator potential; and the spontaneous frequency, which refers to impulses occurring in the absence of a light stimulus. All three components follow a similar time course after application of the glutamic acid. There does not appear to be differentiated action on any particular component and examination of the membrane potential records indicates a nonspecific depolarizing action. The flushing in of another solution (GABA) after 14 min gave rise to a transient increase in the various components before the action of the second drug occurred. This transient was probably due to flushing more glutamate solution into the region of the cell under test and, as will be shown later, is not a concomitant of GABA action.

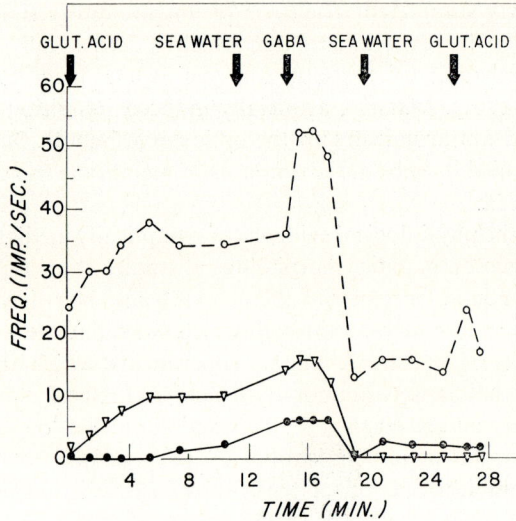

FIG. 2

Action of glutamic acid and GABA on the response to light. Spike frequencies during transient (upper curve) and steady-state (middle curve) components of generator potential and during spontaneous (lower curve) activity in the absence of a light stimulus. Flow applications of glutamic acid and GABA until bath concentrations were between 1·0 and 10·0 mM.

The catechol- and indole-amines, norepinephrin, epinephrin and serotonin (5-HT), are known to excite sympathetic and CNS neurons and smooth muscle in various mammals (Eccles, 1964; Krnjevic and Phillis, 1963). 5-HT excites snail neurons (Kerkut and Cottrell, 1963) and the D-cells of *Aplysia* (Gerschenfeld and Tauc, 1961), but I have not seen any recent reports of the action of the catechol-amines on invertebrate neurons. Norepinephrin (norep.), epinephrin (epin.) and 5-HT excite the eccentric cell in *Limulus*. Figures 3 and 4 illustrate the response to norep. washed onto the cell in the flow chamber to a concentration somewhere between 0·1 and 1·0 mM. The changes in spike frequency parallel changes in the related membrane potential components, the rise in spike frequency being related to membrane depolarization. Localized application of norep. by means of pressure ejection from a

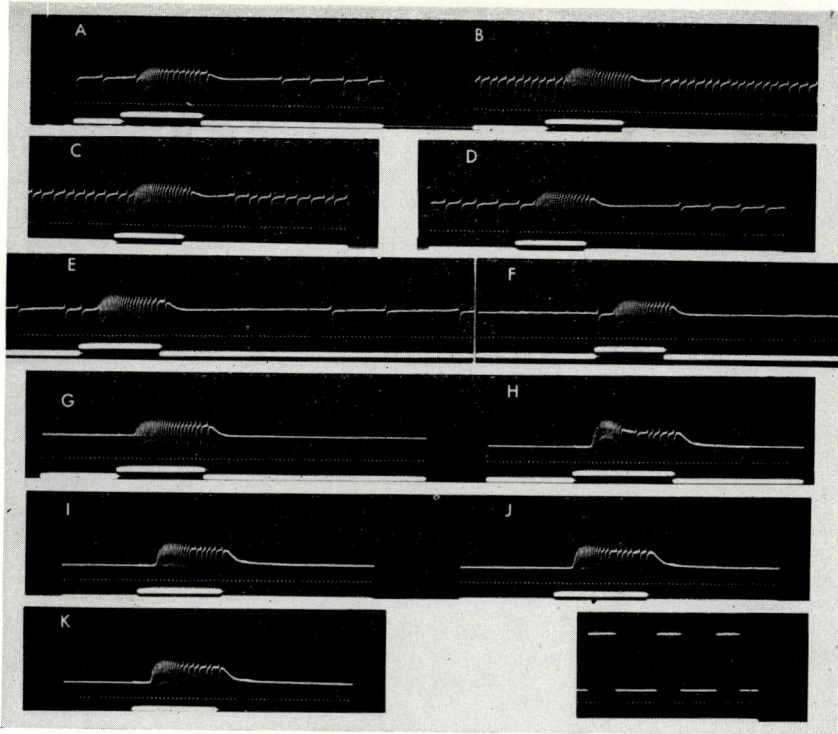

FIG. 3

Action of norepinephrin on the response to light. Top trace is intracellularly recorded membrane potential. Middle trace, 0·1 sec time marks. Bottom trace, light stimulus marker. Records taken every 30 sec after flow application of norep. before (A), and a sea water flush before (H). Calibration, 50 mV.

micropipette rather than nonspecific application by a gross flow technique give rise to a similar series of events. Although the pipette ejection technique ostensibly results in a slug or norep. in the region of the ommatidium under examination, it still is grosser than electrophoretic ejection from a multi-barreled pipette, for example. The ejection pipette used in these experiments was a separately manipulated unit with tip diameter of the order of 10 μ and which probably ejected several tenths of a microliter of solution.

The responses to 5-HT, pressure-ejected from a micropipette onto an ommatidium, are shown in Fig. 5. There is an abrupt rise in membrane potential which is accompanied by the appearance of spontaneous spike activity and a four- or five-fold increase in spike frequency during the tonic component of the generator. As the membrane potential continues to rise, although much more slowly than initially, the spike frequencies of the various components decrease, possibly due to a depolarization blocking action.

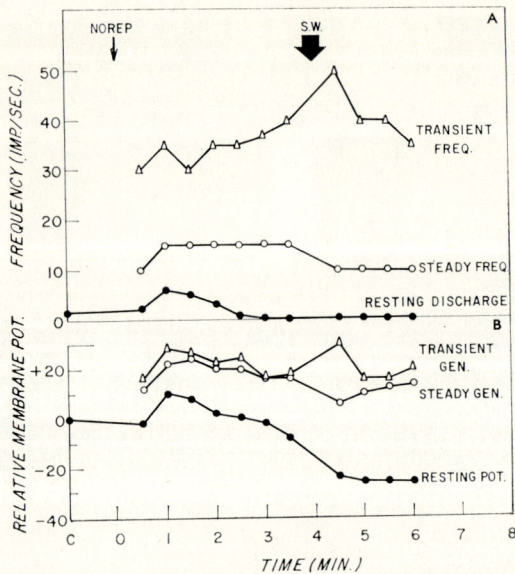

Fig. 4

Action of norepinephrin on the response to light. (A) Spike frequency, and (B) relative membrane potential as functions of time. See text for explanation of various components.

It was of interest to know the effect of the monoamines on the spontaneous subthreshold potentials (SPFs). The frequency of the SPFs does not appear to be affected, although their amplitudes are affected (Fig. 6). The membrane potential continuously depolarized in response to the application of epinephrin, in this case. This is not seen in this figure since the trace was readjusted continuously to keep it centered on the scope face. As the recording progresses, spikes appear at infrequent and sporadic intervals initially, and later at increasing frequency and regularity. During this progression the SPFs' frequency does not noticeably increase but their amplitudes do diminish. An analogous situation occurs in the frog neuromuscular junction (Martin, 1955). There, the decrease in miniature end-plate potential amplitude with increased quantum content of the EPP is ascribed to the nonlinear conductance–potential relationship in the postsynaptic membrane. Each quantum of acetylcholine is thought to give rise to a constant conductance increase which results in an end-plate depolarization that depends on initial membrane potential.

Reserpine is known to cause the release of bound catechol-amines and 5-HT, and to block their uptake by sympathetic nervous system tissues (Vogt, 1959). When reserpine is applied to the ommatidium the most marked effect is a transient depolarization of membrane potential followed by a somewhat

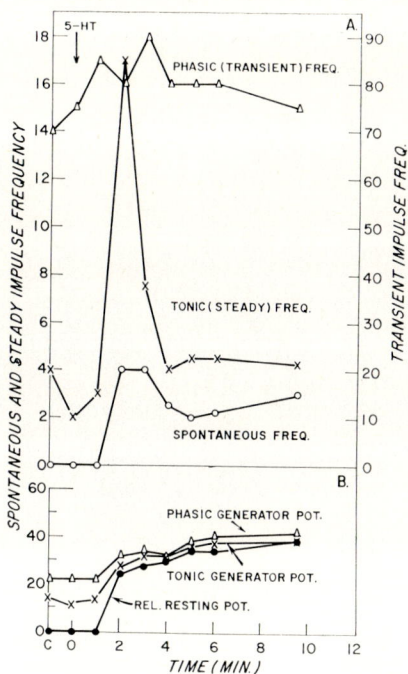

FIG. 5

Action of serotonin (5-HT) on the response to light. (A) Spike frequency, and (B) relative membrane potential as functions of time. 5-HT pressure-ejected from pipette immediately preceding time zero. See text for explanation of various components.

longer lasting hyperpolarization (Fig. 7). In the case illustrated, which was a cell giving a response characterized by a large generator potential (*ca.* 35–40 mV) and no spikes in response to light, the peak resting potential depolarization following drug application was more than 20 mV. The magnitudes of the transient and steady components of the generator potential are proportional to the differences between the resting potential curve and the curves for the transient and steady generator potentials, respectively. In addition to the marked effect on the resting potential, reserpine had a suppressing action on the magnitudes of the transient and steady components of generator potential. In another reserpine experiment the spike frequencies of a cell having moderate sized spikes (*ca.* 20–30 mV) followed the time course of the absolute value of membrane potential, i.e. a transient increase followed by a decrease.

An experiment testing the action of isoniazid (0·4 mg/ml) gave equivocal results. One eccentric cell previously untreated with isoniazid responded with hyperpolarization of the resting potential and decreased transient and steady

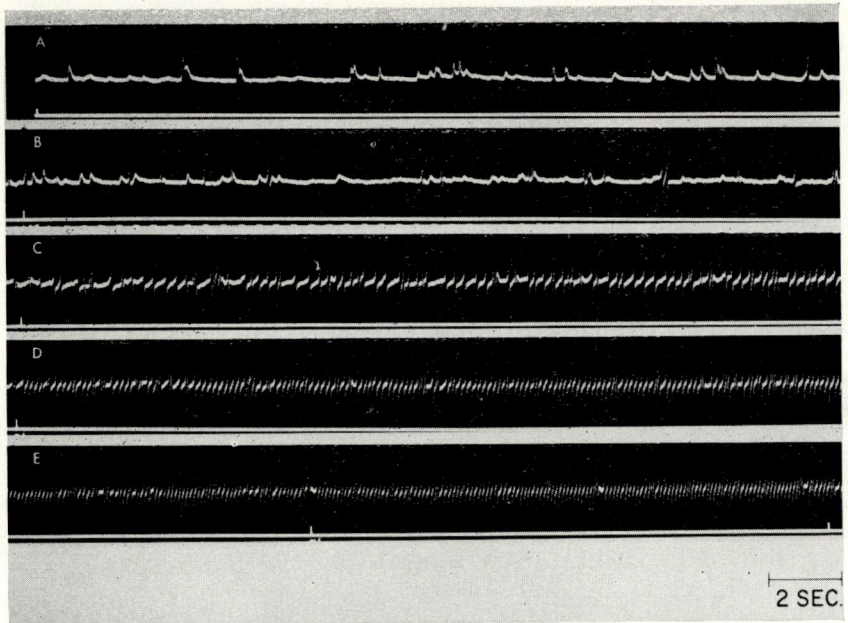

FIG. 6

Action of epinephrin on spontaneous activity. Segments showing SPFs and base-line portions of spikes (A) 2 min, (B) 3 min, (C) 4 min, (D) 5 min and (E) 7 min after flow application of epinephrin to a concentration of 0·1 mM. Amplitudes of largest SPFs were about 5 mV. Spike amplitudes about 40 mV, so that tops of spikes were out of the recording range. Time calibration, 2 sec.

spike frequencies, following application of the drug. A second eccentric cell in the same retinal slice, which had been bathed in the isoniazid for over ½ hour at the time it was tested, gave a slight depolarization of its resting potential (35%) in response to a further dose of the drug.

Few invertebrate excitatory synapses appear to be cholinergic; the *Aplysia* D-cell and leech neuromuscular junction are two of the unusual ones (Eccles, 1964). Atropine acts to block the depolarizing action of ACh on those synapses. ACh (as 1 mM ACh–Cl) and atropine (1 mM) were not found to affect the ommatidial neurons in the *Limulus* eye. These ACh-atropine results are preliminary ones which are based on three experiments. The lack of marked response to these agents led to discontinuation of testing their effects.

INHIBITORY AGENTS

The possible role of gamma-aminobutyric acid (GABA) as an inhibitory transmitter substance in invertebrate and vertebrate nervous systems has been widely investigated (Eccles, 1964; Roberts, 1960; Florey, 1961). Although

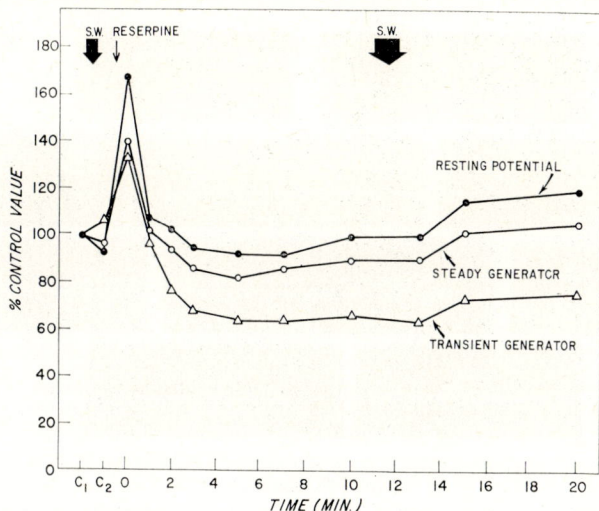

FIG. 7

Action of reserpine on generator potentials. Time course of components of a "pure" generator potential. Concentration of reserpine probably 10^{-6} to 10^{-4} M, but not known exactly since drug is almost insoluble in sea water.

GABA acts to depress the activity of vertebrate central neurons, Eccles (1964) cites the absence of hyperpolarizing membrane potential shifts and failure of strychnine to block the depressant action as evidence that GABA and its analogues are unlikely to be the usual postsynaptic inhibitory transmitters. The evidence that GABA or a related substance may be the inhibitory transmitter in invertebrates, especially crustacea, is more compelling (Kuffler and Edwards, 1958; Hagiwara *et al.*, 1960; Edwards, 1960).

GABA blocks spike action potentials but apparently does not interfere with excitatory processes in the *Limulus* ommatidium (Figs. 2 and 8). There is often a hyperpolarization of the eccentric cell membrane potential which accompanies the blocking action and which probably depends on the resting potential level in relation to the equilibrium potential for the inhibitory process. According to Purple (1964) the inhibitory equilibrium potential may be -70 mV in the region of synaptic action in the ommatidium. As measured in the soma membrane, the shifts of potential during inhibition from the resting level (*ca.* 45–55 mV) are not as great as the 15–25 mV inhibitory driving potentials which may occur in the neuropilar region. When the effects of GABA are tested while recording from within a retinular cell, as judged by physiological criteria (Adolph, 1963), the usual inhibition of spike frequency and attenuation of spikes and generator potentials are seen, but little if any change in resting potential occurs.

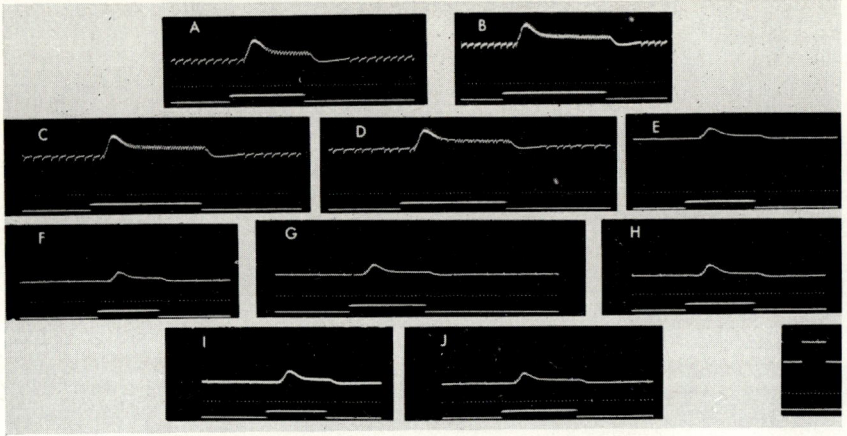

FIG. 8

Action of GABA on the response to light. Top trace is intracellularly recorded membrane potential. Middle trace, 0·1 sec time marks. Bottom trace, light stimulus marker. (A) Immediately before, and (B) 30 sec after flow application of GABA to a concentration between 1·0 and 10·0 mM. (C) 1½ min, (D) 2½ min, (E) 4 min after GABA. (F) 1 min after sea water flush, (G) 3 min, (H) 5 min, (I) 7 min and (J) 8 min after sea water. Baseline manually shifted between records (E) and (F). 10 mV calibration. Refer also to Fig. 2.

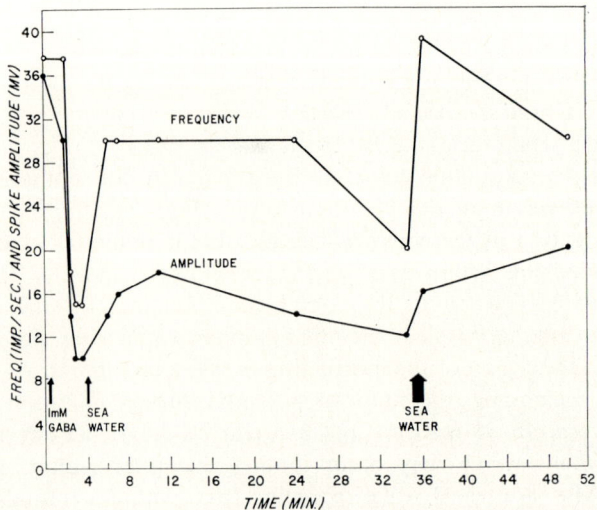

FIG. 9

Action of GABA on the response to light. Spikes during transient component. Flow application of 1·0 mM GABA until bath concentration about 0·1 mM.

Membrane conductance increases during the action of GABA on the ommatidium. Measurements of membrane resistance at the pipette show a drop from a resting value of 8 megohms to 1 megohm during the peak of GABA action. Figure 9 shows the reduction in spike amplitude, which parallels frequency inhibition during GABA action.[*] The localized action of GABA, perhaps in the neuropil region, which is a prerequisite for GABA to be considered as the inhibitory transmitter, may be indicated in Fig. 8 by the relative difference in amplitude reduction of the generator potential in comparison to spike amplitude. Differences in time course of the GABA inhibition may also indicate something about its localized action. Pressure ejection of GABA from micropipettes in the region just proximal to the ommatidium under test usually results in a faster inhibitory response than when the GABA is applied by a gross flow technique (see Figs. 10 and 11 as compared to Figs. 2 and 9).

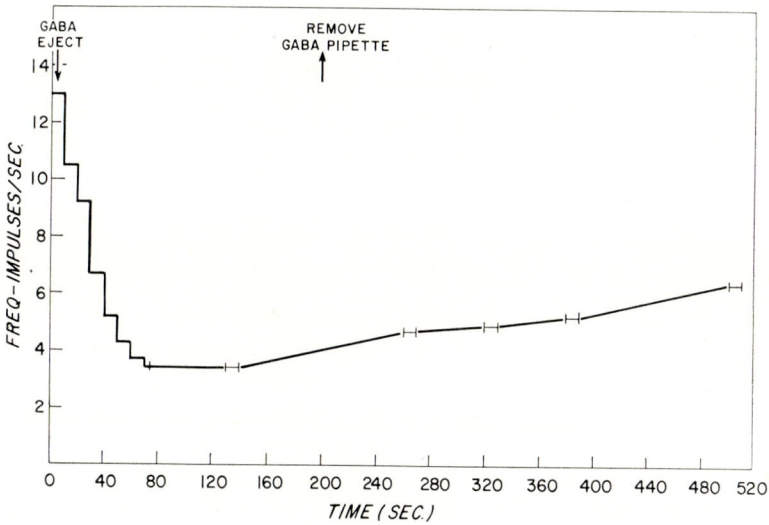

FIG. 10

Action of GABA on spontaneous activity. GABA pressure-ejected from micropipette in region proximal to ommatidium. Average spike frequency during indicated 10 sec periods.

The convulsant drug picrotoxin is known to block the inhibitory action of GABA and of natural inhibition in the crayfish stretch receptor (Edwards, 1960). The same results obtain in the *Limulus* ommatidium. This antagonism between GABA and picrotoxin is shown in Figs. 12 and 13. In Fig. 12 the

* Hagiwara, Kusano and Saito (1960) found conductance changes of 5 to 7 times in response to 10^{-4} M GABA applied to the crayfish stretch receptor.

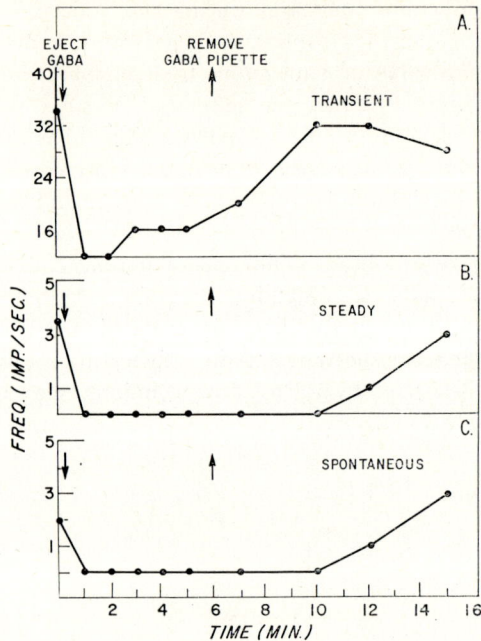

Fig. 11

Action of GABA on the response to light. GABA pressure-ejected from micro-pipette proximal to ommatidium. See text for explanation of various response components.

ejection of GABA (*ca.* 10^{-4} M) onto the proximal region of the ommatidium causes a drop in spike frequency in response to a current stimulus to the eccentric cell. The inhibition is abated by a sea water flush of the cell. The gross application of picrotoxin (0·1–1·0 mM) results in a slight increase in spike frequency. A further short flush with sea water is insufficient to remove the picrotoxin acting on the ommatidium; the simultaneous application of GABA and picrotoxin later on does not result in any inhibition by the GABA as was produced earlier by the GABA alone. When the drugs are applied in the reverse order, as is depicted in Fig. 13, a depolarizing action of the picrotoxin can be clearly seen. This depolarizing response is often, although not invariably, seen.

When picrotoxin is applied to an eye in which the test ommatidium is being inhibited by antidromic stimulation of the optic nerve, the inhibition appears to be blocked (Fig. 14). In this case the test unit was orthodromically stimulated by a depolarizing current step and a train of antidromic stimuli was delivered at a fixed rate (30 per second) and pulse duration (4 msec). By plotting the inhibitory decrement in frequency as a function of

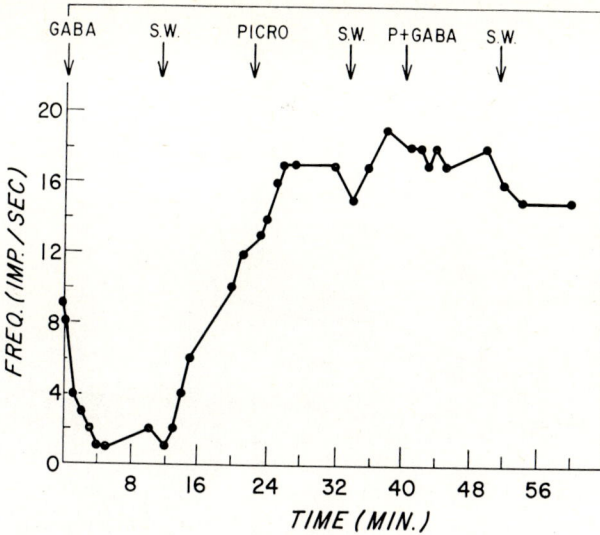

Fig. 12

Action of GABA and picrotoxin in response to current stimulus. GABA (0·4 mM) pressure-ejected from micropipette proximal to ommatidium. Gross application of picrotoxin until bath concentration about 0·1 mM. Current stimulus was a 4 nA depolarizing step.

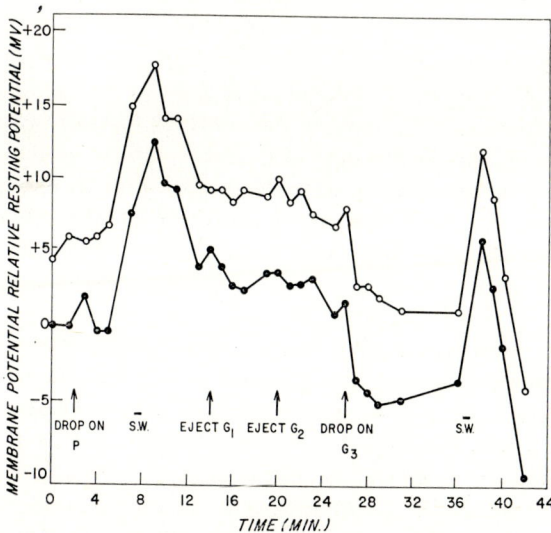

Fig. 13

Action of picrotoxin and GABA on membrane potential. Lower curve, relative membrane potential immediately preceding light stimulus. Upper curve, relative membrane potential 2 sec after end of 2·5 sec light stimulus.

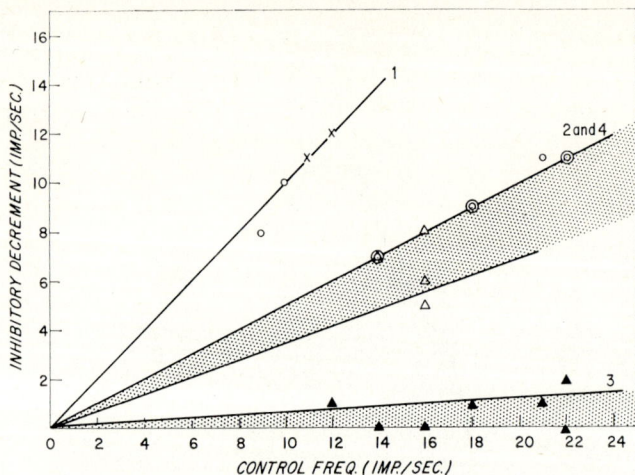

Fig. 14

Action of picrotoxin on antidromic inhibition. Orthodromic stimulus, 2 nA depolarizing current step. Antidromic frequency, 30 per sec. Region 1: controls (x), and during first minute (o) after picrotoxin (0·1 mM). Region 2: second to fifteenth minutes (o). Region 3: eighteenth to fortieth minutes (▲), with two short sea water flushes. Region 4: forty-fifth to sixtieth minutes (△), with one long (3 min) sea water flush.

pre-inhibitory control frequency one may obtain some indication of the "efficiency" of the inhibitory processes from the slope of the plotted lines. A line with a slope of one, i.e. complete inhibition, being one limiting case, and a slope of zero, i.e. no inhibition, the other limit.

The experimental results plotted in Fig. 14 show that before and just after the addition of picrotoxin the slope was one (complete inhibition). During the following 15 min period the slope decreased to about one-half. For the next 20 or so minutes, a period when two short sea water flushes were applied, further "washing in" the picrotoxin, the slope decreased to zero (no inhibition). A final 15 min period, which included a long sea water flush, partially restored the slope.

Strychnine, a convulsant drug which has been found to block inhibition in mammalian central nervous systems (Eccles, 1964) but not in invertebrate neurons, did not appear to have any effect on the *Limulus* eye. Aminooxyacetic acid (AOAA), which in mammals inhibits the metabolism of GABA via its transaminase pathway (van Gelder, 1965), did not show any marked effects on antidromic inhibition of the *Limulus* eye. The time span over which these effects were examined was about 30 min; in mammals, systemic applications of AOAA may require at least this long, and possibly longer, to develop effects. In addition, the metabolic paths of GABA in invertebrates may be different from those in mammals. It should be understood that these results cited for strychnine and aminooxyacetic acid are of a preliminary nature and were obtained in single experiments involving a total of only three or four neurons.

A number of compounds structurally related to GABA have inhibitory actions on mammalian neurons (Krnjevic and Phillis, 1963) and on the cray-fish stretch receptor (Edwards, 1960). of the omega-amino acids, beta-alanine is one that is effective on both the mammalian and invertebrate neurons, although not so effective as GABA. Figure 15 shows the effect of beta-alanine (0·1 mM) on spontaneous spikes in the *Limulus* ommatidium. It is

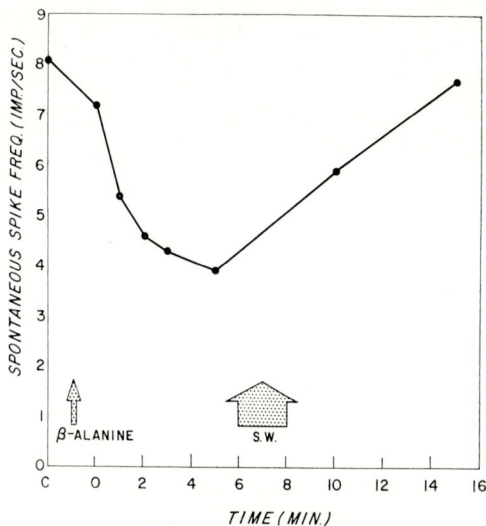

FIG. 15

Action of beta-alanine on spontaneous activity. Gross application of beta-alanine until bath concentration was between 0·1 and 0·2 mM.

difficult to draw conclusions regarding the relative potencies of beta-alanine and GABA from diverse experiments, but the reduction in spike frequency by a factor of 2 by beta-alanine should be compared with reductions by factors of 3 to 10 in similar experiments using GABA. Taurine, which was approximately as effective as beta-alanine in its inhibitory action on the ommatidium, has also been found to inhibit the crayfish neuromuscular junction and stretch receptor (Kravitz *et al.*, 1963; Edwards, 1960).

BIOCHEMICAL ANALYSES

High-voltage electrophoreses of rather crude extracts of the ommatidial tissue were carried out. The extracts were obtained by homogenizing the tissue and precipitating out some of the protein fraction with sodium acetate

solution. The tissues were stripped from within the eye chamber and contained ommatidia, nerve fibers and connective tissue. A control run using
connective tissue from a non-eye region of the animal showed that the connective tissue did not give the ninhydrin positive spots obtained with the eye
tissue. Two regions, of differing mobilities, were obtained from the eye
extracts (Fig. 16). There was a third region of very low mobility near the origin
which probably contained a good deal of protein and tissue fragments.
Standards of the various agents studied physiologically were run along with
the tissue extracts.

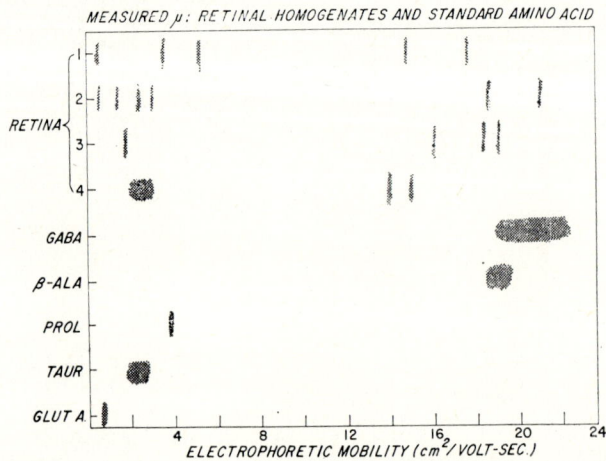

FIG. 16

Electrophoretic mobilities of eye tissue extracts and standard amino acids. High
voltage (*ca.* 50 V/cm) paper electrophoresis in acetate buffered pyridine, pH 3·5.
Hatched areas indicate approximate ranges of mobilities of different components
and amino acids, found in four experiments.

While no positive identifications of these substances in the eye tissue can be
made on the basis of these crude separations, it is of interest to note that
GABA and beta-alanine run with mobilities similar to the fast retinal tissue
group. Also, taurine runs with a mobility falling in the range of the slower
retinal tissue group. Glutamic acid, which behaved as a cation at the pH (3·5)
of the pyridine–acetate solvent, was one of the least mobile substances and its
spot was in the mobility range of the slowest group. In recent experiments, with
results not indicated in Fig. 16, an electrophoresis using a GABA standard
mixed in with the tissue extract and comparing its mobility to the mobility of
GABA alone showed a retardation of the GABA peak due to the ionic environment presented by the tissue salts. Norep. and epin. gave spots with mobilities
comparable to the fast moving tissue group (i.e. about 16 V/cm² sec).

SUMMARY

Glutamic acid, norepinephrin, epinephrin and 5-hydroxytryptamine produce excitation of electrical activity in the eye. The form of the excitation is a membrane depolarization and increased frequency of spikes. The eye does not appear to be responsive to acetylcholine or atropine. The Q_{10} of the spontaneous miniature subthreshold potentials (SPFs) is between 3 and 4, similar to other synaptic subthreshold processes. The various excitatory substances do not appear to directly stimulate an increased frequency of SPFs but rather to act directly on the receptor membrane and produce an increased ionic conductance.

Impulse blockade and membrane hyperpolarization are produced by gamma-aminobutyric acid (GABA) and, to a lesser extent, by beta-alanine and taurine. These inhibitory agents do not appear to affect the generator potential mechanism. Picrotoxin blocks the action of GABA and blocks lateral inhibition produced by antidromic stimulation of the optic nerve.

ACKNOWLEDGEMENTS

The work reported in this communication was performed under support of Public Health Services grant NB-03489.

REFERENCES

ADOLPH, A. R. 1963. A stochastic model of neuron function and its application to subthreshold processes in the *Limulus* photoreceptor and frog neuromuscular junction. Ph.D. Thesis, The Rockefeller Institute.

ADOLPH, A. R. 1964. Spontaneous slow potential fluctuations in the *Limulus* photoreceptor. *J. Gen. Physiol.* **48**, 297.

ECCLES, J. C. 1964. *The Physiology of Synapses*. Academic Press, New York.

EDWARDS, C. 1960. Physiology and pharmacology of the crayfish stretch receptor. In *Inhibition in the Nervous System and Gamma-Aminobutyric Acid* (E. Roberts, ed.). Pergamon Press, New York.

FATT, P. and KATZ, B. 1952. Spontaneous subthreshold activity at motor nerve endings. *J. Physiol.* **117**, 109.

FLOREY, E. (ed.). 1961. *Nervous Inhibition*. Macmillan, New York.

GERSCHENFELD, H. M. and TAUC, L. 1961. Pharmacological specificities of neurones in an elementary central nervous system. *Nature*, **189**, 924.

HAGIWARA, S., KUSANO, K. and SAITO, S. 1960. Membrane changes in crayfish stretch receptor neuron during synaptic inhibition and under action of gamma-aminobutyric acid. *J. Neurophysiol.* **23**, 505.

HARTLINE, H. K., RATLIFF, F. and MILLER, W. H. 1961. Inhibitory interaction in the retina and its significance in vision. In *Nervous Inhibition* (E. Florey, ed.). Macmillan, New York.

KERKUT, G. A. and COTTRELL, G. A. 1963. ACh and 5-HT in the snail brain. *Comp. Biochem. Physiol.* **8**, 53.

KRAVITZ, E., KUFFLER, S. W., POTTER, D. and VAN GELDER, N. 1963. Gamma-aminobutyric acid and other blocking compounds in crustacea. II. Peripheral nervous system. *J. Neurophysiol.* **26**, 729.

KRNJEVIC, K. and PHILLIS, J. W. 1963. Iontophoretic studies of neurons in the mammalian cerebral cortex. *J. Physiol.* **165**, 274.

KUFFLER, S. W. and EDWARDS, C. 1958. Mechanism of gamma-aminobutyric acid (GABA) action and its relation to synaptic inhibition. *J. Neurophysiol.* **21**, 589.

KURIYAMA, H. 1964. The effect of temperature on neuromuscular transmission in the vas deferens of the guinea-pig. *J. Physiol.* **170**, 561.

LILEY, A. W. 1956. An investigation of spontaneous activity at the neuromuscular junction of the rat. *J. Physiol.* **132**, 650.

MARTIN, A. R. 1955. A further study of the statistical composition of the end-plate potential. *J. Physiol.* **130**, 114.

PURPLE, R. 1964. The integration of excitatory and inhibitory influences in the eccentric cell in the eye of *Limulus*. Ph.D. Thesis, The Rockefeller Institute.

ROBERTS, E. (ed.). 1960. *Inhibition in the Nervous System and Gamma-Aminobutyric Acid.* Pergamon Press, New York.

SALMOIRAGHI, G. C. and BLOOM, F. E. 1964. Pharmacology of individual neurons. *Science,* **144**, 493.

VAN GELDER, N. M. 1965. The histochemical demonstration of gamma-aminobutyric acid metabolism by reduction of a tetrazolium salt. *J. Neurochem.* **12**, 231.

VOGT, M. 1959. Adrenaline and noradrenaline in nervous tissue. In *Biochemistry of the Central Nervous System* (F. Brücke, ed.). Pergamon Press, London.

CLOCK-SPIKES IN THE *CALLIPHORA* OPTIC LOBE AND A HYPOTHESIS FOR THEIR FUNCTION IN OBJECT LOCATION

J. T. Leutscher-Hazelhoff and J. W. Kuiper

Department of Biophysics, Natuurkundig Laboratorium der Rijks Universiteit, Groningen

INTRODUCTION

In the optic lobe (or 3rd ganglion layer) of the blowfly there are action potentials which fire at a very constant rate. The repetitive firing goes on almost as long as the fly is alive; on one occasion it was observed for 11 hr, with no appreciable changes in frequency up to the very end.

In the following pages we will describe the phenomenon, and an analysis will be given of the statistical properties of long spike trains of 10,000 to 100,000 spikes, which have been recorded on magnetic tape. We will conclude with the presentation of a hypothesis regarding its function, namely, as a timing mechanism in object location. A preliminary report has already been published as a letter to the editor in *Nature*, 1965.

MATERIAL AND METHODS

More than a hundred experiments were done on animals that were intact except for a small piece of chitin cut away from the back of the head, so that the visual system and optic lobe were visible. The spikes were picked up either centrally in the optic lobe, on some occasions even in the region adjoining the central nervous system, or more peripherally, in most cases on the ventral side of the optic lobe.

Several different types of electrodes have been used for recording, for example Pt–Ir glass-coated electrodes, and either KCl-filled or metal-filled pipettes (tip diameter $10-20\ \mu$). Both single-ended and differential pre-amplifiers, with direct as well as capacitive interstage coupling, were used. We used batteries as well as line-fed power supplies. Checks were performed with an electrometer tube input whose grid current was less than 10^{-12} amp.

In experiments in which the temperature was varied, the animal was fixed in a double-walled, close-fitting house made of brass, in such a way that there was no electrical contact between the animal and the house; water from a constant-temperature bath (temperature variations smaller than $0\cdot01°C$) was pumped through at high speed. A small thermocouple was kept in the thorax of the animal and the temperature was recorded on a micrograph.

ORIGIN OF THE SPIKES

It was ascertained that the spikes actually originate in the optic lobe or in the central nervous system: in experiments on isolated heads, or on animals in which all tissue peripheral to the optic lobe was cut through, the spikes were found to persist for a short time. The left and right optic lobe fire completely independently.

THE WAVEFORM

At room temperature, the spikes vary in amplitude between 200 and 1500 μV, and their duration varies between 1 and 8 msec. The shorter-lasting spikes are picked up centrally in the optic lobe, and are biphasic as a rule; the longer-lasting ones are picked up more peripherally, are sometimes biphasic, sometimes monophasic and usually accompanied by afterpotentials. Apart from the site of recording, the waveform was found to depend very much on the temperature. In Fig. 1 a centrally recorded spike is shown at different temperatures; in each picture, about a hundred spikes are superimposed, all triggered on the downgoing slope, demonstrating that at a given temperature all spikes are very nearly identical. The biphasic character of the spike and the afterpotentials that are seen at the higher temperatures disappear completely below $10°C$, where only a long-lasting monophasic form remains. In penetration experiments, spikes could be picked up over a range of 200–400 μ, in most cases without appreciable changes in form.

In a few experiments, using two separate channels, each with a differentially recording amplifier, we picked up central and peripheral sets of spike trains simultaneously. It was found that there is an absolute correlation between the timing of the two, but that the peripheral spike lags behind the central one by 1–2 msec. The speed of propagation calculated from such experiments amounted to $\frac{1}{2}$–1 m/sec.

THE RATE OF FIRING

The rate of firing is very constant, and at room temperature is about 50–60 spikes/sec.* In dying animals, and in animals brought under CO_2 anaesthesia, the spikes do not change in amplitude, but the rate of firing becomes gradually higher with sudden reversals; sometimes spikes evidently start to be dropped from the train.

* Suspicions of a spurious effect due to the fact that our power line frequency is 50 c/s may be definitely allayed; we have been aware of the possibility of interference and we have performed sufficient checks to exclude this.

When the interspike interval becomes as short as 2–5 msec the spikes disappear. In the case of CO_2 anaesthesia this is completely reversible. The only other way to change the rate of firing proved to be changing the temperature; mechanical stimulation has no effect, nor have various forms of light stimulation. Neither photic nor electric driving could be accomplished.

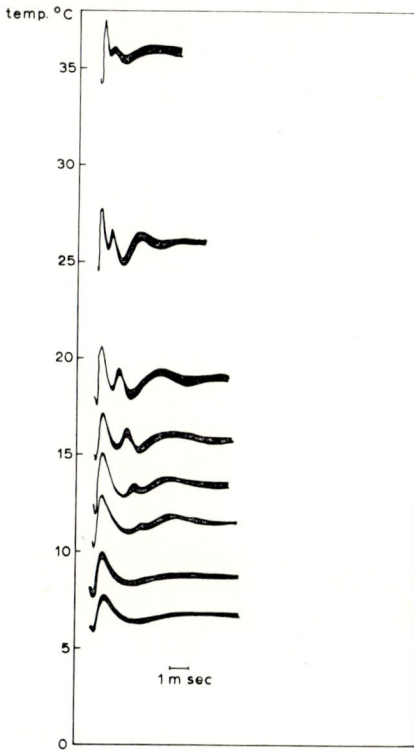

FIG. 1

Waveforms of a centrally recorded spike at different temperatures. In each picture, about a hundred spikes are superimposed, all triggered on the first downgoing slope.

Light flashes of 10 μsec duration from a stroboscopic lamp—which elicited an electroretinogram that came through in the recording three times as large as the spikes themselves—failed to bring the spikes into frequency and phase when the frequency of the applied flashes was very near to the spike frequency, or even when the flashes were triggered by the spikes themselves. Similarly, an electrical current did not affect the spikes until it actually cooked the tissue.

INFLUENCE OF TEMPERATURE ON THE REPETITION RATE

The repetition rate of the spikes could be altered very considerably by changing the temperature. Values were obtained from about 10 spikes/sec at low temperatures to about 125 spikes/sec at high temperatures. The relation between temperature and repetition rate is essentially linear except at the extremes of the temperature range (6–36°C), as can be seen in Fig. 2.

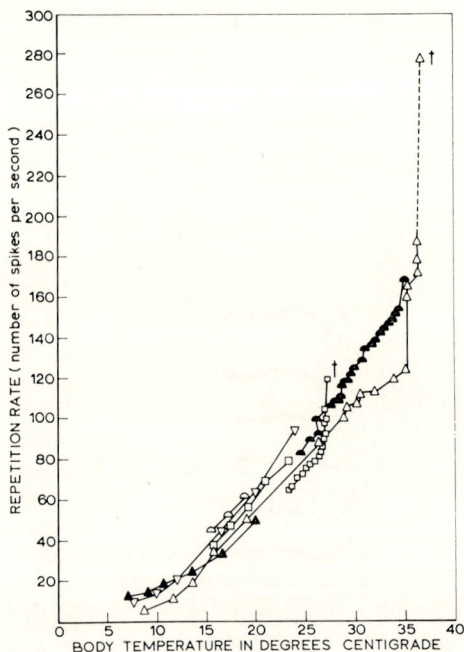

FIG. 2

Relation between the temperature and the repetition rate, for five different animals.
† means death of the animal.

The increase in repetition rate averages 5·5 spikes/sec per degree centigrade. There are individual differences: at 7–8°C the repetition rate was 10 and 12 spikes/sec in two cases, and 5·5 spikes/sec in another. In this last instance cooling below 7°C resulted in a continual slowing down to 2·2 spikes/sec after which the firing stopped altogether. This temperature effect was completely reversible.

The same cannot be said for what happens at the higher temperatures: with individual differences, at some point between 25 and 36°C the repetition rate rises, even without further rise in temperature, up to values of 200 spikes/sec, and the picture becomes essentially the same as that of a dying or anaesthetized animal. Unlike the effect of CO_2 anaesthesia, however, this effect was always irreversible.

The values of these temperature limits might be considered somewhat surprising; temperatures of more than 36°C are not exceptional in the natural habitat. If the spikes are of vital importance to the animal, they should not stop functioning under these circumstances. We should consider the possibility that indeed they do not. In the tsetse fly, body temperature regulation in dry air is effected by evaporation resulting in a maximal depression of body temperature of 1·6°C (Edney and Barass, 1962). Furthermore, these animals always tend to seek shelter in relatively cool places (37°C) whenever they are not actively feeding. Possibly blowflies also normally protect themselves from overheating. As for short-lasting high temperatures, we have observed in a preliminary experiment on *Eristalis* that the firing stopped 30 sec after the fly was exposed to the heat of a strong lamp; switching off the lamp immediately thereafter brought the spikes back in 20 sec. Unfortunately, we have no idea of the value of the body temperature of the animal in this experiment. It points, however, to the possibility that the speed of the change in temperature must be taken into consideration. The lower temperature limit of about 7°C is also remarkable. Flies kept in the refrigerator at this temperature behave very sluggishly; they crawl about, but do not fly.

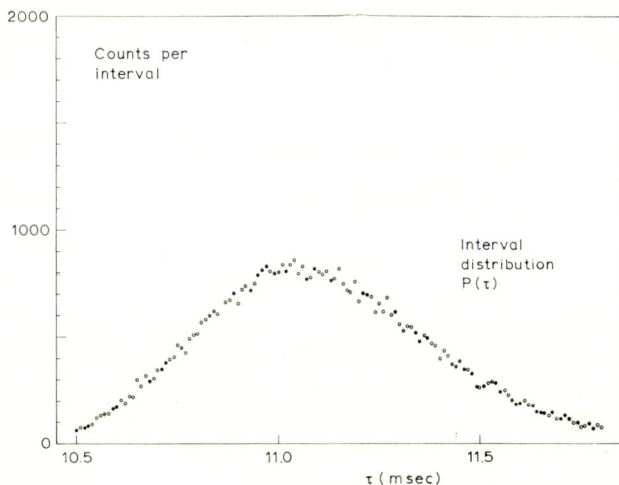

FIG. 3

Distribution of the interspike intervals in a constant-temperature experiment.

STATISTICAL ANALYSIS OF THE PROPERTIES OF THE SPIKES
IN CONSTANT-TEMPERATURE EXPERIMENTS

In several experiments the body temperature of the fly was kept constant within 0·1°C, and trains of 10,000 to 100,000 spikes were recorded on magnetic tape. After analog to digital conversion the data was fed into a computer.

Figure 3 shows an example of the distribution of the interspike intervals in a train of 60,000. It is seen that the distribution deviates but little from a Gaussian. The standard deviation, calculated from the best-fitting Gaussian distribution, amounts to less than 3 % of the mean value of the interspike interval. There are individual differences: we have found values of standard deviation which vary from 1·6 to 4%. Spike trains recorded at different temperatures revealed that this percentage is the same for all values of the interspike interval in a given fly (see Fig. 4).

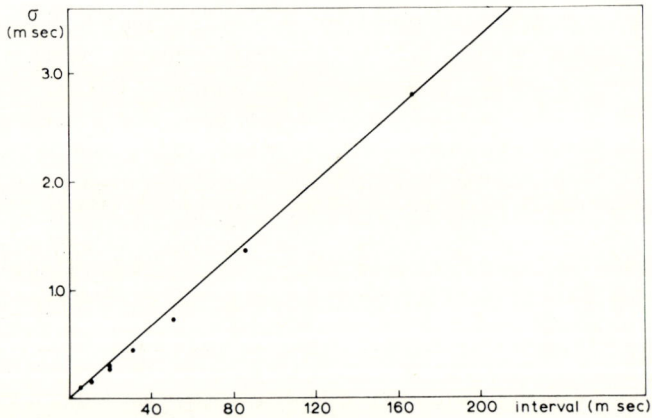

FIG. 4

Relation between the interspike interval values (obtained in one animal at different temperatures) and their standard deviation.

Because we suspected the existence of a correlation between subsequent interspike intervals, we determined the distributions of the scaled intervals (that is, the double, the triple, the quadruple interval, etc.). Up to the 10-fold interval, the distributions remain reasonably close to a Gaussian, though there is an increasing tendency for the ascending slope to be a little steeper than the descending one. The standard deviations calculated from the best-fitting Gaussians are related to the mean interval values as shown in Fig. 5.*

* The values plotted in Fig. 5 were obtained by Drs. H. van Barneveld and T. Sinnema. (By earlier but less advanced analysis a similar relationship was also shown up in two instances, but the points strayed rather more.) Recently they have succeeded in extending their analysis up to the 80-fold interval.

This proves the existence of a correlation: if there were no correlation at all, for a Gaussian distribution the standard deviation of the *n*-fold interval would equal $\sqrt{n}$ times the standard deviation of the single interval.

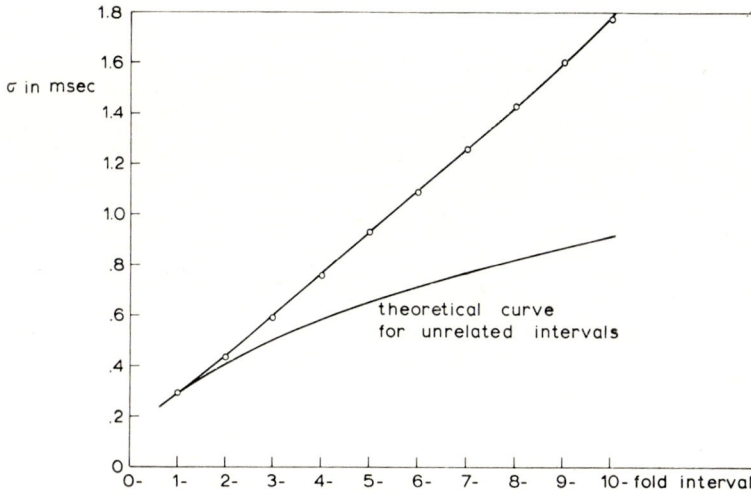

FIG. 5

The standard deviations of the scaled intervals up to 10, and the theoretical curve for a Gaussian distribution of unrelated intervals.

In addition, we calculated that a positive correlation of about 0·1 exists between two subsequent intervals. This means that the results of Fig. 5 cannot be explained by this correlation, i.e. by a first-order correlation alone.

The notion that the correlation extends over more than one interval does not seem improbable when one considers the picture of the building up of the distribution on the computer screen during the data processing. One sees that the histogram is built up in jerks—the points tend to stray to one flank of the distribution for a while, then to the other, and then back again, in a highly irregular fashion. Whether or not such extended correlations will provide sufficient explanation for the results of Fig. 5 will have to be ascertained in the future.

We are not as yet far enough advanced with our analysis to be able to propose a model for the mechanism underlying the high-precision firing. For the time being, we think that a random-walk model such as has been proposed by Gerstein and Mandelbrot (1964)* may be used as a first approximation.

---

* This random-walk model supposes that the generator potential is built up in small steps, all of which have the same height and appear at random, perhaps started by noise. When the generator potential has reached a certain limit a spike is fired off, and the whole process starts all over again. Several more complex random-walk models have also been proposed.

THE FUNCTION

Although the high-precision of the firing and its mechanism are absorbing in themselves (the only case we have found that can be remotely compared with it was found by Horn (1962) in the cat striate cortex), the problem of their function is even more intriguing.

The idea of a physiological clock was rejected as soon as we saw the effect of the temperature. Though it is known that in the honeybee pulses of cold (5–7°C) or high (40°C) temperatures will delay or hasten, respectively, the time of feeding (Kalmus, 1934; Renner, 1957), their time sense is independent of temperature between 18 and 35°C (see also Sweeney and Hastings, 1960). We think, even without corresponding evidence in the case of the blowfly, that the great temperature effect we find makes these spikes useless as a clock.

They can also be counted out as a pacemaker for wing-beating. The distributions of interspike intervals found in flight nerve and muscle differ strongly from those reported here (Wyman, 1965).

Neither are we attracted by the idea of a thermometer in the optic lobe, or, for that matter, any other function that has nothing to do with vision, especially since the spikes move from the centre of the optic lobe to the periphery.

So, looking for a function in the visual system, we have first turned our thoughts to a scanning mechanism: a signal, pointing out selectively, one after the other, clusters of sense cells (or more centrally lying units) for the momentary transmission of signals to the central nervous system. However, we have never been able to find a delay of more than 2 msec between spikes picked up at different sites, whereas we would expect delays up to the value of the interspike interval itself. Apart from that, the high critical flicker-fusion values that are found in electrophysiological experiments (about 300 c/s) make it rather difficult to support this idea.

Instead, we think at present along the following lines: when a distinct object is viewed during flight, it is seen by different clusters of sense cells in succession. We suppose that comparison between different clusters (of one eye) seeing the same object is timed by the high-precision firing. For the fly's distance to the object we may write (see Fig. 6)

$$d = \frac{N\tau v \, \sin \beta}{\sin \alpha}$$

when d = distance between insect and object, N = number of interspike intervals elapsed between the viewing of the object by the first and the second cluster, v = velocity of the insect, τ = interspike interval, β = angle between the optical axis of the first-viewing cluster of ommatidia and the direction of flight, and α = angle between the first- and second-viewing cluster of ommatidia.

In this formula the only parameter that may be unknown to the insect is its velocity; possibly it has an intrinsic knowledge of this, but if it has not it may relate the distance to the velocity. We believe that this is how we judge distances ourselves; when travelling at a speed we are not used to, we always make mistakes in distance judgement at first.

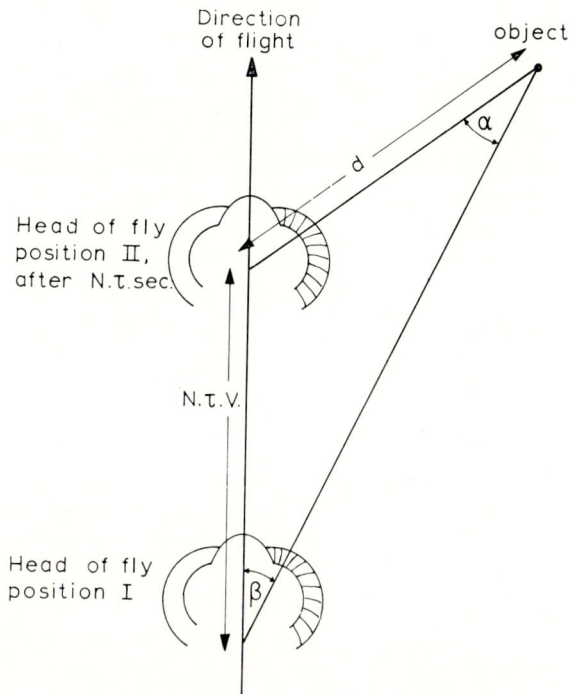

FIG. 6

Hypothesis for the calculation of d = distance between insect and object, N = number of interspike intervals elapsed between the viewing of the object by the first and the second cluster of ommatidia, v = velocity of the insect, τ = interspike interval, β = angle between the optical axis of the first-viewing cluster and the direction of flight, and α = angle between the first- and second-viewing clusters of ommatidia.

If our hypothesis is true, object location will be somewhat more resistant to temperature changes than the spikes themselves, since τ and v change in opposite directions. At lower temperatures, slow movements and long interspike intervals go together. This is also the case in other species of insects: there are especially marked differences in repetition rate between slow- and fast-moving species of Syrphidae.

A consequence of this hypothesis is that the animals should be able to locate objects with one eye. Therefore we have done a few experiments in which one eye was coated with black paint. We have observed in two instances that such insects, having grown accustomed to this situation after a few hours, were able to navigate in a horizontal plane, carefully avoiding obstacles.

More behaviour experiments are needed for the testing of our hypothesis. Among other things, a clue might be provided by optomotor experiments in which the light is provided by a stroboscope lamp triggered by the spikes. If the flashes coincide exactly with the spikes, the animal should, according to our hypothesis, be able to make a normal comparison and react as if steady light were used, but not if the flashes come between the spikes. As such an experiment would be very hard to carry out, we might instead, without knowing exactly what to expect, observe what happens to light-spikes when the stroboscope is triggered by the clock-spikes, with or without a delay.

Another reaction that might be used as a test is the landing response described by Goodman (1964) in experiments on *Lucilia*. Insects that are in a fixed position with dangling legs stretch out their legs when they see an object approaching. Goodman concluded that the percentage of landing responses is linearly related to the product of the number of ommatidia stimulated, the logarithm of the relative decrease in intensity, and the rate of decrease in intensity. The number of ommatidia stimulated is linearly related to the increase in angle under which the approaching object is seen; this angle differs only by a factor of 2 from our angle α.

The velocity of the animal with respect to the object is here expressed as the rate of decrease in intensity. The fact that in our formula v and $\sin \alpha$ have an opposite effect on d whereas in Goodman's empirical formula v and α are both linearly related to the percentage of landing responses would not seem to be exactly promising for our hypothesis. At any rate, we think it may be worthwhile to repeat Goodman's experiments with our hypothesis in mind, in a perhaps somewhat different experimental set-up.

Whether or not our hypothesis is true, it is evident that clock-pulses that are independent of the incoming information are very valuable in the processing of this information.

REFERENCES

EDNEY, E. B. and BARASS, R. 1962. The body temperature of the tsetse fly. *J. Insect Physiol.* **8**, 4, 469.

GERSTEIN, G. L. and MANDELBROT, B. 1964. Random walk models for spike activity of a single neuron. *Biophys. Journal.* **4**, 1, 41–69.

GOODMAN, L. J. 1964. The landing responses of insects. *J. Exp. Biol.* **41**, 403–15.

HORN, G. 1962. Regular impulse activity of single units in the cat striate cortex. *Nature*, **194**, 4833, 1084–5.

KALMUS, H. 1934. Ueber die Natur des Zeitgedächtnisses bei Bienen. *Zeitschr. f. vergl. Physiol.* **20**, 405–19.

KUIPER, J. W. and LEUTSCHER-HAZELHOFF, J. T. 1965. High-precision repetitive firing in the insect optic lobe and a hypothesis for its function in object location. *Nature*, **207**, 4989, 1158–60.

RENNER, M. 1957. Neue Versuche über den Zeitsinn der Honigbiene. *Zeitscher. f. vergl. Physiol.* **40**, 85–118.

SWEENEY, B. M. and HASTINGS, J. W. 1960. Effects of temperature on diurnal rhythms. *Cold Spring Harbor Symp.*, **25**, 87–104.

WYMAN, R. 1965. Probabilistic characterization of simultaneous nerve impulse sequences controlling dipteran flight. *Biophys. Journal*, **5**, 4, 447–71.

POLAROTAXIS AND PRIMARY PHOTORECEPTOR EVENTS IN CRUSTACEA*

T. H. WATERMAN

Department of Biology, Yale University, New Haven, Connecticut, U.S.A.

INTRODUCTION

WHILE the ommatidium is obviously the structural building block of compound eyes, the extent to which it is the basic functional unit remains controversial. That such basic ambiguity can persist despite the large amount of work already done on these important visual receptors, testifies to the substantial gaps remaining in our knowledge of comparative visual physiology.

Probably the most crucial point here is the operational relation of an ommatidium's typically seven or eight component retinular cells to their collective entity, the retinula. In the detection of visual stimulus parameters does each retinular cell constitute an information channel at least partly independent of its close-packed neighbors or do two or more such neurosensory elements in a retinula act as a unit? At one extreme there would be seven or eight separate neural channels per ommatidium whereas at the other extreme there would effectively be only one.

In any case it is certain that various visual stimulus parameters are processed in different specific ways so that they are partitioned into distinct axonal channels at the level of optic nerve interneurons (Waterman and Wiersma, 1963; Waterman, Wiersma and Bush, 1964). These higher order fibers always were found to carry information integrated over many ommatidia, but in the present review attention will be directed mainly to the early steps in information processing as they occur in a single ommatidium.

Beyond the initial dioptric influences the information handling capability of such sensory systems must be dependent on the primary event of photon absorption by the visual pigment concerned. In fact some channeling of information appears already to be determined at this molecular photochemical level. Evidence for this is available for polarized light perception and for color vision as discussed below.

Clearly the overall problems raised here are complex since data relevant to their solution may come from dioptric, biochemical, morphological,

* Aided by NIH grant NB 03076 and NSF grant G24055.

neurological and behavioral levels. Furthermore a wide range of input parameters should be encompassed in any general explanation. However, in the present report attention is focused particularly on an input of linearly polarized light and on output responses measured in various ways, but mainly in terms of the resulting oriented polarotactic behavior. In addition, most of the data discussed are restricted to crustaceans, with which we have mainly worked.

Specific effects of polarized light have been reported in ninety or more different animal species of which twenty-six are crustaceans assigned to six different orders of the class (Waterman, 1965b). Similar responses certainly could be demonstrated in many more Crustacea, Insecta and Cephalopoda if they were tested. So far, in crustaceans only those with compound eyes can be firmly included in such a list, but work in progress indicates that comparable responses apparently occur in aquatic forms possessing median eyes but not compound eyes. However, dorsal eyes of spiders, simple eyes in water mites and perhaps dorsal and lateral ocelli of insects have previously been shown to be specifically sensitive to polarized light (references in Jander and Waterman, 1960).

SPECIFIC e-VECTOR SENSITIVITY

In assessing the respective contributions of retinular cells and retinulas to this capacity of detecting the e-vector of polarized light a crucial question is whether direction and intensity of illumination can be consistently discriminated from polarization. If so, the polarized light must be perceived as such. A similar question must be answered affirmatively to demonstrate color vision.

Since visual responses to intensity and direction of light are nearly universal, unequivocal demonstration of polarized light sensitivity requires considerable care. This is particularly so because artifacts resulting from differential reflection and refraction as well as differential scattering can convert a simple polarized irradiance pattern to a complex one including intensity distributions which will surely affect responses. Such possible artifacts are ubiquitous both in nature and in laboratory set-ups.

However, when suitable precautions and controls are observed, nearly all the arthropods studied, and several cephalopod mollusks as well, have been clearly shown to perceive the plane of linearly polarized light as a distinct stimulus parameter (von Frisch, 1948; Stockhammer, 1959; von Frisch, Lindauer and Daumer, 1960; Jander and Waterman, 1960; Moody, 1962; Jander, Daumer and Waterman, 1963; Waterman, 1965b). The most direct laboratory demonstration of this specific polarized light sensitivity comes from experiments in which polarotaxis is not affected by changing the sign of the phototactic responses from positive to negative. In contrast, phototaxis itself shows the predicted 90° shift in orientation when its sign is changed with the animal swimming in an illumination pattern of two horizontal unpolarized light sources separated by 180° (discussed further below).

THE ANALYZER MECHANISM

In polarotactic animals with compound eyes, behavioral evidence indicates that a single ommatidium must be able to analyze the plane of polarization (discussion in Jander and Waterman, 1960). This capacity was in fact taken for granted in the model for polarized light sensitivity proposed for the honey-bee's eye by von Frisch (1949) and Autrum (Autrum and Stumpf, 1950). In this model diametrically opposite pairs of the eight retinular cells were supposed to have their analyzers in the same orientation whereas those in the four different pairs were aligned in distinctive directions.

Direct evidence from spike activity in optic fibers, from ERG's and from intracellular receptor potential responses has provided some information about the actual underlying mechanism in *Limulus* and in insects. Thus the first electrophysiological work to demonstrate polarized light sensitivity was in single fibers of the *Limulus* optic nerve (Waterman, 1950). The frequency of visual spikes was found to be a sinusoidal function of stimulus *e*-vector orientation and had a period of 180°. Further experiments, however, showed that the polarized light response of this preparation depended on oblique light entry into the ommatidium being studied and was marginal or absent when the stimulus direction was parallel to the optic axis (Waterman, 1954a). Such a reflection–refraction mechanism does not seem physiologically interesting or related to true polarotaxis. In any case, the *Limulus* eye is so aberrant that *e*-vector discrimination by a single ommatidium responding via its eccentric cell would seem inherently impossible. Consequently, our attention shifted to forms with more typical compound eyes, mainly Crustacea.

About the same time as the first *Limulus* paper cited, the on-wave of the ERG in the honey-bee and in *Calliphora* was reported to be invariant with *e*-vector rotation (Autrum and Stumpf, 1950). Such absence of amplitude modulation with changing planes of polarization was attributed to radial symmetry of the ommatidia in *Apis'* eye. This explanation was made more plausible by the subsequent demonstration in the aquatic hemipteran *Notonecta* that the ERG amplitude was actually modulated with a 180° period by rotation of the *e*-vector of the stimulating light (Lüdtke, 1957). In this water bug each ommatidium is bilaterally symmetrical rather than radial as in the bee. This morphological lack of radial symmetry was used to explain *Notonecta's* demonstrable *e*-vector response.

On the other hand, failure to find any effect of *e*-vector rotation on ERG amplitude in the honey-bee eye was interpreted by other workers as evidence that, despite all the extensively documented behavioral work supporting specific polarized light sensitivity in *Apis*, there might not, in fact, be an intraocular analyzer (Kennedy and Baylor, 1961). This conclusion was reached particularly because these workers in an interesting experiment could find no trace of the selective adaptation which would be expected of a retinal *e*-vector analyzer.

Taken at face value, this left our understanding in an apparently contradictory state: behavioral evidence, on the one hand, required a retinal analyzer within a single ommatidium and some negative electrophysiological evidence, on the other, indicated that no such analyzer was present. However, in the light of subsequent developments, particularly our demonstration of selective adaptation in the crab *Cardisoma* (mentioned later) and Tasaki's analogous results in *Octopus* (1965), restudy of this matter in insect eyes would seem imperative.

DIPTERAN ELECTROPHYSIOLOGY

Intracellular recording in *Lucilia* and in *Calliphora* had already shown that the receptor potential of single retinular cells is sensitive to the orientation of the plane of stimulus polarization (Kuwabara and Naka, 1959; Burkhardt and Wendler, 1960; Autrum and von Zwehl, 1962). However, these results were rather preliminary in *Lucilia* while in *Calliphora* they would seem to indicate that only some of the cells tested were sensitive to polarization, a situation which would not logically fit a simple version of the von Frisch–Autrum hypothesis.

Extracellular retinal recordings in the compound eyes of *Calliphora* and *Musca* also have given response amplitude modulation with a 180° period on *e*-vector rotation (Giulio, 1963). Specifically, maximum responses were evoked when the plane of stimulus polarization was parallel to the long axis of the rhabdom microvilli. In these experiments the direction of the stimulating light was perpendicular to the optic axis of the ommatidium in question. Hence the direction of the maximally effective *e*-vector was also normal to the optic axis.

However, because of the alignment and cylindrical shape of individual microvilli apparent in electron micrographs, axially incident (normal) illumination should also be differentially absorbed by the dichroic visual pigment with the maximum again occurring when the *e*-vector parallels the tubules' longitudinal axes. This is different from the situation in vertebrate rod or cone outer segments where the complex membrane structures enclosing the visual pigment are flat disks perpendicular to the optic axis (Sjöstrand, 1961). There, no dichroism is evident looking parallel to the optic axis, which is the normal direction of visible light, but dichroism is strong in lines of light parallel to the disks (Wald, Brown and Gibbons, 1962).

THE DICHROIC MODEL

In the dipteran results there are some discrepancies between data and model as well as others between intra- and extracellular recordings which make further experiments highly desirable. Nevertheless, the available electrophysiological results for these insects generally are consistent with the hypothesis that the microvilli in the rhabdom constitute a dichroic analyzer. Its properties would depend on the highly regular parallel arrangement of the tubules in a single rhabdomere and the likely location within these membrane elements of oriented rhodopsin molecules with their major axes parallel to tubule direction and hence perpendicular to the normally incident illumination (Stockhammer, 1959; Waterman, 1965a, 1966). On the other hand, the four sets of analyzers originally hypothesized have not been identified physiologically in any of this insect work; also the relevant data available are sufficiently fragmentary and inconsistent that they do not clearly settle the problem of mechanism. Furthermore, the fine structural evidence itself contradicts a four channel system in *Apis*. Only two microvillus directions have been reported in the eight rhabdomeres of this ommatidium (Goldsmith, 1962).

Currently we are developing electrophysiological evidence from the ERG of the crab eye that directly demonstrates a close correlation between fine structure of the rhabdom and the polarized light detector mechanism (Waterman and Horch, 1965; Eguchi and Waterman, 1966). Both electron micrographs and electrophysiological experiments using selective adaptation indicate that there is actually a two channel analyzer functioning in these decapod crustacean compound eyes. These results will be reported in detail elsewhere (Waterman and Horch, 1965). Suffice it to say here that the new data strongly support the dichroic model cited above except that only two, instead of four, channels originally postulated by von Frisch and Autrum are present.

Before the present series of experiments using ERG responses to flashes were done, our work on decapod visual systems, recording spikes from single fibers in the optic nerve, failed to demonstrate any units which were convincingly sensitive to plane of polarization independently of various possible extraocular sources of intensity variation (Waterman and Wiersma, 1963; Waterman, Wiersma and Bush, 1964).

POLAROTAXIS

Another important kind of experimental data which may be useful in trying to determine the mechanism of polarized light perception is that relating to the oriented behavior of arthropods and cephalopods when exposed to a pattern of polarized light. In this respect the freshwater cladoceran *Daphnia* is one of the most important experimental animals because its polarotactic behavior has been extensively studied beginning with the pioneer work of Verkhovskaya (1940) followed by Baylor and Smith (1953), Eckert (1953) and others.

As in the general case, it was important with *Daphnia* to establish that polarized light was perceived as such and not as an intensity artifact originating outside the retina. For aquatic animals the differential scattering of polarized light by the medium will establish intensity patterns to which any animal might react whether it were capable of analyzing polarized light or not. The importance of this factor was clearly shown in *Daphnia* and for the marine mysid, *Mysidium*, in both of which turbidity of the medium strongly affected orientation in polarized light (Baylor and Smith, 1953; Bainbridge and Waterman, 1957, 1958).

Systematic study of the relationship between polarotaxis and turbidity of the medium demonstrated significant interactions between phototactic responses to intensity pattern and polarotactic responses to the *e*-vector (Waterman, 1960). The data strongly implied, however, that the behavior observed represented a superposition of two distinct orienting mechanisms and that polarotaxis itself was mediated by a specific sensory modality. The clinching evidence for this was found when both positively and negatively phototactic *Daphnia* were shown to orient in the same way in a vertical beam of linearly polarized light, namely, strongly perpendicular to the *e*-vector (Jander and Waterman, 1960; Hazen and Baylor, 1962).

Thus *Daphnia* must distinguish polarization patterns from intensity patterns within the retina itself. All extraocular and extraretinal intraocular analyzing mechanisms (Hazen and Baylor, 1962) would produce different motor outputs for different phototactic signs; but this does not occur. Hence the analyzer must be retinal in location.

ACTION SPECTRUM IN *DAPHNIA*

New experiments on the action spectrum of *Daphnia* polarotaxis (Daumer and Waterman, 1965, in preparation) provide independent evidence that the polarized light discrimination system is quite distinct from the phototactic receptor channel. They also raise some interesting questions relative to the number and distribution of photopigments in the *Daphnia* ommatidium as well as the more general problem of the channeling mechanism involved in processing the visual sensory input. No previous quantitative data are available on the wavelength sensitivity of polarized light responses, but von Frisch (1954) has reported that the honey-bee can orient in the near ultraviolet band of blue sky light between 300–400 nm and that wavelengths longer than 500 nm cannot be used for such orientation. However, a systematic effect of *e*-vector orientation on the amplitude of receptor potentials in *Calliphora* has been reported at wavelengths near 606 nm by Giulio (1963), whereas no polarized light sensitive response at 603 nm in the same species was found by Burkhardt and Wendler (1960). Preliminary analysis of our *Daphnia* action spectrum data demonstrates some facts which are important in the present context.

Tests were run at 20 nm intervals throughout the visible spectrum and down to 320 nm in the near UV. Orientation was measured photographically by taking flash exposures in the far red which did not affect the *Daphnia's* behavior. Significant responses to the *e*-vector in a vertical beam of linearly polarized light were obtained between 360 nm and 580 nm and through a range of intensities which extended over four log units in the central region of the effective spectrum. When the reciprocals of the number of quanta required to evoke equal orientation responses are plotted from these data, peak sensitivity appears in the blue–violet at 440 nm falling quite sharply on either side of this wavelength (Fig. 1). A shoulder in the curves between 480 nm and 520 nm suggests a possible blue–green second component in this response.

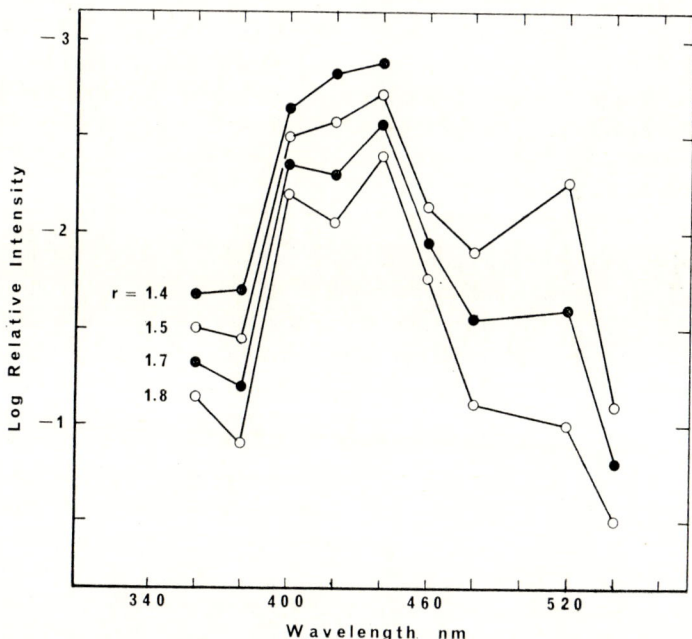

FIG. 1

Action spectrum for the polarotaxis of *Daphnia magna* swimming in a vertical beam of linearly polarized light. Narrow band interference filters transmitting equal numbers of quanta were used every 20 nm from 320 nm to 600 nm. Significant polarotactic responses 90° to the *e*-vector were found between 360 nm and 580 nm but suitable data for equal degrees of orientation (*r*) were available only as plotted. These equal response curves are essentially parallel whether the polarotaxis was relatively strong (*r* = 1·8) or weak (*r* = 1·4). (Daumer and Waterman, 1965, in preparation.)

Clearly, the most effective λ for orientation by *Daphnia* is not in the near UV although this band of wavelengths has been reported to be within the range of sensitivity of these animals (Viaud, 1938) and seems to constitute a color for them (Heberdey, 1949), as it does for *Apis* (Daumer, 1956). The 440 nm peak for polarotaxis is not far from the λ_{max} at 460 nm for the natural polarization of the clear blue sky (Sekera *et al.*, 1955). Underwater polarization, however, is not very sensitive to wavelength but decreases slightly with the λ of greatest penetration which is at 465 nm for clear oceanic water (Ivanoff and Waterman, 1958) and at longer wavelengths for more turbid natural waters (Hutchinson, 1957).

The visual action spectra reported in the literature for *Daphnia* phototaxis and eye movement are maximal from 530 nm to 540 nm (Viaud, 1938; Scheffer, Robert and Médioni, 1958). Hence the most effective λ for polarotaxis is very different from that for phototaxis. This demonstrates that more than one kind of cell must be present in the retina and that the visual channel processing polarotactic input involves cells with different wavelengths of maximal sensitivity than those in the phototactic system. A somewhat similar wavelength dependent situation has been found in the frog where the phototactic sensitivity curve implies that the green rods and to some extent the cones mediate this response whereas the red rods inhibit it (Muntz, 1963).

RELATION TO COLOR RECEPTION

Returning to the wavelength sensitivity in the Crustacea, two kinds of information are relevant here in addition to orientation behavior. One is the electrophysiological demonstration of selective wavelength adaptation comparable in concept and significance with respect to color to our *Cardisoma* work with respect to linear polarization. The other is extraction and spectrometric characterization of the visual pigments concerned. The latter is reviewed *in extenso* by Goldsmith and Fernández (1966).

No pigment extractions have yet been reported for *Daphnia*, but some relevant information is available for specific color receptors. For example, on the basis of phototactic intensity discrimination using two stimulating lights of different λ, Heberdey (1949) reported a sort of Purkinje shift with light adaptation and concluded there were three receptor types in *Daphnia*: UV, blue–violet and yellow. However, he did not prove that all three were present in the compound eye as distinct from the naupliar eye or generalized light sensitivity. Blue and yellow receptors in the compound eye have been postulated on the basis of *Daphnia's* wavelength-differential swimming behavior patterns (Baylor and Smith, 1957). Other workers found non-ocular light responses in *Daphnia* to have a peak sensitivity at 420 nm or less (Scheffer, Robert and Médioni, 1958), but the possible relevance of this for polarized light responses is not obvious at present.

A considerable amount of data is available on various decapod crustaceans. Selective adaptation has revealed two separate maxima in a number of forms. Two kinds of crayfish (*Orconectes*, *Procambarus*), a marine prawn (*Palaemonetes*) and two quite remotely related brachyuran crabs (*Carcinus*, *Libinia*) are among those which have been studied (Wald, 1963). Two pigments with different absorption peaks have also been extracted from several crayfish species and a freshwater prawn in the genus *Palaemonetes* (see Goldsmith and Fernández, 1966, Table 1).

While the $\lambda_{max's}$ of the various extracted pigments cover a considerable range, the λ_{max} found for selectively adapted peaks is in several instances at a lower wavelength than for any extracted pigment. In addition, the overall spectral sensitivity curve may have yet another λ_{max}. For example, in *Procambarus clarkii* maximum spectral sensitivity, electrophysiologically determined from the ERG, was 570 nm (Kennedy and Bruno, 1961), yet differential adaptation demonstrated peaks at 445 and 575 nm and two pigments extracted had peaks at 525 and 557 nm respectively (Wald, 1963). Undoubtedly, complex synergistic and antagonistic interactions are involved in some of these differences.

A considerable body of relevant information is available in insects. In general this is not unlike the crustacean data but shows some points of further interest (Burkhardt, 1962; Goldsmith, 1964). Recording from single retinular cells, three types can be found in the dipteran *Calliphora* (Burkhardt, 1962). Each of these has two absorption maxima, one at about 350 nm and the others at 490 nm (green), 470 nm (blue) and 520 nm (yellow–green) respectively. Of these three types the green are considerably more common. Burkhardt (1962) has suggested that the observed frequency distribution of the three types might be accounted for by assuming that a single retinula has five green receptors, one blue one and one yellow–green type. Intensity would be some sort of an integrated overall function of these three color channels. Direct spectrophotometric evidence for more than one pigment type in a single dipteran insect retinula has recently been reported (Langer and Thorell, 1966).

POLAROTAXIS AND PHOTOTAXIS

In *Daphnia* one might propose a somewhat similar model where several receptor cell types are present and where light is mediated by one type with a maximal sensitivity near 440 nm, with a possible minor contribution from a second absorption peak or a second, less common, cell type near 500 nm. The phototactic sensitivity in such a model would be dominated by some other receptor type with a λ_{max} at longer wavelengths such that the overall response of the retinal population affected would be in the range observed, namely, 520–530 nm.

But such an hypothesis runs into some perplexing difficulties. In *Daphnia*, as in most other crustaceans studied, the rhabdom consists of regularly arranged microvilli with their long axes normal to the ommatidial optic axis (Figs. 2 and 3). Within each rhabdom the seven constituent rhabdomeres fall into two groups with their tubules mutually perpendicular. The *Daphnia* rhabdom is not layered along its optic axis in the typical decapod pattern (Eguchi and Waterman, 1966) but has its two different rhabdomere types sandwiched across the rhabdom in another characteristic manner (Fig. 4). A somewhat similar rhabdom fine structure occurs in the predatory cladoceran *Leptodora* (Wolken and Gallik, 1965).

On the basis of the dichroic rhabdom model discussed above, all seven of the *Daphnia* retinular cells should be sensitive to orientation of the *e*-vector of incoming illumination. Consequently one would not expect that differential wavelength sensitivity in the various neurosensory cells of a single retinula would give any one cell type a predominant role in polarotaxis provided each retinular cell constitutes a more or less independent data channel. Yet our action spectrum for this orientation shows that it has a maximum in quite a different part of the spectrum from that reported for phototaxis.

In explanation of this, such differences might be assumed to arise in the information processing mechanism where more than one sensory channels interact. If, for instance, the phototaxis involved only summation of all channels participating, whereas at least some subtraction occurred in polarotaxis, the first could have an average population response whereas the second could have a quite distinctly different action spectrum depending on the specific details of the visual information processing.

To study this matter further, probably the first step necessary is to re-examine phototaxis in *Daphnia* with essentially the same technique as that used in the polarotactic work so that directly comparable data are available. Then the action spectrum of polarized light sensitivity should be worked out in other arthropods where electrophysiological experiments are more feasible. The latter might, in such cases, allow direct tests of the model hypotheses. Another important parameter that should be systematically examined is location of the retinula under study within the total retina because different parts of the eye might be responsible for different types of response.

Areal specialization of various sorts occurs widely in compound eyes (for review see Waterman, 1961) and might possibly provide quite separate sites for analysis of polarized light, color and intensity patterns.

Optomotor responses to *e*-vector rotation in the fiddler crab *Uca tangeri* have been interpreted to indicate that the special job of polarized light detection is a function only of the skyward-looking apical ommatidia of the eye (Korte, 1965). However, there has been no suggestion so far that the orderly pattern of rhabdom microvillus alignment, which is nearly ubiquitous in arthropods and in cephalopod mollusks, and which seems almost certainly

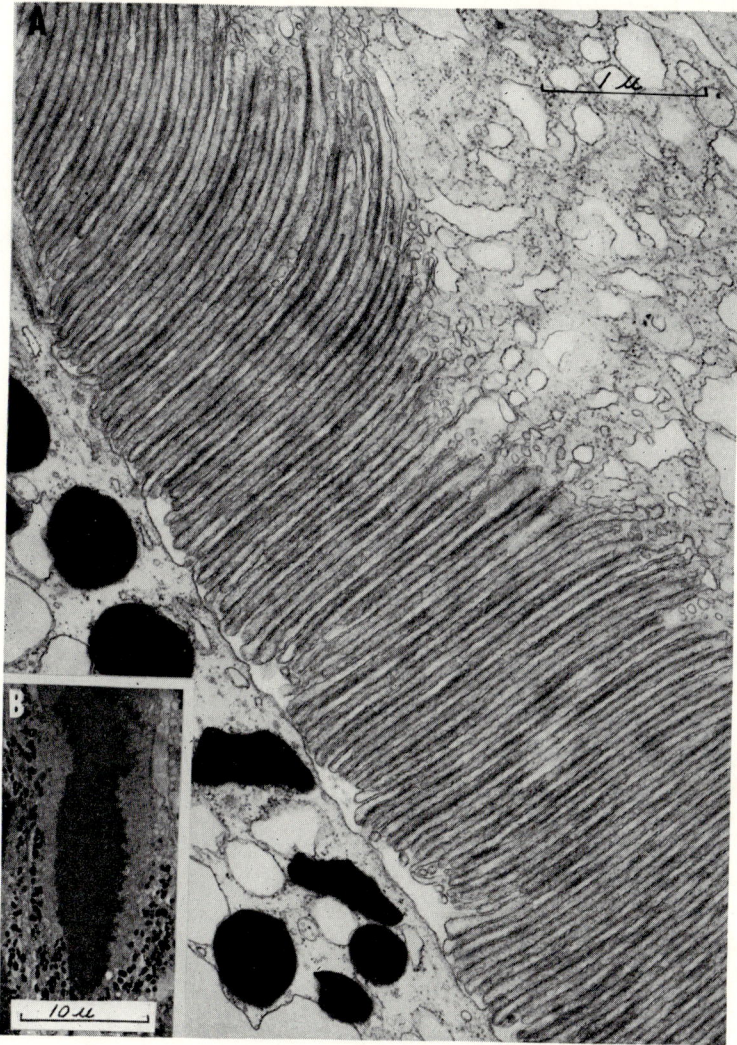

FIG. 2

Fine structure and location of *Daphnia* rhabdom. A, Longitudinal section through a rhabdom showing its component regularly arranged microvilli. The optical axis of the ommatidium to which this detail belongs runs from upper left to lower right with distal being upward to the left. Only one rhabdomere is visible and its tubules arise, as can be seen, from the retinular cell in the upper right corner. Another retinular cell with prominent pigment granules is located in the lower left corner but does not contribute to the rhabdomere shown. B, Low power electron micrograph showing the axial rhabdom surrounded by retinular cells of which its constituent rhabdomeres are parts. The optical axis of the ommatidium shown is vertical and the distal direction is up. (Eguchi and Waterman, 1965, in preparation.)

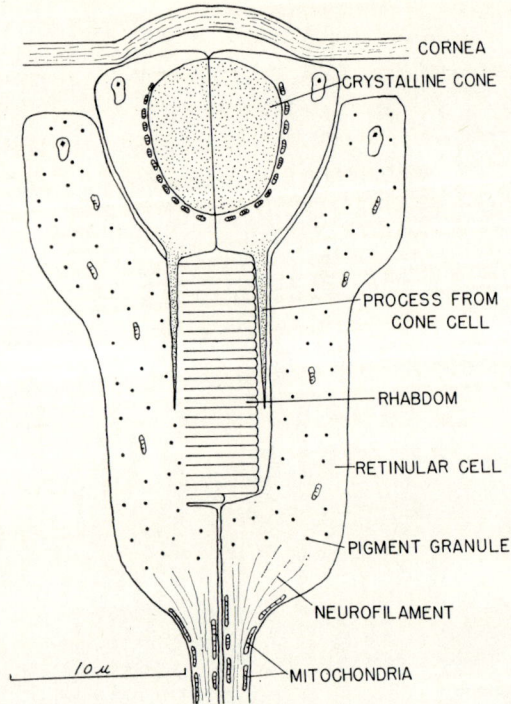

Fig. 3

Schematic reconstruction of a *Daphnia* ommatidium showing in longitudinal section the relation of the details shown in Fig. 2 to the whole ommatidium. (Eguchi and Waterman, 1965, in preparation.)

responsible for their polarized light sensitivity, occurs only in some restricted regions of the retina. Other behavioral and electrophysiological data have yet to be considered in relation to such a specialized area hypothesis, which still lacks quantitative support.

INFLUENCE OF DEGREE OF POLARIZATION

A number of additional problems relating polarotaxis to visual information processing in *Daphnia* are now obvious. One of the most interesting of these relates to the influence of degree of polarization on the strength of the resulting polarotaxis (Waterman, 1961; Waterman and Jander, 1965, in preparation). A series of extensive tests have shown that as the percent of polarization decreases from near 100%, little effect on orientation appears until about 80%, where a slow deterioration begins and extends down to about 20% polarization. Below this point a rapid decrease occurs in orientation accuracy. Even so, significant alignment perpendicular to the *e*-vector may occur with as little as 10% polarization, but not always nor in all individuals.

These results indicate that over the wide range from 20 to 100 % polarization a significant degree of orientation relative to the *e*-vector is present and that the accuracy decreases but slowly as polarization decreases. This suggests, somewhere in the system, the presence of a feedback mechanism which maintains significant orientation down to low levels of polarization.

From the point of view of natural polarization patterns underwater, this is an interesting finding since maximum degrees of polarization between 20 % and 60 % are commonly present in clear water (Waterman, 1954b; Ivanoff and Waterman, 1958; Ivanoff, Jerlov and Waterman, 1961). Therefore polarotaxis may be a considerable factor in the normal behavior of *Daphnia* and other polarized light sensing animals in the field.

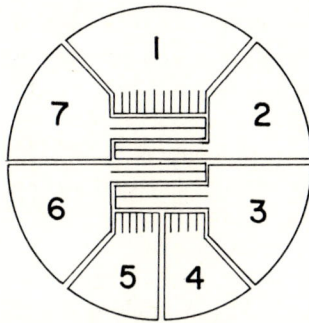

FIG. 4

Schematic reconstruction of a *Daphnia* ommatidium showing a cross-section at the mid-rhabdom level. The seven constituent retinular cells and their corresponding rhabdomeres are shown. Note that although the axial layering typical of the decapod rhabdom (Eguchi and Waterman, 1966) is absent (Fig. 3) the microvillus pattern still shows only two perpendicular axial directions. In the retinula diagrammed, three cells give rise to tubules running in one direction while the remaining four contribute those at right-angles. In some other retinulas examined only cells 1 and 4 produce the rhabdomeres at the ends of the row while 2, 3, 5, 6 and 7 give rise to the intermediate five at right-angles. (Eguchi and Waterman, 1965, in preparation.)

MULTIPLE-PEAK ORIENTATION

Another phase of polarotaxis about which considerable information is available is the occurrence of multiple-peaked orientation responses. Extensive series of experiments on *Daphnia* showed that a single-peaked polarotaxis at 90° to the *e*-vector was characteristic under the usual laboratory stimulus conditions where a high intensity of unidirectional illumination was present. However, at lower intensities or with less sharply directional light patterns additional maxima appeared in the polarotactic responses so that four peaks were present within 180°: 0°, 45°, 90° and 135°, relative to the *e*-vector

(Jander and Waterman, 1960). One, two or four peaks occur in the polarotaxis of a number of other organisms. Clearly, the presence of single or multiple-peaks in the oriented response must be explicable in terms of the functional organization of the retinula or in terms of the subsequent processing of the polarized light information in the visual tract. In any case, the occurrence of multiple-peaked responses presents difficulties in obtaining and analyzing data which require the use of special techniques (Waterman, 1963; Batschelet, 1965).

Further insight into the visual input processing mechanism in *Daphnia* was obtained from a demonstration that the turning tendency controlling polarotaxis was a sinusoidal function of the angular difference between the *e*-vector orientation being perceived and the actual direction of swimming (Jander, 1963); this function was determined by opposing a fixed response to gravity to various directions of the *e*-vector in a horizontal beam of polarized light. The implications of such a trigonometric output for the polarotactic mechanism have been considered elsewhere from the point of view of elementary systems analysis (Waterman, 1966).

This approach provides a fairly simple model for the possible mechanism of polarotactic steering in which the directions evoking zero-turning tendency would provide the basic orientation. When a model of this sort is devised with a two channel polarization analyzer, which our fine structure and ERG data require, interesting simulations of oriented behavior can be obtained (Fig. 5). Multiple-response peaks at $0°$, $\pm45°$ and $90°$ can be produced by different ways of integrating the information in the two input channels (Waterman, 1966). In turn, these alternatives suggested by the model provide hypotheses which can be experimentally tested either in the visual tract or in the motor output.

SUMMARY

The above review may be summarized by reference to a schematic diagram of the functional organization of a single ommatidium from a decapod crustacean compound eye (Fig. 6). This embodies, in a simplified way, the relevant facts and the hypotheses which appear most likely for their explanation. If such a schema has any merit, it is to make explicit some of the basic puzzles remaining in our understanding of the functional organization of compound eyes.

Incoming light stimuli are directed by the dioptric system onto the axial cluster of seven retinular cells. Altogether these absorb quanta over a broad energy range, embracing the animal's visibility curve, and their total output could provide the information needed by an intensity channel. Within the seven retinular cells specialization is assumed to be present in the particular quantal energy ranges to which their photopigments are tuned. Explicitly, a

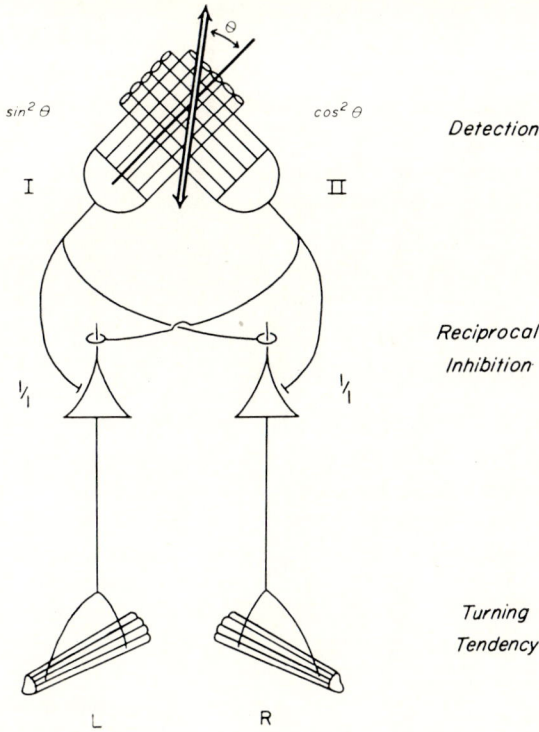

FIG. 5

Model for a two channel polarized light analyzer hypothesized to account for the orientation patterns observed in polarotactic animals. The two sets of perpendicular dichroic microvilli would produce responses proportional to $\cos^2\theta$ and $\sin^2\theta$ respectively. If these two channels were connected to the motor output mechanism for azimuth orientation by the reciprocal excitatory and inhibitory network shown, behavior comparable to that observed in animals orienting in a vertical beam of linearly polarized light could be obtained from the model. The presynaptic loops in the diagram are inhibitory, the presynaptic bars excitatory and transmission is assumed to be 1:1 in both types. Note that addition of the output of the two detector-analyzer channels could yield information proportional to illumination intensity and independent of polarization because $\cos^2\theta + \sin^2\theta = 1$. (Waterman, 1966.)

three channel color analyzing system is specified with the differently absorbing cells present in a frequency ratio of 5:1:1 as suggested by some of Burkhardt's data.

Furthermore, these photopigments are assumed to be localized in the microvilli of the seven rhabdomeres constituting the rhabdom. A regular orientation of receptor molecules relative to the rhabdom membrane system is hypothesized so as to endow the microvillus array with a substantial part of the dichroism present in individual rhodopsin molecules. The tubules are

STIMULUS   INPUT

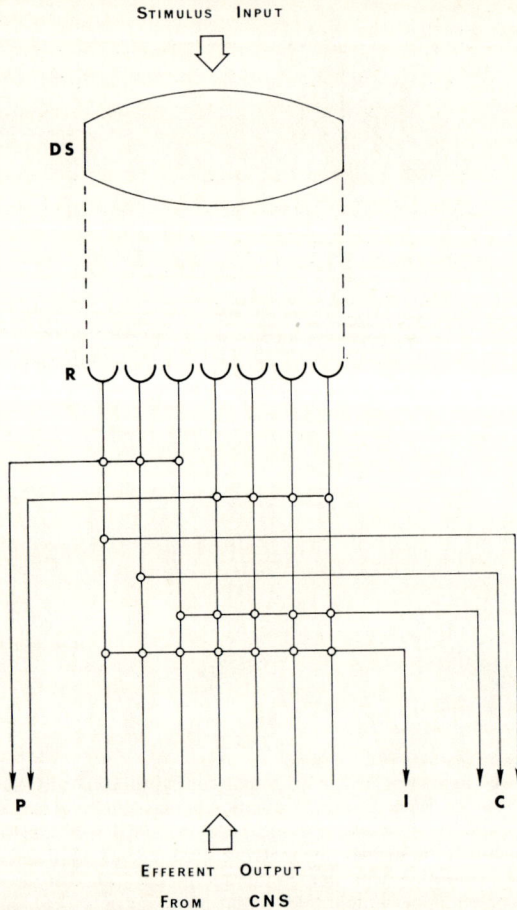

FIG. 6

Schematic circuit representing some of the information channeling functions of a
single decapod crustacean ommatidium. This is based on the available data (still
far from complete) and hypotheses (most of them only partially tested) reviewed
in the text. These submodalities of vision are identified by two channels analyzing
e-vector direction (*P*), three determining color sensitivity (*C*) and one signaling
intensity (*I*). In addition, the demonstrated extensive efferent traffic in the optic
nerve is indicated as a potential influence on the afferent information processing.
The nature and extent of such influences remain largely to be demonstrated. *DS*,
dioptric system; *R*, retinula comprising seven photoreceptive cells.

known to be oriented at 90° to the optic axis with their own longitudinal axes
regularly aligned in only two perpendicular directions. Hence the polarization
analyzing mechanism has two channels fed respectively by three and four of
the seven retinular cells. Direct evidence for such an analyzer is provided by
our differential adaptation experiments.

While this scheme is deliberately quite unspecific about how and precisely where in the visual system the requisite channeling takes place, it does indicate an important additional feature. This is the substantial and varied efferent traffic demonstrated to be present in the optic nerve (Waterman and Wiersma, 1963; Wiersma, Bush and Waterman, 1964; Bush, Wiersma and Waterman, 1964). Such information outflow must reach at least the innermost of the four optic ganglia in these stalk-eyed crustaceans. How much further distally it travels and what its functional significance may be remain to be determined.

At present, further research would seem more fruitful than more discussion of these matters. Interest and knowledge of the information encoding and transmitting system involved are sufficiently high and varied that substantial continuing progress in our understanding can be confidently expected.

REFERENCES

AUTRUM, H. and STUMPF, H. 1950. Das Bienenauge als Analysator für polarisiertes Licht. *Z. Naturforsch.* **5b**, 116–22.

AUTRUM, H. and VON ZWEHL, V. 1962. Die Sehzellen der Insekten als Analysatoren für polarisiertes Licht. *Z. vergl. Physiol.* **46**, 1–7.

BAINBRIDGE, R. and WATERMAN, T. H. 1957. Polarized light and the orientation of two marine Crustacea. *J. Exp. Biol.* **34**, 342–64.

BAINBRIDGE, R. and WATERMAN, T. H. 1958. Turbidity and the polarized light orientation of the crustacean *Mysidium*. *J. Exp. Biol.* **35**, 487–93.

BATSCHELET, E. 1965. *Statistical Methods for the Analysis of Problems in Animal Orientation.* AIBS Monogr., Washington, D.C. 57 pp.

BAYLOR, E. R. and SMITH, F. E. 1953. The orientation of Cladocera to polarized light. *Am. Naturalist.* **87**, 97–101.

BAYLOR, E. R. and SMITH, F. E. 1957. Diurnal migration of plankton Crustaceans. In *Recent Advances in Invertebrate Physiology* (B. T. Scheer, ed.), pp. 21–35, University of Oregon Publications, Eugene.

BURKHARDT, D. 1962. Spectral sensitivity and other response characteristics of single visual cells in the arthropod eye. In *Biological Receptor Mechanisms* (J. W. L. Beament, ed.). *Symp. Soc. Exptl. Biol.* **16**, 86–109, Cambridge University Press, London.

BURKHARDT, D. and WENDLER, L. 1960. Ein direkter Beweis für die Fähigkeit einzelner Sehzellen des Insektauges, die Schwingungsrichtung polarisierten Lichtes zu analysieren. *Z. vergl. Physiol.* **43**, 687–92.

BUSH, B. M. H., WIERSMA, C. A. G. and WATERMAN, T. H. 1964. Efferent mechanoreceptive responses in the optic nerve of the crab, *Podophthalmus*. *J. Cell. Comp. Physiol.* **64**, 327–46.

DAUMER, K. 1956. Reizmetrische Untersuchung des Farbensehens der Bienen. *Z. vergl. Physiol.* **38**, 413–78.

ECKERT, B. 1953. Oriéntující vliv polarisovaného světla na perločky. *Ceskoslov. Biol.* **2**, 76–80. (In Czech.)

EGUCHI, E. and WATERMAN, T. H. 1966. Fine structure patterns in crustacean rhabdoms. This volume.

VON FRISCH, K. 1948. Gelöste und ungelöste Rätsel der Bienensprache. *Naturwiss.* **35**, 38–43.

VON FRISCH, K. 1949. Die Polarisation des Himmelslichtes als orientierender Faktor bei den Tänzen der Bienen. *Experientia* **5**, 142–8.

VON FRISCH, K. 1954. Die Fähigkeit der Bienen die Sonne durch die Wolken wahrzunehmen. *Sitzber. Math. Naturw. Kl. Bayer Akad. Wiss. Muenchen* **17**, 197–9.

VON FRISCH, K., LINDAUER, M. and DAUMER, K. 1960. Über die Wahrnehmung polarisierten Lichtes durch das Bienenauge. *Experientia* **16**, 289–301.

GIULIO, L. 1963. Elektroretinographische Beweisführung dichroitischer Eigenschaften des Komplexauges bei Zweiflüglern. *Z. vergl. Physiol.* **46**, 491–5.

GOLDSMITH, T. H. 1962. Fine structure of the retinulae in the compound eye of the honeybee. *J. Cell Biol.* **14**, 489–94.

GOLDSMITH, T. H. 1964. The visual system of insects. In *The Physiology of Insecta*, Vol. I (M. Rockstein, ed.), pp. 397–462, Academic Press, New York.

GOLDSMITH, T. H. and FERNÁNDEZ, H. R. 1966. Some photochemical and physiological aspects of visual excitation in compound eyes. This volume.

HAZEN, W. E. and BAYLOR, E. R. 1962. Behavior of *Daphnia* in polarized light. *Biol. Bull.* **123**, 243–52.

HEBERDEY, R. F. 1949. Das Unterscheidungsvermögen von *Daphnia* für Helligkeiten farbiger Lichter. *Z. vergl. Physiol.* **31**, 89–111.

HUTCHINSON, G. E. 1957. The optical properties of lakes. In *A Treatise on Limnology*, Vol. I pp. 366–425, Wiley, New York.

IVANOFF, A., JERLOV, N. and WATERMAN, T. H. 1961. A comparative study of irradiance, beam transmittance and scattering in the sea near Bermuda. *Limnol. Oceanogr.* **6**, 129–53.

IVANOFF, A. and WATERMAN, T. H. 1958. Factors, mainly depth and wavelength, affecting the degree of underwater light polarization. *J. Mar. Res.* **16**, 283–307.

JANDER, R. 1963. Grundleistungen der Licht- und Schwerkrafts- orientierung von Insekten. *Z. vergl. Physiol.* **47**, 381–430.

JANDER, R., DAUMER, K. and WATERMAN, T. H. 1963. Polarized light orientation by two Hawaiian cephalopods. *Z. vergl. Physiol.* **46**, 383–94.

JANDER, R. and WATERMAN, T. H. 1960. Sensory discrimination between polarized light and light intensity patterns by arthropods. *J. Cell. Comp. Physiol.* **56**, 137–60.

KENNEDY, D. and BAYLOR, E. 1961. Analysis of polarized light by the bee's eye. *Nature* **191**, 34–7.

KENNEDY, D. and BRUNO, M. S. 1961. The spectral sensitivity of crayfish and lobster vision. *J. Gen. Physiol.* **44**, 1089–1102.

KORTE, R. 1965. Durch polarisiertes Licht hervorgerufene Optomotorik bei *Uca tangeri*. *Experientia* **21**, 98.

KUWABARA, M. and NAKA, K. 1959. Response of a single retinula cell to polarized light. *Nature* **184**, 455–6.

LANGER, H. and THORELL, B. 1966. Microspectrophotometry of single rhabdomeres in the insect eye. This volume.

LÜDTKE, H. 1957. Beziehungen des Feinbaues im Rückenschwimmerauge zu seiner Fähigkeit, polarisiertes Licht zu analysieren. *Z. vergl. Physiol.* **40**, 329–44.

MOODY, M. F. 1962. Evidence for the intraocular discrimination of vertically and horizontally polarized light by *Octopus*. *J. Exp. Biol.* **39**, 21–30.

MUNTZ, W. R. A. 1963. The development of phototaxis in the frog (*Rana temporaria*). *J. Exp. Biol.* **40**, 371–9.

SCHEFFER, D., ROBERT, P. and MÉDIONI, J. 1958. Réactions oculomotrices de la Daphnie (*Daphnia pulex* De Geer) en réponse à des lumières monochromatiques d'égale énergie. Sensibilité visuelle et sensibilité dermatoptique. *Compt. rend. Soc. Biol.* **152**, 1000–1003.

SEKERA, Z. *et al.* 1955. Investigation of Polarization of Skylight. Final Report, U.C.L.A., Dept. of Meteorology for the Air Force Cambridge Research Center, pp. 1–68 (and appendices).

SJÖSTRAND, F. S. 1961. Electron microscopy of the retina. In *The Structure of the Eye* (G. K. Smelser, ed.), pp. 1–28, Academic Press, New York.

STOCKHAMMER, K. 1959. Die Orientierung nach der Schwingungsrichtung linear polarisierten Lichtes und ihre sinnesphysiologischen Grundlagen. *Ergeb. Biol.* **21**, 23–56.

TASAKI, K. 1965. The octopus retina as an analyzer for polarized light. (Abstr.) *Symp. on Comparative Neurophysiology*, Tokyo, 1965, p. 7.

VERKHOVSKAYA, I. N. 1940. The influence of polarized light on the phototaxis of certain organisms. *Bull. Moscow Nat. Hist. Soc., Biol. Sect.* **49**, 101–13. (In Russian with French summary and figure legends.)

VIAUD, G. 1938. Recherches expérimentales sur le phototropisme des Daphnies. *Publs. Fac. lettres Strasbourg* **84**, 1–196.

WALD, G. 1963. Single and multiple visual systems in arthoprods. (Abstr.) *Fed. Proc.* **22** (2): 519.

WALD, G., BROWN, P. K. and GIBBONS, I. R. 1962. Visual excitation: a chemo-anatomical study. In *Biological Receptor Mechanisms* (J. W. L. Beament, ed.). *Symp. Soc. Exp. Biol.* **16**, 32–57, Cambridge University Press, London.

WATERMAN, T. H. 1950. A light polarization analyzer in the compound eye of *Limulus*. *Science* **111**, 252–4.

WATERMAN, T. H. 1954a. Polarized light and angle of stimulus incidence in the compound eye of *Limulus*. *Proc. Natl. Acad. Sci. U.S.* **40**, 258–62.

WATERMAN, T. H. 1954b. Polarization patterns in submarine illumination. *Science* **120**, 927–32.

WATERMAN, T. H. 1960. Interaction of polarized light and turbidity in the orientation of *Daphnia* and *Mysidium*. *Z. vergl. Physiol.* **43**, 149–72.

WATERMAN, T. H. 1961. Light sensitivity and vision. In *The Physiology of Crustacea*, Vol. II (T. H. Waterman, ed.), pp. 1–64. Academic Press, New York.

WATERMAN, T. H. 1963. The analysis of spatial orientation. *Ergeb. Biol.* **26**, 98–117.

WATERMAN, T. H. 1965a. Visual information processing in crustaceans. (Abstr.) *Symp. on Comparative Neurophysiology*, Tokyo, 1965, p. 17.

WATERMAN, T. H. 1965b. Specific effects of polarized light on organisms. In *Handbook of Environmental Biology* (P. L. Altman, ed.), Fed. Amer. Soc. Exptl. Biol. (In press).

WATERMAN, T. H. 1966. Systems analysis and the visual orientation of animals. *Amer. Scientist* (In press).

WATERMAN, T. H. and HORCH, K. W. 1965. The polarized light analyzer in a crab compound eye. (Abstr.) *Symp. on Information Processing in Sight Sensory Systems* (G. D. McCann, ed.), California Institute of Technology, Pasadena (In press).

WATERMAN, T. H. and WIERSMA, C. A. G. 1963. Electrical responses in decapod crustacean visual systems. *J. Cell. Comp. Physiol.* **61**, 1–16.

WATERMAN, T. H., WIERSMA, C. A. G. and BUSH, B. M. H. 1964. Afferent visual responses in the optic nerve of the crab, *Podophthalmus*. *J. Cell. Comp. Physiol.* **63**, 135–56.

WIERSMA, C. A. G., BUSH, B. M. H. and WATERMAN, T. H. 1964. Efferent visual responses of contralateral origin in the optic nerve of the crab, *Podophthalmus*. *J. Cell. Comp. Physiol.* **64**, 309–26.

WOLKEN, J. J. and GALLIK, G. J. 1965. The compound eye of a crustacean *Leptodora kindtii*. *J. Cell Biol.* **26**, 968–73.

THE RETINA OF THE LOCUST

G. A. HORRIDGE

Gatty Marine Laboratory and Department of Natural History, St. Andrews, Scotland

INTRODUCTION

THE following account is a summary of work which has been pursued at St. Andrews over the past 2 or 3 years. I must stress that many of the electrophysiological measurements have been made by J. Scholes and separately by J. Tunstall and will eventually appear in detail under their names. The effect of light on the movement of the palisade has already been published (Horridge and Barnard, 1965), a brief summary of the statistical properties of miniature potentials has appeared (Scholes, 1964) and more is in press (Scholes, 1966). However, in view of the fact that we have applied a variety of techniques to a particular preparation which has been the source of some controversy, it seems appropriate to draw together our work, even though prematurely, for presentation in this symposium.

ANATOMY

The retina of the locust has a rather uniform geometrical arrangement of eucone ommatidia, of apposition type, which form a hexagonal array. The rhabdomeres of the six or seven retinula cells form equal closely fused segments of the long rhabdom, and as one looks along a vertical section through the retina the densely staining rhabdoms stand out as a series of columns which run from the bases of the crystalline cones to the basement membrane. The principal anatomical features are summarized in Figure 1A, and further details are presented in the plates.

The cone, 30 μ at widest diameter and 60–90 μ long, is divided into four segments, as in many insects. There is a granular boundary between the substance of the cone and the cytoplasm of the cells which form it, and as revealed under the interference microscope the density changes suddenly at this point. The cytoplasm of the cells which form the cone is devoid of pigment grains, remarkably clear, and of a watery appearance. Towards their pointed ends the four sections of the cone each contain about a hundred long hollow tubules of about 20 mμ diameter. These four parts of the cone tip separate from each other where they meet the distal end of the rhabdom, and each continues as a long rod-shaped extension of the cone, 0·5–2·0 μ diameter, which has been seen in Diptera (Waddington and Perry, 1960) and in the bee

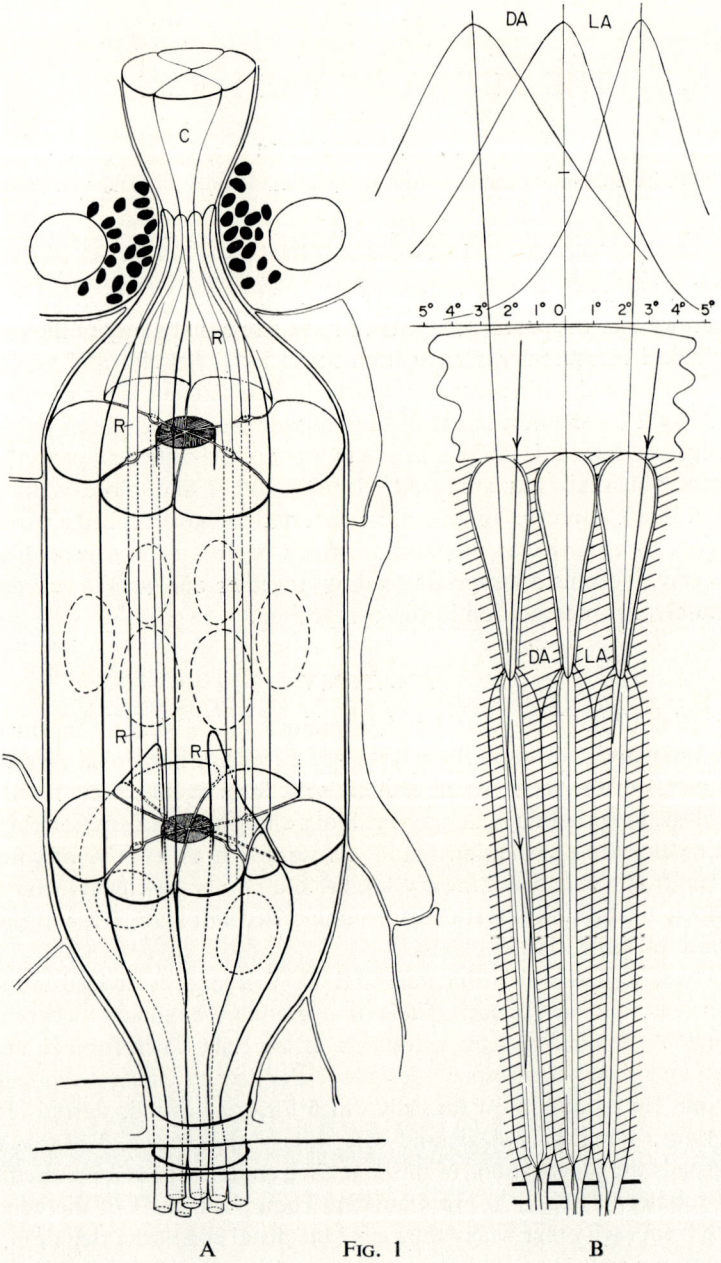

A   FIG. 1   B

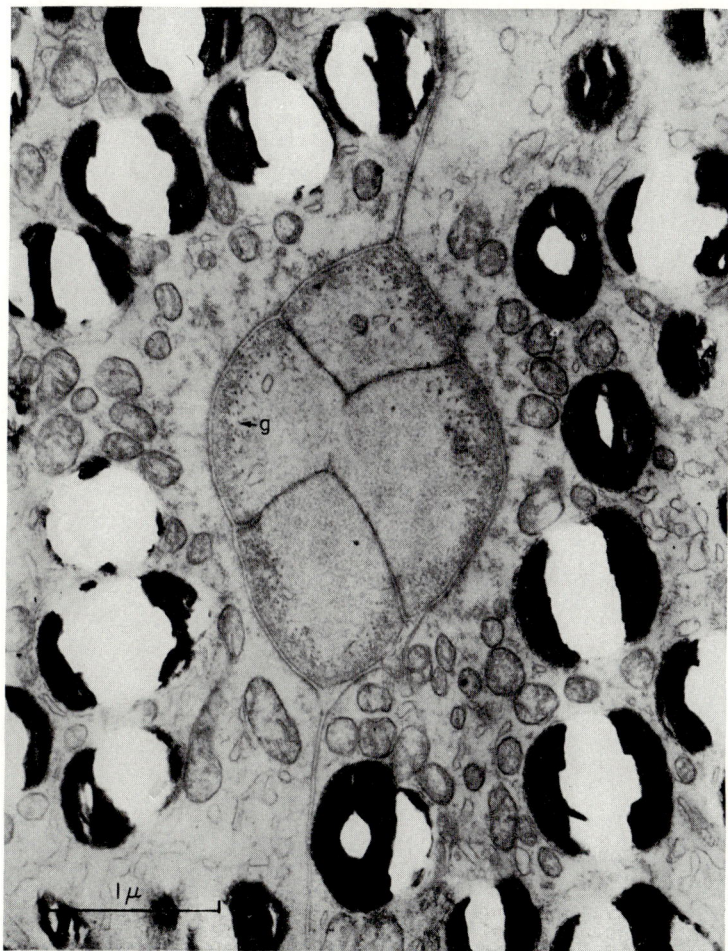

FIG. 2

Transverse section through the narrow portion of the cone showing the proximity of the surrounding pigment granules, which are hard and are split by the glass knife. The small granules (g) in the periphery of the cone are long tubules which extend far into the roots of the cone.

FIG. 1 (opposite)

Summary of anatomical and physiological conclusions. A, Structure of a locust ommatidium, showing how the roots (r) of the cone (c) spread round the rhabdom, which is composed of the rhabdomeres of (in this case 6) retinula cells. Two basal retinula cells, without rhabdomeres, are shown. B, Scale drawing showing conclusions concerning light pathways, in the dark-adapted (left) and light-adapted (right) states. Note the palisade. The curves at the top show the corresponding acceptance angle curves. There is no information of the fate of other light rays, and we are especially ignorant of the properties of the margin and peripheral end of the cone.

(Goldsmith, 1962) and which can be traced as far as the basement membrane, Fig. 1. These fibrous rods presumably provide mechanical support and hold each group of retinula cells directly beneath its corresponding cone.

Two large primary iris pigment cells surround the narrow region where the cone runs between the distal ends of the retinula cells and where it finally breaks up into four. These cells contain pigment grains which are much

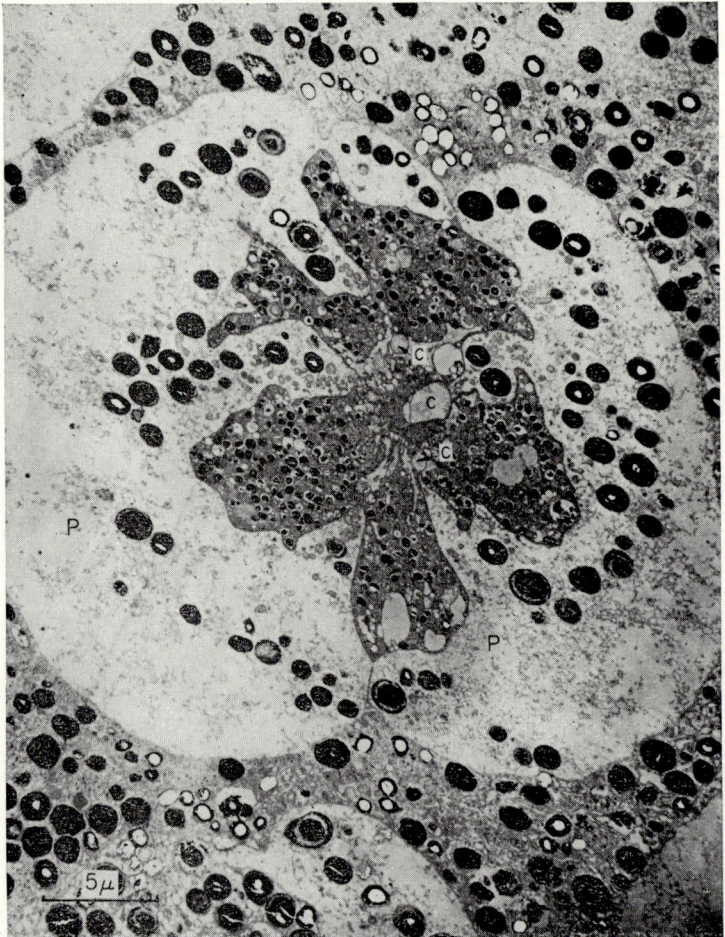

FIG. 3

Transverse section through the upper part of an ommatidium of a locust in the region where the cone (c) runs into the retinula cells. The small pigment grains lie within the darker cytoplasm of the retinula cells. The larger pigment grains are in the primary pigment cells (p) which surround the cone. Two parts of the cone have already split off from the other two.

larger than those of the nearby retinula cells, as shown in Figs. 2, 3, and 5. This is the crucial region of narrowest aperture, where the pigment grains are arranged thickly round the apparent path of the light at the narrowest point in the cone (Fig. 2). The pigment grains are extraordinarily abundant, even in electron microscope sections, so that it is easily supposed that no light makes its way through them in the solid structure. Light microscope sections have to be less than about 2 μ thick before it is possible to distinguish the individual pigment grains in this region. No movement of this pigment under the influence of light has been found although sought.

The retinula cells of one ommatidium together form a cylinder which is 350–500 μ long. A series of sections across this cylinder show that six or seven of the retinula cells stretch from top to bottom, and contribute a segment (called a rhabdomere) of the rhabdom for the whole length (Figs. 1A, 4 and 7). There are however a total of eight cells in each ommatidium, and eight corresponding axons in the small bundle from each ommatidium through the basement membrane. The other one or two cells are restricted to the basal third of the column, have no rhabdomere, and a cytoplasmic appearance which is quite distinct from the others. These are the basal retinula cells, which have the same orientation over large areas of the retina (Fig. 9).

The retinula cells have a richly-filled cytoplasm, containing numerous, rather typical, components (Figs. 4, 6 and 7), Numerous layers of endoplasmic reticulum, in parallel arrays or whorls, occur all along the cell, mainly in the outer parts away from the rhabdomere. Golgi bodies are very small, about 1 μ across, but otherwise typical. Large onion bodies of 10–30 concentric rough membranes, which are similar to endoplasmic reticulum, are scattered through the cytoplasm. There are also large dense-core vesicles with uniformly smooth contents. Mitochondria of 1–3 μ long by 0·5–1·0 μ broad, are very numerous and are concentrated near the rhabdom in light-adapted eyes (Figs. 4 and 6).

Where the retinula cells meet at the centre of the column the membrane is broken up into tubules which are about 0·05 μ in diameter, forming the rhabdomere which is considered the site of the visual pigment and process of reception. Its exact form is therefore of importance. The slightly granular contents of the tubules are in continuity with the cytoplasm of the retinula cell (Figs. 7 and 8). The membranes of adjacent tubules are pressed against each other, especially in the central regions, where there is a regular hexagonal array of tubules (Fig. 6). Where they meet, the tubules of adjacent retinula cells are pressed against each other in exactly the same way as between those of one cell, and it is noteworthy that nowhere is there any intracellular space which could be specialized as a line of ionic current flow. Where the adjacent retinula cell bodies meet at the margin of the rhabdom they are attached together by obvious elongated desmosomes (Figs. 6 and 7) which clearly have the function of holding the cells together round the central

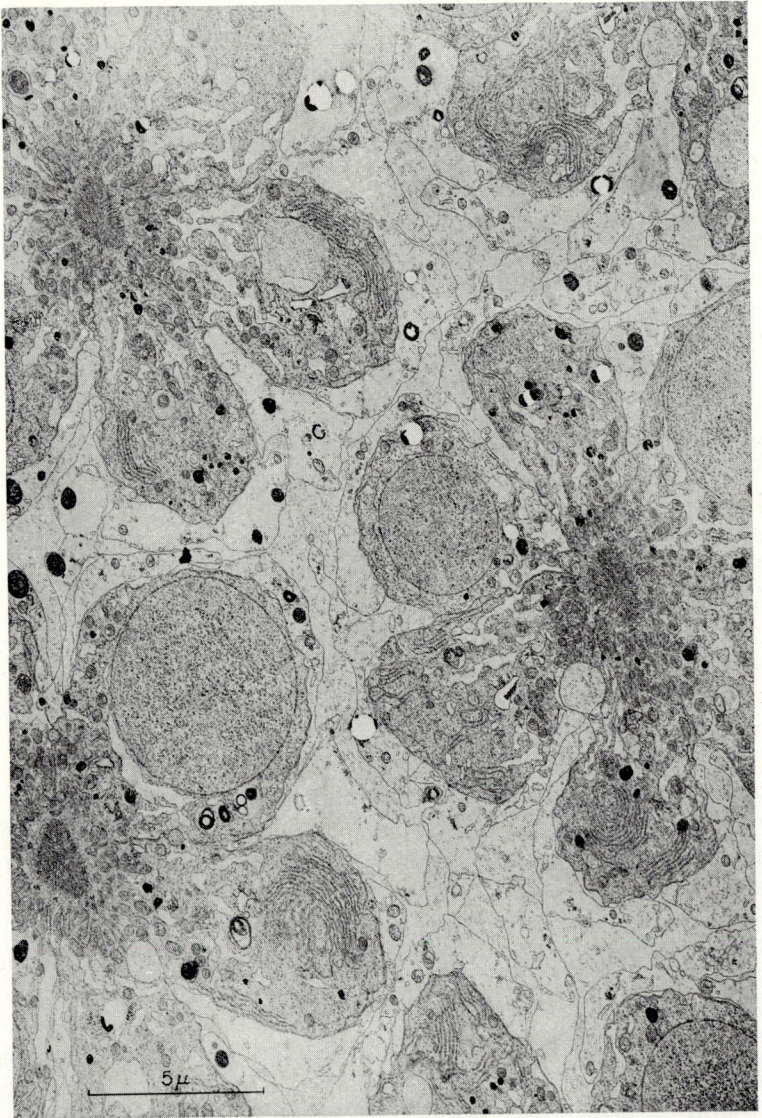

FIG. 4

Ommatidia of locust eye in transverse section above the basal retinula cells through the region where each ommatidium has six retinula cells. Note their nuclei, endoplasmic reticulum and the loose sheaths of glial cells between which there are haemocoel spaces around the ommatidia. This is a light-adapted eye and the mitochondria lie close to the rhabdom.

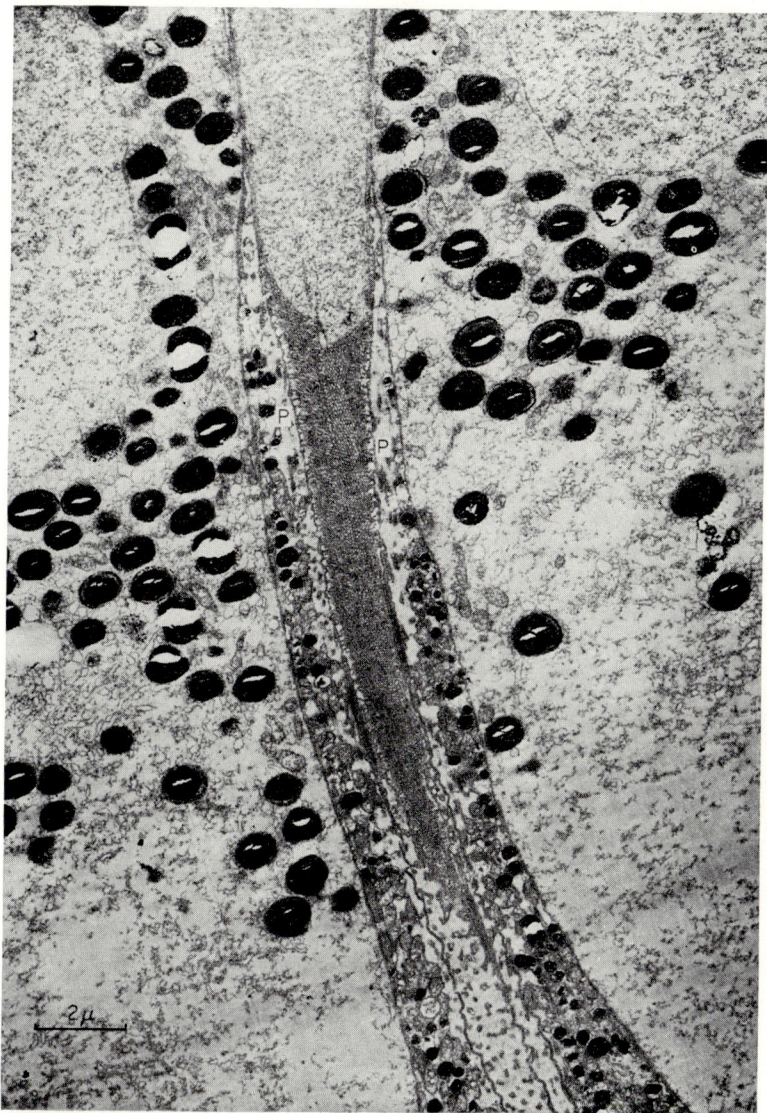

FIG. 5

Longitudinal section through the upper part of a dark-adapted ommatidium, showing at the top parts of the two primary pigment cells and the cone. The upper end of the rhabdom, where it meets the cone, is almost entirely surrounded by fluid-filled palisade (*p*), which is again seen extensively where the section runs off the rhabdom at the foot of the picture.

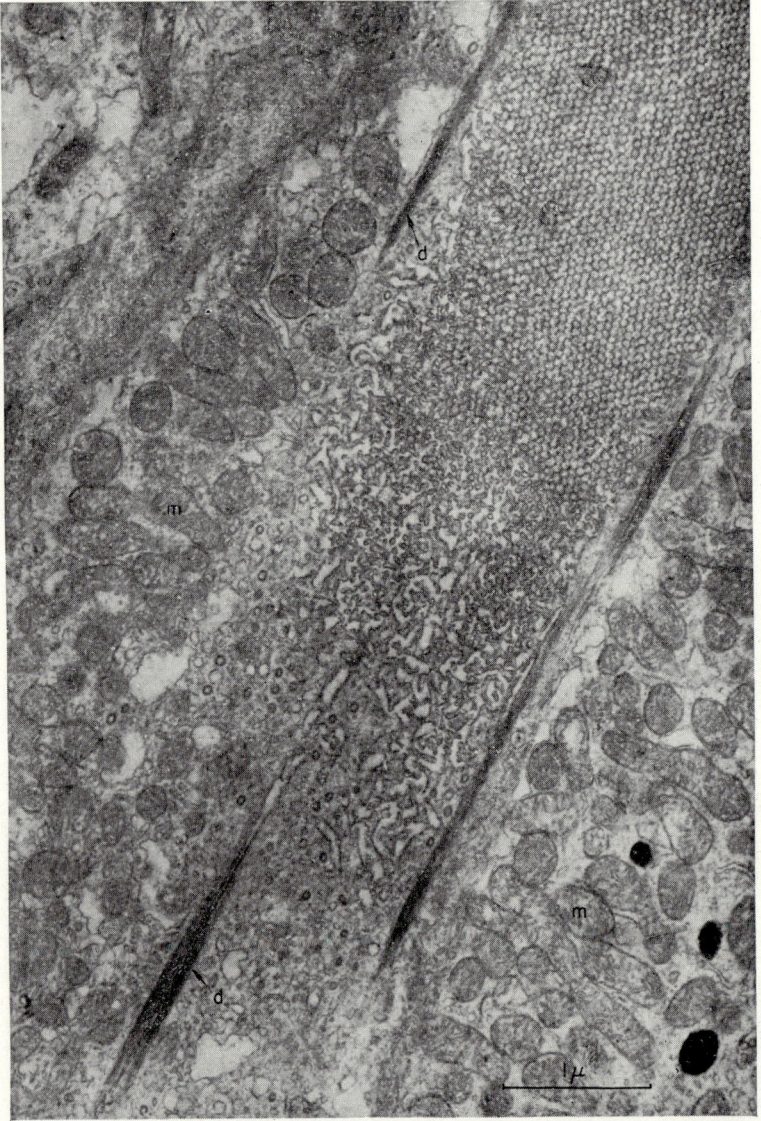

FIG. 6

Glancing longitudinal section along the side of the rhabdom of a light-adapted eye, showing the close approximation of the mitochondria (*m*) to the sides of the rhabdom, and the elongated form of the desmosomes (*d*) where the retinula cells meet at the rhabdom edge. The fusion of rhabdomeres of the separate retinula cells is so complete that it is impossible to distinguish them here.

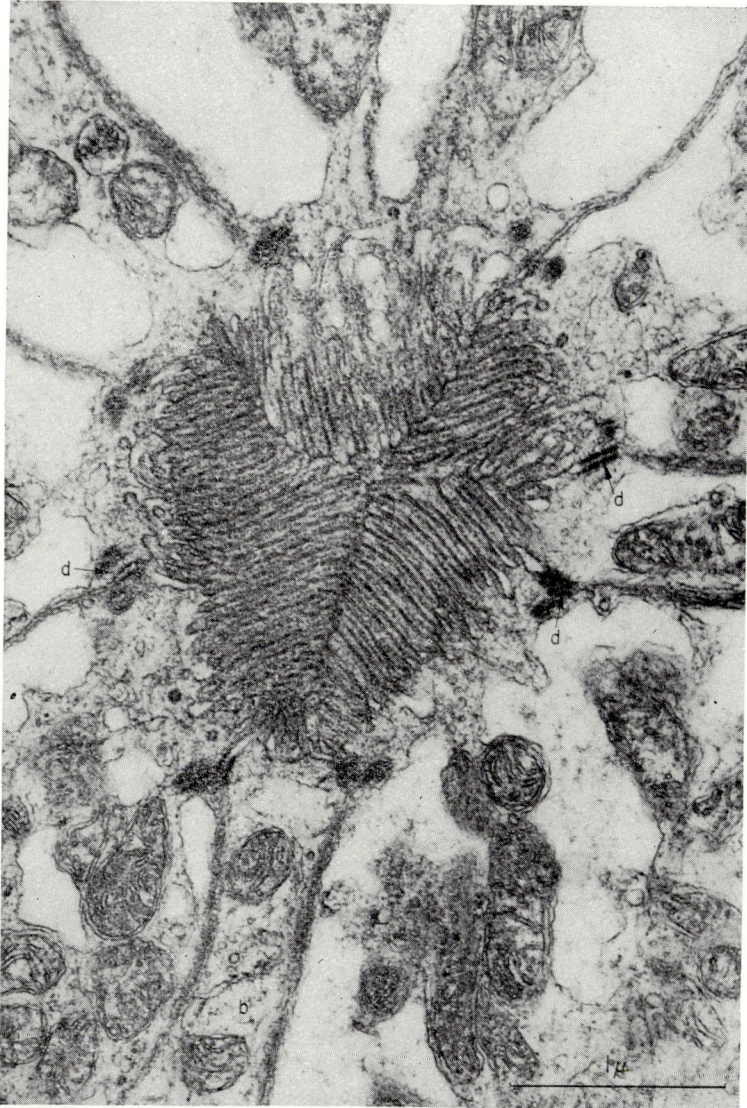

FIG. 7

Enlarged view of the rhabdom of a dark-adapted eye showing seven retinula cells
with palisade. The basal retinula cell (*b*) has no palisade. The desmosomes (*d*)
differ in appearance because most are cut obliquely.

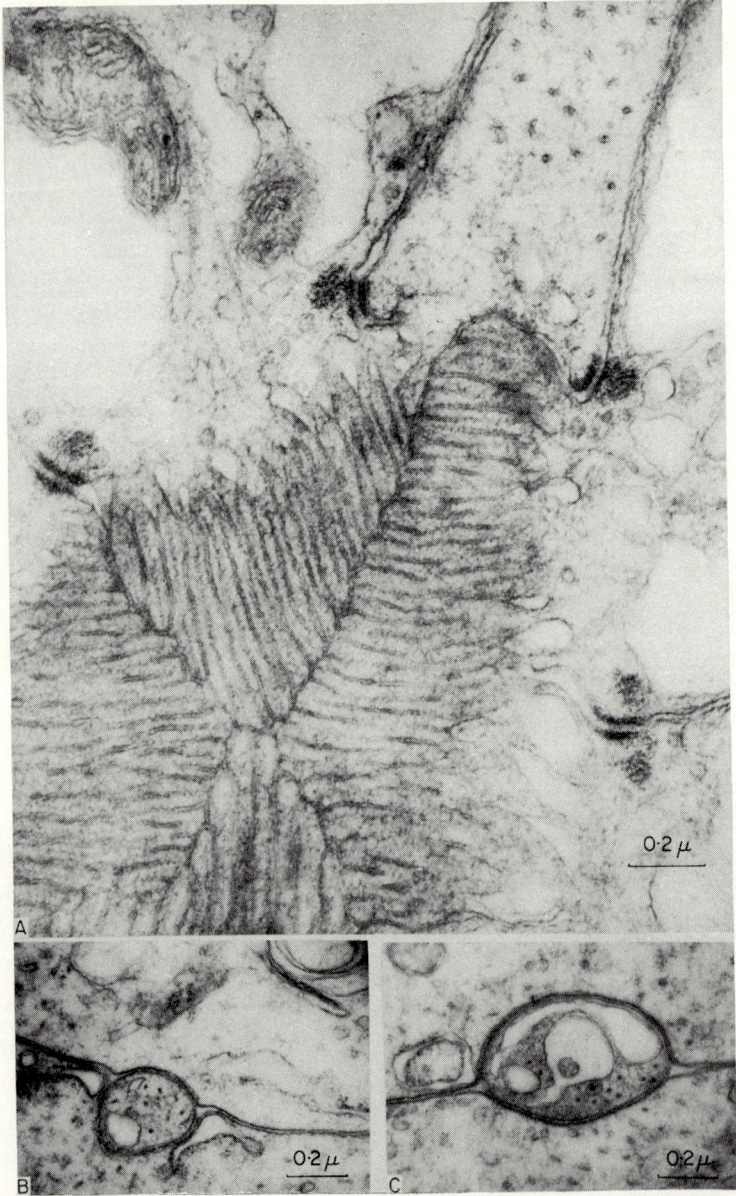

FIG. 8

A, The end of a basal retinula cell where it approaches the rhabdom. Note the different directions of the tubules and their continuity with the cytoplasm. B and C, Sections through the extensions of the cone, four of which run to the basement membrane, with tubules in each.

rhabdom region. This arrangement must presumably tend to block a low resistance radial pathway for ionic currents between the retinula cells as suggested by Goldsmith (1962). The desmosomes extend from the cone to the base of the rhabdom, which reaches almost to the basement membrane. They have a strand of densely staining fibres on each side along their whole length (Figs. 7 and 8). The basal retinula cells number either one or two per ommatidium, and are arranged in a definite position in the ring of retinula cells, in a pattern which is repeated across the eye (Fig. 9). Where there are two, one is dorsal and the other ventral, at least in the limited sample examined. The main part of the basal retinula cell lies away from the rhabdom in the outer part of the ring of cells, as seen in cross-section, but sends a narrow blade-shaped protrusion as far as the rhabdom between two adjacent retinula cells (Figs. 1A and 8). This protrusion bears a few minute rhabdomere tubules, but it always terminates against the rhabdom in the region of the ring of desmosomes, to which it also contributes. The cytoplasm of the basal retinula cells is relatively free from organelles, as compared with the typical retinula cells. There are no pigment grains, onion bodies or endoplasmic lacunae (see below), while mitochondria, endoplasmic reticulum and multivesicular bodies are relatively rare. Neurotubules are a constant feature of the basal cell cytoplasm, but in the other cells lie mainly in the axons.

Glial, or pigment, cells surround each ommatidium and form a continuous sheath from cone to basement membrane. Two large primary pigment cells which surround the narrowest part of the cone, at its base, have a large clear cytoplasm with numerous pigment grains commonly arranged closely round the nuclear and cell membranes (Fig. 3). The glial cells round the ommatidia appear to be more numerous than the retinula cells, in that many outlines are seen in any one section (Figs. 4 and 9). However, judging from the small number of nuclei between the ommatidia, these long processes spread from cells which have nuclei near the basement membrane. All the glial cells have pigment grains which are much larger than those of the retinula cells. Pigment grains are especially abundant in the glial cells which surround the axon bundles as they pass below the basement membrane. Also in the basement membrane region, and associated with glial cells, are tracheoles, which enter the retina and run in the glial sheath around the ommatidia. There is no special tapetal layer of trachea in the locust. From each ommatidium eight axons pass through the basement membrane in a discrete bundle (Fig. 10).

CHANGES WITH DARK–LIGHT ADAPTATION

The following changes have already been described (Horridge and Barnard, 1965). In the light-adapted eye the cytoplasm of the retinula cells is crowded with mitochondria in the region adjacent to the rhabdom (Figs. 4 and 6) and fluid-filled endoplasmic lacunae are spread through the cell. In the dark-

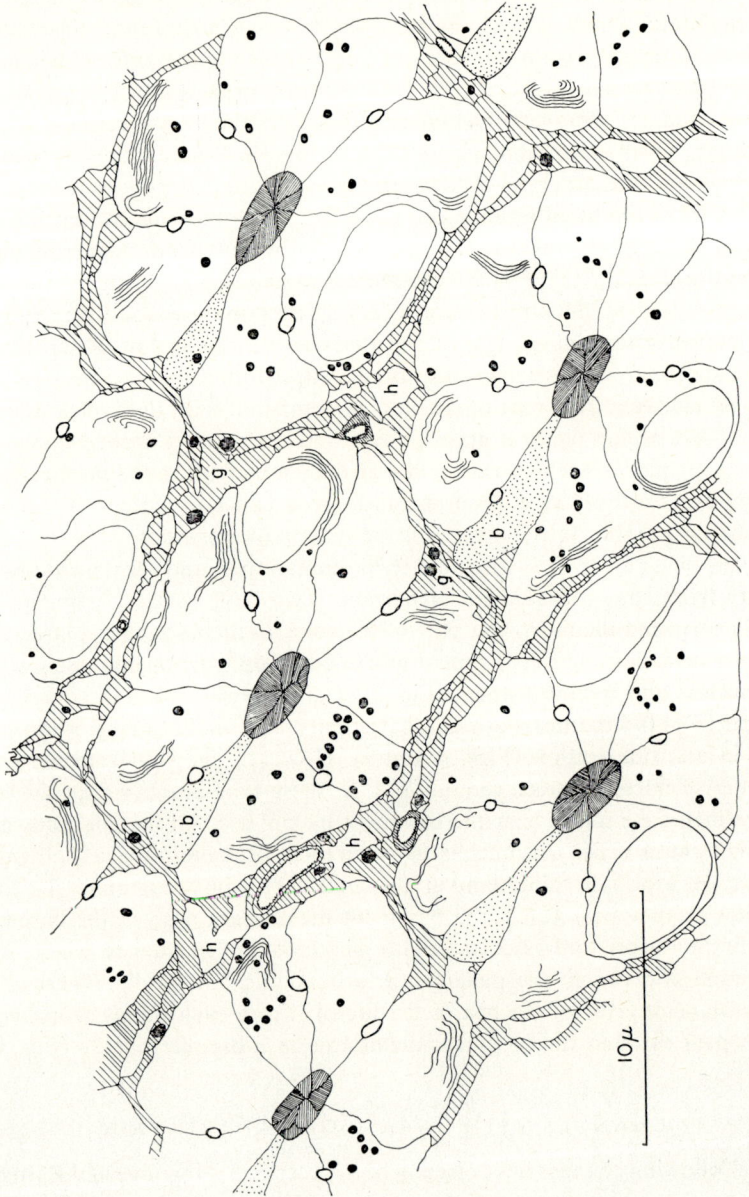

FIG. 9

adapted eye, by contrast, the mitochondria have moved away from the rhabdom and their place has been taken by large fluid-filled lacunae which form a palisade (Figs. 5, 7, and 8). The fluid-filled spaces, which are large enough to be visible in the light microscope, are surrounded by membranes of the endoplasmic reticulum in each case, and it is not clear whether they migrate in bulk or whether the fluid is transported from one set of membranes to a different set. The basal retinula cells do not participate in these changes. Despite a careful search, no noticeable pigment movements have been found in either glial or retinula cells.

On the wave-guide theory of the rhabdom (Exner, 1891, p. 31; Kuiper, 1962), to reduce the refractive index by palisade round the rhabdom will have the effect of retaining light over a great angle of internal reflection. Having realized that this constitutes a test whether the acceptance angle for the ommatidium is limited by internal reflection in the rhabdom, we set out at St. Andrews, to measure angles of acceptance for the same retinula cell in the two states. Measurements made by J. Tunstall show that the angle of acceptance does in fact become wider on dark adaptation and, moreover, the time course of this change agrees with the appearance of the palisade and not with the time course of the large increase in sensitivity which also takes place in dark-adaptation.

ACCEPTANCE ANGLE CURVES

The measurements are made in the following way. A locust eye is mounted at the centre of a circle upon which a movable arm swings in calibrated horizontal and vertical directions. With citrate or KCl-filled glass electrodes, probings are made blindly into the retinula cell region until a cell is found with a stable resting potential. Values of 30–60 mV are treated as being from reliable cells. On the movable arm is a very small tungsten light source, a shutter and a set of neutral filters. The light is a point source, without focusing lenses. The response is usually measured to the top of the dynamic phase, or initial peak, because some of the light flashes are short and give responses without a plateau. This has negligible effect on the resulting angles, so long as measurements are all made on the same variable. The intensity to give a required response is measured for various angles at either side of the position of maximum response. The state of adaptation of the cell is changed by varying the duration of the light-pulse or the intervals between successive pulses, and letting the cell come to a new steady state. To follow the angles

---

FIG. 9 (*opposite*)

Tracing from a montage of *EM* sections through the eccentric cell region of the retina, showing the similar orientation of the basal retinula cells (*b*) in each ommatidium. The outlines of the glial cells (*g*) and of haemocoel spaces (*h*) are also shown.

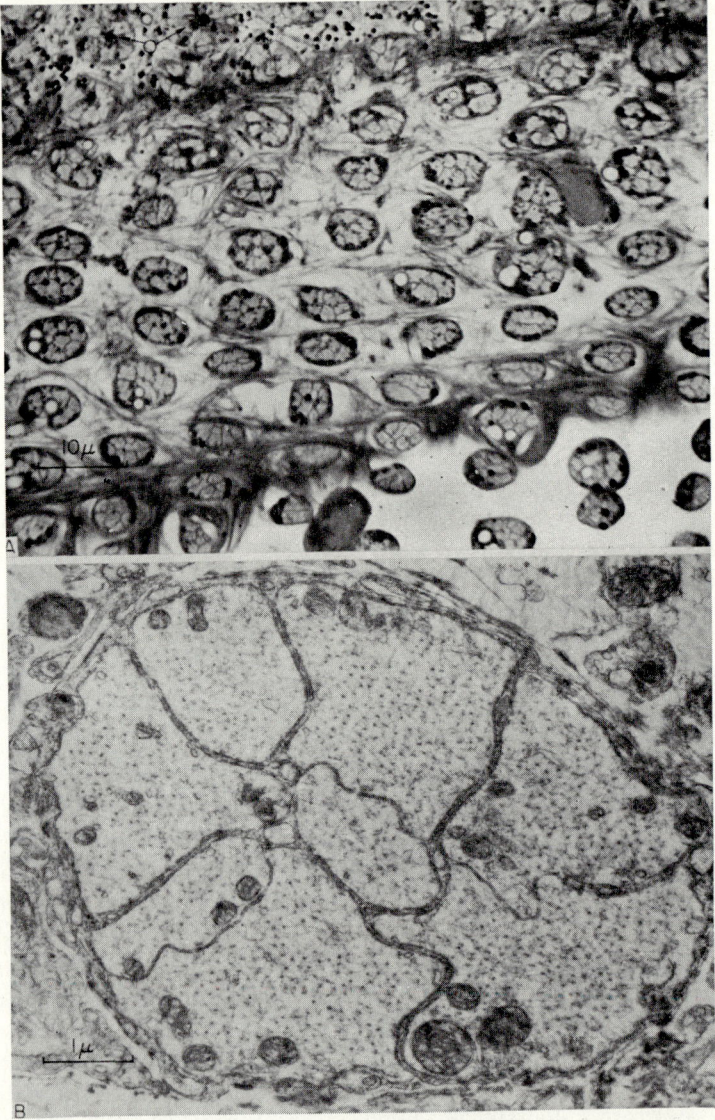

FIG. 10

A, Light microscope picture running obliquely through the basement membrane with ommatidia (*o*), having pigment grains in the glial cells and retinula cells. The central part of the picture shows the bundles of eight axons, each bundle from one ommatidium. B, A single bundle, showing the eight axons within it. Six or seven of these are of retinula cells and two or one are of basal retinula cells. All axons have neurotubules and mitochondria.

during light-adaptation other measurements were taken at various times with the cell continually illuminated after a long period of darkness. A few measurements were taken on the time course of dark adaptation by use of brief flashes at long intervals, but these measurements are almost impossible to make when many trials with filters are required to adjust the intensity at each angle. In fact, one has usually to be content with measuring the angle at which a light must be twice the intensity which is required on the axis to elicit the same response (called the half-linear sensitivity). Repeated checks of the state of adaptation are made with the light on the axis of the cell.

Because the sensitivity increases by a factor of about 1000 during the course of dark adaptation in the range we use, care must be taken to ensure that the cell stays in the same average illumination over the period of one test. For this reason most measurements were taken in one of the extreme states. A fuller account is in preparation. Curves of the acceptance angle of three adjacent light-adapted ommatidia are shown in Fig. 11. Interommatidial angles are 2·4° in the horizontal plane. Curves for the dark-adapted state ($\Delta\rho = 6\cdot5°$) are more spread out with respect to angle than those of the light-adapted cell ($\Delta\rho = 4\cdot4°$) where $\Delta\rho$ is the angle at half-linear sensitivity. Moreover, during dark adaptation, the increase in sensitivity is completed in 1–2 min whereas the change in angle has hardly started by that time, and takes 6 min to complete (Figs. 12 and 13). Measurements of the time course of the migration of the palisade around the rhabdom are inevitably open to criticism because (a) the tissue has to be sectioned and is therefore liable to fixation and shrinkage artefacts, and (b) the changes in the palisade are most noticeable at the peripheral end of the cell, where there is most light. In a series of preparations in which all eyes had exactly the same histological treatment but were kept in the dark or exposed to light for differing intervals before fixation, the palisade becomes visible and increases in size after about 3 min in darkness. It continues to increase after 6 min, up to even 15 min but the additional palisade adds nothing to the effect on angle.

On the theory set out by Kuiper (1962) light rays which enter the rhabdom are kept within it by internal reflection (Fig. 1B). That such a process occurs can be directly observed, for when a cut slice of the eye is seen from behind, the rhabdomes shine as bright spots when the front of the eye is illuminated. In fact, because the rhabdom is of higher refractive index than surrounding tissue, light must be internally reflected to some extent until finally absorbed. We would like to know what in fact is the critical angle, whether the critical angle determines the angle of acceptance for the whole ommatidium (see Fig. 1B), what fraction of the light of normal intensities is absorbed in the rhabdom, and whether a significant amount of light from the facet of one ommatidium ever reaches the rhabdom of the neighbouring one.

Figures for refractive indices are not easy to obtain, but a rough calculation can be made if some assumptions are made. The refractive index of rhabdom

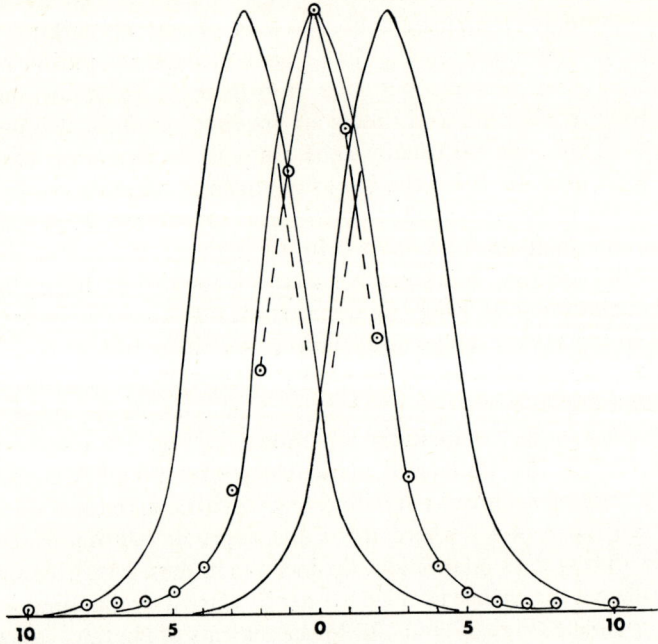

FIG. 11

Fig. 11

Acceptance angle curves for three light-adapted retinula cells in adjacent ommatidia of *Locusta* to show extent of overlap. The vertical ordinate is a linear percentage measure of the effective brightness of a distant point source which is moved through small angles from the axis of the cell. Circles show measured values for one cell; smooth lines show Gaussian curves which fit the experimental points in the lower part, but are too wide in the upper part of the figure, so that a cell has greater acuity than the smooth curve would predict. The two lateral curves are set at an angular distance equal to the interommatidial angle from the central one. It cannot be assumed that all retinula cells of one ommatidium have the same axis, but experiment shows that the angles between axes of randomly selected cells are usually the same as, or multiples of, the interommatidial angle, presumably because the rhabdomeres are fused in the locust. The smooth Gaussian curves ignore the slight asymmetry which is typical of acceptance angle curves.

is high, for they shine as refractile bodies under the microscope. The refractive index of membrane material, of which the rhabdom mainly consists, is put as high as 1·6 by Thompson (1964), that of vertebrate rod distal segments is 1·405–1·411 and of cones 1·387–1·396 (Barer, 1957). The contents of the palisade seems to be body fluid, with a refractive index estimated at 1·347–1·350, whereas that of the concentrated mass of mitochondria which replaces the palisade is observably near that of the rhabdom in the interference microscope; the mitochondria are also rich in membrane. The ellipsoid of the vertebrate eye is a mass of mitochondria of R.I. 1·390–1·398, compared with

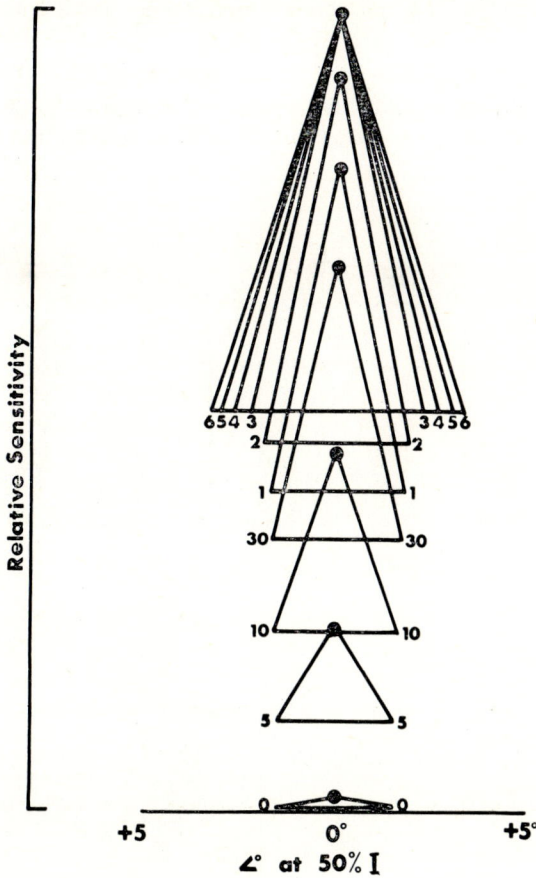

FIG. 12

Each triangle represents three points on an angle of acceptance curve. The points are the apex (sensitivity on axis) and the two points which show the angle at half this sensitivity ($\Delta\rho$, or angle at half-height in Fig. 11). The numbers show periods of dark adaptation, at 5, 10, 30 secs and 1, 2, 3, 4, 5, 6 min. For the first 2 min in the dark the change is predominantly one of sensitivity. Thereafter the angle of acceptance increases without change in sensitivity,

an R.I. of 1·361–1·364 for cytoplasm of rods and cones (Barer, 1957). From these figures it may be reasonable to base a rough calculation for the locust on guesses of R.I. = 1·39–1·40 for rhabdom, 1·37–1·39 for the mitochondria and 1·35 for palisade. These figures show that internal reflection, measured from the axis, in the light-adapted eye could range all the way from 0 (giving great selectivity to axial rays) to 12°, and then on dark adaptation it could increase to 13·5–15°. Clearly this is a large change right across the range of interest. The migration of the mitochondria is bound to cause a considerable

C.E.—2M

change, because under the interference microscope they are not distinguishable from the rhabdom in refractive index.

This hypothesis as to the cause of the changes in angle brings together several features of the available data, and no observations contradict it. The change in acceptance angle seems to be experimental evidence that some of

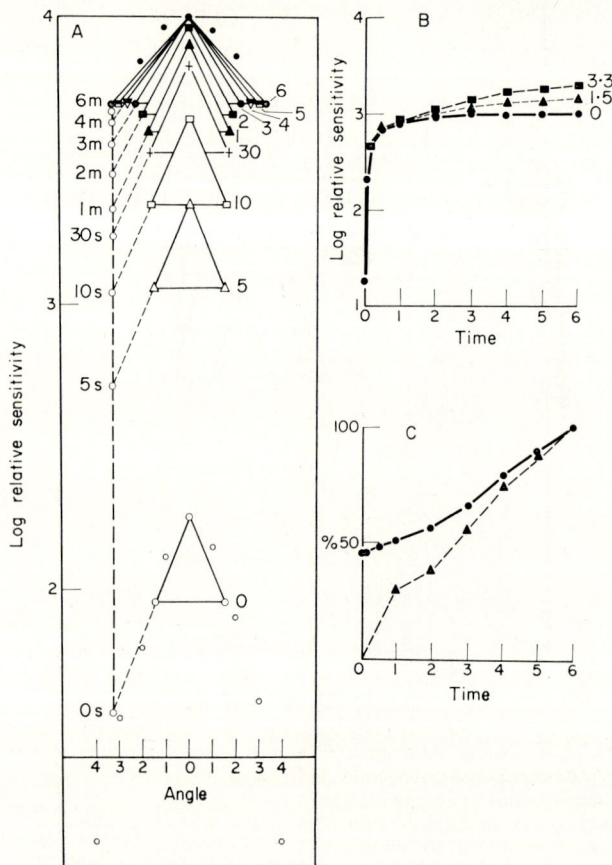

FIG. 13

A, The data of Fig. 13 plotted on a logarithmic vertical scale, together with additional data. Solid circles at top show angle of acceptance measurements for the dark-adapted eye; open circles at bottom show the same for the light-adapted eye. Adaptation to a light on the axis is shown by the triangles and times, as in Fig. 12. Adaptation to a light which is 3·3° from the axis is slower, as shown by the sensitivities plotted along the vertical dashed line, but eventually reaches the same level on account of the change in acceptance angle. B, Increase in sensitivity with dark adaptation over various times to a light: (a) on-axis, (b) at 1·5°, (c) at 3·3° from axis. C, Increase in acceptance angle (solid line) with time as percentage of the dark-adapted value and the increase in palisade (dashed line) with time as percentage of the 6 min value. The palisade continues to increase after 6 min but has no further apparent effect on internal reflection in the rhabdom.

the light suffers internal reflection in the rhabdom, and that the rhabdom is truly the receptor. Several complexities have been brushed over. Firstly, the optical pathway includes the air–cuticle, cuticle–cone and cone–rhabdom interfaces, and these will tend to widen the angle in so far as they scatter light and refract off-axis rays. The narrow ends of the cones are pulled out to long columns, where they are not necessarily straight, as seen in vertical sections. This curvature may be an artefact, but we have no proof that in life the axis of the cone corresponds to the axis of its rhabdom below. Angle of acceptance curves sometimes have a double peak and are almost always asymmetrical, which may arise from the asymmetry of the retinula cell itself. However, the optical properties of an ommatidium are measurable by the available response of the retinula cell. These should agree approximately with the geometry of the dioptric apparatus, but simple anatomical observation shows a variability of curvatures, lengths of cone and geometry of the critical point of the cone where it meets the rhabdom; and neither cone nor rhabdom is a cylinder of perfectly circular section.

SUMMATION BETWEEN FACETS

As shown by Rogers (1962) a regular array of lenslets can produce an image of a regularly repeated contrasting pattern by a process which involves summation of light from several facets. Strong arguments against the application of this theory to insect eyes have been put forward by Goldsmith (1962). Burkhardt (1962) shows that a little light of a wavelength 616 m μ will spread to adjacent ommatidia by a pathway which absorbs light of shorter wavelengths, and he infers that in *Calliphora* the pigment normally prevents light from spreading between adjacent ommatidia except in the red, where the extinction of the ommochrome is feeble. Even if this happens in the locust, after being scattered by pigment grains the light would be unlikely to form a diffraction image. The anatomical arrangement of the long rhabdom means that such images could not be sorted out even if they occur.

Over the past few years the question of the acuity of the eye of the locust has aroused considerable interest, in particular because the structure of the eye is difficult to reconcile with direct measures of the sensitivity. The story began when Burtt and Catton (1960) reported that impulses can be recorded in large fibres of the ventral cord when a pattern of equal black and white stripes is moved before the eye. The stripes were moved across a window in a screen: the repeat distance of the narrowest effective stripes subtended an angle of $0.3 \pm 0.08°$ at the eye of the locust. Comparable figures were $0.28°$ for *Calliphora* and $0.3°$ for *Phormia* (Burtt and Catton, 1962). As in optomotor experiments, this smallest repeat distance is defined as the resolution towards stripes. The argument then turned to the theoretical resolution of a single ommatidium. Arguing from telescope theory, Q equals $1.22 (\lambda/\alpha)$, where

Q is the smallest resolvable separation of two points in radians, and λ and α are the wavelength of the light and the diameter of the aperture in the same units. The theoretical value for the locust ommatidium, taking $d = 32\ \mu$, is 0·74° for a single cone aperture. Actual observation of two point sources through an eye-slice of the locust gave 1·08 ±0·03°. Burtt and Catton therefore argued that the animals' known sensitivity to stripes or to movement of a single light by 0·1–0·3° must depend on a resolution which is only obtainable by combination of light from more than one lenslet.

Deeper images of regular stripe patterns were then found behind actual eye slices, and Rogers (1962) developed a diffraction theory whereby summed images (of a regular stripe pattern) could be formed behind a regular array of pinholes or small lenses. Meanwhile, Kuiper (1962) put forward the view that the cone, together with the rhabdom below, acts as a light-guide in apposition eyes, but the theoretical resolution of stripes by such a system has not been worked out. Theoretical objections to a summation theory are as follows. (a) The amount of pigment in the retinula cells is so great that they appear as dense chocolate coloured masses through which only the most powerful light penetrates in eye-slices. (b) The cytoplasm of the retinula cells is by no means homogeneous, but is permeated by watery cisternae, pigment grains and endoplasmic reticulum, while the spaces between retinula cells of adjacent ommatidia are filled with sinuses and glial cells which are distinctly different from retinula cells. The medium for diffraction is therefore not homogeneous. (c) Recordings from retinula cells at wide angles of acceptance show no second hump which would be positive evidence of spread from adjacent ommatidia. (d) A subsequent publication from McCann and MacGinitie (1965) shows that when revolving stripes of varying widths are accurately made, the resolution by the fly's eye is no better than expected for single facets, but with striped drums as ordinarily made, the irregularities cause higher but spurious values of the acuity to stripes.

Recently Palka (1965) showed that the window plays a part in the response to the movement across it of fine stripes which subtend 1°. When the edge of the window is not parallel with these stripes, the resolution found by Burtt and Catton (1962) falls, and the response to 1° stripes is indistinguishable from spontaneous activity when the edge of the window subtends 30° to the stripes. Palka therefore interprets the anomalously fine resolution found by Burtt and Catton as arising from an effective shift of the average window position when the stripes are moved, i.e. to a lower spatial harmonic which the eye can resolve. Optomotor experiments with stripes of various widths provide another means of testing the acuity but with a window which runs all round the animal. Measurements by Thorson (1965), with the optomotor method are consistent with the values given in this paper, of the width of the acceptance angle curve at half-linear response (called $\Delta\rho$ in Figs. 11 and 15) and a resolution (depending on contrast) which agrees with Palka's findings.

Burtt and Catton (1965) now find an extraordinary high resolution of rotating radial stripes on a disc, but the precision and eccentricity were not defined. Apart from this, the generally accepted conclusion is that a very high sensitivity to changes in intensity will explain all anomalous acuity, and that no special optical summation is required.

Of the actual light fluxes at different depths, the electrophysiological and behavioural results say nothing. Kuiper's theory, outlined in this Symposium, is acceptable only if quantitatively compatible with the actual acceptance angle curves and acuity for single retinula cells.

MODERN MOSAIC THEORY

Historically a major advance came with the analysis by Götz, (1964, 1965) of the contrast seen by a visual receptor when stripes pass in front of it, as a function of the width of the receptor's angle of acceptance curve. Götz assumes, from experimental evidence of the blowfly (Washizu, Burkhardt and Streck, 1964), that the acceptance angle curve is a normal Gaussian curve with width $\Delta\rho$ at half-linear height (the angle from axis where twice as much light is required to give the same response as on the axis). He defines the contrast from the striped pattern as $m_e = J_{max}-J_{min}/2$ average J, where J is a measure of brightness, and he shows that the contrast in similar terms as seen by a single retinula cell will be

$$m_e = e^{-\left[\frac{\Pi^2}{4\ln 2}\right]\left[\frac{\Delta\rho}{\lambda}\right]^2}$$

where $\Delta\rho$ is the angle at half-height of the acceptance curve and λ is the stripe period. When $\lambda = \Delta\rho$, the calculated contrast from the above is a ratio of 0·027, i.e. contrast theoretically falls to 2·7% when stripe repeat angle falls to the acceptance angle at half-height. Götz assumes that the optomotor response makes full use of all the contrast available, and on this basis can derive a value of $\Delta\rho$ for an animal from its optomotor responses to stripes of different repeat distance. Differences between ommatidia are neglected. On this theory the limit of resolution applies to an infinite field of stripes. For some critical stripe period the responses appear out of noise, and the threshold stripe period (which is approximately $\Delta\rho$) depends on the exact method used, the nature of the response, the noise level and the number of observations which can be averaged to give statistical significance. However, Götz makes two assumptions which for the locust are unnecessary and lead to small errors, but which he has been obliged to make for his studies on *Drosophila*. First, in the locust the acceptance angle curve can be measured, and in the light-adapted eye it turns out to be more pointed than a Gaussian of equivalent width; secondly, in the locust, the contrasts seen by a retinula cell can be measured directly while stripes are presented to it.

RESOLUTION OF RETINULA CELLS BY DIRECT TEST

The measurements have been made by J. Tunstall at St. Andrews; the method was to move patterns of stripes of various widths at a constant steady speed in front of a retinula cell from which intracellular recordings were made simultaneously. The striped area fills the field of view of the retinula cell: movement of the stripes was sufficiently slow (actually 2 cm/sec) to ensure that the membrane potential could follow. Records appear as in Fig. 14. Narrowing of the stripes reduces the humps in potential caused by each stripe. The response of the cell is not linear with respect to light, so the potentials are first converted to equivalent light intensities, of which the maxima L_{max} and minima L_{min} represent the passage of white and black stripes respectively across the axis of the retinula cell. Values of the contrast $L_{max} - L_{min}/2$ average L, which varies from 0 to 1 are plotted in Fig. 15 together with theoretical curves for various values of $\Delta\rho$. According to this, the dark-adapted retinula cell agrees with the theory based on a Gaussian curve with $\Delta\rho = 5\cdot4°$, while the light-adapted cell behaves as if it had a value of $\Delta p = 3\cdot8°$ for stripes over the range $\lambda = 5$–$15°$, but to narrower stripes improves its performance so that stripes of $3°$ are resolved. Presumably this is because the acceptance angle curve is sharper than a normal Gaussian curve of the same width at half-linear height. Götz assumes that in the optomotor response an insect makes full use of all the contrast available to its retinula cells from the striped pattern. We cannot exclude, however, that the animal has resolution to spare in the retina and loses some during nervous processing in the ganglion. Our calculations from actual retinula cell responses to stripes show that the calculation of retinal properties from optomotor responses as made by Götz and by Thorson are essentially correct. Therefore Burtt and Catton's fine resolution must have another explanation, which is presumably that which Palka gives it.

RETINULA CELL SPIKE FREQUENCIES

The intensity changes in the retinula cells are reflected as spike frequencies presumably in the retinula axons but the relation cannot be observed directly during illumination because the light stimulus lowers the membrane resistance and also the space constant and this has the effect of reducing the spike height to zero, as recorded by an electrode in a retinula cell. However, by use of a double-barrel electrode, through one side of which passes pulses of current of the order of 10^{-9} amp, the membrane potential can be displaced and spikes are now observed from retinula cells. As now known in *Limulus* (Kikuchi and Ueki, 1965), it is possible that the spikes do not originate in retinula cells although recorded from them. However, Naka and Eguchi (1962) recorded spikes in the drone bee, where there are no basal retinula cells. Measurements on the locust have been made by J. Scholes, and further details are in press (Scholes, 1966).

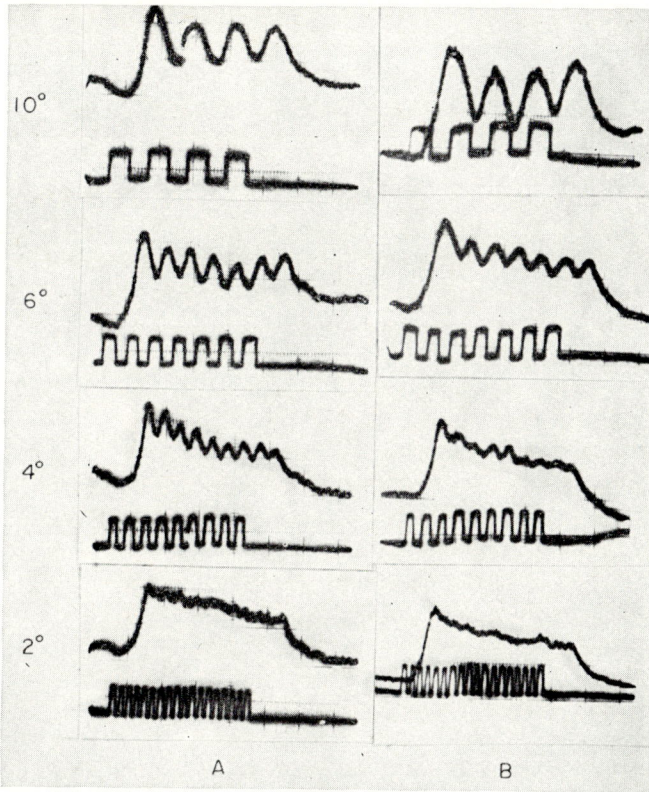

Responses of retinula cells to the movement of equal width black and white stripes of repeat periods subtending 10°, 6°, 4° and 2° at the eye. On the left (A) the eye is light-adapted, on the right (B) dark-adapted. The intensity is cut down about a thousandfold in B as compared with A. Despite the fact that the responses at 10° are less in A than in B due to inexact adjustment of the starting conditions, the responses at 6°, 4° and 2° are greater in A, as a result of the narrower angle of acceptance.

The spike frequency in the locust adapts for a maintained depolarization of the membrane. Initially the frequency will increase by 10 impulses per second for each millivolt of depolarization, up to about 50 sec and thereafter at about half that rate, whereas the steady state frequency after the first 0·1 sec changes only from 10 to 20 sec for a depolarization by 10 mV, as in Fig. 16. Therefore a small light stimulus moving in the visual field of a locust will be in a position where it moves across the steepest part of the slope of the acceptance angle curve of some receptors, giving maximum response in these per degree of movement round the eye. A light giving a few lux at the eye will cause a change of a millivolt by a movement of about 0·1°. A large number of

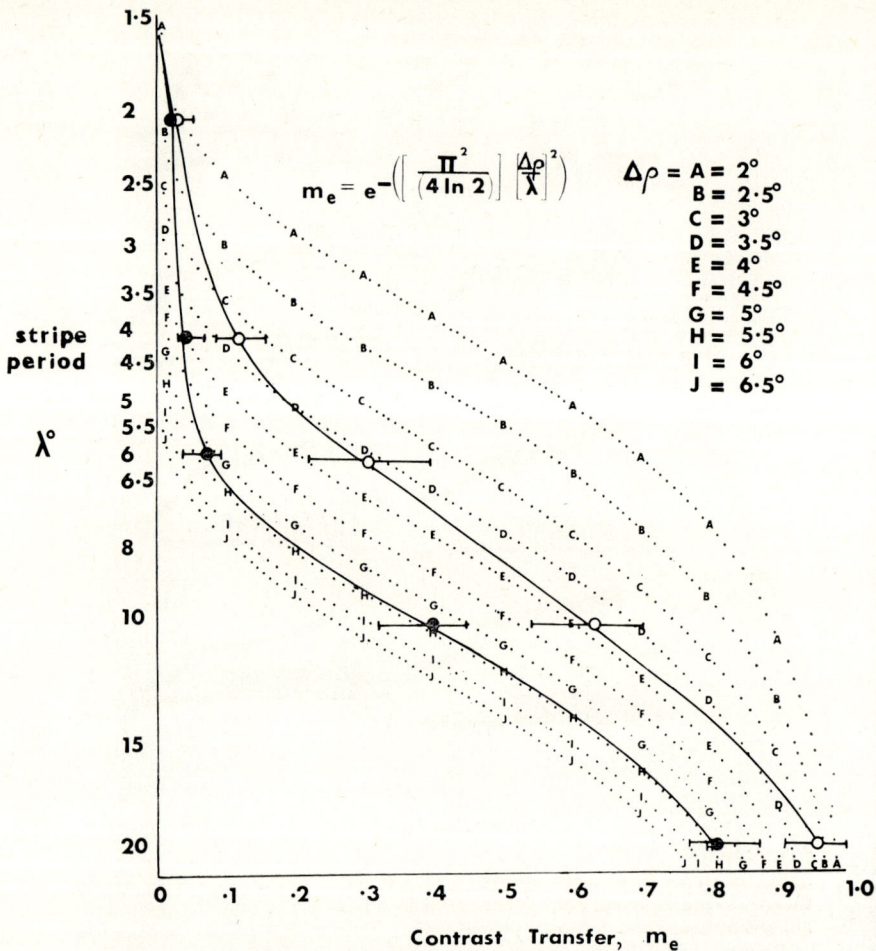

$$m_e = e^{-\left(\left[\dfrac{\pi^2}{(4\ln 2)}\right]\left[\dfrac{\Delta\rho}{\lambda}\right]^2\right)}$$

$\Delta\rho = $ A = 2°
B = 2·5°
C = 3°
D = 3·5°
E = 4°
F = 4·5°
G = 5°
H = 5·5°
I = 6°
J = 6·5°

stripe period

$\lambda°$

Contrast Transfer, m_e

FIG. 15

Theoretical (dotted) and experimental (solid line) contrast of peaks and troughs in the response of a retinula cell when moving stripes of various repeat periods subtending $\lambda°$ at the eye are moved in front of it. These curves show how contrasts, as seen by the cell increase with increasing λ, and do so more quickly for cells with smaller acceptance angles, $\Delta\rho$. Solid circles, dark-adapted locust eye; open circles, light-adapted. The disagreement (which is not serious) between theory and experiment for the light-adapted cells is presumed to lie in the non-Gaussian form of the actual acceptance angle curve.

retinula cells will be in this position and we have no knowledge of the extent to which their spike frequencies are accurately measured further back in the optic lobe by summation over long times over many inputs. There is no question of a threshold except in terms of the minimum change which a retinula cell, a ganglion cell, or a whole animal can record in an experiment.

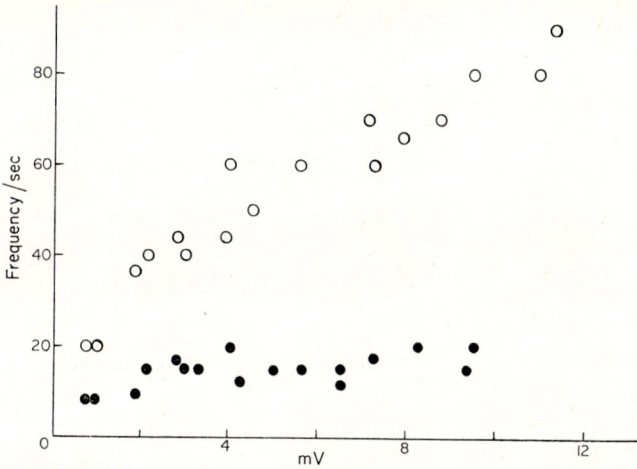

FIG. 16

Spike frequencies at various membrane depolarizations in a locust retinula cell as a result of passing current through a second electrode. Open circles, initial peak frequency; solid circles, frequency in the partially adapted plateau after 50–250 msec of depolarization. (The points are recalculated from data of Scholes, 1966.)

INTENSITY THRESHOLDS

Values of least light or depolarization to cause a response are also illusory except in statistical terms. The most extreme example in the locust is the firing of a cell by a single miniature potential (Fig. 17), which in turn seems to be produced by the capture of a single photon. At very low light intensities locust retinula cells yield miniature potentials which have the following features (Scholes, 1964). The intervals between them are randomly distributed. Their frequency is linearly proportional to light intensity up to frequencies where they fuse. There is no summation of stimuli apart from the addition of probabilities of occurrence, i.e. below frequencies where miniature potentials fuse together, no non-linearities of possible neural origin are introduced by summation of two light stimuli. The probability of occurrence of miniature potentials is proportional to the product of intensity and duration of a light pulse over a 100:1 ratio. A forced change in membrane potential changes the height but not the frequency of miniature potentials. The above are properties of photons, and the miniature potentials are not easily understood except as indicators of photon arrivals. The startling feature is that when a dark-adapted retinula cell is near spike threshold it may be fired by one miniature potential (Fig. 17). At the other extreme, a light-adapted retinula cell has about one-thousandth of the sensitivity of the dark-adapted state. When there is one light in the visual field, retinula cells not illuminated by it will be in a dark-adapted state. The great size of the dark–light adaptation

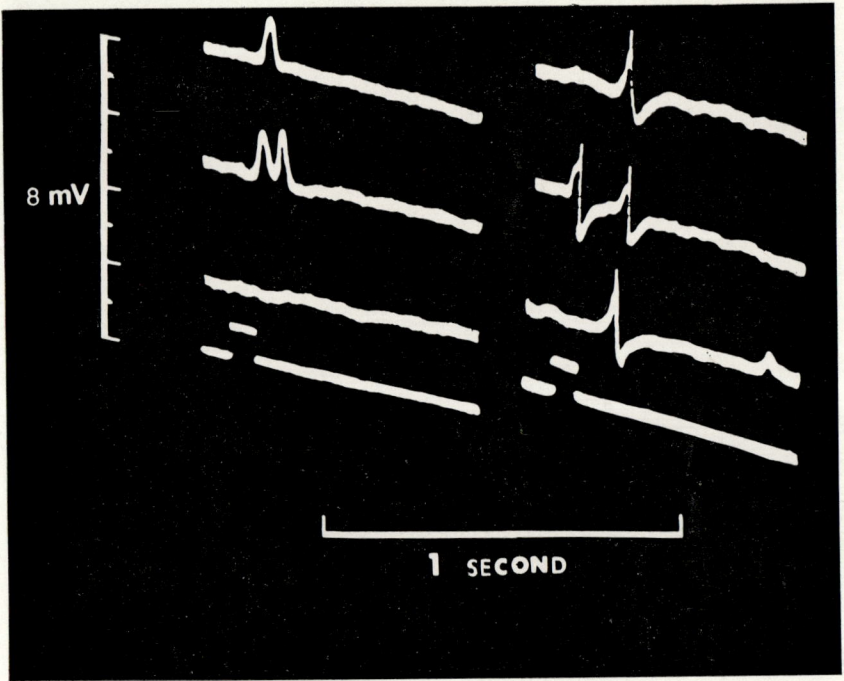

FIG. 17

Miniature potentials (left) and spikes (right), as recorded from a locust retinula cell.
(From Scholes, 1966.)

change, together with this compartmentalization of the retina, means that great care is necessary in devising and interpreting experiments in which the stimulus moves across the eye.

RETINAL LATERAL INHIBITION

A further complication, not yet accurately described, is the lateral inhibition which certainly occurs when light falls on the eye. This seems to be caused by some kind of current flow through the locust retina as a whole and through its basement membrane. The size of a receptor potential, as recorded internally in a retinula cell, can be reduced by a flash falling nearby on the eye. The same phenomenon was briefly suggested by Burkhardt and Autrum (1960) for *Calliphora*. Our general but unproven impression is that the effect is caused by currents which flow through the basement membrane as a result of potentials which arise asymmetrically from the ERG. This must greatly modify the probability of spike initiation by retinula cell axons, because the small height of these spikes, as seen in internal recordings from retinula cells, suggests that they do indeed originate in the region of the basement membrane.

UNITS OF THE OPTIC LOBE

In a recently published paper (Horridge *et al.*, 1965) we list about twenty types of unit in the optic lobe, from extracellular recordings, confirming and extending previous work (Burtt and Catton, 1960; Ishikawa, 1962). Besides the "on", "off", and "on–off" types, there are others which are found less frequently. The most interesting are "novelty units" which respond to any new movement, one-way movement receptors, and others with inhibitory centres and excitatory surround, or the converse. Many units change their properties with dark–light adaptation; some visual units respond also to sound received by the tympanum. Small field units are present but rare and therefore are probably small fibres. Further details are given in the reference quoted.

SENSITIVITY TO SMALL MOVEMENTS

Ability to detect a slight movement of lights or of large objects which may be seen with fuzzy edges is astonishingly well developed in the locust, but not closely related to acuity. This is illustrated as follows. A locust is clamped by the thorax at the centre of an illuminated, striped drum, left for a few minutes and then the light is turned off. With the animal seeing nothing, the drum is turned through a small angle and the light is then restored. The locust responds with an optomotor response showing that it perceives movements of $0\cdot1°$ which have occurred during a dark period of 10 sec. This is perhaps as remarkable as the findings by Thorson (1965) that optomotor movements of the head follow the movements of a coarsely striped drum down to angles of amplitude $0\cdot03°$ or less. There is no question of resolution in these experiments, but there is a high sensitivity to general displacement of an object of which the edges may not be seen very clearly. Sensitivity to the movement of a small light is of the same kind.

CONCLUSION

Tentatively it is worth putting together the simplest account of the mechanism of the locust eye which seems to fit the anatomical, optical, neurophysiological and behavioural facts. Axial light enters the aperture of the ommatidium, passes down the cone and is absorbed by the rhabdom, which is elongated in exactly the appropriate way to achieve maximum sensitivity to axial light. Non-axial light up to about 2° off-axis follows the same path but there is electrophysiological evidence for internal reflection in the rhabdom. At angles greater still the light is lost to the pigment and there is no evidence of any spread to other ommatidua. For lack of evidence of its optical properties we might almost as well consider the cone as merely holding back the pigment to maintain a clear path. At present it cannot be decided whether the closely fused rhabdomeres of one ommatidium have any measure of independent directionality. It is likely that locust retinula cells in one ommatidium fall into several classes which differ in sensitivity to polarized light and to colours, but that topic remains for a future discussion. Even if there are these differences, the possibility of interaction between retinula cells, which is now evident in *Limulus* (Kikuchi and Ueki, 1965), casts a shadow over any interpretation based upon recordings from one cell at a time in the same ommatidium. The sensitivities and function of the basal retinula cell and the origin of spikes cannot be discussed for lack of experimental data. Acuity of stripes seems to be compatible with the angle of acceptance curves and must not be confused with an astonishing ability to detect very slight displacement of any contrasting object which nevertheless may be seen with fuzzy edges. Unlike the situation in the crab (Horridge, 1966) it has not been shown in any insect that small eye movements are effective in sharpening up the edges of contrasting objects.

SUMMARY

Anatomically there are six or seven retinula cells and correspondingly two or one basal retinula cells in each ommatidium, all with axons to the lamina. Rod-like extensions of the cone reach the basement membrane. Pigment movements have not been found. Physiologically, recordings from individual retinula cells show that the angle of acceptance is wider in dark-adapted ($\Delta\rho = 6\cdot0-6\cdot5°$) than in light-adapted eyes ($\Delta\rho = 3\cdot0-3\cdot5°$). The time course of this change is correlated with the replacement of fluid-filled palisade by a dense packing of mitochondria round the rhabdom. The correlation between these two changes is evidence of internal reflection in the rhabdom of the dark-adapted eye and of the sensory nature of the rhabdom. Summation between facets is considered unlikely. Direct tests of the acuity of single retinula cells to equal black and white stripes of various repeat period show reasonable agreement with theory based on a Gaussian shape of the acceptance angle curve and $\Delta\rho = 5\cdot5°$ for the dark-adapted eye, but the curve for the light-adapted eye ($\Delta\rho = 3\cdot8°$) is more pointed than a Gaussian, conferring a somewhat greater than expected acuity for narrow stripes. An account of miniature potentials and of the relation between depolarization and spike frequency leads to the conclusion that the threshold for detection of an intensity change, which is the limiting factor on the response at a deeper level, has a meaning only in relation to the nature of the response and the background noise at the level recorded. At a deeper level, say in the ganglion, or in behaviour, the thresholds depend on the amount of convergence of axons and the time over which the response is integrated. On this account threshold responses to small displacements of contrasting objects (and the memory of them) can be much less than the acuity to equally spaced stripes.

REFERENCES

BARER, R. 1957. Refractometry and interferometry of living cells. *J. Opt. Soc. Amer.* **47**, *Soc. Exp. Biol.* **16**, 72–85.

BURKHARDT, D. 1962. Spectral sensitivity and other response characteristics of single visual cells in the arthropod eye. *Symp. Soc. Exp. Biol.* **16**, 86–109.

BURKHARDT, D. and AUTRUM, H. 1960. Die Belichtungspotentiale einzelner Sehzellen von *Calliphora erythrocephala* Meig. *Z. Naturf.* **15**, B, 612–16.

BURTT, E. T. and CATTON, W. T. 1960. The properties of single-unit discharges in the optic lobe of the locust. *J. Physiol.* **154**, 479–90.

BURTT, E. T. and CATTON, W. T. 1962. The resolving power of the compound eye. *Symp. Soc. Exp. Biol.* **16**, 72–85.

BURTT, E. T. and CATTON, W. T. 1965. Perception by locusts of rotated patterns. *Science* **151**, 224.

EXNER, S. 1891. *Die Physiologie der facettirten Augen von Krebsen und Insecten.* Deuticke, Leipzig.

GOLDSMITH, T. 1962. Fine structure of the retinulae in the compound eye of the honeybee. *J. Cell Biol.* **16**, 489–94.

GOLDSMITH, T. 1964. The visual system of insects, In *Physiology of Insecta.* Vol. I. (M. Rockstein, ed.). Academic Press.

GÖTZ, K. G. 1964. Optomotorische Untersuchungen des visuellen Systems einiger Augenmutanten der Fruchtfliege *Drosophila. Kybernetik* **2**, 77–92.

GÖTZ, K. G. 1965. Die optischen Übertragungseigenschaften der Komplexaugen von *Drosophila. Kybernetik* **2**, 215–21.

HORRIDGE, G. A. 1966. Perception of edges versus areas by the crab *Carcinus. J. Exp. Biol.* (In press).

HORRIDGE, G. A. and BARNARD, P. B. T. 1965. Movement of palisade in locust retinula cells when illuminated. *Quart. J. Micr. Sci.* **106**, 131–5.

HORRIDGE, G. A., SCHOLES, J. H., SHAW, S. and TUNSTALL, J. 1965. Extracellular recordings from single neurones in the optic lobe and brain of the locust. In *The Physiology of the Insect Central Nervous System.* (J. E. Treherne and J. W. L. Beament, eds.), Academic Press.

ISHIKAWA, S. 1962. Visual response patterns of single ganglion cells in the optic lobe of the silkworm moth, *Bombyx mori* L. *J. Insect Physiol.* **8**, 485–91.

KIKUCHI, R. and UEKI, K. 1965. *Localization of Action Potentials Arising Within Single Ommatidia of Horseshoe Crab, Tachypleus tridentatus.* Paper 831. Internat. Physiology Congress. Tokyo, 1965.

KUIPER, J. W. 1962. The optics of the compound eye. *Symp. Soc. Exp. Biol.* **16**, 58–71.

McCANN, G. D. and MacGINITIE, G. F. 1965. Optomotor response studies of insect vision. *Proc. Roy. Soc. B,* **163**, 369–401.

NAKA, K. and EGUCHI, E. 1962. Spike potentials recorded from the insect photoreceptor. *J. Gen. Physiol.* **45**, 663–80.

PALKA, J. 1965. Diffraction and visual acuity of insects. *Science* **149**, 551–3.

RCGERS, G. L. 1962. A diffraction theory of insect vision. II. Theory and experiments with simple model eye. *Proc. Roy. Soc. B,* **157**, 83–98.

SCHOLES, J. H. 1964. Discrete subthreshold potentials from the dimly-lit insect eye. *Nature, Lond.* **202**, 572–3.

SCHOLES, J. H. 1966. Discontinuity of the excitation process in locust visual cells. *Cold Spring Harbor. Symp. Quant. Biol.* (In press.)

THOMPSON, T. E. 1964. The properties of bimolecular phospholipid membranes. In *Cellular Membranes* (M. Locke, ed.), p. 83–96, Academic Press.

THORSON, J. 1965. Thesis, Univ. of California, Los Angeles.

WADDINGTON, C. H. and PERRY, M. M. 1960. The ultra-structure of the developing eye of *Drosophila. Proc. Roy. Soc. B.* **153**, 155–78.

WASHIZU, Y., BURKHARDT, D. and STRECK, P. 1964. Visual field of single retinula cells and interommatidial inclination in the compound eye of the blowfly, *Calliphora erythrocephala. Z. vergl. Physiol.* **48**, 413–28.

OPTOKINETIC MEMORY AND THE PERCEPTION OF MOVEMENT BY THE CRAB, *CARCINUS*

P. R. B. SHEPHEARD

Gatty Marine Laboratory and Department of Natural History, St. Andrews

AT THE end of 1964 I was trying with G. A. Horridge to analyse the perception of movement by the crab. Using a striped drum we wanted to apply a movement which was itself not seen and, to accomplish this, we turned out the light during the course of a drum movement through a few degrees. When the light was turned on, the eye followed in the same direction but never travelled through as great an angle as the drum. We found that when the dark period in which a drum movement was made was increased from a few to many seconds, the response still remained but became progressively smaller with increasing dark period. We concluded that a persistent but slowly fading impression of the original drum position is retained. This was termed optokinetic memory.

G. A. Horridge used the optokinetic memory as a technique to examine other aspects of the crab's visual system. Visual feedback was eliminated by stimulating a clamped eye in what is termed the open loop situation and he found that eye tremor enhanced the perception of edges at the partial expense of areas of intensity.

I have recently used this open loop technique with W. J. P. Barnes to examine the time course of the build up of optokinetic memory.

INTRODUCTION

Perception of movement in the visual field is dependent upon a relation being derived from the visual input at one time with a changed visual input at a succeeding time.

The stalked eyes of a crab will follow movement of a vertically striped drum which is rotated horizontally around the animal. The eye moves more slowly than the drum and the relative movement of the two is the stimulus. The eye is capable of following movements of a drum or single light down to velocities as low as $10-20°/\text{hr}$ which is slower than the speed of movement of the sun or moon across the sky (Horridge and Sandeman, 1964) and the eye does in fact follow the sun's movement with a latency of 10 sec and a speed $10-40\%$ that of the stimulus (Horridge, 1966a).

A free eye exhibits continual tremor of amplitude $0 \cdot 02 - 0 \cdot 2°$ at a frequency of around 1 or 2 per second. Besides the tremor there are irregularly appearing flicks and wandering movements. These are all superimposed on the opto-kinetic response and, for low drum speeds near the lower limit of response, the input must be averaged over several seconds before movement is deduced. Such slow movement could be deduced if the crab were able to compare the position of contrasts in the visual field with their position, relative to the receptor array, at an earlier time. Some form of memory of past visual input would be necessary before such a comparison could be made.

In the following experiments visual memory is demonstrated by the optokinetic response when the light is turned on, to a movement of the striped drum made in the preceding dark period. A preliminary account has already appeared (Horridge and Shepheard, 1966).

MATERIALS AND METHODS

The crab is held horizontally in a clamp at the centre of a vertically striped drum (Fig. 1). The stripe repeat pattern of the drum used subtended about

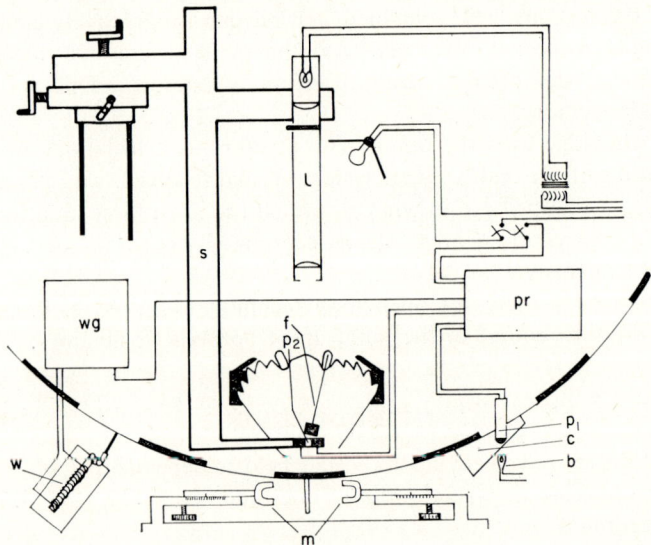

FIG. 1

The experimental set up. Drum movement is controlled by a modified pen writer (w), which is activated by a L.F. waveform generator (wg) or may be moved by hand between adjustable magnetic stops (m). Drum movement is recorded by the photocell (p_1), shaded from a light (b), by an obliquely cut card (c). The crab is clamped with the seeing eye over the axis. A flag (f), cuts a parallel beam of infra-red light which impinges on a pair of photocells (p_2) which are clamped to the same adjustable support (s) as the lamphouse (l). The drum and eye movements and the on–off of general illumination can all be recorded on the pen recorder (pr). (From Horridge, 1966a.)

30° at the crab's eye. The eye position is recorded by means of a rectangular flag on the end of a small nylon fibre, attached to the eye with insect wax. The flag casts a shadow from a light-beam on a pair of photocells arranged back to back. A filter passing infrared light is inserted in the lamp house and the resulting light-beam is not visible to the crab. The lamp house and photocells are mounted together on a miniature lathe cross-bed and so may be adjusted relative to the flag on the crab's eye without changing the calibration of the photocells or moving the crab relative to the drum.

The drum may be controlled mechanically by a linear pen recorder actuator driven by a low frequency waveform generator or moved by hand in a dark period so that a steel peg on the drum moves between two fixed magnets whose separation determines accurately the angular rotation. A card with an inclined edge, attached to the outside of the drum, shades another photocell to record various extents of drum movement. The eye movement, drum movement, the on–off of general illumination and a time scale may all be recorded on one pen recorder.

Either one or both eyes may be presented with a visual stimulus and the movement of either eye recorded. The basic situation is with both eyes free to move and see but one eye may be painted over to eliminate binocular complications. Both eyes follow, but lag behind, the moving drum and, if one eye is blind, it is driven by the seeing eye so that both move at approximately the same speed. This is termed the closed loop situation (Fig. 2A).

When one eye sees but is fixed to the carapace and the other eye is blinded by painting, the visual feedback due to the following movement is cut out and the fixed seeing eye drives the blind free eye through several times the angle moved by the drum. This is termed the open loop situation (Fig. 2B). This and many other observations confirm that eye movement is visually and not proprioceptively controlled (Horridge and Sandeman, 1964).

In both situations the eye movement is several times greater than the relative movement of the stripes across the seeing eye (the effective stimulus) and the ratio of the two is termed the forward gain. This gain is demonstrated directly in the open loop situation by removal of the visual feedback (Fig. 2C).

With a crab arranged in one or other of the above situations it is possible to demonstrate various aspects of visual memory. The drum is moved in the dark through a small angle and, although no actual movement is seen, the eye responds to the apparent movement when the light is turned on.

RESULTS

With Visual Feedback (closed loop)

When the eye has stabilized relative to the stationary drum for a period of at least 1 min, the light illuminating the drum is turned off. In the dark period the eye usually drifts from its stable position and, when the light is again turned on, recovers towards its previously stable position (Fig. 3a, b, c). If a small drum movement is made in the dark period, so producing an apparent movement, the eye recovers, when the light is turned on, not towards its *previous position in space* but towards its previous *position relative to the drum* (Fig. 3d, e). In practice a recovery is usually complete within 3 min, and another experiment is not performed until at least a minute has elapsed after completion.

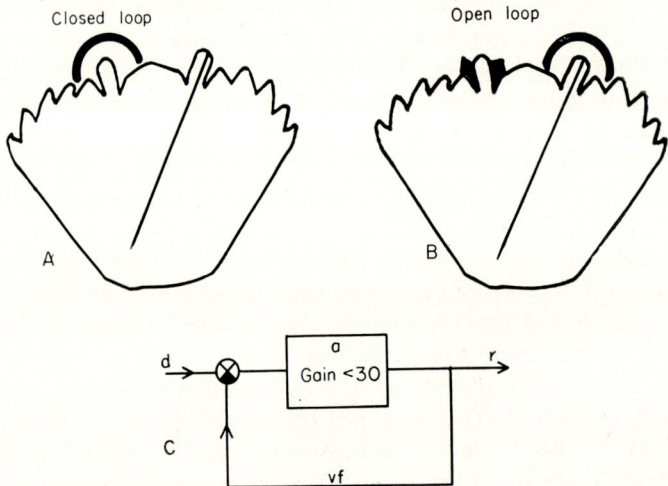

FIG. 2

A, Closed loop. The left eyes of the crab is blinded by painting over. Movement of the right seeing eye is measured. B, Open loop. The left seeing eye of the crab is firmly clamped to the carapace. The right eye is blinded by painting over and its movement measured. C, The drum displacement (*d*) is observed and amplified (*a*) with a forward gain of up to × 30, producing an eye response (*r*). The visual feedback loop (*vf*) is closed when the eye is free to follow the drum displacement, but is removed in the open loop situation.

To discover whether drift of the eye has any effect in addition to producing apparent drum movement, two series of experiments are conducted. In the first, the apparent drum movement is entirely due to drift of the eye in the dark period, whereas, in the second, the apparent drum movement is mainly due to actual drum movement in the dark. Eye movement is plotted against apparent drum movement (Fig. 4) and both series of points are seen to fall into the same area, which confirms that the stimulus is the apparent drum movement, and that the recovery is dependent upon correlation of new visual input with memory of the previous input.

The eye may sometimes remain partially retracted and this leads to a reduction in the response, possibly due to partial obstruction of the field of view by the carapace. For this reason the line drawn through the points of maximum eye movement is taken to represent the maximum capability of the system for compensation after a dark period of 1 min. The slope of the line multiplied by 100% is termed the percentage following.

As the duration of the dark period is increased the time taken for the response to reach completion is lengthened but rarely exceeds 3 min. The percentage following also falls off with increasing dark period (Fig. 5) and this is taken to represent a degeneration of the optokinetic memory with time. The exponential curve drawn through the points has a time constant of 150 sec and falls from 80% to 40% following in 10 min. A response has been observed to drum movement through 1° in a dark period of 15 min.

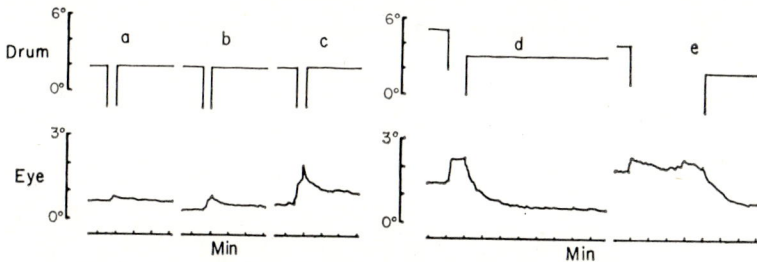

FIG. 3

Eye movements (lower traces) in response to drum movements (upper traces) which are completed during a period of darkness. The two vertical lines on the drum trace indicate the duration of the dark period. a, b, and c, The eye drifts in the dark period during which no drum movement is made. Upon re-illumination the eye recovers towards its previous position. d, A drum movement is made in a dark period of 1 min. Upon re-illumination the eye responds to an apparent drum movement which is equal to the actual drum movement minus the drift of the eye in the dark. e, As for d, except the dark period is 4 min. The response upon re-illumination is slower and not so large.

The Build-up of Visual Memory

The time taken for memory of a visual input to built up cannot be easily examined under closed loop conditions. Using the open loop condition (Fig. 2B), the drum is presented for a predetermined time to a fixed eye at a *test* position and moved, during a fixed dark period, to a second (*response*) position (Fig. 6). The left fixed seeing eye drives the right blind eye through an angle that must depend on correlation of the memory of the *test* input with the input at the *response* position.

Since a crab can remember a visual input for more than 10 min (at least in the dark), one visual presentation may well have an effect on several succeeding experiments. For this reason the visual events are presented in a strictly ordered fashion (Table 1).

TABLE 1

Light	Drum	Time
On	*Pr*	1 min
Off	*Pr→Pt*	10 sec
On (test)	*Pt*	*x* sec
Off	*Pt→Pr*	10 sec
On	*Pr*	1 min

Pr = drum in response position, *Pt* = drum in test position.

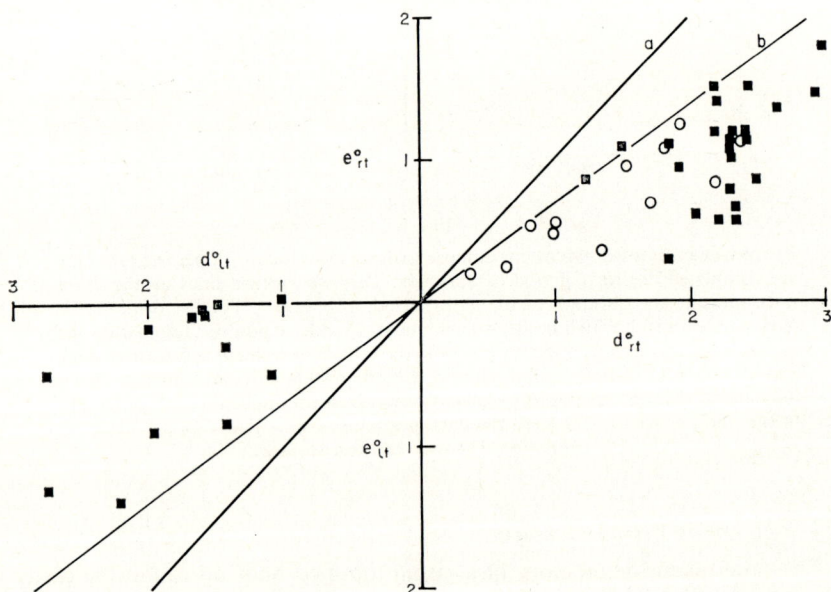

FIG. 4

The angular movement of the eye ($e°$) as a response occurring during 3 min after the light is turned on, plotted against the apparent drum movement ($d°$) through various angles up to 3° to the left (*lt*) and right (*rt*) made during a dark period of 1 min. The line (*a*) shows where eye movement would equal drum movement, which is never realized. The line (*b*) shows the maximum observed percentage following (69%) for a dark period of 1 min. Points representing eye movement due to apparent drum movement caused by eye drift in the dark are represented by open circles (○). Points representing eye movement due to apparent drum movement composed mainly of drum movement in the dark are represented by filled squares (■).

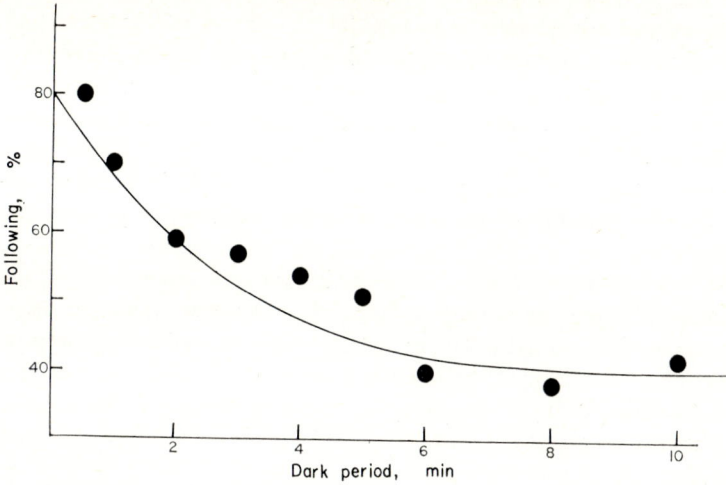

FIG. 5

The percentage following of the eye to a drum movement made during a dark period, plotted against the length of the dark period in minutes. The exponential curve shows a decay from 80% to 40% with a time constant of 150 sec. (From Horridge and Shepheard, 1966.)

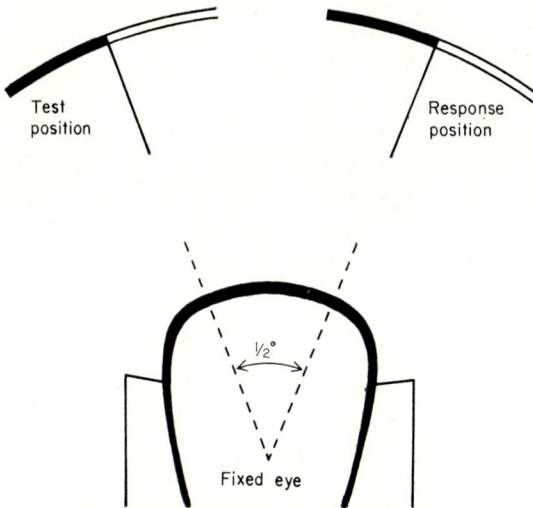

FIG. 6

The fixed seeing eye of a crab in the open loop situation is presented with a striped drum in only two alternative positions. The drum is presented at the test position for a fixed time and then moved in a dark period through $\frac{1}{2}°$ to the response position. The fixed seeing eye (shown) drives the free blind eye through an angle that must depend on correlation of the memory of the *test* input with the input at the *response* position.

The response depends on the angular movement of the drum and, for small angles, the free blind eye is driven through up to thirty times the stimulus angle and often exhibits a fast phase of nystagmus. The slow phase encompasses about 15° and so, to avoid the fast phase, a stimulus angle of $\frac{1}{2}°$ is chosen.

There are only two drum positions at which the light is turned on and the only stimulus variable is the time for which the drum is presented at the test position.

First, the cycle of events (Table 1) is repeated several times with no presentation of the test stimulus. There is no response from the crab. The test stimulus time (x) is then increased for each successive cycle in a regular manner until the response reaches a maximum. Finally, the test stimulus time is decreased through the same sequence and the gain (= response/drum angle) is plotted against the test time (Fig. 7). In this way the complete history of stimulus presentation and response is known.

At irregular intervals the crab moves its legs and, preceding such leg movements, the gain increases erratically. During leg movements the eye

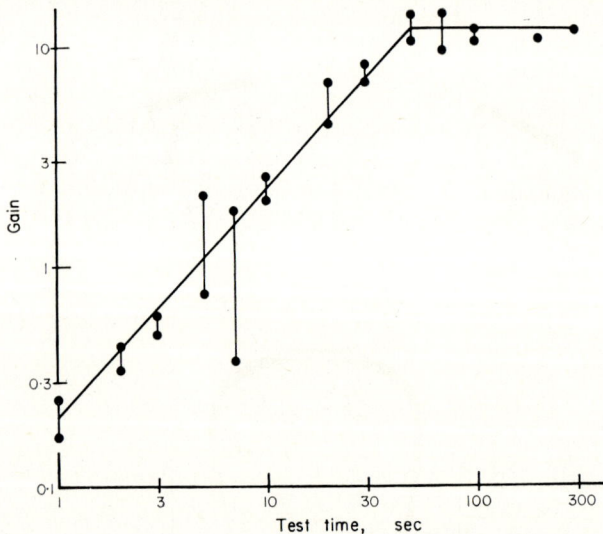

Fig. 7

The build up of optokinetic memory with time. Gain (movement of blind eye/drum movement) is plotted against the time of presentation of the drum in the test position. The responses were measured for both an increasing and decreasing series of test times. The two values for each test time are joined by a vertical line. One value, for 200 sec test time, is omitted as it was invalidated by eye flicking. The optokinetic memory would appear to build up approximately linearly to saturation within 50 sec.

wanders and flicks so that no measurements are possible. An experimental series was not interrupted to repeat a particular test time and, as the crab from which these results were obtained was more stable than many, only one response was invalidated by eye flicking.

The experiment was repeated for a number of crabs and each gave essentially the same results. With different crabs the curve reached a maximum gain of between 10 and 30 at presentation times of between 40 and 100 sec. The results for the increasing series of test times were not consistently either higher or lower than those for a decreasing series, and are therefore not distinguished in the graph. Memory of one visual input would not therefore seem to have any appreciable effect on a succeeding experiment. However, several pieces of evidence tend to show that this is not the case and one certainly cannot assume that memory of the previous visual input is all erased during a response. We may conclude that the curve approximately represents build-up of memory of the test input with time.

To examine the degeneration of memory that has been allowed to build up to various extents, the drum is presented at the test position for a fixed time and the following dark period varied. As before, the visual events are presented in a strictly ordered fashion (Table 2).

TABLE 2

Light	Drum	Time
On	Pr	1 min
Off	$Pr \rightarrow Pt$	10 sec
On	Pt	x sec (fixed)
Off (D.P.)	$Pt \rightarrow Pr$	y sec
On	Pr	1 min

Pr = drum in response position, Pt = drum in test position, $D.P.$ = dark period.

The only stimulus variable is the length of the dark period following presentation of the drum at the test position. The test time (x) is fixed at 10 sec. First, the cycle of events (Table 2) is repeated several times for a dark period of 10 sec until consistent responses are obtained. The dark period (y) is then increased for each successive cycle in a regular manner until little or no response remains. This series is repeated for several different fixed test times and gain (calculated as before) is plotted against the length of dark period for each fixed test time (Fig. 8).

The response due to memory allowed to build up for 10 sec fades rapidly to near zero in a dark period of 50 sec, whereas the response due to memory allowed to build up for 70 sec is still present after 5 min. This corresponds well with the result of the experiment on degeneration of optokinetic memory in closed loop and also with the experiment on build up of memory.

The results from all crabs used are essentially similar, although some specimens showed higher gain or shorter memory. These particular results were chosen because both the build up and degeneration of memory were examined in the same specimen and the responses were not erratic. Leg movement, eye retraction, or fatigue led with several crabs to incomplete results.

It is concluded that memory of a visual input builds up to a maximum within 40–100 sec and fades from this maximum roughly exponentially, an appreciable response being obtained to movement of $\frac{1}{2}°$ in a 5 min dark period on open loop or to $1°$ in 15 min on closed loop.

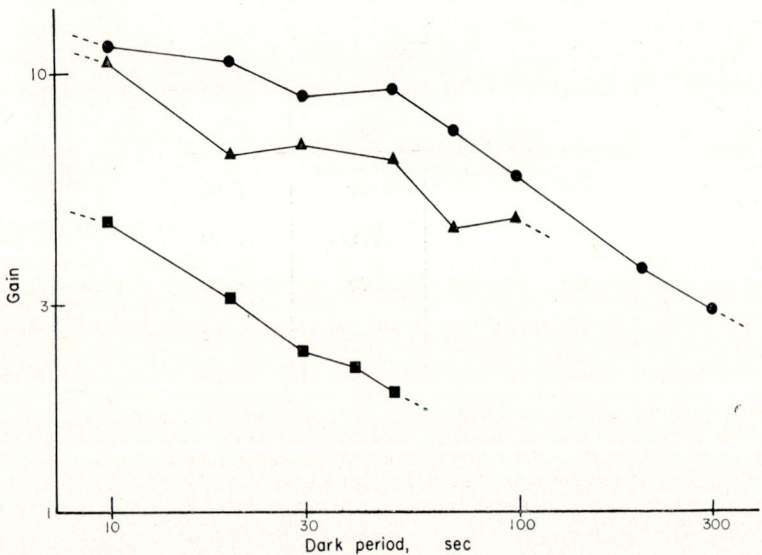

FIG. 8

The degeneration of optokinetic memory that was allowed to build up for several different fixed times. The drum was presented at the test position for a fixed time (■ = 10 sec, ▲ = 50 sec, ● = 70 sec), and moved during a measured dark period to the response position. Gain (movement of blind eye/drum movement) is plotted against the length of the dark period in seconds.

Other Properties of the Visual System

The memory response has been used as a tool to demonstrate certain other properties of the visual system of the crab in the following way. First, tremor accentuates the perception of intensity edges of the drum relative to the black or white areas. The upper and lower lines in Fig. 9 represent the drum positions before and after a shift to the right in a dark period through various fractions of a period of the stripe pattern. The human interprets shift through up to $\frac{1}{2}$ period as a movement to the right (Fig. 9A). Shift through $\frac{1}{2}$ period may be interpreted either to the left or right or as no movement, and shift through more than $\frac{1}{2}$ period is interpreted as movement to the left. The eye response passes through one period as the drum shift passes through one period of the stripe pattern.

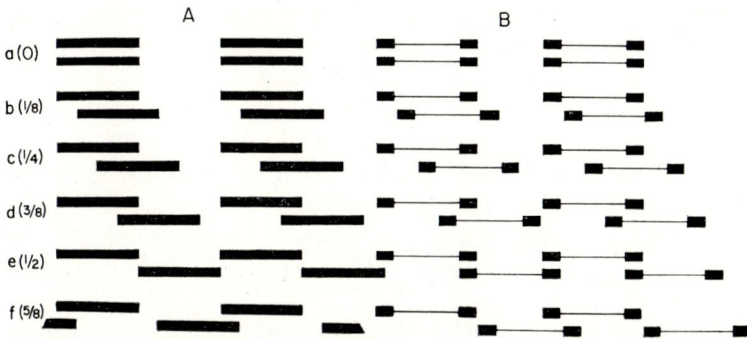

FIG. 9

The relative positions of the drum before and after a dark period are shown in the upper and lower line of each pair. Perception of intensity areas (A) is compared with perception of intensity edges (B). Lines (a) to (f) show successively larger drum movements increasing by intervals of $\frac{1}{8}$ stripe period. In (a) there is no movement. In (b) apparent movement is to the right. In (c) there is a large apparent movement of areas to the right but no apparent movement of edges. In (d) the movement of areas is to the right but of edges to the left. In (e) there is no movement of edges but areas may be interpreted as apparent movement to the left or right or as no movement. For the second half period of drum movement the apparent direction of movement is reversed and so in (f) the apparent movement of areas is to the left and of edges to the right. (From Horridge, 1966a.)

If the drum were seen in terms of intensity edges rather than areas of intensity (Fig. 9B), shift through up to $\frac{1}{4}$ period would be interpreted as movement to the right and movement through $\frac{1}{4}$ to $\frac{1}{2}$ period to the left. Shift through $\frac{1}{4}$ period could be interpreted either to the left or right or nil and shift through $\frac{1}{2}$ period must be interpreted as zero. The eye response would pass through two periods as the drum shift passed through one period of the stripe pattern.

In the closed loop the seeing eye is free to move, and so any visual effect of prevention of tremor cannot be examined. However, the crab may be set up in the open loop condition and effective tremor exhibited to the fixed seeing eye by oscillating the drum. Two sets of experiments are performed where the drum is moved through various angles in a short dark period with or without imposed oscillation and the movement of the free blind eye is measured. Further details are given in the original description (Horridge, 1966a).

For small stimulus angles the gain is large and, for both sets of results, the response reaches a maximum at about $\frac{1}{4}$ stripe period (when a period is about 30°). When the stripes are moved through $\frac{1}{2}$ period, black areas replace white and the response in both experiments is zero. However, for angles just less than and just more than the $\frac{1}{2}$ period a distinct difference is noticed, the two classes of response being most different in the region of $\frac{3}{8}$ period and $\frac{5}{8}$ period. Without imposed tremor the response at $\frac{3}{8}$ period is always to the right whereas with imposed tremor the response is usually to the left, there being variation from crab to crab.

The same effect can be recognized in the closed loop response where the eye is free to tremor (Horridge and Shepheard, 1966). The results show, as with imposed drum oscillation, that for drum movement of $\frac{3}{8}$ period the response can be to the left, and is consistently so in some crabs.

If note were taken only of intensity edges the response would be towards the left for all regions between $\frac{1}{4}$ period and $\frac{1}{2}$ period and not just between a little less than $\frac{3}{8}$ and $\frac{1}{2}$.

The crab thus interprets the situations in terms of areas when tremor is prevented but when tremor is allowed, or effective tremor superimposed; many crabs take note of intensity edges at the partial expense of areas.

When an eye is free to tremor before a stationary drum, receptors facing areas of consistent intensity may adapt so that contrast fades, but receptors which face an intensity edge are continually stimulated by changes of intensity induced by the tremor so that adaptation is reduced or prevented.

The function of the memory system is not known but it may well act as a stabilizing system and be important in the perception of slow movement. It is well known that the environment is partially stabilized, relative to the eyes of a moving crab, by compensatory eye movements induced by the statocysts. Small eye movements in the crab, as in ourselves, improve the contrast in the visual field. An optokinetic memory system with a time constant of several minutes, such as has been demonstrated, would allow perception of slow movements in the visual field, or confer additional long-term stability of the visual input, in the presence of body vibration and eye tremor.

The gain in the open loop, as has been shown, may be up to thirty or even more. This is equivalent to saying that the eye moves thirty times further than the stimulus. In the closed loop the eye follows the drum movement but again moves many times further than the stimulus which is the relative movement of the drum. The higher the gain, the greater the percentage following in closed loop but, due to the visual feedback, the response is always less than the drum movement.

When the visual feedback is closed in a memory response to apparent movement, the drum must appear to move across the eye in the reverse direction as a consequence of the eye's own movement. However, the percentage following can be just as large to apparent movement in a dark period, as to continuous slow drum movement in the light when movement of stripes across the eye in the latter is in the same direction as eye movement. This would suggest that the signals from both types of correlation are amplified in a common channel and that the perception of slow movement depends upon the optokinetic memory.

Optokinetic memory takes many seconds to build up, but response to fast movement occurs with very small latency, and with increasing speed the gain gradually falls off. This suggests that there may be two separate but possibly related systems, one a fast velocity system and the second the memory and slow movement system, although the first could be a part or an expression of the second.

Several observations point out some aspects of the output from the movement perception mechanism. The drum is moved through a few degrees in a dark period and then oscillated through a small angle. Upon re-illumination the response to the oscillation is superimposed on the slow response (Fig. 10). A new, changing visual input is thus effective in producing a response independent of the over-riding memory response. The response to fast movement can be adapted out by oscillating the drum. The drum is then moved fast through a small angle, the oscillation being maintained in the new position and the eye then responds to the fast overall movement as if the drum had been moved slowly. These results suggest that there are at least two channels in the output from the movement correlation mechanism, one conveying signals from fast, and the other from slow, real or apparent movement in the visual field, and that their effect is additive. Horridge (1966b) has further evidence for parallel channels of different time constant.

Movement receptor neurons that respond to different rates of traverse across the visual field have been demonstrated in the optic nerve of several crabs (Waterman, Wiersma and Bush, 1964), although none have been reported that respond to the extreme slow movements demonstrated in Carcinus. Information resulting from both memory and velocity correlations may well be carried in these interneurons, and work is at present in progress upon examination of the situation in Carcinus.

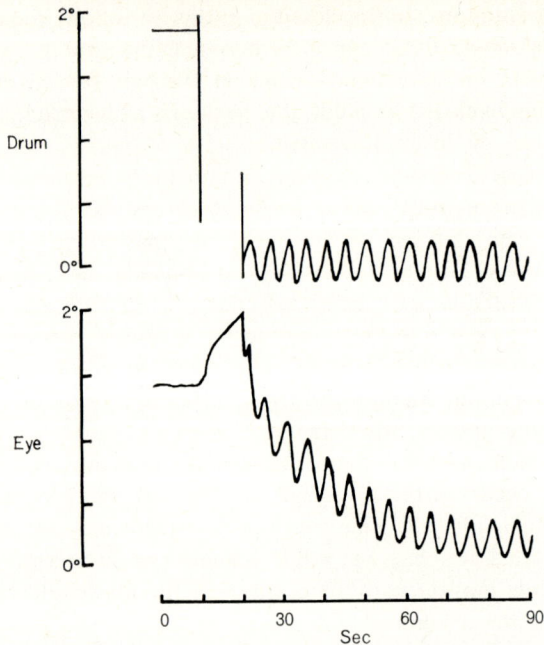

Fig. 10

Eye movement (lower trace) as a response to a drum movement (upper trace) made
in a dark period of 10 sec when a small oscillation is applied to the drum before
re-illumination. The oscillation is superimposed on the slow recovery of the eye.
The two vertical lines on the drum trace indicate the duration of the dark period.

SUMMARY

1. A crab remembers the former position of a striped drum moved to a
new position in a dark period. Upon re-illumination movement is deduced
and demonstrated by a following movement of the eye.

2. When a stationary contrasting object is presented to a crab, memory
of the visual input builds up to a maximum within 40–100 sec and fades
from this maximum roughly exponentially with a time constant of 150 sec,
and may still be present after 15 min in the dark.

3. Contrasting stripes of a drum are seen by the crab as areas of intensity
when eye tremor is prevented but, when tremor is allowed, many crabs take
note of intensity edges at the partial expense of areas.

4. A crab responds to apparent movement of the drum in a dark period
(memory system) and also to the real movement of the drum in the light
(velocity system). It is suggested that the perception of slow movement is
dependent upon the optokinetic memory and that the perception of fast
movement may be inherent in the same or a separate system.

5. At least two output channels from the movement perception mechanisms are postulated, one conveying signals from fast, and the other from slow movement in the visual field (either real or apparent). It is further postulated that the effects of the two output channels are additive.

REFERENCES

HORRIDGE, G. A. 1966a. The optokinetic response. (A series of papers.) *J. Exp. Biol.* (In press).

HORRIDGE, G. A. 1966b. A study of a system, as illustrated by the optokinetic response of the crab. *Symp. Soc. Exp. Biol.* (In press).

HORRIDGE, G. A. and SANDEMAN, D. C. 1964. Nervous control of optokinetic responses in the crab *Carcinus. Proc. Roy. Soc. B.* **161**, 216–46.

HORRIDGE, G. A. and SHEPHEARD, P. R. B. 1966. Perception of movement by the crab. *Nature, Lond.* **209**, 267–69.

WATERMAN, T. H., WIERSMA, C. A. G. and BUSH, B. M. H. 1964. Afferent visual responses in the optic nerve of the crab *Podophthalmus. J. Cell. Comp. Physiol.* **63**, 135–55.

CORRELATED STUDIES
OF
INSECT VISUAL NERVOUS SYSTEMS

G. D. McCann, Y. Sasaki and M. C. Biedebach

California Institute of Technology, Pasadena, California, U.S.A.

I. INTRODUCTION

SUCH insects as the flies and locusts have been shown to possess some unusual visual properties. They react to motions as small as a few minutes of arc, and conversely their optokinetic responses are altered if eye movements of the same amount are permitted (McCann and MacGinitie, 1965). They can detect motions as slow as 0·75° per minute and their light intensity sensitivity thresholds are as low as in humans. They react to isolated discontinuities in patterns with very thin lines or small spots and to rotating cylinders made of plain white paper if adequately illuminated.

Such visual responses have led some investigators to the belief that insect visual acuity exceeds that possible if, in the initial visual stage, the retinular cells are simple sampling stations with fields characterized by half-sensitivity angles of several degrees.

An extensive study of the optokinetic responses of the house-fly *Musca domestica* has been described previously (McCann and MacGinitie, 1965). This provided considerable information on this question. In particular, correlations of the responses to constant velocity rotating precision striped patterns with a histological and limited retinular cell microprobing study (Vowles, 1965) indicated that the initial sensory information transduced by each retinular cell of an ommatidial group is largely determined by the total light flux introduced into the ommatidium. Ommatidial fields are characterized by half-sensitivity angles of about 3–5° and a model of expected variations of light flux signals for critical variations in visual moving patterns was partially verified. This indicated that all observed optokinetic reactions were only from the spatial frequency components of any pattern whose wavelength exceeded about 3°.

It was found that migration of the red shielding pigment of the eye decreases the ommatidial field under light adaptation conditions thereby reducing its general sensitivity but increasing its acuity. In addition, it was found that the steady state optokinetic flight responses to constant velocity striped patterns

* The research described in this paper is supported by the National Institutes of Health, United States Public Health Service.

can be described as a saturable summation of a series of unit first order cross-correlation processes involving adjacent ommatidia in the direction of pattern motion (such as described by Reichardt (1961) for *Chlorophanus*) but complicated by variations in the geometry of the ommatidia throughout the eyes.

The interesting properties of the insect visual system indicated the desirability for further work. In particular it was deemed important to correlate more thoroughly information at several points up through the nervous system. Numerous experiments, for instance, have been made to determine correlations between stimuli and retinular cell responses. No correlations, however, have revealed the information content of the retinular cell responses used in higher stages. It was also considered desirable to make direct correlations between the visual nervous systems of different insects. The additional insects chosen for this purpose were the fly *Calliphora erythrocephala*, the locust *Schistocerca gregaria* and a white-eyed mutant of *Musca domestica* provided to us by Professor Robert R. Sokal at the University of Kansas. The actual points now under investigation in the insect nervous system are indicated in Fig. 1.

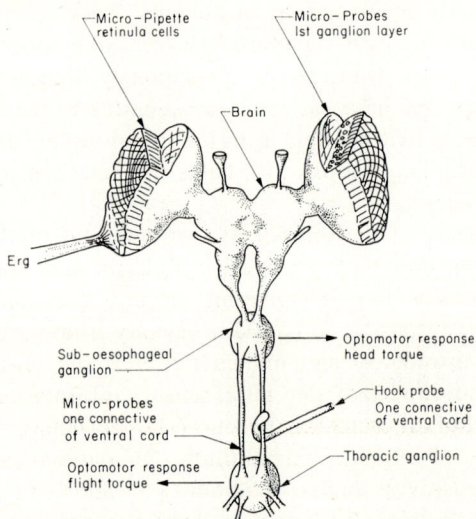

FIG. 1

Positions in insect nervous system where responses to light stimuli are being studied.

II. GENERAL DESCRIPTION OF EXPERIMENTAL TECHNIQUES

An extensive correlation of this sort is greatly facilitated by the organization of several cooperating research teams each developing satisfactory probing preparations in different portions of the nervous systems. After conducting certain individual experiments, they can then combine their techniques and conduct simultaneous probing and optokinetic response studies at a number of points in the nervous system.

Hook Probes in Ventral Cords

A new series of ventral cord hook probe preparations have been developed by Madey and Ray (1966) which are applicable to all of the insects listed above. Through the use of new non-toxic sealants, it is possible to make an implantation stable for several days or weeks. Freedom of insect movement is permitted and simultaneous probings with flight reaction studies are quite practicable. Such probes can be designed to record only the "giant" fiber of the ventral cord or to record as many as 8 or 10 of the larger fibers in such a manner that their individual responses can be separated out by computer analysis (Keehn, 1966).

Microelectrode Multi-unit Probing

Bishop (1966) has developed new etched stainless steel microelectrodes with lacquer-coated films having multi-spot activation by sparking. This provides electrode tips of very small dimension but low impedance (10–20 megohms). The use of this electrode with a new low noise pre-amplifier so raises the signal-to-noise ratio that a greater frequency band width can be used in recording extra cellularity in interneurons and fiber bundles. The incorporation of this technique with the spike separation procedure developed by Keehn (1966) permits the simultaneous recording on one electrode of 5 to 10 interneurons or fibers in a bundle. These are preparations where the electrode can be advanced in successive stages and its position marked at the end of its penetration to explore an extensive region of cells or fibers.

Retinular Cell Probing

The initial retinular cell probing technique prepared in our laboratory by Vowles (1965) involved the penetration of the eye from the front as indicated schematically in Fig. 1. This had the disadvantage of rapid drying in the exposed ommatidia. Vowles also placed the indifferent electrode in the thorax and this raised the question of induced ERG effects. Correlations of his results with those of Washizu, Burkhardt and Streck (1964) indicated the possibility that induced potentials of this sort were increasing the apparent field of the retinular cell. It was decided therefore to change to the Washizu, Burkhardt and Streck technique. Dr. Washizu was kind enough to visit our laboratory and assist in the preparation. The indifferent electrode is placed in a corner of the eye and the microelectrode penetrates from the back or side of the eye.

General Survey

A number of general survey studies have been made of the response characteristics at the various probing points now developed. It is the intent of this paper to treat in detail only studies made to determine more accurately

C.E.—20

the information processing characteristics of the retinular cells. However, it is interesting to note that the more general studies reveal rich visual pattern abstracting properties in the optic ganglia, brain and ventral cords of these insects.

III. MODEL ANALYSIS OF OMMATIDIUM
AS BASIS FOR NEW EXPERIMENTS

This paper concentrates on the determination of the role of the ommatidium as the first sampling stage of the visual system. A model analysis of possible critical characteristics is desirable as a basis for the design of actual experiments. This will start with the analysis described in the previous paper (McCann and MacGinitie, 1965). Perhaps one of the first questions to consider is the assumption that the sensory information of the retinular cells is determined primarily by the total light flux entering the ommatidium rather than to important distributed variations of the light intensity within the ommatidium. A possible method of testing this question is to combine a series of two or more point light sources in different field positions so as to produce the same total flux as a single source in accordance with the pre-measured field sensitivity curves. Such a procedure might be feasible if studies could be conducted which covered a wide range of extensive field patterns built up in this manner. However, when only a few point sources are used, very high individual intensities are required to obtain measurable responses (Vowles, 1965) and the resulting high concentration of light intensity in different regions of the ommatidium does indeed provide accentuated discontinuity effects. Thus in the limit as defined by this unnatural stimulus, the responses appear to be sensitive to light flux distribution variations.

A more rational approach would appear to be one which provides a general large field pattern so designed as to vary detail in terms of a few well defined parameters which can, however, adequately test the general properties of acuity. A pattern composed of combinations of spatial sinusoids can do this and correlates with the previous studies (McCann and MacGinitie, 1965) when the pattern is given motion. Such a series of patterns provides a combination of spatial detail or wavelengths and a varying range of pulsating or temporal frequencies.

Referring to Fig. 2, it then becomes convenient to consider the relationships between the light pattern $I(\varphi,t)$, the ommatidial flux $F(t)$ and the retinular cell potential $V(t)$ in terms of such parameters as the average values of the three functions, the magnitudes of the pulsating components $\triangle F$ and $\triangle V$ resulting from the various spatial wavelength components of $\triangle I$ and their various frequencies and phase relations.

Effect of Ommatidial Field on Average Flux

The first significant point to note is that the average light flux in an ommatidium is proportional to its field area or to the square of such field defining

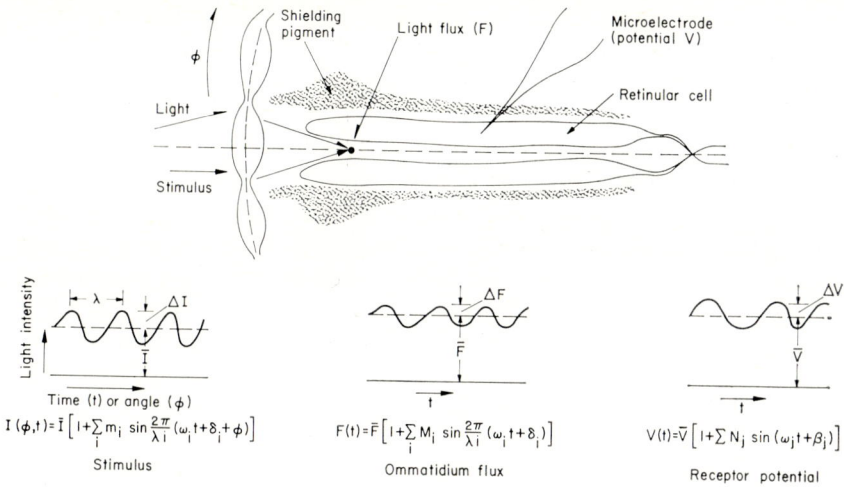

FIG. 2

Schematic diagram of insect eye showing relationships to be investigated between moving light patterns, ommatidium flux and resulting retinular cell potential.

parameters as the half sensitivity angle α. If, for instance, the field can be described by a simple Gaussian distribution, it was shown in Reference 1 that the average flux in an ommatidium has the form

$$\bar{F} = \frac{\pi \alpha^2}{4 \ln 2} \bar{I}. \tag{1}$$

Responses measured at constant signal level $\triangle I$ but varying average light intensity $\bar{I}$ and in receptors with different measured values of α could determine whether signal sensitivity variation with average light level is dependent upon $\bar{I}$ or $\bar{F}$.

Variation of Contrast Function with Pattern Wavelength

The previous paper dealt with this point in detail and Fig. 3 is reproduced simply to emphasize again the rapid predicted roll-off of the ripple content of the flux $\triangle F$ and possibly the response $\triangle V$ as pattern wavelength is reduced. These curves are computed from the formula

$$M_i = m_i e^{\frac{-\pi^2}{4 \ln 2}\left(\frac{\alpha}{\lambda_i}\right)^2}. \tag{2}$$

Also reproduced from Reference 1 is a harmonic analysis (Fig. 4) of a pattern typical of previous investigations and a precision pattern developed for our investigations. This clearly shows appreciable subharmonics in the less accurate pattern which can provide stimuli with wavelengths greater than 10° even though the intended pattern wavelength is in the range of 0·1–1°.

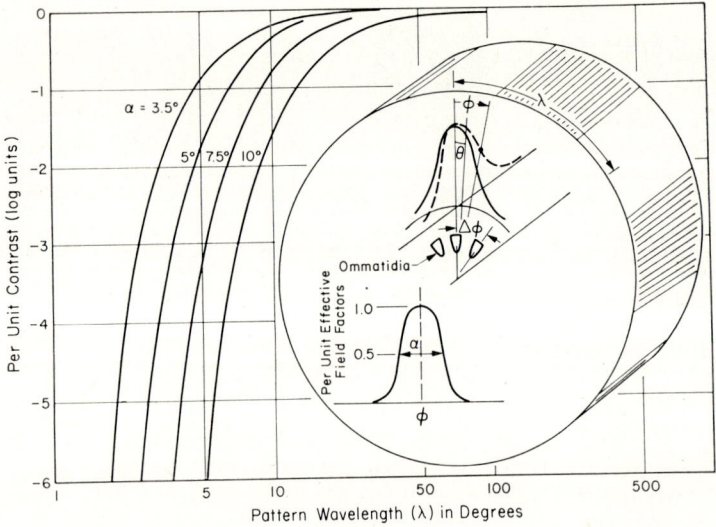

Fig. 3

Ommatidium light flux contrast functions computed from eqn. 2.

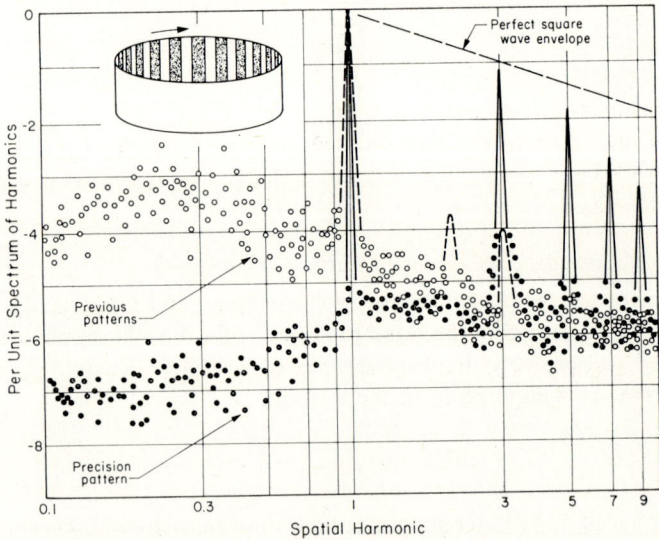

Fig. 4

Power spectrum analysis of striped patterns.

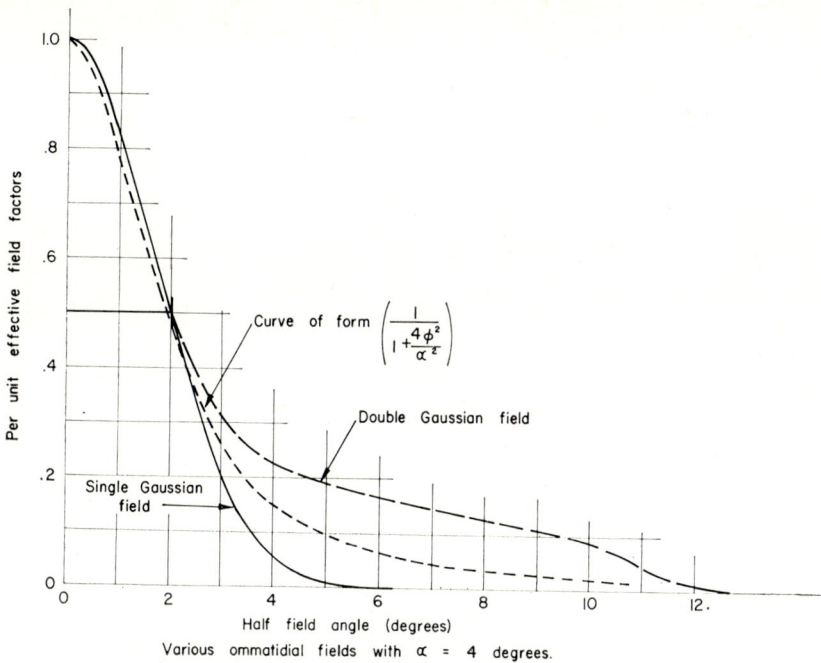

Various ommatidial fields with $\alpha = 4$ degrees.

Fig. 5

Variations from simple Gaussian ommatidial visual field used for the analyses in Figs. 6 and 7.

Effect of Ommatidial Field Shape

Definition of the receptor field by the single parameter α is of course an oversimplification. Figure 5 shows a range of variations from the simple Gaussian that are indicated by our probing experiments in *Musca domestica* and by the work of Washizu *et al.* on *Calliphora*. Typical calculations of contrast functions for these variations are presented in Fig. 6. This shows that measured deviations from a single Gaussian in the region beyond the half-sensitivity angle have only small effects. However, changes in the field gradient in the central region of the field have appreciable effects. Rapid roll-off or attenuation with decreasing wavelength beyond a critical value is always characteristic, however.

Discontinuities and Restrictions of Field

Communications engineers are well acquainted with the band width extension afforded by the interposition of sharp boundaries or windows between wide band width information and sampling windows having such low pass cutoff properties as shown in Fig. 3. This suggested the importance of studying the effect of placing stationary edges or slits between the ommatidium and the moving pattern. Several such conditions have been calculated

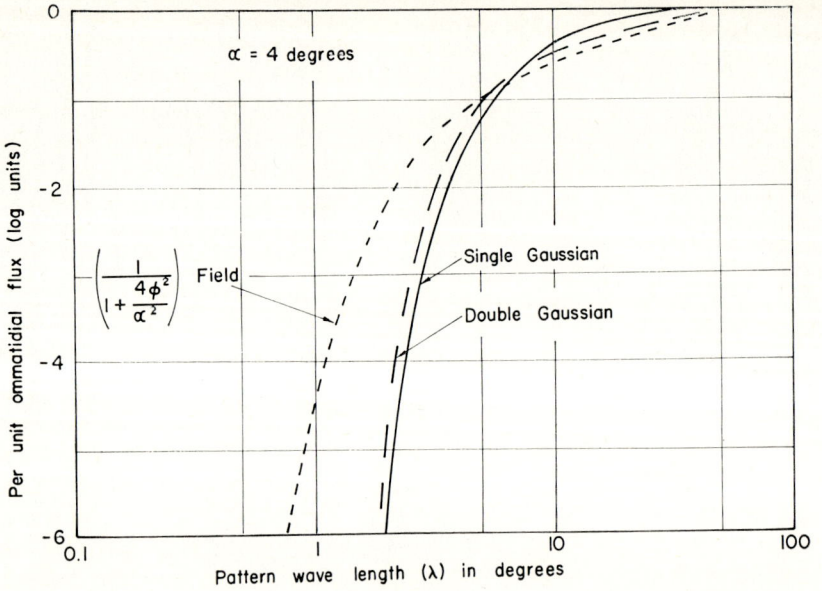

FIG. 6

Calculated variations in receptor light flux contrast functions using the fields of Fig. 5.

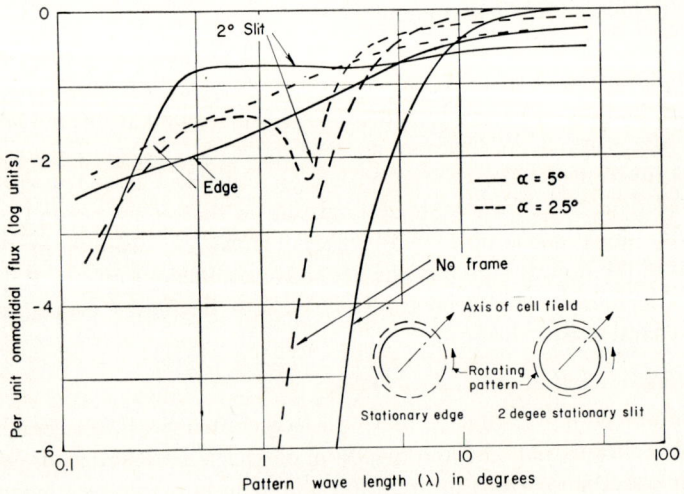

FIG. 7

Calculated effects on flux contrast functions when stationary boundaries are interposed between ommatidium and moving pattern.

by numerical integration on a digital computer (McCann and Ray, 1965) as shown in Fig. 7. The marked changes in acuity from this effect and its variation with ommatidial field provides the basis for an important series of experiments. The detailed character of the contrast function curve is quite critical to the shape of the receptor curve and the relative position of the slit when slits of width comparable to the half-sensitivity angle α are used. Thus the dip in the curve of Fig. 7 for the 2° slit and $\alpha = 2\cdot5°$ might not be found in experimental data or may be appreciably different.

IV. DESCRIPTION OF RETINULAR CELL EXPERIMENTS

After developing the improved retinular cell probing technique, a series of retinular cell field measurements were made using the same point source stimulus conditions described by Vowles (1965) and typical also of those used by Washizu et al. (1964). These were made under average light intensity adaptation conditions in the range to be employed in all of the experiments described later (0·01 to 0·05 lumens per steradian). For these measurements, the point light intensity was varied to give equal peak responses to square wave stimuli and the fields were defined by the resulting inverse sensitivity points. The new preparation showed a greatly decreased range of field variations between retinular cells as compared to those measured by Vowles (1965). Probings were restricted to the central region of the eye and no significant difference could be found between the fields of *Musca domestica* and of *Calliphora* as tested in our laboratory and as reported by Washizu et al. (1964).

Half-sensitivity Field Angle α

It was decided to establish a rapid method of determining the half-sensitivity angle α in the horizontal direction of the eye (the direction of pattern motion in later experiments) as an index to be determined for each experiment. This was done by first finding the maximum response position at the center of the field, then doubling the light pulse intensity and finding the angular change required for the same response amplitude. The statistical distribution of α as determined in this manner is shown in Fig. 8.

Difficulties in Retinular Cell Probing

Although the general life of an experiment was extended by the improved preparation it is still a difficult procedure with frequent failures to obtain preparations whose stable response life is greater than 10–20 min. For this reason, it was considered desirable to provide pattern stimulus conditions rich in individual stimulus information and alternating between condition variations that would provide repeated reference checks during the life of the experiment.

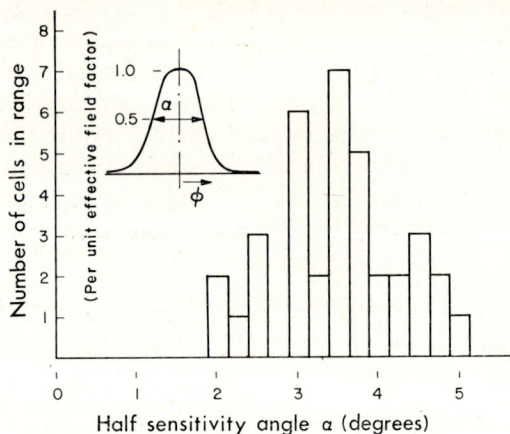

FIG. 8

Histogram of measured ommatidial field angle α (36 probings).

The experimental set up developed for this is shown in Figs. 9 and 10. This provides mechanical isolation between the microprobing preparation and the visual stimulus. During the initial electrode preparation the rotating pattern portion of the stimulus is raised out of the way through a hydraulic lift and the microscope swung into position. After the initial placing of the electrodes, the hydraulic lift repositions the rotating pattern system and the micro electrode is advanced in fractional micron steps by remote control.

Three separate types of light sources are shown in Fig. 10. One of these is the uniform light reflected from the spherical surface. This provides the ΔI function (Fig. 2) as the moving cylinder lies between it and the insect. A second light source reflects light from stationary gel to provide variations in the average intensity $\bar{I}$ essentially independent of ΔI. A third source is the point source (shown in Fig. 10) that can be moved into the visual field by remote control. This is fixed in position relative to the rotating pattern and any slits or edges that might be used. The whole system is gimbaled with two angular degrees of freedom and can be quickly lined up with the axis of the retinular cell field as determined with the point light source.

Moving Patterns

Square wave patterns were used for most stimulus conditions. These were constructed to high precision and to minimize subharmonic effects (McCann and MacGinitie, 1965). They also provide simultaneously several spatial wavelengths. Referring to Figs. 3 and 8, it will be seen that high sensitivity should be found in the retinular cell responses for pattern wavelengths above 8–10°. Thus, if a square wave pattern is used whose fundamental wavelength

FIG. 9

Photograph of light stimulus system used for insect experiments.

is about 36°, one should find simultaneous responses to the third and fifth harmonics whose ideal characteristics are given in Fig. 12. As the wavelength of the fundamental is reduced below this number, the harmonics should first start to rapidly attenuate and then the fundamental.

It was further found that the two halves of the cylinder could have two separate square wave patterns for alternate checks between two stimulus conditions since the transient period of the response change is very short

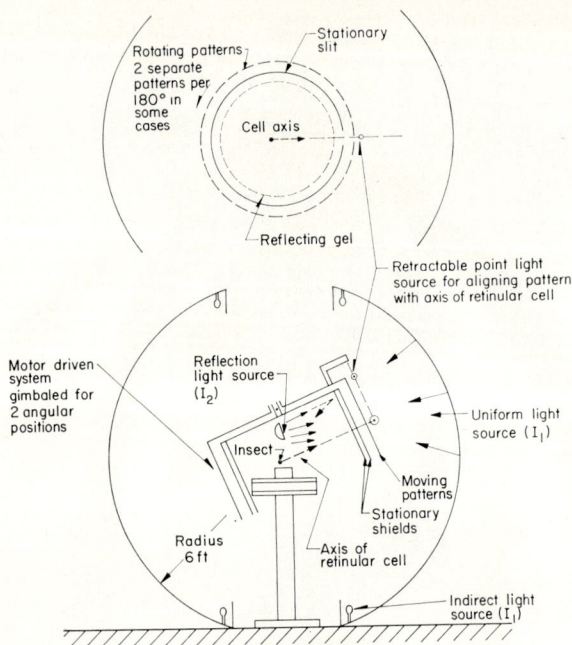

FIG. 10

Schematic diagram of stimulus system.

compared to the duration of each unit stimulus at cylinder speeds in the frequency range of interest. Three other sets of alternating variations that could be introduced either individually or in various combinations are the change in $\triangle I$, the change in $\bar{I}$ and the placement and removal of stationary slits.

Calibration of Pattern and Data Reduction

Control of pattern accuracy is extremely important. This was provided by means of the photomultiplier sensing device shown in Fig. 11. This device has a field of only a few minutes of arc. To calibrate a pattern, this was placed in the position of the insect and signals from it were digitized by an A/D converter at 3000 samples per pattern cylinder revolution. Repetitions of the sampling for several hundred revolutions provided high calibration accuracy from the computer-averaged harmonic analysis. This was the method used for obtaining the data of Fig. 4. Accurate control of $\triangle I$ and $\bar{I}$ by precalibration was also effected in this manner. Calibrations of the three patterns used for obtaining data to be presented below are shown in Table 1. The on-line digital data processing system described by Burtt and Catton (1962) was used for all stimulus and response analyses. Receptor potentials were digitized by the A/D converter for their harmonic analysis.

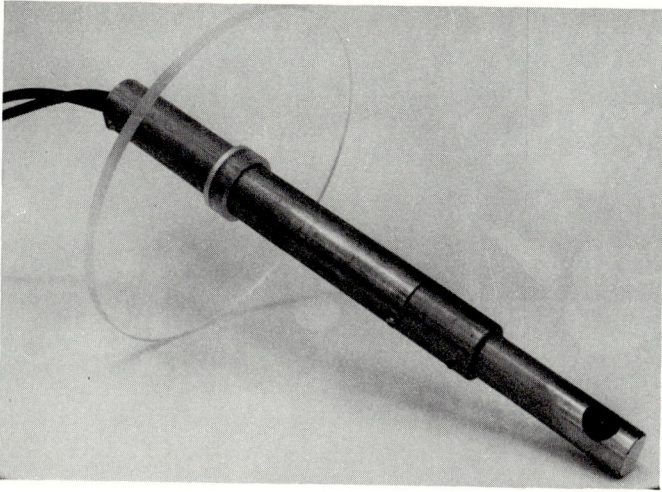

FIG. 11

Photomultiplier for calibrating light patterns. Slit and optical system provide field of only a few minutes of arc.

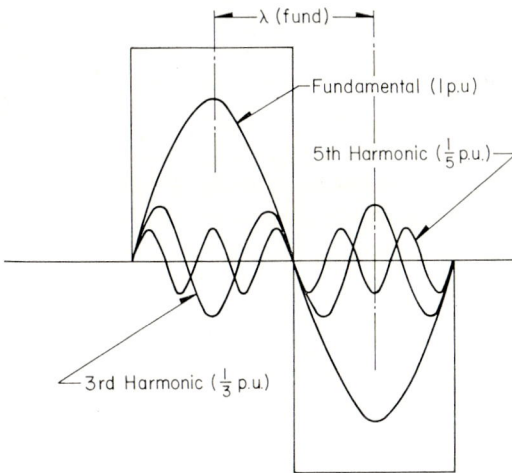

FIG. 12

Harmonic properties of first three components in perfect square wave.

V. EXPERIMENTAL RESULTS

1. *Retinular Cell Studies*

Consideration will be given first to the relative significance of the pulsating components of the receptor potentials $\triangle V$ and the average potential $\overline{V}$ or uncorrelated variations. In some of the preparations stable repeatable values

TABLE 1

CALIBRATION OF SQUARE WAVE STIMULUS PATTERNS

Pattern	Relative harmonic amplitudes		
	Fundamental	3rd harmonic	5th harmonic
36°	1·0	0·33	0·20
4·8°	1·0	0·29	0·14
3·6°	1·0	0·26	0·11

of the $\triangle V$ responses could be obtained for 10 min or more. In others there were 15–30 % variation in this period. Data from these are included by insuring first that the per-unit changes between the successive variations in stimulus conditions were repeated accurately. Poorer preparations with rapid response decay were not used. However, in all conditions there were appreciable low frequency drift variations in the receptor potential both with and without stimuli. A frequency analysis of the fluctuations showed that with no visual stimulation the larger component amplitudes had frequencies below 0·2 c/s. In the region between 0·2 and 10 c/s such variations were much smaller (0·005–0·010 mV in penetrations where the $\triangle V$ responses to light stimuli $\triangle I$ might be as high as 1–5 mV. This determined the threshold level for the detection of pattern response signals which were confined to this frequency range.

It is to be noted that unless the retinular cell potential contains motion correlation information produced at an earlier stage, all pertinent information to be used by the higher stages of the nervous system should be contained in the pulsating signals ($\triangle V$) that are the result of the pulsation components of the stimulus ($\triangle I$).

Effects of pattern ripple frequencies. A survey was made of the affect of varying the frequencies induced by the various harmonics by running the square wave cylinders at different velocities. This disclosed the fact that apparently uncorrelated variations in the receptor potential with frequency components below about 0·2 c/s caused large fluctuations in the responses to stimuli whose frequencies were below 0·2 c/s. Amplitudes of component response did not attenuate appreciably until the corresponding frequency exceeded about 10 c/s. When the 36° square wave stimulus was used at the intensity range of 0·01 to 0·07 lumens per steradian the fundamental, third and fifth harmonic components always appeared in the response when their respective frequencies lay in the range of 0·2–10 c/s. This was not the case, however, when the shorter 3·6° and 4·8° wavelength patterns were used. Only the fundamental component was measurable. The amplitudes of the response components to the 36° pattern fundamental ranged from 1–5 mV and were used as the reference for conversion of other components to per-unit magnitudes. The various experiments described below all involve repetitions of from 10 to 100 cycles of each stimulus fundamental. Thus the averaging technique used for the computer analyses reduced the effective noise level by a factor of from 3 to 10. With a general noise level of about 50 μV this produces a per-unit range of detectable amplitude of from 0·01 to 1·0.

Small signal linearity of $\triangle V$. The data plotted in Fig. 13 were obtained with a double square wave pattern of alternate 36° and 3·6° basic wavelengths

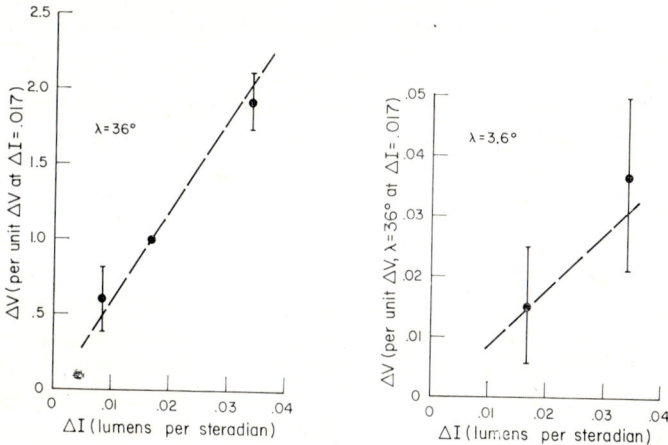

FIG. 13

Relation of pulsating responses ($\triangle V$) to stimulus $\triangle I$ for small signals and constant I (0.036 lumens per steradian).

running at fixed speeds to provide corresponding fundamental pulsating frequencies of 0·30 c/s and 3·0 c/s. By combined precalibrated adjustments of the reflected light from the spherical surface and the light reflected from the stationary gel, $\bar{I}$ was held constant at 0·034 lumens per steradian and $\triangle I$ was varied from 0·0085 to 0·017 to 0·034 lumens per steradian. The corresponding total responses $\triangle V$ for the two patterns are normalized in Fig. 13 to the response from the 36° pattern at $\triangle I = 0·034$ in each unit experiment. Each probing experiment consisted of 10 to 15 sets of 16·6 second runs on each alternating pattern and the response data used was the average response from the 10 to 15 sets at each wavelength and amplitude. Six such runs are represented in Fig. 13. The amplitude of the responses $\triangle V$ to the 36° pattern at $\triangle I$ of 0·034 ranged from 2·1 to 3·5 mV. Figure 13 indicates approximate linearity of the response signals in this stimulus range. The marked attenuation of the responses to the 3·6° pattern are to be noted as predicted from Fig. 3. Unfortunately, no calibrations of the field angle α were obtained from this series.

Dependence of signal $\triangle V$ on average light flux $\bar{F}$. A second series of experiments was run in which $\triangle I$ was held constant but with $\bar{I}$ (the average stimulus intensity) as the variable. The purpose of this was to determine whether or not the signal component sensitivity of the receptor potential $\triangle V$ is primarily a function of the average total ommatidial flux $\bar{F}$ or the average light intensity $\bar{I}$. The data for this, analyzed in two ways, are presented in Table 1 and Fig. 14. A fixed cylinder speed was used throughout giving a frequency of 0·5 c/s for the 36° pattern and 3·75 c/s for the 4·8° pattern. Data were obtained at two values of $\triangle I$ (0·017 and 0·034 lumens per steradian). This represents the lower limit at which $\bar{I}$ could be adjusted ($\bar{I}$ minimum $= \triangle I$) and the corresponding increases of $\bar{I}$ are shown in Table 2. Because of the presumed importance of

TABLE 2

VARIATIONS OF $\triangle V$ FOR SINGLE SQUARE WAVE PATTERN AS FUNCTION
OF AVERAGE LIGHT INTENSITY $\bar{I}$ WHEN $\triangle I$ IS CONSTANT

Exp $a°$		$\bar{F}_n{}^1$	$\triangle \bar{V}_o{}^1$	$\triangle \bar{V}_1{}^1$	$\bar{F}_n$	$\triangle \bar{V}_o$	$\triangle \bar{V}_1$	$\bar{F}_n$	$\triangle \bar{V}_o$	$\triangle \bar{V}_1$
		$15\lambda = 4·8°$								
		$\triangle I = 0·017^1$	$I = 0·017$		$I = 0·034$			$I = 0·135$		
1	3·5	0·023	0·915	0·87	0·046	0·74	0·70	0·18	0·35	0·33
2	4·75	0·043	0·915	0·78	0·086	0·76	0·65	0·34	0·19	0·16
3	2·0	0·0075	0·915	0·97	0·015	0·85	0·90	0·06	0·59	0·62
4	3·5	0·023	0 915	0 87	0 046	0 86	0 82	0·18	0·41	0·39
5	3·0	0·017	0·915	0·92	0·034	0·81	0·81	0·135	0·41	0·41
		$\triangle I = 0·034$	$I = 0·034$		$I = 0·068$			$I = 0·152$		
6	4·2	0·068	0·825	0·66	0·136	0·53	0 42	0·30	0·31	0·25
7	2·5	0·022	0·825	0·87	0·044	0·72	0·77	0·10	0·49	0·46
8	3·5	0·046	0·825	0·77	0·092	0·71	0·66	0·21	0·38	0·35
9	2·25	0·019	0·825	0·90	0·038	0·68	0·74	0·085	0·48	0·52
		$\lambda = 36°$								
		$\triangle I = 0·017$	$I = 0·017$		$I = 0·034$			$I = 0·135$		
10	4·2	0·034	0·915	0·83	0·068	0·83	0·75	0·27	0·31	0·28
11	2·5	0·011	0·915	0·95	0·022	0·90	0·93	0·089	0·61	0·63
12	3·0	0·017	0·915	0·92	0·034	0·81	0·81	0·14	0·38	0·38
13	4·0	0·030	0·915	0·84	0·060	0·82	0·75	0·24	0·36	0·33
14	3·0	0·017	0·915	0·92	0·034	0·88	0·88	0·14	0·32	0·32
15	3·5	0·023	0·915	0·87	0·046	0·87	0·83	0·18	0·41	0·39
		$\triangle I = 0·034$	$I = 0·034$		$I = 0·068$			$I = 0·152$		
16	4·5	0·075	0·825	0·63	0·150	0·59	0·45	0·33	0·22	0·17
17	3·4	0·044	0·825	0·78	0·087	0·53	0·50	0·19	0·43	0·41
18	3·5	0·046	0·825	0·76	0·092	0·70	0·65	0·21	0·27	0·25
19	2·7	0·028	0·825	0·75	0·055	0·65	0·67	0·12	0·40	0·41

[1] Stimulus light intensities I and $\triangle I$ are in lumens per steradian. $\bar{F}_n$ is a normalized average flux; $\bar{F}_n = I$ when $a = 3°$; $\bar{F} = I \, 4\pi a^2/4 \ln 2°$; $\triangle \bar{V}_o$ is normalized by fitting actual $\triangle V$ for lowest I to curve of Fig. 10 at actual I. They are plotted to actual I. $\triangle \bar{V}_n$ is normalized by fitting actual $\triangle V$ for lowest I to curve of Fig. 10 at corresponding $\bar{F}$. They are plotted as function of $\bar{F}$.

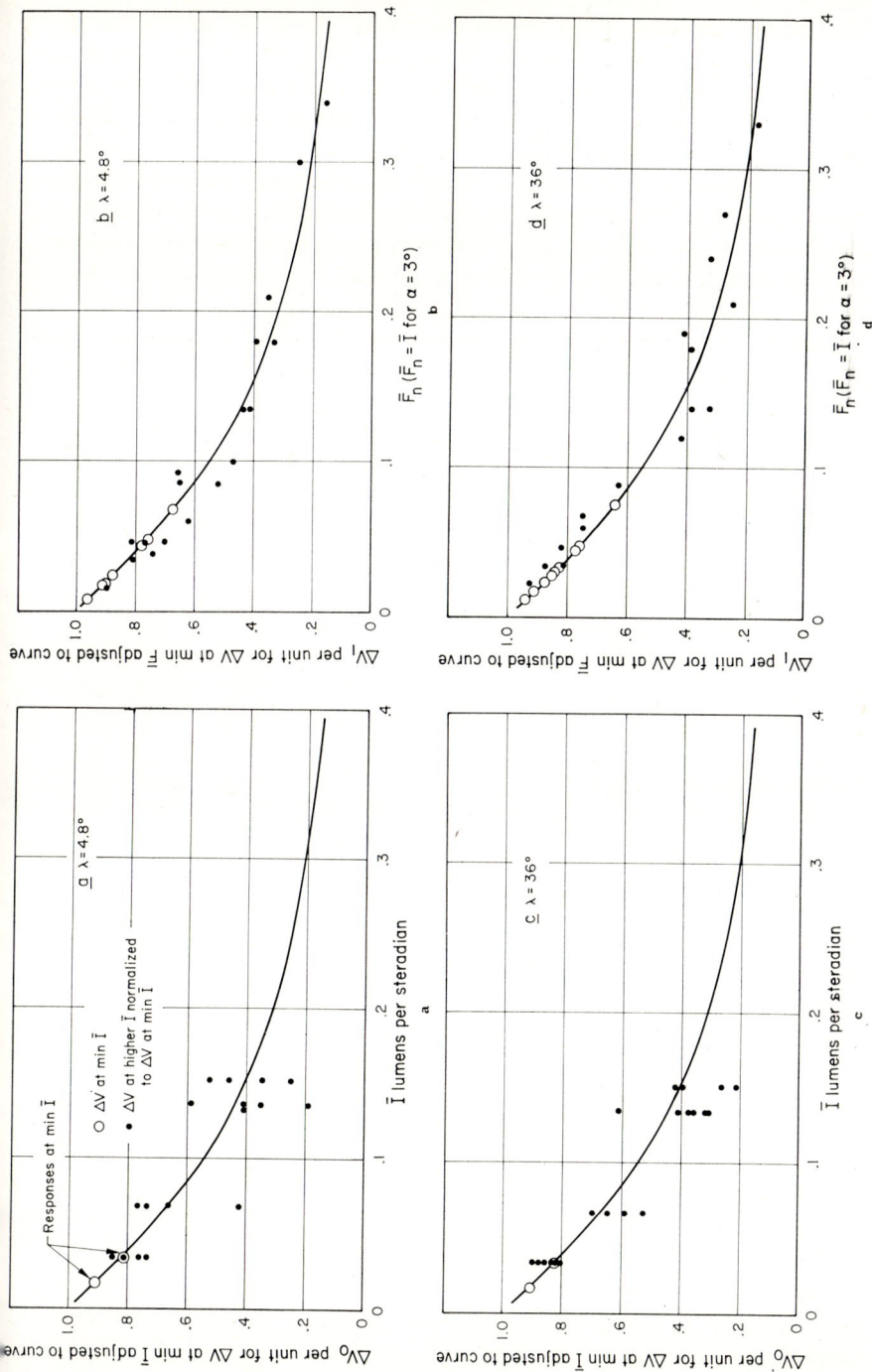

FIG. 14

Dependence of ripple signals ΔV on average light intensity $\bar{I}$ and average ommatidial flux $\bar{F}$. (Data of Table 1.)

the field angle α, it was measured for each preparation at the start as described earlier. Each preparation experiment consisted of a series of 2 min runs at the three values of $\bar{I}$ starting at the minimum value, going successively to each of the other two values but returning to the minimum between each change as a normalization check.

The data have been analyzed in two ways to investigate the relative importance of average light intensity $\bar{I}$ and average ommatidial flux $\bar{F}$. All are based on normalization to a single presumed light adaptation sensitivity curve that was obtained from a curve fit of the data plotted as a function of $\bar{F}$. Having chosen a single curve, the data plotted as a function of average intensity $\bar{I}$ was normalized by fitting the response at the lowest value of $\bar{I}$ to this curve and then using the same normalizing factor for the other two values of $\bar{I}$ obtained in the unit run.

The data for the responses $\triangle V$ as a function of average ommatidial flux $\bar{F}$ were obtained by computing first a normalized average flux coordinate for each experiment. This was done by multiplying each average intensity by the factor $\alpha^2/(3)^2$. This normalized the flux data to an ommatidial field characterized by an α of 3°. Then each response $\triangle V$ for a given penetration was normalized by fitting the response at the lowest value of $\bar{F}$ in the run to the standardized curve plotted as a function of $\bar{F}$.

Comparison of the data as plotted in Fig. 14 thus points up the fact that the signal response sensitivity is primarily a function of average ommatidial flux rather than average light intensity. This is also indicated to be independent of pattern wavelength over the modest temporal frequency range given by the two pattern wavelengths.

Effects of pattern frequencies and wavelengths. Table 3 summarizes all of the additional data presented here from the retinular cell probing studies. These are a series of response measurements and digital computer harmonic analyses obtained with the double (two wavelength) square wave pattern. Each run alternated repeatedly between the condition of unconstricted exposure of the retinular cell to the pattern and constriction by placing a 2° stationary slit between the eye and the moving pattern symmetric with the axis of the field of the cell being probed.

Dependence of signals on pattern wavelength. One of the most significant facts pointed up by the data of Table 3 is the rapid roll-off of response signal $\triangle V$ to the wavelength of the pattern component producing the respective signal component. It is seen, for instance, that the fundamental and the third and fifth harmonics are reproduced in the receptor potential for the 36° pattern, whereas only the fundamental can be detected for either the 3·6° or 4·8° patterns. The relative amplitudes of the three component responses for the 36° pattern stimulus are also in approximate ratio to the corresponding amplitudes of the stimulus as modified by the appropriate contrast function roll-off curve.

TABLE 3

Computer harmonic analysis of retinular cell responses to square wave
moving patterns with both full field and 2° slit

Exp.[1]	$a°$	$\triangle I^2$	$\lambda°$	f(c/s)	Full field		2° slit	
					Amp(pu)	Phase°	Amp(pu)	Phase°
●	4·6	0·034	36	0·2	1·00	5	0·32	−7
			12	0·6	0·30	75	0·22	61
			7·8	1·0	0·042	8	0·048	15
			3·6	2·0	—		0·32	21
○	3·2	0·034	36	0·2	1·0	−8	0·60	−3
			12	0·6	0·321	35	0·26	70
			7·8	1·0	0·039	−15	0·030	4
			3·6	2·0	0·013	−9	0·30	2
			1·2	6·0	—		0·038	80
×	3·0	0·034	36	0·2	1·0	10	0·52	5
			12	0·6	0·29	65	0·24	78
			7·8	1·0	0·11	−10	0·09	15
			3·6	2·0	—		0·40	15
△	3·0	0·017	36	0·2	1·0	15	0·61	−2
			12	0·6	0·33	20	0·29	15
			7·8	1·0	0·041	13	0·034	−3
			3·6	2·0	0·030	−3	0·28	16
			1·2	6·0	—		0·031	29
▽	2·7	0·034	36	0·2	1·0	5	0·66	8
			12	0·6	0·33	83	0·29	70
			7·8	1·0	0·016	5	0·031	11
			3·6	2·0	0·019	−3	0·16	16
			1·2	6·0	—		—	
□	2·4	0·034	36	0·2	1·0	5	0·76	−13
			12	0·6	0·31	21	0·24	36
			7·8	1·0	0·038	3	0·043	−8
			4·8	1·5	0·46	8	0·71	3
			1·6	4·5	—		0·027	35
			0·96	7·25	—		—	

[1] Symbols used in Fig. 15.
[2] Maximum $\triangle I$ (lumens per steradian) for both complete square waves ($I = \triangle I$).

Effect of stationary slit. The added information obtained by the alternative
use of the stationary 2° slit permits a more detailed correlation between the
actual response characteristics and those predicted by the model analysis
summarized by Figs. 3, 6 and 7. This is shown by the analysis given in Fig. 15.
Here the normalized $\triangle V$ response components before and after the introduction of the slit are plotted as a function of the corresponding wavelength
of the stimulus pattern component and compared with the predicted effects
of Fig. 7. It should be noted that changes in the two light sources were determined by the calibration so as to maintain both $\bar{I}$ and $\triangle I$ constant as the slit
was added or removed.

C.E.—2P

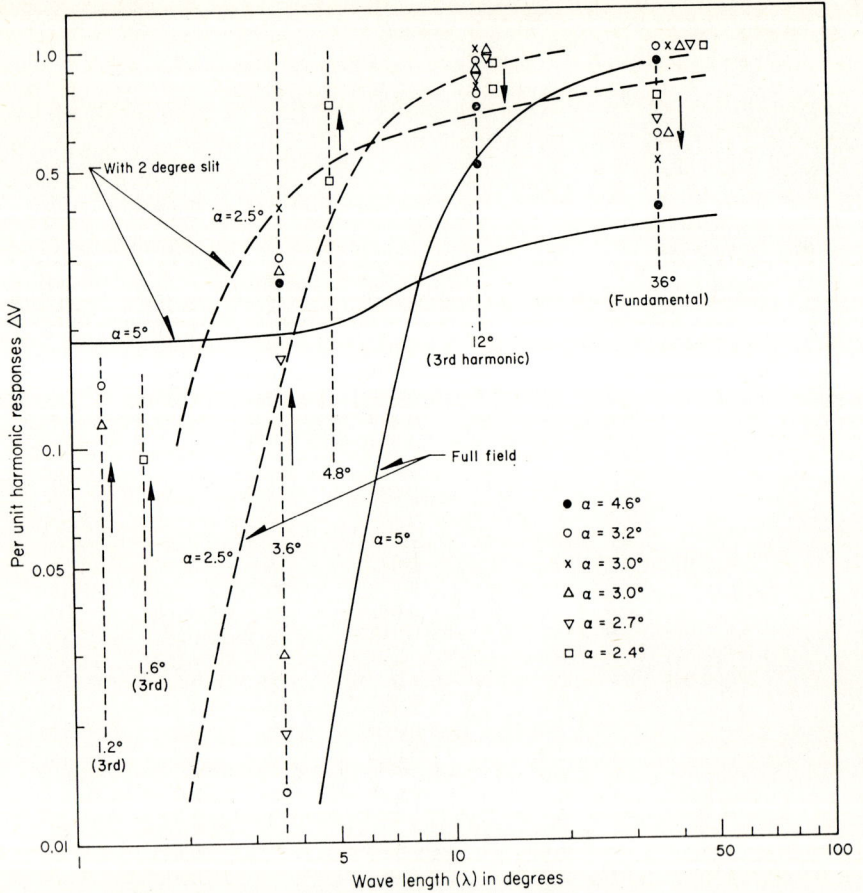

FIG. 15

Variation of harmonic components of receptor potential signals ($\triangle V$) with the wavelength (λ) of the corresponding stimulus components ($\triangle I$) and with the addition of a $2°$ slit symmetric to axis of receptor field. (Data of Table 3.)

The arrows for each set of plotted points indicate the direction of change of the component response when the slit was introduced. When only one point is shown for a given case, the corresponding signal before adding the slit was not detectable. The general correlation of the data with the predicted curves is good. It might seem remarkable that the introduction of the slit for the short $3·6°$ wavelength pattern raises the corresponding response signal for both the fundamental and third harmonic from a very low value (undetectable in most cases) to signals one or more orders of magnitude greater. The predicted effect of field angle α is also to be noted in the results.

2. Ventral Cord Studies

It was hoped that the same general properties of the retinular cell responses could be detected higher up in the nervous system and appropriate studies were made at both the ventral cord and in the optokinetic responses. The ventral cord studies on the locust *Schistocerca gregaria* were chosen for presentation here since evidence of high visual acuity and possible complex optic data processing characteristics in the ommatidia have been reported for this insect (Burtt and Catton, 1962). The data presented here is part of a more general study by Madey and Ray (1966).

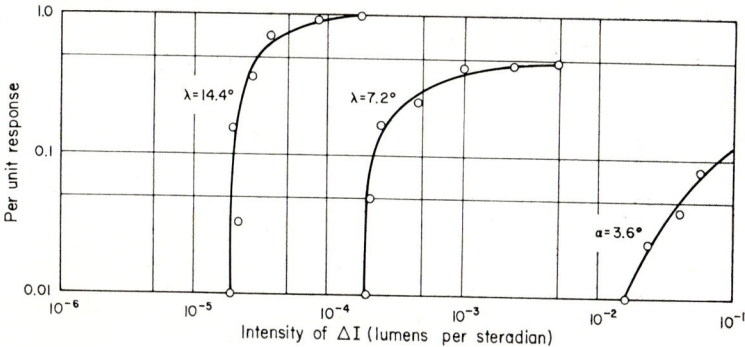

FIG. 16

Typical ventral cord response curves for the same *Schistocerca gregaria* with variations in pattern wavelength (λ) and signal intensity ($\triangle I$). (From Madey and Ray, 1966.) (Responses are per unit of largest for long wavelength pattern.)

Figure 16 summarizes a study of the effect of varying the pattern wavelength λ and signal level $\triangle I$ for full field vision (360°) in the direction of pattern motion. A hooked probe preparation was used in this experiment which permitted the recording of the individual spikes elicited from about 8 individual fibers. The experiment was performed by constantly exposing the insect to a given static pattern and light condition then suddenly starting the pattern into constant velocity motion. The response index used in Fig. 16 is the increase in the total number of fiber spikes generated per unit time and over a 3 sec interval as a result of the sudden pattern motion. This curve shows the same general effect of pattern wavelength on acuity as found for *Musca domestica* (McCann and MacGinitie, 1965) and predicted by the model analysis. For instance, the ratios of thresholds for the three patterns in Fig. 14 are predicted by a half-sensitivity field angle (α) of about 4·5°.

The predicted increase in acuity for short wavelength patterns and reduction of sensitivity to long wavelength patterns by the insertion of a narrow window is shown by the data of Fig. 17 also obtained by Madey and Ray (1966).

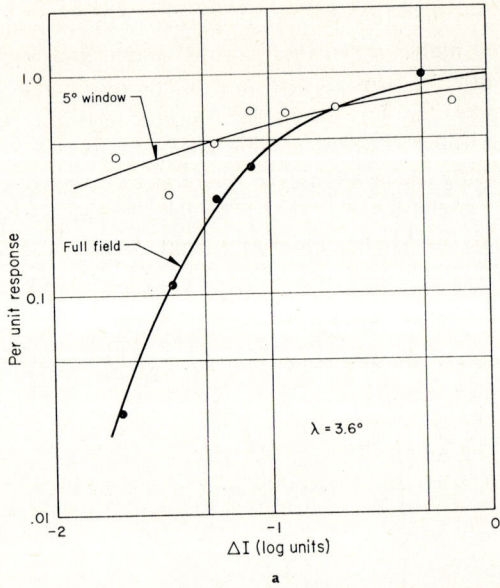

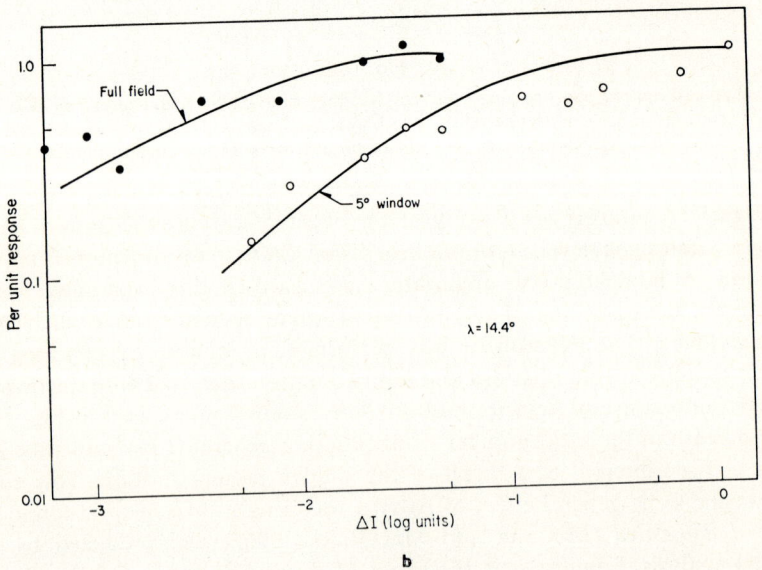

FIG. 17

Comparison for ventral cord responses in *Schistocerca gregaria* for full field and 5°
window conditions (each figure for different insects). (a) $\lambda = 3 \cdot 6°$, (b) $\lambda = 14 \cdot 4°$.

3. *Studies of White-eyed Musca*

Histological studies of the comparative physiology of the eye of the mutant and the normal red-eyed fly show no differences in ommatidial geometry. Extensive measurements of the distribution of ommatidial spacings and diameters were made with no differences disclosed. For instance, the mutant has the same statistical distribution and average values for the ommatidial spacings as reported by Vowles (1965). Photographs of ommatidial sections taken under various conditions of non-staining, staining and pigment bleaching show only one type of difference; the shielding pigment is completely absent in the white-eyed mutant.

It has not yet been possible to conduct a significant retinular cell probing study of this insect. A number of optokinetic response studies have been carried out, however, and they are summarized in Fig. 18. The data pertaining to the red-eyed fly are reproduced from Reference 1. Figure 18 shows a comparative optokinetic analysis between the red- and white-eyed *Muscas* similar to the ventral cord study of Fig. 16. This shows no marked change in acuity for the mutant as adaptation conditions are changed in contrast to the red-eyed insect. It does show a lowering of general sensitivity.

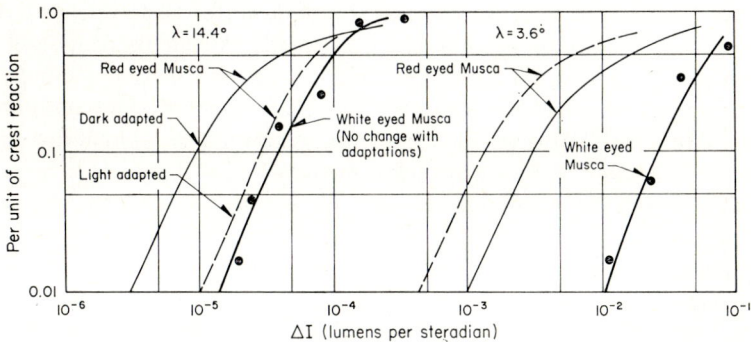

FIG. 18

Musca domestica Yaw flight torque reactions for two pattern wavelengths (λ) as a function of ΔI. (Data for red-eyed fly from McCann and MacGinitie, 1965.)

4. *Correlation with Responses to Other Patterns*

It is pertinent to ask whether or not the model for the initial visual input described above is adequate for observed responses to patterns differing widely from those so far described.

Comparison of stationary and moving patterns. For example, is the retinular cell response to stationary pulsating patterns the same as for moving striped patterns when the computed total light flux variations within the cell are the same? Is the motion detection process therefore higher up in the nervous system? This point was investigated for a variety of stationary pattern shapes and in all cases the same receptor response signals were measured as long as the computed light flux conditions as defined from the pattern shape and intensity and the measured receptor field were held constant.

External moving patterns. Studies too extensive to describe here were also conducted (using optokinetic responses in *Musca*) on patterns with small oscillatory motion (McCann and MacGinitie, 1965), and with constant angular velocity but having very small isolated discontinuities on a uniform white or dark background. In all of these cases the measured thresholds of reaction all occurred at essentially the same computed receptor light flux signal amplitudes as for the thresholds to the uniform striped patterns.

VI. CONCLUSIONS

Detailed studies of the retinular cell responses in the insect *Musca domestica* when precision square wave rotating patterns are used show that the essential properties of the information transduced by the photoreceptors can be described from an analysis of the corresponding ommatidial light flux variations as defined by the ommatidial visual fields. These fields are characterized by half-sensitivity angles α ranging from 2 to 5° and a most frequent value of 3·0°. Such visual fields produce rapid attenuation of responses to pattern detail as the wavelength of such detail goes below about 8–10°. However, restriction of the field of the cell by sharp boundaries greatly extends its acuity and any responses to apparent extremely fine detail in patterns can be attributed to the longer wavelength components they produce as a result of discontinuities.

Absolute signal sensitivity is dependent upon average total light flux in the ommatidium rather than average light intensity.

No essential differences could be detected between the response characteristic of the retinular cells in *M. domestica* and in *Calliphora* and the same basic response properties were found in the ventral cord information of the locust *Schistocera gregaria* and a white-eyed mutant of *M. domestica*.

This mutant has no shielding pigment and no evidence of variation of ommatidial field angle with light adaptation was found in contrast to the red-eyed fly.

SUMMARY

Correlations of the responses in insect retinular cells and ventral cords with optokinetic reactions to stimulation by accurately defined patterns have established the fundamental properties of the initial stages of form perception in the insects *Musca domestica*, *Calliphora erythrocephala* and *Schistocerca gregaria*. These correlations for responses to precision moving patterns with various combinations of spatial wavelengths and temporal frequencies confirm the assumption that the initial information transduced by the photoreceptors can be determined primarily from the total light flux entering the receptor as defined by a measurable optic window or field.

REFERENCES

BISHOP, L. G. 1966. (California Institute of Technology) Selective Microprobing in Insect Nerve Cords. (In preparation.)

BURTT, E. T. and CATTON, W. T. 1962. *Proc. Roy. Soc. B* **157**, 53–82.

KEEHN, DANIEL G. 1966. An Iterative Spike Separation Technique. *Transactions IEEE*, BME Vol. 13, 1.

MCCANN, G. D. and MACGINITIE, 1966. An Information Processing and Control System for Biological Research. *Proc. Roy. Soc. B* **128**, 830.

MCCANN, G. D. and RAY, C. B. An Information Processing System for Biological Research. *Annals N. Y. Academy of Science*, Symposium on Advances in Biomedical Research, June 3–5, 1965.

MADEY, J. M. J. and RAY, C. B. (California Institute of Technology) Ventral Cord Studies of Insect Vision. (Paper in preparation.)

REICHARDT, W. 1961. *Ssnsory Communication*. John Wiley and Sons.

VOWLES, D. M. 1965. *Proc. Roy. Soc.* (In publication.)

WASHIZU, Y., BURKHARDT, D. and STRECK, P. 1964. *Zeitschrift für Vergleichende Physiologie* **48**, 413–28.

AUTHOR INDEX

Figures in **bold type** refer to the first page of the author's article in this volume.

Figures in roman type refer to the page on which the author is cited.

Roman figures given in parentheses refer to a page where the author is cited as other than first author.

Figures in *italics* refer to a page containing the reference list in which the author is cited.

Name in parentheses is the name under which the author has been cited (in the text) only as "*et al.*", "and others", etc.

ADAMS, J. R. (377 DETHIER), (*396*)
ADAMS, R. G. 156, *160*, (329 HAGINS), (*336*)
ADOLPH, A. R. 232, *249*, 335, *336*, 445, 448, 461, 463, *463*, **465**, 465, 466, 473, *481*
ADRIAN, E. D. 9, 10, *10*, 208, *217*
ANDRÉ, W. 9, *10*
AOTO, J. (93), (97), (*100*)
AUTRUM, H. 39, *50*, 60, *62*, 138, 140, 142, *143*, 160, *160*, 175, 177, 180, *185*, 195, 205, 207, 208, 213, 215, 216, *217*, (222), 223, 225, (225), *229*, (*229*), (252), (264), (266), 293, (293), 305, *306*, (*306*), 360, *362*, 495, 496, *509*, (538), (*541*)
AUTRUM, I. (160), (*160*)

BACCETTI, B. 171, 172, 174, 180, *185*, 309, *327*
BAINBRIDGE, R. 174, *185*, 498, *509*
BARASS, R. (487), (*492*)
BARER, R. 528, 529, *541*
BARKER, R. J. (127), (128), (130), (*143*), (153), (*161*)
BARLOW, H. B. 35, 47, *50*, 61, *62*, 65, 75, 187, *191*, 448, *448*
BARLOW, R. B. JR. 408
BARNARD, P. B. T. (109), (116), (*123*), (513), (523), (*541*)
VAN BARNEVELD, H. 488
BARRNETT, R. J. (106), (*124*)
BATSCHELET, E. 506, *509*
BAUMANN, F. (406), (*424*)
BAYLOR, E. R. 174, (174), *185*, (*186*), (496), 498, (498), 500, *509*, (*510*)
BECKER, J. A. 323, *325*
BEDINI, C. (171), (172), (174), (180), (*185*), (309), (*327*)

BEHRENS, M. E. 231, *249*, 406, *423*
BENNITT, T. 90, *99*
BENOLKEN, R. H. 225, *229*, 231, **231**, 232, 240, 245, *249*, 260, *266*
BENSCH, K. (106), (*124*)
BERGER, H. (9)
BERNHARD, C. G. **1**, 21, **(21)**, (21), 23, 25, 30, 33, *33*, (*33*), 39, *50*, 77, *88*, 195, 200, 204, *205*, 208, 215, *217*, 223, *229*, 251, 263, *266*, 341, *362*
BERTKAU, P. 171, *185*
BICKART, T. (210), (211), (*217*)
BICKING, L. A. 448, *448*
BIEDEBACH, M. C. **(559)**
BIEKERT, E. (89 BUTENANDT), (*100*)
BISHOP, L. G. 561, *583*
BLISS, D. E. 92, *99*
BLOOM, F. E. (467), (*482*)
BODENSTEIN, D. **(207)**, *217*
BOERHAAVE, H. 1, 3
BOISTEL, J. 214, *217*
BORN, M. 40, *50*
BOTTEMA, M. 39, 40, *50*
BOWMAN, T. E. 93, *99*
BOWNESS, J. M. 153, (153), *160*, (*162*)
BOYNTON, R. M. 309, *327*
BRAITENBERG, V. 288
BRIGGS, M. H. 135, *143*, 153, *161*
BROWN, F. A. JR. 93, (94), 96, *99*, (*101*)
BROWN, K. T. 156, *161*
BROWN, P. K. (152), (*162*), 329, *336*, (496), (*511*)
DE BRUIN, G. H. P. 90, 98, *100*
BRUNO, M. S. (501), (*510*)
BULLOCK, T. H. 373, *375*, 383, 385, 392, *396*, (441 PERKEL), (*449*)
BURG, S. P. (152), (*162*)
BURGESS, P. R. (93, 95 KLEINHOLZ), (*101*)

585